REFERENCE GUIDE FOR **BUILDING OPERATIONS AND MAINTENANCE**

v4

COPYRIGHT

DISCLAIMER

U.S. Green Building Council
2101 L Street, NW
Suite 500
Washington, DC 20037

TRADEMARK

LEED Reference Guide for Building Operations and Maintenance
2013 Edition
ISBN # 978-1-932444-16-2

ACKNOWLEDGMENTS

The LEED Reference Guide for Building Operations and Maintenance, 2013 Edition, has been made possible only through the efforts of many dedicated volunteers, staff members, and others in the USGBC community. The Reference Guide drafting was managed and implemented by USGBC staff and consultants and included review and suggestions by many Technical Advisory Group (TAG) members. We extend our deepest gratitude to all of our LEED committee members who participated in the development of this guide, for their tireless volunteer efforts and constant support of USGBC's mission:

LEED Steering Committee

Joel Todd, Chair	Joel Ann Todd
Bryna Dunn, Vice-Chair	Moseley Architects
Felipe Faria	Green Building Council Brasil
Elaine Hsieh	KEMA Services
Susan Kaplan	BuildingWrx
Malcolm Lewis	Cadmus Group
Muscoe Martin	M2 Architecture
Lisa Matthiessen	Integral Group
Brend Morawa	Integrated Environmental Solutions
Tim Murray	Morris Architects
Sara O'Mara	Choate Construction Company
Bruce Poe	Modus Architecture Collaborative
Alfonso Ponce	Deloitte Finance
David Sheridan	Aqua Cura
Lynn Simon	Thornton Tomasetti
Doug Gatlin (Non-voting)	U.S. Green Building Council
Scot Horst (Non-voting)	U.S. Green Building Council
Brendan Owens (Non-voting)	U.S. Green Building Council
Peter Templeton (Non-voting)	U.S. Green Building Council

LEED Technical Committee

Susan Kaplan, Chair	BuildingWrx
Maureen McGeary Mahle, Vice-Chair	Steven Winter Associates
Jennifer Atlee	BuildingGreen
Steve Baer	Five Winds International
Ted Bardacke	Global Green USA
Steve Benz	OLIN
Neal Billetdeaux	SmithGroupJJR
David Bracciano	Alliance for Water Efficiency
Daniel Bruck	BRC Acoustics & Audiovisual Design
David Carlson	Columbia University
Jenny Carney	YR&G
Mark Frankel	New Buildings Institute
Nathan Gauthier	EA Buildings
George Brad Guy	Catholic University of America
Michelle Halle Stern	The Green Facilitator
Malcolm Lewis	Cadmus Group
John McFarland	Working Buildings LLC
Jessica Millman	The Agora Group
Neil Rosen	North Shore LIJ Health System
Thomas Scarola	Tishman Speyer
Chris Schaffner	The Green Engineer
Marcus Sheffer	7group
Sheila Sheridan	Sheridan Associates
Bob Thompson	U.S. Environmental Protection Agency
Alfred Vick	University of Georgia

LEED Market Advisory Committee

Lisa Matthiessen, Chair	Integral Group
Holley Henderson, Vice-Chair	H2Ecodesign
Liana Berberidou-Kallivoka	City of Austin
Jeffrey Cole	Konstrukt
Walter Cuculic	Pulte Homes
Rand Ekman	Cannon Design
Richard Kleinman	LaSalle Investment Management
Craig Kneeland	NYSERDA
Muscoe Martin	M2 Architecture
Cindy Quan	Goldman Sachs & Co.
Matt Raimi	Raimi + Associates
Jon Ratner	Forest City Enterprises
Marcus Sheffer	7group
Rebecca Stafford	University of California, Office of President
Gary Thomas	CB Richard Ellis
Keith Winn	Catalyst Partners

Implementation Advisory Committee

Brenda Morawa, Chair	Integrated Environmental Solutions
Adam Fransen, Vice-Chair	CB Richard Ellis
Michelle Malanca	Michelle Malanca Sustainability Consulting
Brad Pease	Paladino and Co.
Ken Potts	McGough
Richard Schneider	U.S. Army Engineer Research and Development Center
Greg Shank	Altura Associates
David Sheridan	Aqua Cura
Natalie Terrill	Viridian Energy & Environmental
Bill Worthen	Urban Fabrick Design
Max Zahniser	Praxis | Building Solutions

Location and Planning TAG

Jessica Millman, Chair	The Agora Group
John Dalzell, Vice-Chair	Boston Redevelopment Authority/ City of Boston
Eliot Allen	Criterion Planners
Laurence Aurbach	Office of Laurence Aurbach
Ted Bardacke	Global Green USA
Erin Christensen	Mithun
Andy Clarke	League of American Bicyclists
Fred Dock	City of Pasadena
Bruce Donnelly	Auricity
Victor Dover	Dover, Kohl, and Partners
Reid Ewing	University of Utah
Doug Farr	Farr & Associates
Lois Fisher	Fisher Town Design
Tim Frank	Sierra Club
Randy Hansell	Earth Advantage Institute
Justin Horner	Natural Resources Defense Council
Ron Kilcoyne	Lane Transit District
Todd Litman	Victoria Transport Policy Institute
Dana Little	Treasure Coast Regional Planning Council
Art Lomenick	Parsons Brinckerhoff
Steve Mouzon	New Urban Guild

Lynn Richards	U.S. Environmental Protection Agency
Harrison Rue	ICF International
Shawn Seamen	PN Hoffman
Anthony Sease	Civitech
Laurie Volk	Zimmerman/ Volk Associates
Patricia White	Defenders of Wildlife

Sustainable Sites TAG

Jenny Carney, Chair	YR&G
Neal Billetdeaux, Vice-Chair	SmithGroupJJR
Michele Adams	Meliora Environmental Design
Joby Carlson	University of Arkansas
Laura Case	Southface Energy Institute
Stephen Cook	VIKA
Richard Heinisch	Acuity Brands Lighting
Heather Holdridge	Lake | Flato Architects
Jason King	Greenworks, PC
Katrina Rosa	The EcoLogic Studio
Kyle Thomas	Natural Systems Engineering
Alfred Vick	University of Georgia
Teresa Watkins	St. John's Water Management District
Steve Benz	OLIN

Water Efficiency TAG

Neil Rosen, Chair	North Shore LIJ Health System
Doug Bennett, Vice-Chair	Las Vegas Valley Water District / Southern Nevada Water Authority
Damann Anderson	Hazen & Sawyer
Gunnar Baldwin	TOTO USA
Robert Benazzi	Jaros Baum & Bolles
Steve Benz	OLIN
Neal Billetdeaux	SmithGroupJJR
David Bracciano	Alliance for Water Efficiency
David Carlson	Columbia University
Ron Hand	E/FECT. Sustainable Design Solutions
Bill Hoffman	H.W. Hoffman and Associates
Winston Huff	SSR Engineers
Joanna Kind	Eastern Research Group
Heather Kinkade	Forgotten Rain
Gary Klein	Affiliated International Management
John Koeller	Koeller and Company
Shawn Martin	International Code Council
Don Mills	Clivus Multrum
Geoff Nara	Civil & Environmental Consultants
Karen Poff	Austin Energy
Shabbir Rawalpindiwala	Kohler
Robert Rubin	NCSU
Stephanie Tanner	US Environmental Protection Agency
David Viola	International Association of Plumbing and Mechanical Officials
Bill Wall	Clivus New England
Daniel Yeh	University of South Florida
Rob Zimmerman	Kohler

Energy and Atmosphere TAG

Nathan Gauthier, Chair	EA Buildings
Jeremy Poling, Vice-Chair	Goby
John Adams	General Services Administration
Amanda Bogner	The Energy Studio
Kevin Bright	Harvard University
Lane Burt	Natural Resources Defense Council
Allan Daly	Taylor Engineering
Charles Dorgan	University of Wisconsin-Madison
Jay Enck	Commissioning & Green Building Solutions
Ellen Franconi	Rocky Mountain Institute
Scott Frank	Jaros Baum & Bolles
Gail Hampsmire	Low Energy Low Cost
Tia Heneghan	ZIA for Buildings
Rusty Hodapp	Dallas/Fort Worth International Airport Board
Brad Jones	Sebesta Blomberg
Dan Katzenberger	Engineering, Energy, and the Environment
Doug King	King Sustainability
Chris Ladner	Viridian
Richard Lord	Carrier Corporation
Bob Maddox	Sterling Planet
Rob Moody	Organic Think
Brenda Morawa	BVM Engineering
Paul Raymer	Heyoka Solutions
Erik Ring	LPA
David Roberts	National Renewable Energy Laboratory
Michael Rosenberg	Pacific Northwest National Laboratory
Greg San Martin	PG&E
Chris Schaffner	The Green Engineer
Marcus Sheffer	7group
Gordon Shymko	G.F. Shymko & Associates
Jason Steinbock	The Weidt Group
Jorge Torres Coto	MBO
Tate Walker	Energy Center of Wisconsin

Materials and Resources TAG

Steve Baer, Chair	PE INTERNATIONAL/ Five Winds Strategic Consulting
Brad Guy, Vice-Chair	Material Reuse
Paul Bertram	Kingspan Insulated Panels, North America
Paul Bierman-Lytle	Pangeon/ iMCC Management Consulting
Steve Brauneis	Rocky Mountain Institute
Amy Costello	Armstrong World Industries
Chris Geiger	San Francisco Department of the Environment
Barry Giles	BuildingWise
Avi Golen	Construction Waste Management
Lee Gros	Lee Gros Architect and Artisan
Rick Levin	Kahler Slater
Joep Meijer	The Right Environment
Xhavin Sinha	CH2M HILL
Raymond Smith	U.S. Environmental Protection Agency
Wes Sullens	StopWaste.Org of Alameda County
Denise Van Valkenburg	Eurofins

Indoor Environmental Quality TAG

Daniel Bruck, Chair	BRC Acoustics & Audiovisual Design
Michelle Halle Stern, Vice-Chair	The Green Facilitator
Sahar Abbaszadeh	The Cadmus Group
Terry Brennan	Camroden Associates
Aida Carbo	UL Environment
Randal Carter	Steelcase
Wenhao Chen	California Department of Public Health
Nancy Clanton	Clanton & Associates
Dan Dempsey	Carrier
Larry Dykhuis	Herman Miller
Dwayne Fuhlhage	PROSOCO
Stowe Hartridge Beam	Scientific Certification Systems
Dan Int-Hout	Krueger
Alexis Kurtz	The Sextant Group
Matt Latchford	Lam Partners
David Lubman	David Lubman & Associates
Richard Master	USG Corporation
John McFarland	WorkingBuildings
Bud Offermann	Indoor Environmental Engineering
Reinhard Oppl	Eurofins Product Testing A/S
Ozgem Ornektekin	New York University
Charles Salter	Salter Associates
Chris Schaffner	The Green Engineer
Dana Schneider	Jones Lang LaSalle
Dennis Stanke	Trane Commercial Systems
Don Stevens	Panasonic Home and Environment Company
Bob Thompson	U.S. Environmental Protection Agency
Ellen Tohn	Tohn Environmental Strategies
Prasad Vaidya	The Weidt Group

Pilot Credit Library Working Group

Marc Cohen (Chair)	The Cadmus Group
Lindsay Baker	Mary Davidge Associates
Cheryl Baldwin	GreenSeal
James Bogdan	PPG Industries
Carlie Bullock-Jones	Ecoworks Studio
Paul Firth	UL Environment
Mick Schwedler	Trane
Steve Taylor	Taylor Engineering
Richard Young	Fisher-Nickel

Integrative Process Task Group

Lindsay Baker	Mary Davidge Associates
John Boecker	7group
Penny Bonda	Ecoimpact Consulting
Jenny Carney	YR&G
Joel Todd	Joel Ann Todd
Bill Reed	Integrative Design Collaborative
Heather Rosenberg	The Cadmus Group
Linda Sorrento	National Academy of Environmental Design
Keith Winn	Catalyst Partners
Bill Worthen	Urban Fabrik
Max Zahniser	Praxis | Building Solutions

A special thanks to USGBC and GBCI staff for their invaluable efforts in developing this reference guide, especially to the following for their technical expertise: Emily Alvarez, Eric Anderson, Theresa Backhus, Lonny Blumenthal, Amy Boyce, Steve Brauneis, Sarah Buffaloe, Sara Cederberg, Christopher Davis, Robyn Eason, Corey Enck, Sean Fish, Asa Foss, Deon Glaser, Scott Haag, Gail Hampsmire, Jason Hercules, Jackie Hofmaenner, Theresa Hogerheide, Mika Kania, Heather Langford, Christopher Law, Rebecca Lloyd, Emily Loquidis, Chrissy Macken, Chris Marshall, Batya Metalitz, Larissa Oaks, Lauren Riggs, Jarrod Siegel, Micah Silvey, Ken Simpson, Megan Sparks, Rebecca Stahlnecker, and Tim Williamson.

A special thanks to Jessica Centella, Selina Holmes, and Dave Marcus for their graphics support and eye for design.

A thank you also goes to Scot Horst, Doug Gatlin, and Brendan Owens for their vision and support, and Meghan Bogaerts for her hard work, attention to detail and flair for writing. A very special thanks to Dara Zycherman, staff lead on the development of the LEED v4 Reference Guide suite, for her unwavering commitment to quality and her dedication to the production of the guides.

A special thanks to the consultant team which included Arup, CBRE, C.C. Johnson & Malhotra, Criterion Planners, Goby, Paladino & Co., Post Typography, West Main, and YR&G, and the unique artwork created for this publication by RTKL Associates.

TABLE OF CONTENTS

ENERGY AND ATMOSPHERE 186

MATERIALS AND RESOURCES 304

INDOOR ENVIRONMENTAL QUALITY 388

INNOVATION 532

REGIONAL PRIORITY 544

APPENDICES 550

THE CASE FOR GREEN BUILDING OPERATIONS AND MAINTENANCE

Green buildings are an integral part of the solution to the environmental challenges facing the planet.

Today we use the equivalent of 1.5 Earths to meet the resource needs of everyday life and absorb the resulting wastes. This measure of our planet's carrying capacity means that it takes Earth 18 months to regenerate what is used in only 12 months. If current trends continue, estimates suggest, by the year 2030 we will need the equivalent of two planets.[1] Turning resources into waste faster than they can be regenerated puts the planet into ecological overshoot, a clearly unsustainable condition that we all must address.

The forces driving this situation are numerous. Human population has increased exponentially in the past 60 years, from about 2.5 billion in 1950 to more than 7 billion today. Our linear use of resources, treating outputs as waste, is responsible for the toxins that are accumulating in the atmosphere, in water, and on the ground. This pattern of extraction, use, and disposal has hastened depletion of finite supplies of nonrenewable energy, water, and materials and is accelerating the pace of our greatest problem—climate change. Buildings account for a significant portion of greenhouse gas emissions; in the U.S., buildings are associated with 38% of all emissions of carbon dioxide[2]. Globally, the figure is nearly one-third.[3] The problem is anticipated to worsen as developing countries attain higher standards of living. The problem is anticipated to worsen as developing countries achieve higher standards of living.

These forces are bringing us to a tipping point, a threshold beyond which Earth cannot rebalance itself without major disruption to the systems that humans and other species rely on for survival.

The impetus behind development of the Leadership in Energy and Environmental Design (LEED) rating systems was recognition of those problems, coupled with awareness that the building industry—from construction and renovation to operations and maintenance—already had the expertise, tools, and technology to transform daily operations and make significant advances toward a sustainable planet. LEED projects throughout the world have already demonstrated the benefits of taking a green operations and maintenance approach that reduces the environmental harms of existing buildings and restores the balance of natural systems. The opportunity that existing commercial buildings represent is enormous: as world population continues to increase, people have begun to use old buildings in new ways. About 40 percent of the energy consumed in the U.S. and other developed nations is attributable to building operations, and 80 million square feet of the operating building stock is commercial space[4].

1. *Global Footprint Network, footprintnetwork.org/en/index.php/gfn/page/world_footprint/, accessed 9/11/2012*
2. *Energy Information Administration* (2008). *Assumptions to the Annual Energy Outlook*
3. *unep.org/sbci/pdfs/SBCI-BCCSummary.pdf*
4. *iea.org/aboutus/faqs/energyefficiency/.*

ABOUT LEED

Developed by the U.S. Green Building Council, LEED is a framework for identifying, implementing, and measuring green building and neighborhood design, construction, operations, and maintenance. LEED is a voluntary, market-driven, consensus-based tool that serves as a guideline and assessment mechanism for the design, construction, and operation of high-performance green buildings and neighborhoods. LEED rating systems currently address commercial, institutional, and residential building types as well as neighborhood development.

LEED seeks to optimize the use of natural resources, promote regenerative and restorative strategies, maximize the positive and minimize the negative environmental and human health consequences of the building industry, and provide high-quality indoor environments for building occupants. LEED emphasizes integrative design, integration of existing technology, and state-of-the-art strategies to advance expertise in green building and transform professional practice. The technical basis for LEED strikes a balance between requiring today's best practices and encouraging leadership strategies. LEED sets a challenging yet achievable set of benchmarks for interior spaces, entire structures, and whole neighborhoods.

LEED for New Construction and Major Renovations was developed in 1998 for the commercial building industry and has since been updated multiple times. Over the years, a variety of other rating systems have been developed to meet the needs of different market sectors.

Since its launch, LEED has evolved to address new markets and building types, advances in practice and technology, and greater understanding of the environmental and human health effects of the built environment. These ongoing improvements, developed by USGBC member-based volunteer committees, subcommittees, and working groups in conjunction with USGBC staff, have been reviewed by the LEED Steering Committee and the USGBC Board of Directors before being submitted to USGBC members for a vote. The process is based on principles of transparency, openness, and inclusiveness.

LEED'S GOALS

The LEED rating systems aim to promote a transformation of the construction industry through strategies designed to achieve seven goals:

- To reverse contribution to global **climate change**
- To enhance individual **human health** and well-being
- To protect and restore **water resources**
- To protect, enhance, and restore **biodiversity** and ecosystem services
- To promote sustainable and regenerative **material resources** cycles
- To build a **greener economy**
- To enhance social equity, environmental justice, **community** health, and quality of life

These goals are the basis for LEED's prerequisites and credits. In the LEED for Building Operations and Maintenance rating system, the major prerequisites and credits are categorized as Location and Transportation (LT), Sustainable Sites (SS), Water Efficiency (WE), Energy and Atmosphere (EA), Materials and Resources (MR), and Indoor Environmental Quality (EQ).

The goals also drive the weighting of points toward certification. Each credit in the rating system is allocated points based on the relative importance of its contribution to the goals. The result is a weighted average: credits that most directly address the most important goals are given the greatest weight. Project teams that meet the prerequisites and earn enough credits to achieve certification have demonstrated performance that spans the goals in an integrated way. Certification is awarded at four levels (Certified, Silver, Gold, Platinum) to incentivize higher achievement and, in turn, faster progress toward the goals.

BENEFITS OF USING LEED

LEED is designed to address environmental challenges while responding to the needs of a competitive market. Certification demonstrates leadership, innovation, environmental stewardship, and social responsibility. LEED gives building owners and operators the tools they need to immediately improve both building performance and the bottom line while providing healthful indoor spaces for a building's occupants.

LEED-certified buildings are designed to deliver the following benefits:

- Lower operating costs and increased asset value
- Reduced waste sent to landfills
- Energy and water conservation
- More healthful and productive environments for occupants
- Reductions in greenhouse gas emissions
- Qualification for tax rebates, zoning allowances, and other incentives in many cities

By participating in LEED, owners, operators, designers, and builders make a meaningful contribution to the green building industry. By documenting and tracking buildings' resource use, they contribute to a growing body of knowledge that will advance research in this rapidly evolving field. This will allow future projects to build on the successes of today's designs and bring innovations to the market.

LEED CERTIFICATION PROCESS

The process begins when the owner selects the rating system and registers the project (see *Rating System Selection Guidance*). The project team then meets the requirements for all prerequisites and for the credits the team has chosen to pursue. After documentation has been submitted for certification, a project goes through preliminary and final reviews. The preliminary review provides technical advice on credits that require additional work for achievement, and the final review contains the project's final score and certification level. The decision can be appealed if a team believes additional consideration is warranted.

LEED has four levels of certification, depending on the point thresholds achieved:

- Certified, 40–49 points
- Silver, 50–59 points
- Gold, 60–79 points
- Platinum, 80 points and above

INITIAL CERTIFICATION AND RECERTIFICATION

The LEED for Building Operations and Maintenance rating system can be applied both to buildings seeking LEED certification for the first time and to projects previously certified under any version of the LEED Design and Construction rating systems. It is the only LEED rating system that requires projects to recertify.

Initial certification is any first-time application for LEED for Building Operations and Maintenance certification. Recertification is the subsequent application(s) for certification after a project has received an initial certification under any version of LEED for Building Operations and Maintenance. To the extent possible, projects will be held to the requirements of the most current rating system version available on the date the project registers for recertification.

REFERENCE GUIDE OVERVIEW

GUIDE STRUCTURE

GETTING STARTED provides a recommended process for achieving certification and addresses issues that cut across the entire rating system.

CATEGORY OVERVIEWS emphasize sustainability topics, market factors, and credit relationships that are specific to a single credit category and information that is applicable to multiple credits within that category.

CREDITS contain content that is specific to the achievement of that credit.

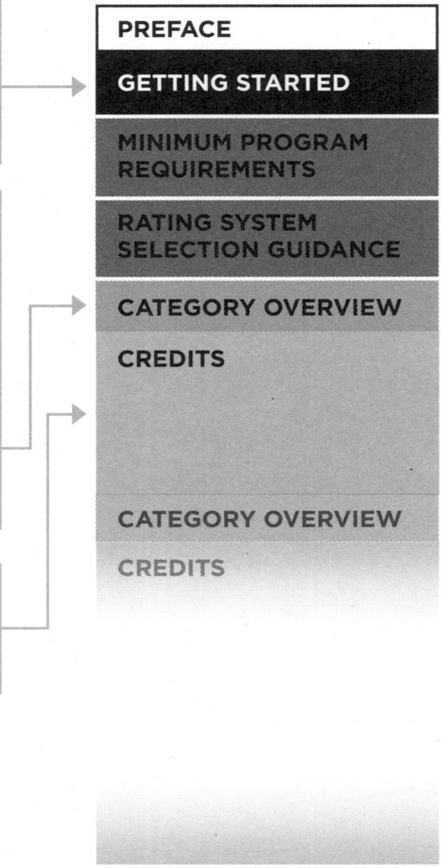

PREFACE
GETTING STARTED
MINIMUM PROGRAM REQUIREMENTS
RATING SYSTEM SELECTION GUIDANCE
CATEGORY OVERVIEW
CREDITS
CATEGORY OVERVIEW
CREDITS

ICONS THAT MAY APPEAR WITHIN EACH CREDIT REFER THE USER TO FOLLOWING SECTIONS:

Getting Started (beginning of book)

Further Explanation (within same credit)

CREDIT STRUCTURE

Each credit category begins with an overview that discusses sustainability and market factors specific to the category. For each prerequisite and credit, readers will then find the following sections:

INTENT & REQUIREMENTS
outlines the rating system requirements for achieving the prerequisite or credit. They were approved through the rating system development process and can also be found on the USGBC website.

BEHIND THE INTENT
connects credit achievement with larger sustainability issues and provides information on how the credit requirements meet the intent stated in the rating system.

STEP-BY-STEP GUIDANCE
suggests the implementation and documentation steps that can be used by most projects, as well as generally applicable tips and examples.

FURTHER EXPLANATION
provides guidance for lengthy calculations or for special project situations, such as tips for nonstandard project types or different credit approaches. It includes a *Campus* section and, sometimes, an *International Tips* section.

REQUIRED DOCUMENTATION
lists the items that must be submitted for certification review.

RELATED CREDIT TIPS
identifies other credits that may affect a project team's decisions and strategies for the credit in question; the relationships between credits may imply synergies or trade-offs.

CHANGES FROM LEED 2009
is a quick reference of changes from the previous version of LEED.

REFERENCED STANDARDS
lists the technical standards related to the credit and offers weblinks to find them.

EXEMPLARY PERFORMANCE
identifies the threshold that must be met to earn an exemplary performance point, if available.

DEFINITIONS
gives the meaning of terms used in the credit.

Getting Started

HOW TO USE THIS REFERENCE GUIDE

This reference guide is designed to elaborate upon and work in conjunction with the rating system. Written by expert users of LEED, it serves as a roadmap, describing the steps for meeting and documenting credit requirements and offering advice on best practices.

Within each section, information is organized to flow from general guidance to more specific tips and finally to supporting references and other information. Sections have been designed with a parallel structure to support way finding and minimize repetition.

CREDIT CATEGORIES

LOCATION AND TRANSPORTATION (LT)

SUSTAINABLE SITES (SS)

WATER EFFICIENCY (WE)

ENERGY AND ATMOSPHERE (EA)

MATERIALS AND RESOURCES (MR)

INDOOR ENVIRONMENTAL QUALITY (EQ)

INNOVATION (IN)

REGIONAL PRIORITY (RP)

MORE ABOUT THE FURTHER EXPLANATION SECTION

Further Explanation contains varied subsections depending on the credit; two of the common subsections are elaborated upon here.

CAMPUS PROJECTS

Campus refers to the Campus Program for Projects on a Shared Site, which certifies multiple buildings located on one site and under the control of a single entity. Examples include buildings on a corporate or educational campus and structures in a commercial development. Only project teams using the Campus Program need to follow the guidance in the Campus section; the guidance is not applicable to projects that are in a campus setting or are part of a multitenant complex but not pursuing certification using the Campus Program.

There are two approaches to certifying multiple buildings under the Campus Program:

- **Group Approach** allows buildings that are substantially similar and are in a single location to certify as one project that shares a single certification.
- **Campus Approach** allows buildings that share a single location and site attributes to achieve separate LEED certification for each project, building space, or group on the master site.

For each approach, the reference guide gives any credit-specific information and notes two possible scenarios:

- **Group Approach**
  - "All buildings in the group may be documented as one." The buildings may meet the credit requirements as a single group by, for example, pooling resources or purchasing, and then submitting a single set of documentation.
  - "Submit separate documentation for each building." Each building in the group project must meet the credit requirements individually for the project to earn the credit.
- **Campus Approach**
  - "Eligible." This credit may be documented once at the level of the master site, and then individual projects within the master site boundary earn the credit without submitting additional documentation.
  - "Ineligible. Each LEED project may pursue the credit individually." Each project within the campus boundary may earn the credit but each project must document compliance separately.

PROJECTS OUTSIDE THE US

The *International Tips* section offers advice on determining equivalency to U.S. standards or using non-U.S. standards referenced in the rating system. It is meant to complement, not replace, the other sections of the credit. Helpful advice for projects outside the U.S. may also appear in the *Step-by-Step Guidance* section of each credit. When no tips are needed or available, the *International Tips* heading does not appear.

Units of measurement are given in both Inch-Pound (IP) and International System of Units (SI). IP refers to the system of measurements based on the inch, pound, and gallon, historically derived from the English system and commonly used in the U.S. SI is the modern metric system used in most other parts of the world and defined by the General Conference on Weights and Measures.

Where "local equivalent" is specified, it means an alternative to a LEED referenced standard that is specific to a project's locality. This standard must be widely used and accepted by industry experts and when applied, must meet the credit's intent leading to similar or better outcomes.

Where "USGBC-approved local equivalent" is specified, it means a local standard deemed equivalent to the listed standard by the U.S. Green Building Council through its process for establishing non-U.S. equivalencies in LEED.

AN INTEGRATIVE APPROACH TO OPERATIONS AND MANAGEMENT

To meet human needs without compromising the bottom line, green building operations require dedication and buy-in from all levels of building and tenant management. The path to sustainable operations requires collaboration, integrative thinking, and a strong team whose members have clearly defined roles and responsibilities.

Successful operations practice engages all team members and emphasizes each person's responsibility for continuing sustainable strategies during transitions and change-over periods. It requires collaborative decision making and information sharing by everyone involved, including staff who oversee waste, chemical applications, or product purchases.

As the team is drafting and implementing a new building policy, for example, an approach that draws on the expertise of all project stakeholders—owner, occupant, engineers, facilities managers, financial managers, contractor—may reveal innovative solutions.

PROJECT GOALS

An integrated team can develop project goals that lay a strong foundation for achievement. The project goals should reflect organizational values and operational realities as well as sustainability targets. Include building stakeholders who understand current facilities practices, such as the owner, building management staff, occupants, and vendors. A diverse team ensures that all operational elements will be considered and the program will be supported by the entire team.

Take a hard look at traditional practices and management and consider the flow of materials, water, and energy through the building and site. For existing buildings, this requires a site study that considers on-site resources and the building's location, orientation, massing, and occupant use patterns. The goal is to identify ways to reduce the loads and environmental harms of each system without increasing those of any others.

Identify existing policies, practices, equipment, contracts, and budgets to set a baseline for improvement. After collecting baseline information, list the areas that may require significant change, moderate change, and low- or no-cost change in operating practices. Identify any organizational issues or pressures that may influence the project goals. Prioritize strategies that are aligned with environmental and organizational values and operational realities.

Environmental Goals

The selection of LEED credits often depends on the project's environmental context, particularly current energy use and site conditions.

- **Energy signature.** To understand how the building behaves in response to the outdoor environment, consider its energy signature—an analysis of measured energy use in relation to seasonal fluctuations in temperature. An energy signature highlights seasonal norms that may prompt operating change and alerts the team to operating inefficiencies. In addition, an energy signature provides insight into whether current systems are meeting the building's heating and cooling needs.
- **Energy benchmarks.** Compare the building's energy use against recognized standards. By benchmarking early, the project team will have time to look at monthly trends in energy use intensity and ENERGY STAR score (where appropriate). Staff will become familiar with recording and reading consumption data and be ready to set efficiency goals.
- **Site analysis.** A detailed site analysis identifies specific conditions—topography, wind patterns, solar availability and shading, water bodies, view corridors—that may guide decisions on rainwater runoff mitigation, landscape water reduction strategies, onsite renewable energy, and other capital investments. Opportunities for improving and preserving the ecological integrity of the site may become clear.

Organizational Goals

Aligning project goals with the owner's and tenants' organizational values allows teams to select green operations strategies that make a strong business case. Examine the following.

- **Corporate social responsibility report.** The owner's or tenant's organizational goals and priorities, articulated in this report, may include aspirations that align with LEED credits.

- **Organizational annual metrics.** Many organizations have requirements for reporting annual statistics on greenhouse gas emissions and waste recycling from their operations. Selecting credits whose achievement improves these metrics will reinforce current efforts.
- **Human resources policies.** These policies and programs may set goals for health initiatives, employee retention, commute trip reduction, or workplace satisfaction, each of which suggests a focus on credits that target employees' well-being.
- **Shareholders' or stakeholders' concerns.** Stakeholders in the organization and project development team may have strongly held ideas about specific sustainability issues. Involving them early in the process ensures that their interests are well represented.

THE CREDIT STRUCTURE OF LEED FOR BUILDING OPERATIONS AND MAINTENANCE

For existing buildings pursuing LEED certification, the establishment period is the time when building infrastructure is assessed, policies are drafted, and programs and processes are put in place to enable ongoing performance measurement. The performance period is the continuous implementation of the strategies set during the establishment period.

Each prerequisite and credit lists the establishment and performance requirements separately. The establishment requirements set projects up for compliance with the performance requirements.

Establishment requirements fall into two categories of credits, those based on building components and site infrastructure and those based on policies and plans:

- Building components and site infrastructure are the characteristics and systems of the building.
- Policies and plans are statements that set goals and outline the implementation of operational management strategies.

ESTABLISHMENT
static and foundational

BUILDING COMPONENTS AND SITE INFRASTRUCTURE
meters, lighting, water fixtures

POLICIES
site management, purchasing

Performance requirements also typically fall into two categories of credits, those that require discrete actions and those that require ongoing tracking and measurement over time:

- Actions are regularly repeated to inform continued performance and to identify opportunities for improvement.
- Ongoing tracking occurs continually, verifying ongoing high performance and upkeep of building systems.

PERFORMANCE
dynamic and recurring

ACTIONS
surveys, audits, testing

POLICIES
energy, purchasing, waste

UNDERSTAND PERFORMANCE PERIODS

LEED for Building Operations and Maintenance certification is based largely on successful outcomes during the performance period, when sustainable operations are being measured. Many prerequisites and credits require that operating data and other documentation be submitted for the performance period. Since the project's certification level is based on these outcomes, the performance period may not have any gaps, defined as any period of time longer than one full week.

The initial performance period is the most recent period of operations preceding the certification application. It must be at least three months but no more than 24 months, except as noted in the credit requirements.

All performance periods must overlap and conclude within 30 days of each other. In the example (Table 1), each performance period is at least three months, and the termination dates range from April 1 through April 26.

TABLE 1. Example performance periods, by credit

Credit	Start	End*	Duration**
WE Credit Outdoor Water Use	February 22, 2014	April 20, 2015	14 months
SS Credit Rainwater Management	April 6, 2014	April 22, 2015	12.5 months
EA Prerequisite Minimum Energy Performance	April 1, 2014	April 1, 2015	12 months
SS Credit Site Management	August 25, 2014	April 25, 2015	8 months
WE Prerequisite Indoor Water Use	January 12, 2015	April 26, 2015	3.5 months

* All performance periods must end with the same 30-day interval.

** Minimum duration = 3 months; maximum duration = 24 months

To ensure that certification is awarded based on current building performance data, LEED for Building Operations and Maintenance certification applications must be submitted for review within 60 calendar days of the end of the performance periods. The 60-day period starts the day after the last day of the latest performance period.

In the example given above (Table 1), the last day of a performance period is April 26; the project team must submit its application in 60 days, counting from April 27.

RECERTIFICATION

Projects must recertify within five years of the previous certification and are eligible as often as every 12 months.

The recertification performance period extends from the date of the previous certification to the date of the recertification application. If projects pursue new credits in the recertification application, they may use the initial certification performance period rules (see *Understand Performance Periods*, above), unless otherwise noted in the credit requirements.

Since buildings do not stop operations while waiting for certification, it is recommended that project teams continue to track building performance during the certification review process.

Projects pursuing recertification are required to submit only performance documentation for review; they are not required to submit establishment documentation unless there have been major changes (e.g., major renovations, major addition, management turnover) that prompt review.

LEED WORK PLAN

It is recommended that LEED applicants follow a series of steps to certification.

STEP 1. SELECT LEED RATING SYSTEM

The LEED system comprises 21 adaptations designed to accommodate the needs of a variety of market sectors (see *Rating System Selection Guidance*). For many credits, *Further Explanation* highlights rating system and project type variations to help teams develop a successful approach.

STEP 2. CHECK MINIMUM PROGRAM REQUIREMENTS

All projects seeking certification are required to comply with the minimum program requirements (MPRs) for the applicable rating system, found in this reference guide and on the USGBC website.

STEP 3. DEFINE LEED PROJECT SCOPE

Review the project's program and initial findings from the goal-setting workshop to identify the project scope. Considerations include multiple buildings and management variations.

Next, map the LEED project boundary to comply with the minimum program requirements.

Finally, investigate any special certification programs that may apply based on the project's scope, such as the Volume Program or the Campus Program. If the owner is planning multiple similar projects in different locations, Volume may be a useful program to streamline certification. If the project includes multiple buildings in a single location, Campus may be appropriate.

STEP 4. DEVELOP LEED SCORECARD

Use the project goals to identify the credits and options that should be attempted by the team. The *Behind the Intent* sections offer insight into what each credit is intended to achieve and may help teams align goals with credits that bring value to the owner, environment, and community of the project.

A gap analysis may identify the feasibility of certain strategies and indicate whether the team should conduct energy audits, commission building systems, or start organizing utility data in preparation for the performance period. Using this information, the team can identify priority and supporting credits.

Finally, establish the target LEED certification level (Certified, Silver, Gold, or Platinum) and identify additional credits needed to achieve it. Make sure that all prerequisites can be met and include a buffer of several points above the minimum in case of changes during the performance period.

STEP 5. ASSIGN ROLES AND RESPONSIBILITIES

Select one team member to take primary responsibility for leading the group through the LEED application and documentation process.

Cross-disciplinary team ownership of credit compliance can help foster integrated implementation while ensuring consistent documentation across credits. On a credit-by-credit basis, assign primary and supporting roles to appropriate team members for credit achievement and documentation; this includes assigning responsibility for crucial tasks like water meter reading, purchases tracking, and vendor management. Clarify responsibilities for ensuring that policy and infrastructure upgrade decisions are fully implemented and documented, and that performance outcomes align with operational intent and goals.

Establish regular meeting dates and develop clear communication channels to streamline the process and resolve issues quickly. Double-check that all assignments for surveys, tracking, and audits are clear and that team members understand their roles.

STEP 6. DETERMINE PERFORMANCE PERIOD

Determining a performance period schedule is necessary for compliance with most credits. All performance periods must end within 30 days of each other and (for a newly attempted credit) last at least three months but no more than 24 months (see *Understand Performance Periods*, above).

STEP 7. DEVELOP CONSISTENT DOCUMENTATION

Consistent documentation is critical to LEED certification success. Designate one person as the single point of contact for all LEED documentation. Data accumulated throughout the performance period, such as purchasing activities, should be uploaded regularly to allow the team to track ongoing progress. The *Maintaining Consistency in the Application* section, below, and the credit category overviews discuss common consistency issues that will affect achievement of multiple credits.

STEP 8. PERFORM QUALITY ASSURANCE REVIEW AND SUBMIT FOR CERTIFICATION

A quality assurance review is an essential part of the work program. A thorough quality control check can improve presentation of the project and avoid errors that require time and expense to correct later in the certification process. The submission should be thoroughly proofread and checked for completeness. In particular, numeric values that appear throughout the submission must be consistent, e.g. site area.

MAINTAINING CONSISTENCY IN THE APPLICATION

Certain issues recur across multiple credits and credit categories and must be treated consistently throughout the submission.

EFFECTIVE POLICY DEVELOPMENT

The following components must be included in policies developed for compliance with LEED prerequisites and credits.

Physical and programmatic scope. Describe the physical and programmatic scope of the policy. If any spaces within the building or site are excluded, describe the exemption and explain the reason.

Duration of applicability. Identify the time period to which the policy applies. For example, "This policy shall take effect on XX/XX/XXXX and shall continue indefinitely or until amended and/or replaced by a subsequent sustainable purchasing policy."

Responsible parties. By full name and title or position, name the person who will implement the policy. If a vendor is responsible for implementing parts of the plan, name both the vendor and the building manager to whom the vendor reports. Including contact information makes it easy for anybody who references the policy to reach the responsible party. If there are multiple responsible parties, consider identifying clearly which components of the policy each oversees.

Sustainability goals and objectives. Identify the sustainability goals of the policy. Goals must be measurable and are typically numerical. For example, "50% of waste (measured by weight) will be diverted from the landfill" or "75% of ice melt purchased will meet sustainability requirements." Although measurable goals must be set, documentation to demonstrate actual achievement of the set goals is not required for these policies.

Performance evaluation metrics. Explain how actual outcomes and sustainability performance for each element of the policy will be measured and tracked over time. For example, "the percentage of waste diverted will be measured by weight" or "the percentage of cleaning purchases that meet sustainability requirements will be measured by cost."

Procedures and strategies for implementation. Outline the procedures, strategies, and best management practices to be used to achieve the goals. For projects with multiple tenants, describe how building managers will provide education and guidance to encourage tenants to comply. To help with implementation, list contacts, websites, past experiences, and other resources.

Quality assurance process. Describe how the responsible party will verify that the policy is being implemented, that the metrics reflect the actual outcomes, and that performance persists over time. This may include periodic checks to make sure the policy is consistently implemented and that the set goals are being achieved.

OCCUPANCY

Many kinds of people use a typical LEED building, and the mix varies by project type. Occupants are sometimes referred to in a general sense; for example, "Provide places of respite that are accessible to patients and visitors." In other instances, occupants must be counted for calculations. Definitions of occupant types are general guidelines that may be modified or superseded in a particular credit when appropriate (such changes are noted in each credit's reference guide section). Most credits group users into two categories, regular building occupants and visitors.

Regular Building Occupants

Regular building occupants are habitual users of a building. All of the following are considered regular building occupants.

> **Employees** include part-time and full-time employees, and totals are calculated using full-time equivalency (FTE).
>
> A typical project can count FTE employees by adding full-time employees and part-time employees, adjusted for their hours of work.

EQUATION 1.

$$\text{FTE employees} = \text{Full-time employees} + (\Sigma \text{ daily part-time employee hours} / 8)$$

For buildings with more unusual occupancy patterns, calculate the FTE building occupants based on a standard eight-hour occupancy period.

EQUATION 2.

$$\text{FTE employees} = (\Sigma \text{ all employee hours} / 8)$$

Staff is synonymous with employees for the purpose of LEED calculations.

Volunteers who regularly use a building are synonymous with employees for the purpose of LEED calculations.

Residents of a project are considered regular building occupants. This includes residents of a dormitory. If actual resident count is not known, use a default equal to the number of bedrooms in the dwelling unit plus one, multiplied by the number of such dwelling units.

Primary and secondary school students are typically regular building occupants.

Hotel guests are typically considered regular building occupants, with some credit-specific exceptions. Calculate the number of overnight hotel guests based on the number and size of units in the project. Assume 1.5 occupants per guest room and multiply the resulting total by 60% (average hotel occupancy). Alternatively, the number of hotel guest occupants may be derived from actual or historical occupancy.

Inpatients are medical, surgical, maternity, specialty, and intensive-care unit patients whose length of stay exceeds 23 hours. **Peak inpatients** are the highest number of inpatients at a given point in a typical 24-hour period.

Visitors

Visitors (also "transients") intermittently use a LEED building. All of the following are considered visitors:

Retail customers are considered visitors. In Water Efficiency credits, retail customers are considered separately from other kinds of visitors and should not be included in the total average daily visitors.

Outpatients visit a hospital, clinic, or associated health care facility for diagnosis or treatment that lasts 23 hours or less.

Peak outpatients are the highest number of outpatients at a given point in a typical 24-hour period.

Volunteers who periodically use a building (e.g., once per week) are considered visitors.

Higher-education students are considered visitors to most buildings, except when they are residents of a dorm, in which case they are residents.

In calculations, occupant types are typically counted in two ways:

Daily averages take into account all the occupants of a given type for a typical 24-hour day of operation.

Peak totals are measured at the moment in a typical 24-hour period when the highest number of a given occupant type is present.

Whenever possible, use actual or predicted occupancies. If occupancy cannot be accurately predicted, one of the following resources to estimate occupancy:

a. Default occupant density from ASHRAE 62.1-2010, Table 6-1

b. Default occupant density from CEN Standard EN 15251, Table B.2

c. Appendix 2 Default Occupancy Counts

d. Results from applicable studies.

If numbers vary seasonally, use occupancy numbers that are a representative daily average over the entire operating season of the building.

If occupancy patterns are atypical (shift overlap, significant seasonal variation), explain such patterns when submitting documentation for certification.

Table 2 lists prerequisites and credits that require specific occupancy counts for calculations.

TABLE 2. Occupancy types for calculations, by project type variation

Prerequisite, credit	Regular building occupants	Average daily visitors	Peak visitors	Other	Notes
LT Credit Alternative Transportation					
Existing Buildings, Data Centers, Warehouses and Distribution Centers, Hospitality, Schools, Retail	X	X	X		Counting hotel guests is not required. Only students of driving age must be counted.
EQ Credit Occupant Comfort Survey					
Existing Buildings, Data Centers, Warehouses and Distribution Centers, Hospitality, Schools, Retail	X				
WE Prerequisite and Credit Indoor Water Use					
Existing Buildings, Data Centers, Warehouses and Distribution Centers, Hospitality, Schools, Retail	X	X			Retail customers are considered separately and not included in average daily visitors.

CONSIDERING OCCUPANT IMPACT IN AN EXISTING BUILDING

Occupants' interaction with a building may enhance or compromise the sustainability and efficiency goals of the operations team and owner. For example, if the occupants have complete control over temperature and lighting, energy consumption may rise, but too little control may increase complaints to facilities staff. Similarly, an open-office layout that allows views to the outdoors could compromise acoustics and productivity and also affect heating and cooling. Energy efficiency and indoor environmental quality goals entail many such trade-offs.

Making decisions that account for occupant preferences is likely to increase their satisfaction with their working environment and encourage them to take interest in achieving the long term sustainability goals of the organization.

Surveying occupants during the establishment period will shed light on their preferences and needs and help inform project goals at the outset. A subsequent survey will indicate how well the new policies and systems are working.

TENANT SPACE EXCLUSION ALLOWANCE

Projects with leased spaces may face particular challenges in earning LEED for Building Operations and Maintenance credits. Whereas the prerequisites address the base building systems or are limited to areas under management control, many credits require commitment and cooperation from tenants. Project teams should review the lease terms and management situation and either obtain commitments from tenants or pursue credits that do not require tenants' participation. Projects that have a few large tenants may be able to satisfy the requirements more easily than buildings with many small tenant spaces.

Projects may exclude up to 10% of the total gross building floor area from the LEED project boundary, which will apply consistently throughout the submission except in EQ Environmental Tobacco Smoke, where the entire building must be considered. Projects may take an additional 10% exemption on a credit-by-credit basis if it is not possible to gather the necessary tenant data for these credits, or the applicant does not have control over the required element (this additional 10% may not be applied to the EA Prerequisite Minimum Energy Performance). The specific spaces excluded as part of the 10% can vary by credit. Project teams must clearly note which spaces have been excluded in which credit when preparing documentation for certification.

MINIMUM OCCUPANCY

EA Prerequisite Minimum Energy Performance includes a minimum occupancy requirement. No other credits specify a minimum occupancy threshold.

VARIABLE OCCUPANCY

When occupancy rates vary over the performance period, that variation should be reflected in credit calculations via a time-weighted average.

Generally, for partially occupied buildings, project teams document the performance of the entire building as if it were fully occupied. Because completely vacant or unused space has no activity and may lack the furnishings, fixtures, and equipment intended for regular operations, however, partial occupancy changes the way the performance is documented for the following credits.

WE Prerequisite Indoor Water Use and WE Credit Indoor Water Use
To determine the annual usage of each plumbing fixture type, use the following rules:

- For floors or separate tenant spaces that are partially occupied during part of the performance period, use the regular procedures to document prerequisite achievement. Extrapolate partial-year data to derive annual values unless circumstances justify an adjustment.
- For floors or separate tenant spaces that are completely vacant or unused throughout the entire performance period, base usage on the estimated occupancy count. Allocate occupants to the building's fixture types in a reasonable way. Create usage groups in the indoor water use reduction calculator to account for the vacant areas.

These rules apply to both base building or core fixtures and tenant space fixtures. If fixture upgrades are required to achieve compliance, it is recommended that project teams first focus on base building or core fixtures.

EQ Prerequisite Minimum Indoor Air Quality Performance

For mechanically ventilated spaces that are partially occupied during part the performance period or completely vacant or unused throughout the entire performance period, use the regular procedures, with the following exceptions.

- Determine the minimum amount of outdoor air that must be supplied at full occupancy. Perform calculations using the estimated occupancy count if needed.
- Measure the outdoor airflow rates to determine whether the systems can deliver sufficient ventilation under assumed normal full-occupancy conditions.
- For actual operation, consider reducing the amount of outdoor air supplied to the partially occupied, vacant, or unused space.

For naturally ventilated spaces, use the normal procedures for this prerequisite.

EQ Credit Enhanced Indoor Air Quality Strategies and EQ Credit Thermal Comfort
For spaces that are completely vacant or unused throughout the entire performance period, the team has two choices:

- Install the appropriate particle filters or air-cleaning devices or monitoring devices, or
- Exclude the vacant or unused space from the credit requirements.

If the space becomes occupied, however, it will need to be included to achieve the credit in future LEED certifications.

Vacant or unused spaces do not need to be monitored or tested during the performance period.

EQ Credit Interior Lighting and EQ Credit Daylight and Views
For spaces that are completely vacant or unused throughout the entire performance period but have furnishings, fixtures, and equipment intended for regular operations, use the regular procedures.

For spaces that are completely vacant or unused throughout the entire performance period, exclude this area from credit calculations and measurements. If a space becomes occupied, however, it will need to be included to achieve the credit in future LEED certifications.

EQ Credit Occupant Comfort Survey
The Occupant Comfort Survey credit requires that survey responses be collected from a representative sample of building occupants, making up at least 30% of the total occupants. For partially occupied buildings, use actual occupancy (or a time-weighted average if occupancy varies through the performance period) to determine how many occupants must be surveyed.

PROJECTS WITH SEVERAL PHYSICALLY DISTINCT STRUCTURES

Primary and secondary school projects, hospitals (general medical and surgical), hotels, resorts, and resort properties, as defined for ENERGY STAR building rating purposes, are eligible to include more than one physically distinct structure in a single LEED project certification application without having to use the Campus Program, subject to the following conditions.

- The buildings to be certified must be a part of the same identity. For example, the buildings are all part of the same elementary school, not a mix of elementary school and high school buildings.
- The project must be analyzed as a whole (i.e., in aggregate) for all minimum program requirements (MPRs), prerequisites, and credits in the LEED rating system.
- All the land area and all building floor areas within the LEED project boundary must be included in every prerequisite and credit submitted for certification.
- There is no specific limit on the number of structures, but the aggregate gross floor area included in a single project must not exceed 1 million square feet (92 905 square meters).

Any single structure that is larger than 25,000 square feet (2 320 square meters) must be registered as a separate project or treated as a separate building in a group certification approach.

QUICK REFERENCE

TABLE 3. Credit Attributes

Category	Prerequisite/ Credit	Credit Name	Exemplary Performance
LT Location and Transportation			
LT	C	Alternative Transportation	yes
SS Sustainable Sites			
SS	P	Site Management Policy	no
SS	C	Site Development--Protect or Restore Habitat	yes
SS	C	Rainwater Management	yes
SS	C	Heat Island Reduction	yes
SS	C	Light Pollution Reduction	no
SS	C	Site Management	no
SS	C	Site Improvement Plan	no
SS	C	Joint Use of Facilities	no
WE Water Efficiency			
WE	P	Indoor Water Use Reduction	no
WE	P	Building-Level Water Metering	no
WE	C	Outdoor Water Use Reduction	no
WE	C	Indoor Water Use Reduction	yes
WE	C	Cooling Tower Water Use	no
WE	C	Water Metering	no
EA Energy and Atmosphere			
EA	P	Energy Efficiency Best Management Practices	no
EA	P	Minimum Energy Performance	no
EA	P	Building Level Energy Metering	no
EA	P	Fundamental Refrigerant Management	no
EA	C	Existing Building Commissioning--Analysis	no
EA	C	Existing Building Commissioning--Implementation	no
EA	C	Ongoing Commissioning	no
EA	C	Optimize Energy Performance	yes
EA	C	Advanced Energy Metering	no
EA	C	Demand Response	no

Points					
Existing Buildings	Schools	Retail	Data Centers	Warehouses and Distribution Centers	Hospitality
15	15	15	15	15	15
Req	Req	Req	Req	Req	Req
2	2	2	2	2	2
3	2	3	3	3	3
2	2	2	2	2	2
1	1	1	1	1	1
1	1	1	1	1	1
1	1	1	1	1	1
N / A	1	N / A	1	N / A	N / A
Req	Req	Req	Req	Req	Req
Req	Req	Req	Req	Req	Req
2	2	2	2	2	2
5	5	5	4	5	5
3	3	3	4	3	3
2	2	2	2	2	2
Req	Req	Req	Req	Req	Req
Req	Req	Req	Req	Req	Req
Req	Req	Req	Req	Req	Req
Req	Req	Req	Req	Req	Req
2	2	2	2	2	2
2	2	2	2	2	2
3	3	3	3	3	3
20	20	20	20	20	20
2	2	2	2	2	2
3	3	3	3	3	3

TABLE 3 (CONTINUED). Credit Attributes

Category	Prerequisite/ Credit	Credit Name	Exemplary Performance
EA	C	Renewable Energy and Carbon Offsets	yes
EA	C	Enhanced Refrigerant Management	no
MR Materials and Resources			
MR	P	Ongoing Purchasing and Waste Policy	no
MR	P	Facility Maintenance and Renovation Policy	no
MR	C	Purchasing - Ongoing	yes
MR	C	Purchasing - Lamps	yes
MR	C	Purchasing - Facility Management and Renovation	yes
MR	C	Solid Waste Management - Ongoing	yes
MR	C	Solid Waste Management - Facility Maintenance and Renovation	yes
EQ Indoor Environmental Quality			
EQ	P	Minimum Indoor Air Quality Performance	no
EQ	P	Environmental Tobacco Smoke Control	no
EQ	P	Green Cleaning Policy	no
EQ	C	Indoor Air Quality Management Program	no
EQ	C	Enhanced Indoor Air Quality Strategies	yes
EQ	C	Thermal Comfort	no
EQ	C	Interior Lighting	no
EQ	C	Daylight and Quality Views	yes
EQ	C	Green Cleaning--Custodial Effectiveness Assessment	no
EQ	C	Green Cleaning--Products and Materials	yes
EQ	C	Green Cleaning--Equipment	yes
EQ	C	Integrated Pest Management	no
EQ	C	Occupant Comfort Survey	no
IN Innovation			
IN	C	Innovation	no
IN	C	LEED Accredited Professional	no
RP Regional Priority			
RP	C	Regional Priority	no

Points					
New Construction	Schools	Retail	Data Centers	Warehouses and Distribution Centers	Hospitality
5	5	5	5	5	5
1	1	1	1	1	1
Req	Req	Req	Req	Req	Req
Req	Req	Req	Req	Req	Req
2	2	2	2	2	2
2	2	2	2	2	2
1	1	1	1	1	1
1	1	1	1	1	1
2	2	2	2	2	2
Req	Req	Req	Req	Req	Req
Req	Req	Req	Req	Req	Req
Req	Req	Req	Req	Req	Req
2	2	2	2	2	2
2	2	2	2	2	2
1	1	1	1	1	1
2	2	2	2	2	2
4	4	4	4	4	4
1	1	1	1	1	1
1	1	1	1	1	1
1	1	1	1	1	1
2	2	2	2	2	2
1	1	1	1	1	1
5	5	5	5	5	5
1	1	1	1	1	1
4	4	4	4	4	4

Minimum Program Requirements

INTRODUCTION

The Minimum Program Requirements (MPRs) are the minimum characteristics or conditions that make a project appropriate to pursue LEED certification. These requirements are foundational to all LEED projects and define the types of buildings, spaces, and neighborhoods that the LEED rating system is designed to evaluate.

1. MUST BE IN A PERMANENT LOCATION ON EXISTING LAND

INTENT

The LEED rating system is designed to evaluate buildings, spaces, and neighborhoods in the context of their surroundings. A significant portion of LEED requirements are dependent on the project's location, therefore it is important that LEED projects are evaluated as permanent structures. Locating projects on existing land is important to avoid artificial land masses that have the potential to displace and disrupt ecosystems.

REQUIREMENTS

All LEED projects must be constructed and operated on a permanent location on existing land. No project that is designed to move at any point in its lifetime may pursue LEED certification. This requirement applies to all land within the LEED project.

ADDITIONAL GUIDANCE

Permanent location

- Movable buildings are not eligible for LEED. This includes boats and mobile homes.
- Prefabricated or modular structures and building elements may be certified once permanently installed as part of the LEED project.

Existing land

- Buildings located on previously constructed docks, piers, jetties, infill, and other manufactured structures in or above water are permissible, provided that the artificial land is previously developed, such that the land once supported another building or hardscape constructed for a purpose other than the LEED project.

2. MUST USE REASONABLE LEED BOUNDARIES

INTENT

The LEED rating system is designed to evaluate buildings, spaces, or neighborhoods, and all environmental impacts associated with those projects. Defining a reasonable LEED boundary ensures that project is accurately evaluated.

REQUIREMENTS

The LEED project boundary must include all contiguous land that is associated with the project and supports its typical operations. This includes land altered as a result of construction and features used primarily by the project's occupants, such as hardscape (parking and sidewalks), septic or stormwater treatment equipment, and landscaping. The LEED boundary may not unreasonably exclude portions of the building, space, or site to give the project an advantage in complying with credit requirements. The LEED project must accurately communicate the scope of the certifying project in all promotional and descriptive materials and distinguish it from any non-certifying space.

ADDITIONAL GUIDANCE

Site

- Non-contiguous parcels of land may be included within the LEED project boundary if the parcels directly support or are associated with normal building operations of the LEED project and are accessible to the LEED project's occupants.
- Facilities (such as parking lots, bicycle storage, shower/changing facilities, and/or on-site renewable energy) that are outside of the LEED project boundary may be included in certain prerequisites and credits if they directly serve the LEED project and are not double-counted for other LEED projects. The project team must also have permission to use these facilities.
- The LEED project boundary may include other buildings.

  - If another building or structure within the LEED project boundary is ineligible for LEED certification, it may be included in the certification of the LEED project. It may also be excluded.
  - If another building within the LEED project boundary is eligible for LEED certification, it may be included in the certification if USGBC's multiple building guidance is followed. It may also be excluded.
- Projects that are phased sites with a master plan for multiple buildings must designate a LEED project boundary for each building or follow USGBC's master site guidance.
- The gross floor area of the LEED project should be no less than 2% of the gross land area within the LEED project boundary.

Building

- The LEED project should include the complete scope of work of the building or interior space.
- The LEED project can be delineated by ownership, management, lease, or party wall separation.
- Buildings or structures primarily dedicated to parking are not eligible for LEED certification. Parking that serves an eligible LEED project should be included in the certification.
- If the project consists of multiple structures physically connected only by circulation, parking or mechanical/storage rooms, it may be considered a single building for LEED purposes if the structures have programmatic dependency (spaces, not personnel, within the building cannot function independently without the other building) or architectural cohesiveness (the building was designed to appear as one building).
- An addition to an existing building may certify independently, excluding the existing building in its entirety. Alternatively, the addition and the entire existing building may certify as one project.

Interiors

- If a single entity owns, manages, or occupies an entire building and wishes to certify a renovated portion of the building that is not separated by ownership, management, lease, or party wall separation, they may do so if the project boundary includes 100% of the construction scope and is drawn at a clear, physical barrier.

Neighborhood

- The LEED neighborhood includes the land, water, and construction within the LEED project boundary.
- The LEED boundary is usually defined by the platted property line of the project, including all land and water within it.
  - Projects located on publicly owned campuses that do not have internal property lines must delineate a sphere-of-influence line to be used instead.
  - Projects may have enclaves of non-project properties that are not subject to the rating system, but cannot exceed 2% of the total project area and cannot be described as certified.
  - Projects must not contain non-contiguous parcels, but parcels can be separated by public rights-of-way.
- The project developer, which can include several property owners, should control a majority of the buildable land within the boundary, but does not have to control the entire area.

3. MUST COMPLY WITH PROJECT SIZE REQUIREMENTS

INTENT

The LEED rating system is designed to evaluate buildings, spaces, or neighborhoods of a certain size. The LEED requirements do not accurately assess the performance of projects outside of these size requirements.

REQUIREMENTS

All LEED projects must meet the size requirements listed below.

LEED BD+C and LEED O+M Rating Systems

The LEED project must include a minimum of 1,000 square feet (93 square meters) of gross floor area.

LEED ID+C Rating Systems

The LEED project must include a minimum of 250 square feet (22 square meters) of gross floor area.

LEED for Neighborhood Development Rating Systems

The LEED project should contain at least two habitable buildings and be no larger than 1500 acres.

LEED for Homes Rating Systems

The LEED project must be defined as a "dwelling unit" by all applicable codes. This requirement includes, but is not limited to, the International Residential Code stipulation that a dwelling unit must include "permanent provisions for living, sleeping, eating, cooking, and sanitation."

Rating System Selection Guidance

INTRODUCTION

This document provides guidance to help project teams select a LEED rating system. Projects are required to use the rating system that is most appropriate. However, when the decision is not clear, it is the responsibility of the project team to make a reasonable decision in selecting a rating system before registering their project. The project teams should first identify an appropriate rating system, and then determine the best adaptation. Occasionally, USGBC recognizes that an entirely inappropriate rating system has been chosen. In this case, the project team will be asked to change the designated rating system for their registered project. Please review this guidance carefully and contact USGBC if it is not clear which rating system to use.

RATING SYSTEM DESCRIPTIONS

LEED FOR BUILDING DESIGN AND CONSTRUCTION

Buildings that are new construction or major renovation. In addition, at least 60% of the project's *gross floor area* must be *complete* by the time of certification (except for LEED BD+C: Core and Shell).

- **LEED BD+C: New Construction and Major Renovation.** New construction or major renovation of buildings that do not primarily serve K-12 educational, retail, data centers, warehouses and distribution centers, hospitality, or healthcare uses. New construction also includes high-rise residential buildings 9 stories or more.
- **LEED BD+C: Core and Shell Development.** Buildings that are new construction or major renovation for the exterior shell and core mechanical, electrical, and plumbing units, but not a complete interior fit-out. LEED BD+C: Core and Shell is the appropriate rating system to use if more than 40% of the gross floor area is incomplete at the time of certification.
- **LEED BD+C: Schools.** Buildings made up of core and ancillary learning spaces on K-12 school grounds. LEED BD+C: Schools may optionally be used for higher education and non-academic buildings on school campuses.
- **LEED BD+C: Retail.** Buildings used to conduct the retail sale of consumer product goods. Includes both direct customer service areas (showroom) and preparation or storage areas that support customer service.
- **LEED BD+C: Data Centers.** Buildings specifically designed and equipped to meet the needs of high density computing equipment such as server racks, used for data storage and processing. LEED BD+C: Data Centers only addresses whole building data centers (greater than 60%).
- **LEED BD+C: Warehouses and Distribution Centers.** Buildings used to store goods, manufactured products, merchandise, raw materials, or personal belongings, such as self-storage.
- **LEED BD+C: Hospitality.** Buildings dedicated to hotels, motels, inns, or other businesses within the service industry that provide transitional or short-term lodging with or without food.
- **LEED BD+C: Healthcare.** Hospitals that operate twenty-four hours a day, seven days a week and provide inpatient medical treatment, including acute and long-term care.
- **LEED BD+C: Homes and Multifamily Lowrise.** Single-family homes and multi-family residential buildings of 1 to 3 stories. Projects 3 to 5 stories may choose the Homes rating system that corresponds to the ENERGY STAR program in which they are participating.
- **LEED BD+C: Multifamily Midrise.** Multi-family residential buildings of 4 to 8 occupiable stories above grade. The building must have 50% or more residential space. Buildings near 8 stories can inquire with USGBC about using Midrise or New Construction, if appropriate.

LEED FOR INTERIOR DESIGN AND CONSTRUCTION.

Interior spaces that are a complete interior fit-out. In addition, at least 60% of the project's gross floor area must be complete by the time of certification.

- **LEED ID+C: Commercial Interiors.** Interior spaces dedicated to functions other than retail or hospitality.
- **LEED ID+C: Retail.** Interior spaces used to conduct the retail sale of consumer product goods. Includes both direct customer service areas (showroom) and preparation or storage areas that support customer service.
- **LEED ID+C: Hospitality.** Interior spaces dedicated to hotels, motels, inns, or other businesses within the service industry that provide transitional or short-term lodging with or without food.

LEED FOR BUILDING OPERATIONS AND MAINTENANCE.

Existing buildings that are undergoing *improvement* work or little to no construction.

- **LEED O+M: Existing Buildings.** Existing buildings that do not primarily serve K-12 educational, retail, data centers, warehouses and distribution centers, or hospitality uses.
- **LEED O+M: Retail.** Existing buildings used to conduct the retail sale of consumer product goods. Includes both direct customer service areas (showroom) and preparation or storage areas that support customer service.

- **LEED O+M: Schools.** Existing buildings made up of core and ancillary learning spaces on K-12 school grounds. May also be used for higher education and non-academic buildings on school campuses.
- **LEED O+M: Hospitality.** Existing buildings dedicated to hotels, motels, inns, or other businesses within the service industry that provide transitional or short-term lodging with or without food.
- **LEED O+M: Data Centers.** Existing buildings specifically designed and equipped to meet the needs of high density computing equipment such as server racks, used for data storage and processing. LEED O+M: Data Centers only addresses whole building data centers.
- **LEED O+M: Warehouses and Distribution Centers.** Existing buildings used to store goods, manufactured products, merchandise, raw materials, or personal belongings (such as self-storage).

LEED FOR NEIGHBORHOOD DEVELOPMENT

New land development projects or redevelopment projects containing residential uses, nonresidential uses, or a mix. Projects may be at any stage of the development process, from conceptual planning through construction. It is recommended that at least 50% of total building floor area be new construction or major renovation. Buildings within the project and features in the public realm are evaluated.

- **LEED ND: Plan.** PProjects in conceptual planning or master planning phases, or under construction.
- **LEED ND: Built Project.** Completed development projects.

CHOOSING BETWEEN RATING SYSTEMS

The following 40/60 rule provides guidance for making a decision when several rating systems appear to be appropriate for a project. To use this rule, first assign a rating system to each square foot or square meter of the building. Then, choose the most appropriate rating system based on the resulting percentages.

The entire gross floor area of a LEED project must be certified under a single rating system and is subject to all prerequisites and attempted credits in that rating system, regardless of mixed construction or space usage type.

PERCENTAGE OF FLOOR AREA APPROPRIATE FOR A PARTICULAR RATING SYSTEM

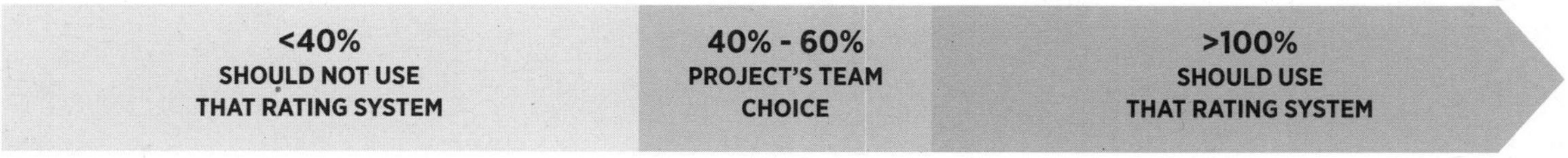

<40%	40% - 60%	>100%
SHOULD NOT USE THAT RATING SYSTEM	PROJECT'S TEAM CHOICE	SHOULD USE THAT RATING SYSTEM

- If a rating system is appropriate for less than 40% of the gross floor area of a LEED project building or space, then that rating system should not be used.
- If a rating system is appropriate for more than 60% of the gross floor area of a LEED project building or space, then that rating system should be used.
- If an appropriate rating system falls between 40% and 60% of the gross floor area, project teams must independently assess their situation and decide which rating system is most applicable.

Location and Transportation (LT)

OVERVIEW

The Location and Transportation (LT) category rewards thoughtful project team decisions about building location and how that location affects commuting patterns. The transportation sector is responsible for about one-quarter of energy-related greenhouse gas emissions worldwide,[1] and these emissions increased 17.5% from 1990 to 2010.[2] A significant portion of these emissions come from conventional commuting—that is, commuting in a single-occupancy vehicle that runs on conventional fossil fuel. Transportation infrastructure and commuting patterns are often intertwined with land-use patterns, and decentralized, disjointed transportation infrastructure can contribute to sprawling, inefficient land development. Thus, alternative transportation is an important part of a project's overall environmental performance.

Understanding the transportation patterns of tenants and providing transportation demand management tools are important first steps, but tracking building occupants' behavior is essential to determining whether projects are achieving results. Building operators and owners who are well informed about their occupants' travel patterns will be able to develop policies and incentives that can encourage changes in transportation habits.

1. *International Council on Clean Transportation, Passenger Vehicles, theicct.org/passenger-vehicles (accessed March 22, 2013).*
2. *cta.ornl.gov/data/chapter11.shtml, Table 11.7.*

LOCATION AND TRANSPORTATION CREDIT

Alternative Transportation

This credit applies to:

Existing Buildings (1–15 points)
Schools(1–15 points)
Retail (1–15 points)
Data Centers (1–15 points)
Hospitality (1–15 points)
Warehouses and Distribution Centers (1–15 points)

INTENT

To reduce pollution and land development effects from automobile use for transportation.

REQUIREMENTS

ESTABLISHMENT E

None.

PERFORMANCE P

OPTION 1. TRANSPORTATION SURVEY (1 POINT)

Conduct a survey of building occupants on their transportation patterns. Regular building occupants must be surveyed. Visitors must be surveyed if either the typical peak or daily average is greater than the number of regular building occupants.

Conduct a transportation survey at least once every five years.

OR

OPTION 2. ALTERNATIVE TRANSPORTATION RATE (3–15 POINTS)

Meet the requirements of Option 1.

Demonstrate an alternative transportation rate in accordance with Table 1. Alternative transportation strategies that contribute to this reduction include human-powered conveyances (e.g. walking or biking), public transit, telecommuting, rideshare options, compressed workweeks, carpools, and green vehicles.

Calculations are performed relative to a baseline case that assumes all regular occupants commute alone in conventional automobiles. The calculations must account for seasonal variations in the use of alternative commuting methods and should indicate the distribution of commuting trips using each type of alternative transportation strategy.

TABLE 1. Points for alternative transportation rate

Alternative transportation rate	Points
10%	3
15%	4
20%	5
25%	6
30%	7
35%	8
40%	9
45%	10
50%	11
55%	12
60%	13
65%	14
70%	15

OR

OPTION 3. COMPREHENSIVE ALTERNATIVE TRANSPORTATION PROGRAM (2 POINTS)

Meet the requirements of Option 1.

Implement an alternative transportation program to reduce the conventional travel rates of building occupants. Include at least one element from each of the following three categories:

Education strategies

- new-hire orientation;
- employee newsletter, flyer, announcements, memos, letters;
- carpool matching website; or

Basic support strategies

- employer carpool events.
- guaranteed return trip;
- preferential parking for rideshare participants;
- flextime schedule; or
- ride-matching service.

Direct strategies

- telecommuting;
- compressed workweek schedule;
- transit subsidy;
- introduction of a parking fee;
- bicycle program;
- parking cash-out;
- employee clean vehicle purchase program; or
- carpool program.

BEHIND THE INTENT

This credit focuses on the transportation patterns of building occupants. Whereas the design and construction LEED rating systems evaluate and reward features that building occupants might use (e.g., nearby transit stops), this operations and maintenance credit determines how building occupants actually travel to and from the project. The credit takes a single, performance-based approach to evaluating a building's transportation characteristics.

A transportation survey is required of all projects attempting this credit. Transportation surveys give building managers a better understanding of the transportation modes used by building occupants. Building managers can then use this information to determine how the building is performing with respect to transportation and the most effective programs for improving alternative transportation rates. Given this, Option 1 is required of all projects so that they can learn about occupants' transportation habits without needing to show a minimum alternative transportation rate.

Once occupants' travel patterns have been determined by the survey, projects can earn additional points through Options 2 and 3. Option 2, worth 3 to 15 points, rewards projects for demonstrating a quantifiable increase in the alternative transportation rate, showing that the building has reduced its transportation-related environmental harms. If the survey results show that the minimum rate has not been achieved, teams can follow Option 3, worth 2 points, and implement a comprehensive alternative transportation program to reduce occupants' reliance on conventional commuting.

STEP-BY-STEP GUIDANCE

Determine whether a regional transportation survey will be implemented during the performance period.

Projects that participate in a local or regional program can use the raw data from those survey results and complete the credit calculations to determine the alternative transportation rate; no additional survey is required. The raw data from a local or regional program can be used only if they are specific to the project building and the results are collected during the performance period.

Option 1. Transportation Survey

STEP 1. CHOOSE SURVEY APPROACH FOR REGULAR BUILDING OCCUPANTS P

Projects pursuing this credit must survey regular building occupants (see *Getting Started, Occupancy*). Determine whether the survey will involve all regular occupants of the project building or use a random sample (see Further Explanation, Surveying Regular Building Occupants).

If the team selects random sampling, determine the minimum survey response size (Table 5).

STEP 2. SELECT SURVEY INSTRUMENT FOR REGULAR BUILDING OCCUPANTS P

Determine the type of survey and whether it will be distributed in person, online, or through another method (see *Further Explanation, Methods for Survey Distribution*)

STEP 3. DETERMINE WHETHER VISITORS MUST BE SURVEYED P

For the space types listed in Table 2, the project team must survey visitors if either their daily average or their typical peak number is greater than the number of regular building occupants.

TABLE 2. Space types and visitors to be surveyed

Space types that may require visitor survey	Visitors to be surveyed
Institution of higher education*	Students
Food sales	Customers
Food service	Customers
Lodging	Guests
Retail (e.g., retail store, enclosed mall, vehicle dealership)	Customers
Healthcare (outpatient)	Outpatients and visitors (nonemergency)
Public assembly (e.g., library, convention center, entertainment, recreation, stadium)	Visitors
Religious worship	Visitors
Services (e.g., vehicle service, post office)	Customers

*Students in K–12 schools are considered occupants rather than visitors.

Based on Table 1, if visitors must be surveyed, determine the best method for distributing the survey (see *Further Explanation, Surveying Visitors*).

STEP 4. DEVELOP TRANSPORTATION SURVEY P

Develop the surveys for regular building occupants and visitors. Both surveys must request information on a variety of transportation modes (see *Further Explanation, Transportation Modes to Survey*).

In the survey, list all transportation modes. Include sufficient descriptions of each to ensure that respondents provide accurate answers. Separate walking, biking, and other human-powered conveyances; do not combine these into one mode of transportation for the purposes of the survey. Although these modes of transportation are equally weighted in the calculation, the distinction between modes is important for planning resources and meeting the needs of occupants.

For regular building occupants, the survey instrument must do the following:

- Collect information on travel during consecutive days of a complete week. This can be a five- or seven-day period, depending on use of the building.
- Ask each respondent to indicate his or her transportation mode to and from the project building; if more than one mode of transportation was used during a trip, the respondent should indicate only the mode used for the longest distance.
- Ask how respondents traveled to and from the building on each day so that they can indicate whether they used different travel modes on different days.
- Collect information on all trips to and from the building, not just during commuting times.
- Apply the same survey approach consistently to all regular building occupants who are surveyed.

For visitors, the survey instrument must do the following:

- Be independent from the survey given to regular building occupants. The visitor survey can be distributed at the same time or on another day.
- Collect information on the alternative transportation rate associated with one typical day of operation.
- Ask each respondent to indicate his or her transportation mode(s) to and from the project building.
- Collect information on all trips to and from the building, not just during peak visitor times.
- Ask respondents whether they work in the building. Responses from participants who work in the building must be excluded from the results to avoid double-counting in the survey of regular occupants.

STEP 5. SCHEDULE SURVEY P

Choose the time period over which the survey will measure travel and the dates it will be distributed. The survey period must reflect the building's typical occupancy patterns.

- Avoid weeks or days with holidays or other events (e.g., a city-sponsored bike-to-work week or a retail sale) that may affect the usage patterns.
- Conduct the survey when the weather is least likely to affect commuting patterns; avoid seasons with extreme weather.

- Account for alternative work arrangements. If employees extend their compressed workweek over two weeks (e.g., take one day off every other week), the team must survey the employees about their trips over the two-week period.

STEP 6. FINALIZE LOGISTICS FOR CONDUCTING SURVEY P

The following best practices can be used to facilitate a smooth survey process:

- Determine who will be involved in the survey, including who will develop the survey language and who will distribute the survey to building occupants.
- Decide whether incentives (e.g., free coffee, raffled-off prizes) are needed to encourage higher response rates. Transportation-related incentives (e.g., transit passes, bicycle locks) cannot be used because they could influence who is more likely to complete the survey.
- If necessary, seek approval from the building owner or other concerned parties for the chosen survey approach.
- Coordinate with security and other building staff to avoid confusion.
- Do not alert survey targets about the nature of the survey in advance (i.e., that it asks about transportation patterns) to avoid influencing behavior or responses.

STEP 7. DISTRIBUTE SURVEY(S) P

Distribute the survey(s) to regular occupants and visitors (if applicable).

- If the project team uses results from a local or regional survey, the survey must have been distributed within the performance period; allow time to collect survey results before the performance period end date.
- If random sampling was used, ensure that the response rate meets or exceeds the minimum (Table 5).

STEP 8. ANALYZE SURVEY RESULTS FOR REGULAR OCCUPANTS P

Calculate the alternative transportation rate for regular building occupants based on the survey results, using the following methodology (see *Further Explanation, Calculations*). Option 1 does not require any minimum alternative transportation rate, but the survey response rate must be at least 5% for both regular occupants and visitors (if applicable).

- Calculate the number of alternative transportation trips using Equation 1.
- Calculate the number of carpool trips using Equation 2.
- Calculate the raw rate of alternative transportation using Equation 3; in this equation, account for regular occupants' absences because of vacation and sick leave.
- Determine the survey response rate using Equation 4.
- Extrapolate the responses to the entire occupant population using the factors in Table 3. If the survey response rate is less than 30%, project teams may not extrapolate the raw rate of alternative transportation to the nonrespondents. After extrapolation, any remaining nonrespondents are assumed to be commuting via single-occupancy vehicles.

TABLE 3. Extrapolation factors

Survey response rate	Extrapolation factor
60%–100%	1.00
50%–59%	0.80
40%–49%	0.60
30%–39%	0.40
< 30%	0.00

- Calculate the total alternative transportation trips using Equation 5.
- Calculate the alternative transportation rate using Equation 6.

STEP 9. ANALYZE SURVEY RESULTS FOR VISITORS, IF APPLICABLE P

Calculate the alternative transportation rate for visitors based on the survey results, using the following methodology (see *Further Explanation, Calculations*).

- Calculate visitors' number of alternative transportation trips using Equation 7.
- Calculate visitors' raw rate of alternative transportation using Equation 8.

STEP 10. CALCULATE OVERALL ALTERNATIVE TRANSPORTATION RATE P

Calculate the overall alternative transportation rate using Equation 9. This equation requires entering regular occupants' and visitors' percentage shares of the building's total population.

Option 2. Alternative Transportation Rate

STEP 1. COMPLETE OPTION 1 P

Follow the steps required to complete the transportation survey.

STEP 2. DEMONSTRATE REDUCTION IN CONVENTIONAL COMMUTING TRIPS P

Review the calculations to determine the percentage reduction in conventional commuting trips by the building's occupants and visitors. Table 1 lists the points earned for reductions of 10% or more.

Option 3. Comprehensive Alternative Transportation Program

STEP 1. COMPLETE OPTION 1 P

Complete all steps in Option 1 to demonstrate the current commuting patterns of building occupants.

STEP 2. DEVELOP ALTERNATIVE TRANSPORTATION PROGRAM P

Use the results of the transportation survey to develop a targeted program aimed at increasing use of alternative modes of transportation. The multistrategy program must include at least one element from each of the three categories listed in the credit requirements.

Track the following elements:

- Frequency of events
- Strategy for marketing and delivery to building occupants and examples of media used for marketing (e.g., website, newsletters, bulletin boards)
- Representative screenshots or photos of the program elements
- Explanation of how the elements are supported by broader organizational policies (optional)

STEP 3. IMPLEMENT INITIATIVES P

All initiatives used for compliance with this option must be implemented before the performance period ends.

FURTHER EXPLANATION

CALCULATIONS

EQUATION 1. Number of alternative transportation trips by regular building occupants

Alternative transportation trips by regular occupants = Trips walking + Trips bicycling + Trips via other human-powered conveyances + Trips via public transit + Trips avoided because of telecommuting + Trips avoided because of compressed work schedule (office spaces only) + Trips via carpool* + Trips via green vehicles + Trips via rideshare (projects outside U.S. only)

* Carpool trips must be computed using Equation 2.

EQUATION 2. Number of carpool trips by regular building occupants

$$\text{Weighted number of carpool trips by regular occupants} = \left\{\text{Vehicle trips in 2-person carpool} \times 1/2\right\} + \left\{\text{Vehicle trips in 2-person-carpool} \times 2/3\right\} + \left\{\text{Vehicle trips in 2-person-carpool} \times \frac{(n - 1)}{n}\right\}$$

EQUATION 3. Raw alternative transportation rate for regular building occupants

$$\text{Raw alternative transportation rate for regular occupants} = \left\{\frac{\text{Alternative transportation trips}}{\text{Total trips} - \text{Absences}}\right\}$$

EQUATION 4. Survey response rate for regular building occupants

$$\text{Survey response rate for regular occupants} = \left\{\frac{\text{Survey respondents}}{\text{Survey recipients}}\right\}$$

EQUATION 5. Total alternative transportation trips of regular building occupants

$$\text{Total alternative transportation trips} = \text{Alternative commuting trips} \times \left\{\left(\text{Nonresponders} \times \text{days/week} \times \text{2 commute trips/day}\right) \times \text{Extrapolation factor} \times \text{Raw alternative transportation rate}\right\}$$

EQUATION 6. Overall alternative transportation rate of regular building occupants

$$\text{Alternative transportation rate for regular occupants} = \left\{\frac{\text{Total alternative transportation trips}}{\left(\text{occupants} \times \text{days/week} \times \text{2 trips/day}\right)}\right\}$$

EQUATION 7. Alternative transportation trips by visitors

$$\text{Alternative transportation trips by visitors} = \text{Trips walking} + \text{Trips bicycling} + \text{Trips via other human-powered conveyances} + \text{Trips via public transit} + \text{Trips via green vehicles}$$

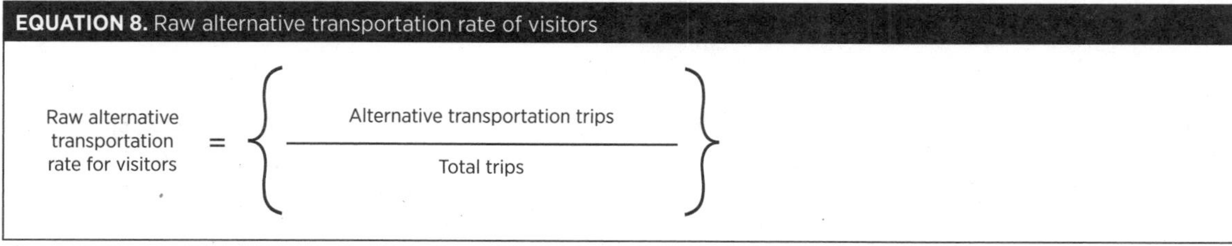

EQUATION 8. Raw alternative transportation rate of visitors

$$\text{Raw alternative transportation rate for visitors} = \left\{ \frac{\text{Alternative transportation trips}}{\text{Total trips}} \right\}$$

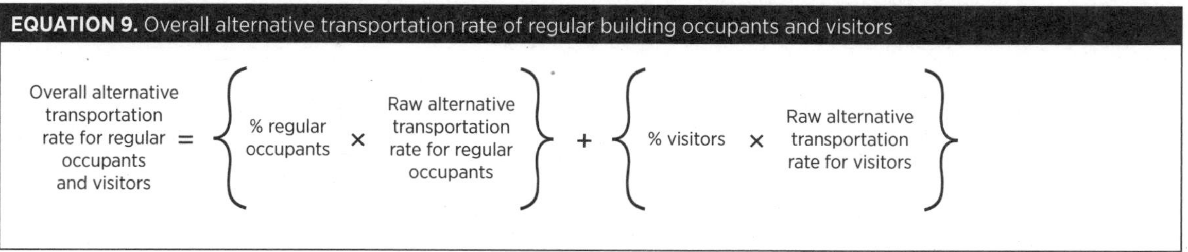

EQUATION 9. Overall alternative transportation rate of regular building occupants and visitors

$$\text{Overall alternative transportation rate for regular occupants and visitors} = \left\{ \text{\% regular occupants} \times \text{Raw alternative transportation rate for regular occupants} \right\} + \left\{ \text{\% visitors} \times \text{Raw alternative transportation rate for visitors} \right\}$$

SURVEYING REGULAR BUILDING OCCUPANTS

Teams can use either of two approaches for regular building occupants: conducting a survey of the entire population, feasible for a small number of occupants or a single tenant, or surveying a random sample, appropriate for a large number of occupants or multiple tenants.

Regular building occupants must be asked about their modes of transportation to and from the project building for a complete week. This can be a five- or seven-day period, depending on the usage patterns in the building.

For example, for an office building with a typical workweek usage pattern (generally Monday–Friday, 8 A.M.–5 P.M.), a five-day period can be used. For a building that is occupied every day of the week (e.g., a museum), a seven-day period may be more appropriate.

Each respondent must have the opportunity in the survey to indicate his or her mode of transportation for a regular workweek (i.e., 10 trips for a five-day week, or 14 trips for a seven-day week). Weeks with holidays or other events (e.g., a city-sponsored bike-to-work week or annual sale) that may affect the usage patterns must be avoided. It is recommended that project teams not conduct the survey during extreme weather (hot or cold).

The survey may be distributed either daily or at the conclusion of the five- or seven-day survey period. Often project teams choose to survey occupants at the conclusion of the week (rather than every day) because it requires less time and resources to collect the survey responses, and respondents generally prefer to be surveyed one time only.

For a Schools project, include only secondary school students of legal driving age in the survey of regular building occupants.

For projects with health care facilities, inpatients do not need to be surveyed.

SURVEYING VISITORS

The visitor survey does not need to be conducted during the same week as the regular building occupant survey, provided it is distributed within the performance period. Project teams should survey a random sample of visitors, since surveying all visitors is likely not feasible.

Visitors must be asked how they traveled to and from the project building on the day of the survey.

If an on-location method is used, surveyors must distribute surveys to visitors throughout an entire primary peak period of at least two hours. If there is a secondary peak period, surveyors must distribute surveys for at least one hour during that period. For example, if a retail mall includes retail shops and a movie theater, distribute surveys at both the peak period for shoppers (e.g., 2:00–4:00 P.M.) and the peak period for moviegoers (e.g., 7:00–8:00 P.M.).

Higher education students are typically considered visitors. Secondary school students of legal driving age are considered regular building occupants.

Hotel guests are not required to be surveyed, though it is encouraged. Hotel guests should be considered visitors and asked either for the most frequently used mode of transportation to and from the hotel during their stay, or for the last mode of transportation used to travel to the hotel and the first mode that will be used on departure.

TRANSPORTATION MODES

The survey language must include the modes of transportation listed in Table 4.

TABLE 4. Survey coverage, for regular building occupants and visitors

Mode	Description	Applicability
Walking	Respondents mark "walking" if they walked to and from building, or if walking was longest distance traveled during multimodal commute.	Regular occupants, visitors
Bicycling	Respondents mark "bicycling" if they bicycled to and from building, or if bicycling was used for longest distance traveled during multimodal commute.	Regular occupants, visitors
Other human-powered conveyances	All human-powered modes of transportation other than walking or bicycling; examples include nonmotorized scooters, skateboards, and pedicabs. Respondents must be asked follow-up question regarding kind of human-powered conveyance.	Regular occupants, visitors
Public transit	Public transit includes bus, light rail, subway, or other transit services that are offered to general public and operate on regular and ongoing basis.	Regular occupants, visitors
Telecommuting	Telecommuting involves work using telecommunications and computer technology from remote location outside building, therefore requiring no transportation. Occupants who telecommute for only part of workday (e.g., work in project building in morning, work from home in afternoon) must complete survey based on commute trip to and from building.	Regular occupants; space types that would otherwise require daily attendance only
Compressed work week	Compressed workweek involves increase in daily hours and reduced number of workdays overall (e.g., employee works extended hours for nine days in two-week period in exchange for *not* working on day 10). Respondents must mark day they are *not* working as compressed workweek day in survey.	Regular occupants; office space types only
Carpool	Carpooling is informal arrangement established by two or more people who drive together. For survey purposes, nondriving-age children do not count as carpoolers. Respondents must be asked to indicate number of people in carpool, for Equation 2.	Regular occupants
Green vehicle	Green vehicles are defined as vehicles with ACEEE green score ≥ 45 (or local equivalent for projects outside U.S.; see *Further Explanation, International Tips*). Respondents must be asked to indicate make, model, and year of vehicle so that project team can determine its eligibility (because respondents are unlikely to know whether their vehicles qualify).	Regular occupants, visitors
Rideshares	Rideshare is transitlike transportation mode that involves independently owned and operated passenger cars or small vans, each seating at least four people. Unlike taxi cabs, rideshares have fixed route, fixed fare structure, continuous daily operation, enclosed passenger seating area, and ability to pick up and drop off multiple riders.	Regular occupants, visitors; non-U.S. projects only
Driving alone in conventional vehicle	Conventional vehicles have ACEEE green score < 45 (or local equivalent for projects outside U.S.). Count motorcycle trips as conventional vehicle trips.	Regular occupants
Absent	Respondents mark "absent" if they did not commute because they were ill, on vacation, serving on jury, etc.	

ACEEE = American Council for an Energy-Efficient Economy

DETERMINING A SAMPLE SIZE

Use Table 5 to determine the number of regular or visitors to survey when using random sampling. For regular or visitor populations not listed in the table, use the sample size for the next highest population. For example, a building with 940 regular building occupants must have a sample size that matches the 1,000 occupant amount (286).

Survey responses must meet or exceed these minimum sample sizes.

TABLE 5. Required sample size, by total population

Regular or visitors	Sample size	Regular or visitors	Sample size
100	81	800	267
125	96	900	277
150	110	1,000	286
175	122	2,000	333
200	134	3,000	353
225	144	4,000	364
250	154	5,000	370
275	163	6,000	375
300	172	7,000	378
325	180	8,000	381
350	187	9,000	383
375	194	10,000	385
400	201	15,000	390
425	207	20,000	392
450	212	25,000	394
500	222	50,000	397
600	240	100,000	398
700	255		

Source: Penn State University Cooperative Extension. "Program Evaluation Tipsheet #60: How to Determine a Sample Size." extension.psu.edu/evaluation/pdf/TS60.pdf. Last accessed on November 21, 2012. The table assumes a +/- 5% margin of error and a 95% confidence level.

SAMPLING A POPULATION

Be prepared to justify how a random sample of the building population was chosen. One possible approach is electronic; another is conducting the survey in a central location, such as a lobby.

Electronic sample selection and survey

Enter all occupants' names into a spreadsheet, randomize the entries, and then scroll down to the row number equal to the random sample size. Everyone from this row up is the random sample. Alternatively, enter all occupants' names into a spreadsheet alphabetically, and then choose every nth occupant (the number that will yield the minimum random sample size). The selected individuals are the random sample.

In multitenant buildings, allocate the total number of surveys across all tenants proportionately, according to their populations. For example, if the minimum sample size is 100, and the largest tenant accounts for 50% of the regular building occupants, that tenant's occupants should receive 50 of the randomly distributed surveys). A sampling across all tenants is desirable, since each tenant may have its own incentives and cultural norms regarding the use of alternative transportation.

Pros and cons for electronic approach
Surveying this way requires less time and resources to distribute the survey but often results in a lower response rate. Consider the ease or difficulty of obtaining email addresses for all regular building occupants in choosing this option. This approach may be preferable if a significant portion of regular building occupants have telecommuting or compressed workweek options.

Lobby blitz survey
The surveyors gather data in person, either by asking the questions and recording the answers, or by asking respondents to fill out paper forms. The surveyors can survey every nth person who enters the building, or every person who enters immediately following the completion of the previous survey.

Station surveyors at all entrance points, including entries that are likely to serve a certain type of commuter (e.g., entrances from parking garages) so as not to bias the results. Select a period of peak activity, when regular building occupants are entering or exiting the building, particularly if the building has a central lobby, security checkpoint, or elevator bank. Include shift changes if appropriate. Even if the minimum sample size has been achieved before the end of a five- or seven-day survey period, surveyors must continue to distribute surveys to regular building occupants to capture all arrivals; ensure that the surveyors stay throughout the entire period.

Pros and cons for lobby blitz approach
Surveying in person requires more time and resources but often results in a higher response rate.

TIPS FOR OPTIMIZING SURVEY RESULTS

To encourage an increase in alternative transportation rates (for Option 2), consider implementing components of an alternative transportation program a few months before (but not right before) the survey.

The following strategies can help the project team achieve higher survey response rates and more accurate results.

- **Incentives.** Offer an incentive to encourage people to respond, such as coffee, a snack, a free lunch, a small-denomination gift card, or something else not related to transportion (e.g., transit passes are not allowed) that will appeal to building occupants but not skew the results.
- **Style.** Do not call it a survey: people are generally survey-averse. If the survey is conducted in person, lead with a survey question rather than asking respondents whether they are willing to participate. They will let the surveyors know if they do not want to.
- **Convenience.** Make the survey quick and easy. Encourage people to take the survey by assuring them that the survey has, say, only three questions or will take only 30 seconds.
- **Strategy.** It may help to notify building occupants the day before the survey, but do not skew the survey results by revealing that the subject is alternative transportation; just alert them that there will be activity in the lobby, with free snacks. Choose the right peak window to survey building occupants; starting too late or ending too early may significantly affect the survey response rate. Do not overlook back doors and other entries that are not the main entrance to the building.

CONSIDERATIONS FOR SURVEYING VISITORS

If the project team can capture contact information for all visitors who enter the building on a particular day, an electronic survey can be distributed to all those visitors the following day. In most circumstances, however, an on-location, in-person survey is more feasible. Conduct the survey during the building's peak period, when visitors are entering or exiting. Choose entries and exits that make it easy to distinguish visitors from regular building occupants, and devise a strategy to avoid double-counting visitors who leave and reenter.

EXAMPLE 1. SURVEY OF ALL REGULAR BUILDING OCCUPANTS

The Frankie B Office Building, with 100 regular building occupants, consists entirely of office space. All regular occupants were asked to complete the alternative transportation survey for a five-day week; 40 occupants responded. The project team performs the following steps.

1. **Determine trips via alternative transportation (Equations 1, 2). Some of the 40 respondents did not work all five days of the survey period because of illness, leaving a total of 392 trips:**

   (40 respondents × 5 days per week × 2 trips per day) − 8 missed trips = 392 total trips

Of the 392 trips, 196 were via single-occupant vehicles and 196 were via mass transit, which qualifies as alternative transportation.

2. **Determine raw alternative commuting rate (Equation 3).**

   Raw rate of regular occupant commuting = 196 / 392 = 50%

3. **Determine survey response rate (Equation 4).**

   40 / 100 = 40%

   The team looks up the extrapolation factor for 40%, which is 0.60 (Table 2).

4. **Determine total number of alternative commuting trips, including nonrespondents (Equation 5).** The team must extrapolate from the data to determine the number of alternative commuting trips attributable to the nonresponders:

   60 occupants × 5 days × 2 trips per day × 0.60 × 50% alternative commuting rate = 180 trips

5. **Determine overall number of alternative commuting trips (Equation 6).** The team sums the known number obtained from the respondents and the extrapolated number for the nonrespondents:

   196 + 180 = 376 alternative commuting trips

6. **Determine reduction in conventional commuting trips (Equation 7).** The team works out the share of alternative commuting as a percentage of the total number of trips and refers to Table 1 to determine the number of points earned.

   (376 alternative commuting trips) / (100 occupants × 5 days × 2 trips per day) = 37.6%

   For this 37.6% reduction in conventional commuting, the team earns 8 points.

EXAMPLE 2. RANDOM SAMPLING OF REGULAR BUILDING OCCUPANTS

The Monster Ball Building, with 1,025 regular occupants, consists entirely of office space. A sample of regular building occupants was randomly selected to receive the survey. The project team then takes the following steps.

1. **Determine minimum random sample size (Table 5).** Regular building occupancy is between 1,000 and 2,000. The team must therefore use the sample size for the next population increment, or 333.
2. **Distribute survey to regular building occupants.** Since the building has five tenants, the project team distributes the surveys proportionately among the tenants. To achieve the required sample size, the project team distributes 500 surveys (exceeding the required minimum of 333). The project team announces that a prize will be raffled to one of the potential 500 respondents.
3. **Determine number of alternative commuting trips (Equation 1).** Of the 500 people who received the survey, 340 completed it. No absences were recorded in the survey results. Of the 3,400 total trips recorded in the survey results, 170 trips were via bicycle, 600 trips were via public transit, and 300 trips were via two-person carpools. Adjusting the carpool number according to Equation 2, the team sums those results:

   [170 bicycle trips + 600 public transit trip + (300 × 1/2 carpool trips)] = 920

4. **Determine raw alternative commuting rate (Equation 3).** The raw rate is the number of alternative commuting trips divided by the total trips made by the respondents:

   920 / 3,400 = 27%

5. **Determine reduction in conventional commuting trips.** Because the entire regular building population was sampled in a statistically valid way and the responses exceeded the required sample size, the project team may conclude that the sample alternative commuting rate is accurate. The 27% reduction in conventional-vehicle commuting trips earns the project 6 points.

EXAMPLE 3. REGULAR OCCUPANTS AND VISITORS

The Nerope Building is occupied by a grocery store. The project team determines that the store has more daily visitors (an average 400 customers) than regular building occupants (20 employees). The team proceeds as follows.

1. **Survey regular building occupants.** Since the number of regular building occupants is low, the project team surveys the entire population of employees, all of whom complete the survey. Since the grocery store is open for seven days per week, the project team surveys the employees for all seven days of store operation.
2. **Determine regular occupants' trips via alternative transportation.** Over the seven-day workweek, each employee works six days. Therefore, each employee avoids two trips (to and from the building) due to absence, or 40 total trips avoided.

   $$\text{Total trips} = (20 \text{ regular occupants} \times 2 \text{ trips/day} \times 7 \text{ days/week}) - 40 \text{ avoided trips} = 240$$

   Of the total trips, 50 trips were by bicycle, 20 via carpool, 20 via green vehicle, and 80 via public transportation, for 170 total alternative commuting trips.
3. **Determine regular occupants' raw alternative commuting rate (Equation 3).**

   $$170 / 240 = 71\%$$

4. **Survey visitors.** The project team must have a sample size of at least 201 customers (Table 4). To create an incentive for customers, the team hands out raffle tickets for free groceries with the survey instrument, which is a paper questionnaire; 215 people complete it.
5. **Determine visitors' number of alternative trips (Equation 7).** The one-day survey shows 430 total trips (215 x 2). Of those trips, 70 were taken by bicycle and 100 by public transit, totaling 170 alternative transportation trips.
6. **Determine visitors' raw alternative transportation rate (Equation 8).**

   $$(170 \text{ alternative transportation trips}) / (430 \text{ total trips}) = 40\%$$

7. **Determine overall alternative transportation rate (Equation 9).** The team combines regular occupants' and visitors' trips, weighted by the percentage of total users that each type of user represents (20 employees and an average 400 customers means a total user count of 420; therefore, employees represent 4.8% of the total, and customers represent 95.2%).

   $$[(20 / 420) \times (0.71)] + [(400 / 420) \times (0.40)] = (0.03) + (0.38) = 0.41$$

For an overall rate of 41%, the project earns 9 points under Option 2.

PROJECT TYPE VARIATIONS

Multifamily Residential

Include residents in the survey of regular building occupants and ask them to indicate their mode of travel to and from work or school.

Exclude noncommuters (e.g., retirees and stay-at-home parents) from the population of regular occupants.

Include full-time students of driving age as regular building occupants; their trip to school is considered their commute. Ask them to indicate any nonschool days (comparable to absences for employees) during the survey period and adjust the results accordingly in Equation 3.

Exclude students under the driving age, and do not count them as part of a carpool.

INTERNATIONAL TIPS

Local equivalent standards to the American Council for an Energy Efficient Economy (ACEEE) Green Book must comprehensively address vehicle fuel economy and vehicle emissions ratings, including particulate matter, nitrogen oxides (NO_x), hydrocarbons, and carbon monoxide (CO). Complete a side-by-side comparison between the methodology of the selected local standard(s) and that of ACEEE.

CAMPUS

Group Approach
All buildings in the group may be documented as one. The credit requirements may be met by performing one survey that encompasses all the regular building occupants in all the buildings within the LEED project boundary. Alternatively, a single survey may be conducted for each individual building and the results may be aggregated.

Campus Approach
Eligible.

REQUIRED DOCUMENTATION

	Documentation	Option 1	Option 2	Option 3
P	Regular building occupant and visitor counts	X	X	X
P	For regular building occupants' survey, description of methodology and how it meets survey requirements	X	X	
P	For visitors' survey (if applicable), description of methodology and how it meets survey requirements	X	X	
P	Survey results, including reduction in conventional commuting trips, trips for each transportation mode, and trips not taken (e.g., sick days, vacation days)	X	X	
P	Narrative describing comprehensive alternative transportation program and implementation			X
P	Supporting documentation for each element of comprehensive alternative transportation program			X

RELATED CREDIT TIPS

None.

CHANGES FROM LEED 2009

- Option 1 has been added to allow projects to earn 1 point for simply surveying their building occupants and submitting the survey results.
- The performance threshold for Option 2 was decreased to allow for a linear increase from threshold to threshold.
- Option 3 has been added to reward projects for implementing a comprehensive alternative transportation program.
- Projects are now required to survey visitors if the daily average number of visitors or typical peak is greater than regular building occupants.
- New ongoing performance standards require teams to conduct a survey every five years.

REFERENCED STANDARDS

American Council for Energy-Efficient Economy (ACEEE) Green Book®: greenercars.org

EXEMPLARY PERFORMANCE

Option 2. Demonstrate an 80% reduction from a conventional commuting baseline.

DEFINITIONS

green vehicles vehicles achieving a minimum green score of 45 on the American Council for an Energy Efficient Economy (ACEEE) annual vehicle rating guide (or a local equivalent for projects outside the U.S.)

light rail transit service using two- or three-car trains in a right-of-way that is often separated from other traffic modes. Spacing between stations tends to be 1/2 mile (800 meters) or more, and maximum operating speeds are typically 40–55 mph (65–90 kmh). Light-rail corridors typically extend 10 or more miles (16 kilometers).

outpatient a patient who is not hospitalized for 24 hours or more but who visits a hospital, clinic, or associated healthcare facility for diagnosis or treatment

rideshare a transit service in which individuals travel together in a passenger car or small van that seats at least four people. It can include human-powered conveyances, which must accommodate at least two people. It must include an enclosed passenger seating area, fixed route service, fixed fare structure, regular operation, and the ability to pick up multiple riders.

Sustainable Sites (ss)

OVERVIEW

The Sustainable Sites (SS) category rewards decisions about the environment surrounding the building, with credits that emphasize the vital relationships among buildings, ecosystems, and ecosystem services. It focuses on restoring project site elements, integrating the site with local and regional ecosystems, and preserving the biodiversity that natural systems rely on.

Earth's systems depend on biologically diverse forests, wetlands, coral reefs, and other ecosystems, which are often referred to as "natural capital" because they provide regenerative services. A United Nations study indicates that of the ecosystem services that have been assessed worldwide, about 60% are currently degraded or used unsustainably.[1] The results are deforestation, soil erosion, a drop in water table levels, extinction of species, and rivers that no longer run to the sea. Recent trends like exurban development and sprawl encroach on the remaining natural landscapes and farmlands, fragmenting and replacing them with dispersed hardscapes surrounded by nonnative vegetation. Between 1982 and 2001 in the U.S. alone, about 34 million acres (13 759 hectares) of open space (an area the size of Illinois) was lost to development—approximately 4 acres per minute, or 6,000 acres a day.[2] The rainwater runoff from these hardscape areas frequently overloads the capacity of natural infiltration systems, increasing both the quantity and pollution of site runoff. Rainwater runoff carries such pollutants as oil, sediment, chemicals, and lawn fertilizers directly to streams and rivers, where they contribute to eutrophication and harm aquatic ecosystems and species. A Washington State Department of Ecology study noted that rainwater runoff from roads, parking lots, and other hardscapes carries some 6.3 million gallons of petroleum into the Puget Sound every year—more than half of what was spilled in the 1989 *Exxon Valdez* accident in Alaska.[3]

Project teams that comply with the prerequisites and credits in the SS category use low-impact development methods that minimize construction pollution, reduce heat island effects and light pollution, and mimic natural water flow patterns to manage rainwater runoff.

In LEED v4, the SS category combines traditional approaches with several new strategies. These include working with conservation organizations to target financial support for off-site habitat protection (Site Development—

1. *UN Environment Programme, State and Trends of the Environment 1987–2001, Section B, Chapter 5, unep.org/geo/geo4/report/05_Biodiversity.pdf.*
2. *U.S. Forest Service, Quick Facts, fs.fed.us/projects/four-threats/facts/open-space.shtml (accessed September 11, 2012).*
3. *Cornwall, W., Stormwater's Damage to Puget Sound Huge, Seattle Times (December 1, 2007), seattletimes.com/html/localnews/2004045940_ecology01m.html (accessed on September 14, 2012).*

Protect or Restore Habitat credit), using low-impact development to handle a percentile storm event (Rainwater Management credit), using three-year aged SRI values for roofs and SR values for nonroof hardscape (Heat Island Reduction credit), and creating a five-year improvement plan for the project site (Site Improvement Plan credit).

SUSTAINABLE SITES PREREQUISITE

Site Management Policy

This prerequisite applies to:

Existing Buildings
Schools
Retail
Data Centers
Hospitality
Warehouses and Distribution Centers

INTENT

To preserve ecological integrity and encourage environmentally sensitive site management practices that provide a clean, well-maintained, and safe building exterior while supporting high-performance building operations and integration into the surrounding landscape.

REQUIREMENTS

ESTABLISHMENT E

Create and implement a site management policy that employs best management practices to reduce harmful chemical use, energy waste, water waste, air pollution, solid waste, and/or chemical runoff for all of the following operational elements on the building and grounds:

- use of low emissions maintenance equipment;
- snow and ice removal;
- cleaning of building exterior, pavement, and other impervious surfaces;
- erosion and sedimentation control (for ongoing operations and for construction activity);
- organic waste management (returned to the site or diverted from landfills);
- invasive and exotic plant species management (through monitoring and eradication);
- fertilizer use (testing soils before using fertilizer to prevent overapplication of nutrients);
- irrigation management (monitor irrigation systems manually or with automated systems at least every two weeks during the operating season for appropriate water usage, system times, leaks, or breaks); and
- storage of materials and equipment.

PERFORMANCE P

None.

BEHIND THE INTENT

Good exterior maintenance practices can significantly affect a project site and its surroundings. Site management best practices not only protect soil, water, and air resources but also yield economic benefits. For example, proactive maintenance and monitoring may detect irrigation system leaks before the wasted water causes unnecessary expense. Moreover, a healthy and well-maintained project site that is appealing to occupants and visitors can benefit human health.

Realization of such benefits begins with a clear, thorough site management policy. Project teams should investigate best practices, assess current practices, and establish measurable goals and objectives. A good site management policy will function as a performance baseline against which a project team can objectively measure shortcomings and achievements; it also can establish a foundation for long-term site management success. Developing and implementing a site management policy early in the LEED process give the team time to optimize products, equipment, and strategies. Finally, a well-crafted site management policy enables a team to address unexpected complications.

STEP-BY-STEP GUIDANCE

STEP 1. REVIEW BEST MANAGEMENT PRACTICES E

Research and review the best management practices for each operational element specified in the prerequisite requirements, as well as any operational elements that may be unique to the project site (see *Further Explanation, Best Practices for Operational Elements*).

STEP 2. GATHER INFORMATION ON CURRENT SITE MANAGEMENT PRACTICES E

Gain a comprehensive understanding of how the project site is currently managed and maintained (see *Getting Started, Effective Policy Development*).

- Learn how current practices align with best management practices. Building management personnel and vendors who oversee site management activities will likely have the most information on existing practices and can help the project team gain a full understanding of how the property is managed.
- Review standard contract documents and template specifications that establish the scope of work performed by site vendors. These documents are a good resource if ownership or management has changed hands but site maintenance contracts have stayed in place.
- Walk the property and observe the existing conditions.
- Identify any opportunities for improvement in current site management operations.
- Collect and review any site management documentation that may be relevant to the policy.

STEP 3. IDENTIFY SITE MANAGEMENT GOALS AND OBJECTIVES E

Establish measurable site management goals and objectives based on the project's site needs and best practices (see *Further Explanation, Setting Goals and Objectives*).

- Owners, property managers, site and grounds managers, and relevant vendors can all help identify goals and opportunities for improving site management.
- Include at least one goal for each operational element applicable to the site. Outline the scope for each goal, including preliminary information on procedures and strategies for implementation.

STEP 4. CREATE PERFORMANCE METRICS AND ASSIGN RESPONSIBILITIES TO TEAM MEMBERS E

Establish performance metrics for each operational element to facilitate performance tracking and evaluation.

- Performance metrics allow teams to gauge ongoing progress.
- Identify the team members who will be responsible for gathering, tracking, and evaluating performance information.

STEP 5. WRITE SITE MANAGEMENT POLICY E

Ensure that the policy includes the following components for each operational element:

- Scope and goals
- Roles and responsibilities
- Standard operating procedures
- Implementation strategies
- Performance measurement and schedule for reassessment
- Quality assurance

For each operational element, explain how the policy is designed to reduce the harms of traditional site management activities.

Multiple vendors may be responsible for the various operational elements covered by this policy. Strategize early with vendors to ensure that the policy is feasible.

For Schools projects, the policy must include any athletic or playing fields within the project boundary.

STEP 6. ADOPT SITE MANAGEMENT POLICY E

Roll out the new site management policy and clearly communicate any new programs, procedures, and activities to the responsible parties.

- Work with vendors to determine which best practices can be adopted immediately, which require phased implementation, and which may be only seasonal.
- Conduct a kick-off meeting a few weeks before the start of the performance period so that all parties understand their roles and responsibilities.
- Familiarize everyone with the intent and requirements of the site management policy and the metrics for tracking and evaluating performance. Highlight the policy's changes and discuss how they compare with previous practices. Post goals, objectives, procedures, and performance metrics as reminders.
- Review the responsibilities and reporting process for performance tracking.
- Include the policy's goals, activities, approved product lists, and performance metrics in staff and vendor training materials, such as binders, online resource pages, and best management practice documents.
- Begin gathering performance data and other documentation on adhering to the site management policy. Performance data are not required for SS Prerequisite Site Management Policy but are required for SS Credit Site Management.

FURTHER EXPLANATION

BEST PRACTICES FOR OPERATIONAL ELEMENTS

Some operational elements may not be applicable to all projects because of site-specific factors. For example, snow and ice removal is not relevant for hot climates, and organic waste management does not apply to projects that have no landscaping or planter boxes. Note any such elements in the policy and explain why they are not relevant, making sure that no operational elements have been overlooked.

All projects must address erosion and sedimentation control, even if the building has a zero or minimal lot line or has established vegetation, for both ongoing operations and potential future construction activity.

Consider the following best practices for working with vendors:

- Review current practices together to determine which standard procedures already meet the prerequisite requirements.
- Review the criteria for compliant equipment, products, and practices and work with vendors to determine feasible options. A list of approved equipment or products can also help vendors adopt best practices.
- Ask vendors about how they train existing and new staff in best practices and different products.
- Consider developing a phase-out schedule for noncompliant equipment, products, and practices.
- Establish a protocol for evaluating additional equipment, products, and practices against the prerequisite criteria.

- Amend contract documents as necessary to support the policy requirements.

Empower property management staff to spot-check actual practices and correct any deviations from the intended practices. Best management practices are designed to outline the best approach for the best outcome. The following table outlines best management practices for each operational element in the prerequisite requirements. The list is not exhaustive, however; project teams are encouraged to research and implement innovative strategies and continue to reduce environmentally harmful activities associated with site management.

TABLE 1. Site management best practices

Operational element	Best practices
Maintenance equipment	Use low- or zero-emissions maintenance equipment. Replace gasoline-powered equipment (including pruning equipment) with electric, manual, or propane-powered equipment and strategies. Maintain and repair equipment according to manufacturers' recommendations. Reduce lawn areas to reduce dependence on powered equipment such as mowers, edgers, trimmers and blowers. Convert lawn to restored habitats, native or adapted plants, mulches, aggregates, or no-mow grasses.
Snow and ice removal	Identify high-traffic areas (e.g., outdoor plazas) that can forgo treatment or require less deicer because traffic helps melt snow and ice. Consider developing drawings to show users or tenants areas not treated. Cone or mark off untreated areas before storms begin. Pretreat pavement with granular or liquid deicers before storms to reduce total amount of product used. Consider using salt-free and environmentally preferred deicers (e.g., potassium acetate, potassium chloride, magnesium chloride, or calcium magnesium acetate CMA). Always plow or power sweep snow before applying deicer. Use vehicles with electronic spreader controls for more precise deicer application in terms of both quantity and location. Apply only enough deicer to loosen ice for plowing; do not use deicer to melt entire depth. Reduce idle time of snow removal vehicles. Use prewetted salt rather than dry salt when possible. Keep records of deicer use (dates applied, quantities used, area treated) and its effect for each snow event to optimize future deicer applications. Save leftover deicers for the next season, using safe storage techniques that fully contain the material. For the performance metric in SS Credit Site Management, track percentage of environmentally preferred deicer used, by cost or quantity (units of weight or volume), or track percentage reduction in area treated with calcium chloride or sodium chloride deicers, from baseline application area.
Building exterior, pavement, and impervious surface cleaning	Use cleaning products that meet requirements of EQ Credit Green Cleaning Products and Materials. Optimize cleaning frequencies to conserve water and reduce emissions. Perform periodic power washing with water only to reduce chemical use. Use water-reclaiming power washers. Maximize use of manual cleaning strategies. Reduce gasoline-powered equipment to limit emissions and noise pollution.
Erosion and sedimentation control for on-going operations	Keep debris, garbage, and organic waste out of storm drains through routine maintenance, such as pavement sweeping. Provide cigarette butt receptacles, empty them regularly, and sweep butts off ground frequently. Regularly inspect, clean, and repair rainwater infrastructure, including roof drains, gutters, and downspouts. Maintain healthy groundcover and vegetation to prevent erosion, especially in sloping areas, and restore any eroded soils by reestablishing vegetative cover, mulching, or adding stone aggregates.
Erosion and sedimentation control for construction activities	Before any future construction project, work with general contractor to develop project-specific plan for controlling erosion and sedimentation. Review local and national rainwater management codes, standards, and prevention measures (e.g., U.S. EPA Stormwater Pollution Prevention Plans for Construction Activities, epa.gov). Develop process for planning, communicating, and implementing erosion and sedimentation control strategies during construction.
Organic waste management	Compost or mulch leaves and waste on site. Use mulching mowers on turf areas. Compost at off-site facility.

Invasive and exotic vegetation species management	Develop list of regionally invasive and exotic vegetation and regularly monitor grounds for their presence. Engage local nursery, county extension agent, or other knowledgeable resource to identify invasive and exotic vegetation. Eradicate any invasive or exotic vegetation found on site through low-impact means. Work with neighboring properties to remove their invasive and exotic vegetation to prevent its spread to project site.
Fertilizer and herbicide use	Test soil to establish soil type (classification and texture); contact extension service for information. Retest every other year for nutrient content and pH. Use no ammonia-based fertilizers, biosolid-based fertilizers formulated for continuous application, synthetic quick-release fertilizers, or weed-and-feed formulations. Use fertilizer derived from animal or vegetable matter, organic or natural fertilizer, and slow-release formulas. Prioritize use of organic waste generated on site (e.g., grass clippings, compost) over traditional fertilizers. Apply fertilizer based on plants' needs (as determined through soil testing) rather than on predetermined schedule. Review local or national sources, such as the U.S.-based Organic Materials Review Institute (OMRI) database for environmentally preferred fertilizer products that comply with USDA organic standards (omri.org). Control turf weeds by spot spraying only; use no blanket applications of herbicides. For performance metric in SS Credit Site Management, track percentage of environmentally preferred fertilizer used, by cost or quantity (units of weight or volume).
Irrigation management	Monitor irrigation systems regularly (at least every two weeks) during operating season for leaks, breaks, irregularities in water usage, and system time settings. Test operation of system components regularly during operating season. Monitor watering schedule regularly and adjust based on plant and soil conditions. Visually inspect landscaped areas for instances of under- or overapplication of irrigation water. Use high-efficiency irrigation systems, drip irrigation, and/or weather-based controllers. Install pressure sensors that respond to water pressure surges by closing mainline. Use weather forecasting data to optimize irrigation. Group plantings according to water requirements to optimize timing and quantity of irrigation. Turn off irrigation zones in areas where plants are established and require supplemental watering only during droughts. Replace plants that are inappropriate to ecoregion and/or natural habitat. Convert cool-season lawns to warm-season grasses (which require less water in summer).
Storage of materials and equipment	Store materials and equipment according to manufacturers' recommendations. Ensure that products and equipment are properly contained and secured to prevent materials and fuels from leaking. Ventilate storage areas so that chemicals and equipment do not degrade indoor air quality.

SETTING GOALS AND OBJECTIVES

Review the performance criteria for SS Credit Site Management to assess whether the policy goals established for this prerequisite will align with the credit compliance options.

Site- or project-specific goals not covered by the prerequisite requirements can be included in the policy. For example, if a creek runs through the property, the project team may choose to develop goals around improving water quality or riparian zone management.

Depending on the goal or objective, the schedule for implementation may be shorter or longer; some activities may warrant multiple goals with different implementation schedules or performance criteria. For example, a team could develop two metrics for maintenance equipment, one for replacing gasoline-powered equipment with environmentally preferred models, and one for reducing the runtime of the old equipment while it is still in use.

EXAMPLE

The policy model provided by USGBC contains useful guidance for developing a compliant policy. The example below demonstrates an appropriate level of detail for one operational element.

Sample documentation narrative for snow and ice removal policy

Building ABC has standard operating protocols for snow and ice removal that prioritize anti-icing strategies, reduce the total quantity of deicer applied, and require the exclusive use of environmentally preferred deicer products. Anti-icing

is performed before major winter storms. This involves applying a small amount of liquid deicer to high-traffic areas to prevent snow and ice from bonding to the hardscape. When deicer is applied after the storm, only the amount necessary to loosen snow and ice from the pavement is used; this avoids overusing materials and creates safer conditions for pedestrians. The snow and ice is then mechanically removed. High-traffic areas receive less deicer, since foot traffic helps mix and melt snow. Deicer is never used to open frozen storm drains. Deicer is spread using equipment with electronic controls to optimize the quantity use and application area. The vendor is instructed to avoid idling snow removal equipment to reduce vehicle emissions. To be considered environmentally preferred, deicer products may not contain any calcium chloride or sodium chloride. Building ABC has approved the use of SnowPRO Ice Wizard, which contains potassium chloride, and Ice-B-Gone, which contains magnesium chloride.

CAMPUS

Group Approach

All buildings in the group may be documented as one.

Campus Approach

Eligible.

REQUIRED DOCUMENTATION

	Documentation	All projects
E	Site management policy document	X
E	Justification for operational elements not included in policy	X

RELATED CREDIT TIPS

SS Credit Site Management. The site management policy is the primary tool for establishing best-practice maintenance procedures that support achievement of the related credit. Carefully review the credit requirements when developing the policy to establish strategies, guidelines, and goals that will facilitate meeting those requirements.

SS Credit Site Improvement Plan. The site management policy can support the use of environmentally preferable practices while site improvement activities are being implemented. Soil testing completed under the site management policy can inform the long-term objectives of the site improvement plan by, for example, influencing the selection of plant material.

SS Credit Site Development—Protect or Restore Habitat. The site management policy can support on-site habitat and biodiversity through maintenance of the site's native or adapted vegetation.

WE Credit Outdoor Water Use Reduction. Coordinate the development of the site management policy with the irrigation strategy pursued under the related credit.

CHANGES FROM LEED 2009

- This is a new prerequisite.
- The prerequisite is derived from two LEED 2009 credits: SS Credit 2, Building Exterior and Hardscape Management Plan, and SS Credit 3, Integrated Pest Management, Erosion Control, and Landscape Management Plan. Integrated pest management is now covered under the EQ credit category.

REFERENCED STANDARDS

None.

EXEMPLARY PERFORMANCE

Not available.

DEFINITIONS

invasive plant nonnative vegetation that has been introduced to an area and that aggressively adapts and reproduces. The plant's vigor combined with a lack of natural enemies often leads to outbreak populations. (Adapted from U.S. Department of Agriculture)

SUSTAINABLE SITES CREDIT

Site Development—Protect or Restore Habitat

This credit applies to:

Existing Buildings (1-2 points)
Schools (1-2 points)
Retail (1-2 points)
Data Centers (1-2 points)
Hospitality (1-2 points)
Warehouses and Distribution Centers (1-2 points)

INTENT

To conserve existing natural areas and restore damaged areas to provide habitat and promote biodiversity.

REQUIREMENTS

OPTION 1. ON-SITE RESTORATION (2 POINTS)

ESTABLISHMENT E

Have in place native or adapted vegetation on 20% of the total site area (including the building footprint), a minimum of 5,000 square feet (465 square meters), to provide habitat and promote biodiversity.

PERFORMANCE P

None.

OR

OPTION 2. FINANCIAL SUPPORT (1 POINT)

ESTABLISHMENT E

Provide financial support equivalent to at least $0.05 per square foot (US$0.50 per square meter) for the total site area (including the building footprint).

Financial support must be provided annually to a nationally or locally recognized land trust or conservation organization within the same EPA Level III ecoregion or the project's state (or within 100 miles [160 kilometers] for projects outside the U.S.). For U.S. projects, the land trust must be accredited by the Land Trust Alliance.

PERFORMANCE P

Provide the specified financial support annually.

BEHIND THE INTENT

Preservation and conservation of intact or high-quality native ecosystems, including their soils, native vegetation, sensitive species habitat, wildlife corridors, and hydrology, contributes to maintaining overall ecosystem health. Restoration of soils, hydrology, and native plants also improves the viability of ecological communities, helps manage and filter rainwater, and can regenerate other ecosystem functions.

When site constraints prevent on-site restoration, consider off-site conservation and restoration. An off-site approach may provide greater total ecosystem benefits than could otherwise be achieved on site. For projects that are unable to provide large, contiguous parcels of on-site land for long-term conservation, providing financial support to a recognized land trust or conservation organization can be an effective tool. Funds may be earmarked for activities that protect or restore of habitat, such as acquiring crucial land parcels, restoring habitat that is essential to certain species, protecting water bodies, and preserving urban green space.

STEP-BY-STEP GUIDANCE

To select the appropriate option for the project, determine whether to pursue on-site restoration (Option 1) and/or off-site financial support (Option 2).

- Option 1 is for projects with large, contiguous parcels of land. The project team must restore a minimum area of 5,000 square feet (465 square meters). Project teams that pursue Option 1 may also support conservation financially (Option 2) but can earn credit for only one option.
- Option 2 is appropriate for projects that do not have enough habitat area to meet the requirements of Option 1 or do not wish to perform on-site restoration.

Option 1. On-Site Restoration

STEP 1. CALCULATE SITE AREA REQUIRED TO HAVE NATIVE OR ADAPTED VEGETATION E

Use Equation 1 to determine the total site area that must have native or adapted vegetation. If the total area available for vegetation is less than the required minimum, the project is not eligible for Option 1 and must pursue Option 2 to earn this credit.

EQUATION 1. Minimum vegetated area

$$\text{Required area for native or adapted vegetation} = \text{Total site area (including building footprint)} \times 0.20$$

- If the currently vegetated area of the site exceeds the required area threshold and meets credit requirements for native or adapted vegetation, no additional restoration is necessary beyond maintenance of the area, which must be tracked during the performance period.
- Site area can be revegetated to meet the minimum vegetated area requirement (see *Further Explanation, Example*).

STEP 2. FACILITATE RESTORATION E

Work with site professionals to identify areas to be restored with native or adapted vegetation, determine restoration strategies, and define the process and method for restoration work (see *Further Explanation, Habitat Protection, Maintenance, and Restoration*).

- Restoration and enhancement of natural site elements can include existing ponds, riparian buffers, vegetation, and other natural features.
- Consider restoring areas adjacent to greenfield areas, bordering natural areas, and contiguous parcels to increase the environmental benefit.
- Areas that naturally do not contain vegetation can count toward restored area. For example, natural rock outcrops, ponds, and desert would all qualify under this credit. There is no need to vegetate areas that are not naturally vegetated. Project teams may need to submit documentation showing that the project site contains naturally unvegetated land or natural water bodies.
- Lawns (turf grasses) qualify as adapted vegetation only if they are able to survive without mowing, fertilization, pesticides, and irrigation.
- Maintenance of the vegetated areas is a best practice and may include: weeding, trimming, removal of invasive species, and other activities to ensure the health and long-tem viability of the plants.

Option 2. Financial Support

STEP 1. DETERMINE AMOUNT OF FINANCIAL SUPPORT E

Using Equation 2, establish the minimum financial support that must be dedicated to a qualifying land trust or conservation organization every year.

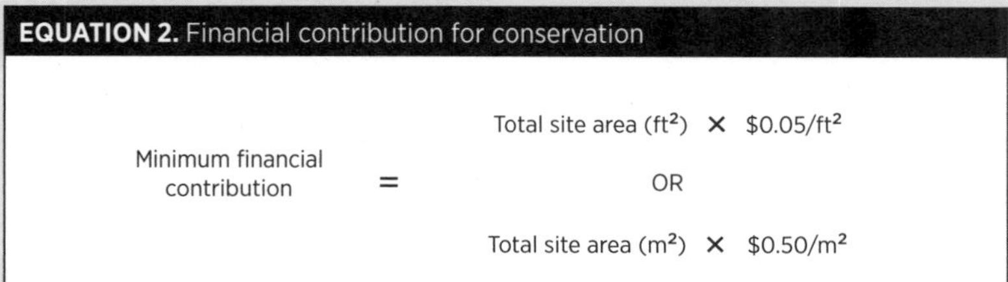

STEP 2. IDENTIFY QUALIFYING PARTNER ORGANIZATION E

Work with an accredited land trust or conservation organization to identify a use for the contribution and establish an agreement with the organization, detailing the use of the funding (see *Further Explanation, Working with Conservation Organizations*).

- The partnering organization must provide financial support to a project that meets the proximity criteria indicated in the credit requirements (see *Further Explanation, Identifying the Project's Ecoregion*).
- Examples of projects include land acquisition or management for natural processes; native habitat restoration; watershed management, restoration, or protection; and public urban green space restoration or revitalization.

FURTHER EXPLANATION

CALCULATIONS

See calculations in *Step-by-Step Guidance*.

HABITAT PROTECTION, MAINTENANCE, AND RESTORATION

Best practices for Option 1 of this credit focus on maintaining the health and viability of native and adapted vegetation, limiting and removing invasive species, and using low-impact management practices that reduce water and chemical use, summarized here as best practices.

Best practices for habitat protection and maintenance

- Clearly delineate the boundary of the habitat area on plans that are part of the site or facilities maintenance documents.
- Establish a five- to seven-year site management plan covering fire management, flooding, and invasive species, if necessary.
- Monitor the area for invasive species and remove them when they are identified.
- Avoid overwatering once plants are established.
- Do not store equipment or materials or dispose of inorganic or organic matter in the habitat area.
- Do not harvest live vegetation, fallen trees, or dead standing trees unless they pose a danger to human safety or create a fire hazard, or as prescribed by a certified forester for the purposes of advancing habitat protection.

Best practices for habitat restoration

- Engage a certified professional to assess the site's soils, water sources, native vegetation, invasive species, and wildlife species to determine how the area should be restored.
- Plan for site-specific environmental conditions; native species planted in inappropriate microclimates will not thrive.
- Source plants from reputable nurseries; find nursery-propagated specimens that originated in the same ecoregion as the project site (i.e., local ecotypes). Avoid nurseries that take plants from natural areas.
- Record the sources and origins of plant material to help inform on-going management.

The Society for Ecological Restoration International provides additional guidance on best management practices.

IDENTIFYING THE PROJECT'S ECOREGION

Project teams in the U.S. can use the classification system of the Environmental Protection Agency (EPA) to identify their Level III ecoregion and its characteristic native vegetation and soils. Refer to EPA's ecoregion map for more information, at epa.gov/wed/pages/ecoregions/level_iii_iv.htm. If EPA ecoregion information is not available for the project's area, ask the state government's environmental agency for comparable information.

Project teams outside the U.S. should also determine their ecoregion to help inform decisions about habitat protection and restoration.

WORKING WITH CONSERVATION ORGANIZATIONS (OPTION 2)

For U.S. projects, the land trust must be accredited by the Land Trust Alliance and be in the same Level III ecoregion or within the same state as the project.

For projects outside the U.S., the land trust or conservation organization must be located within 100 miles (160 km) of the project.

- If there are multiple options for recipients of financial support, project teams may wish to consult with potential recipients to determine the financial need of the organization, the intended use of the contribution, and compatibility with the project's own conservation goals.

EXAMPLE

The project is a small office building. To earn the credit, the project team is increasing the site's vegetated area. The site plan (Figure 1) depicts an existing area of vegetation and the area that will be revegetated, and Table 1 shows how the project is documenting compliance.

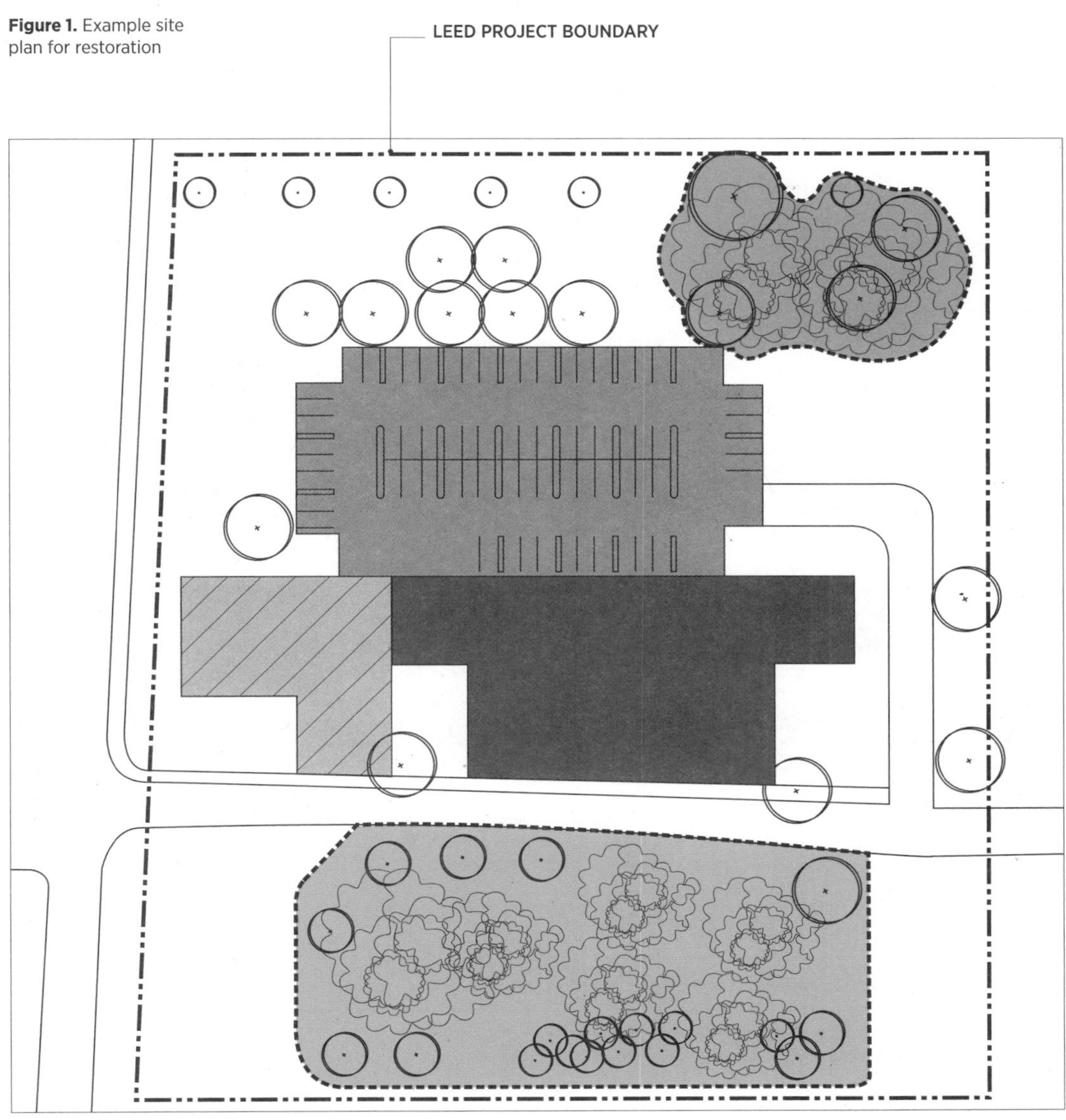

Figure 1. Example site plan for restoration

Total site area = 475,200 sq ft (11 ac)
44 148 sq m (4 ha)

Total native/adapted vegetation area = 119,500 sq ft (3 ac)
11 102 sq m (1 ha)
= 25% of total site area

- Office building to remain
- Existing parking lot to remain
- Proposed building extension area
- Proposed new native vegetation = 31,500 sq ft (2 926 sq m)
- Vegetated area to remain = 88,000 sq ft (8 175 sq m)

TABLE 1. Example calculation for minimum vegetated area		
	Area	**Calculation**
Total site area (including building footprint)	475,200 ft² (44 148 m²)	
Required area for native or adapted vegetation under Option 1	95,040 ft² (1 858 m²)	(475,200 ft² x 0.20) (44 148 m² x 0.20)

INTERNATIONAL TIPS

Project teams must identify the agency in their country that is responsible for land conservation issues. U.S. federal agencies may be a good resource to identify counterparts in other countries. Local entities can provide guidance on restoration activities and information regarding land trust projects within the required distance from the project site for teams pursuing Option 2.

Groups that work internationally include NatureServe Natural Heritage Program, Conservation International, and World Land Trust.

CAMPUS

Group Approach

All buildings in the group may be documented as one.

Campus Approach

Eligible.

REQUIRED DOCUMENTATION

	Documentation	Option 1	Option 2
E	Description of native or adapted vegetation	X	
E	Site plan indicating project boundary and building footprint and highlighting any preserved greenfield area, previously developed area, restored area, native and adapted vegetation, and plant species, other ecologically appropriate features or relevant site conditions	X	
E	Agreement with land trust or conservation organization		X
E	U.S. projects: Confirmation that land trust is accredited by Land Trust Alliance		X
E	Projects outside U.S.: Verification that the conservation organization is nationally or locally recognized; description of qualifications and mission of conservation organization		X
P	Confirmation that financial support will continue to be provided annually		X

RELATED CREDIT TIPS

SS Prerequisite and Credit Site Management Policy. Invasive and exotic species management, which may be necessary for this credit, is required by the related credit. Review the site management policy developed for the related prerequisite when preparing a maintenance plan for this credit, to ensure coordination.

SS Credit Site Improvement Plan. Habitat restoration is an important consideration when a project team develops a site improvement plan under the related credit. When preparing the site improvement plan, consider including plans for on-site restoration.

SS Credit Rainwater Management. Landscaped areas designed for rainwater management under the related credit can be counted toward the vegetated area in this credit, provided these areas use native or adapted vegetation.

SS Credit Heat Island Reduction. Vegetated roofs can be counted for both credits.

CHANGES FROM LEED 2009

- The calculation for the native vegetation threshold has changed to 20% of the total site area (including the building footprint) and a minimum of 5,000 square feet (465 square meters).
- The off-site option was replaced with an option for financial support

REFERENCED STANDARDS

U.S. EPA Ecoregions: epa.gov/

Land Trust Alliance Accreditation: landtrustalliance.org/

EXEMPLARY PERFORMANCE

Option 1. Double the 20% restoration requirement (restore at least 40%).

Option 2. Double the annual financial requirement by donating at least $0.10 per square foot ($1.00 per square meter).

DEFINITIONS

land trust a private, nonprofit organization that, as all or part of its mission, actively works to conserve land by undertaking or assisting in conservation easement or land acquisition, or by its stewardship of such land or easements (Adapted from Land Trust Alliance)

native vegetation an indigenous species that occurs in a particular region, ecosystem, and habitat without direct or indirect human actions. Native species have evolved to the geography, hydrology, and climate of that region. They also occur in communities; that is, they have evolved together with other species. As a result, these communities provide habitat for a variety of other native wildlife species. Species native to North America are generally recognized as those occurring on the continent prior to European settlement. Also known as native plants.

SUSTAINABLE SITES CREDIT

Rainwater Management

This credit applies to:

Existing Buildings (3 points)
Schools (2 points)
Retail (3 points)
Data Centers (3 points)
Hospitality (3 points)
Warehouses and Distribution Centers (3 points)

INTENT

To reduce runoff volume and improve water quality by replicating the natural hydrology and water balance of the site, based on historical conditions and undeveloped ecosystems in the region.

REQUIREMENTS

ESTABLISHMENT E

Use low-impact development (LID) practices to capture and treat water from 25% of the impervious surfaces for the 95th percentile storm event.

Establish and implement an annual inspection program of all rainwater management facilities to confirm continued performance.

PERFORMANCE P

Document the annual inspections, including identification of areas of erosion, maintenance needs, and repairs. Perform necessary maintenance, repairs, or stabilization within 60 days of inspection.

BEHIND THE INTENT

Conventional site development disrupts natural hydrological systems and watersheds through impervious area, soil compaction, loss of vegetation, and loss of natural drainage patterns. The cumulative effect of these changes is disruption to the natural water balance and water flow. Typically, a conventional site's rainwater management technique is to address runoff by piping and conveying it as quickly as possible into centralized, large facilities at the base of drainage areas. However, such a strategy, although intended to prevent flooding and promote efficient drainage, can harm watersheds: it increases the volume, temperature, peak flow, and duration of runoff, eroding streams and causing other ecological damage.

Green infrastructure (GI) and low-impact development (LID) rainwater management strategies and techniques improve upon that conventional approach by mimicking a site's natural hydrology. Rainwater is treated as a resource rather than a waste product. The approaches and techniques in this credit involve minimizing disturbed areas on the project site, limiting the amount of impervious cover on a site, and then infiltrating, filtering, storing, evaporating, or detaining rainwater runoff at or close to its source.

STEP-BY-STEP GUIDANCE

STEP 1. OBTAIN RAINFALL DATA FOR PROJECT LOCATION E

Collect at least 10 years of historical rainfall data, or as much historical data as possible from all seasons to account for seasonal variability. If the team submits less than 10 years' worth of information, explain why additional historical data are not available.

- For projects in the U.S., long-term rainfall data for many locations are available through the National Climatic Data Center. Use this database or another source to identify the reference location closest to the project site where similar precipitation patterns are expected.
- For project locations outside the U.S. or other locations not covered by the National Climatic Data Center, obtain information from local airports, universities, water treatment plants, or other facilities that maintain long-term precipitation records (see *Further Explanation, International Tips*).
- Data must include the location of the monitoring station, the recording time (usually the start of a time-step), and the total precipitation depth during the time-step.
- Collect daily historical rainfall data from a consistent source whenever possible. If data must be combined from multiple monitoring stations, interpolate or average rainfall data from three or more stations around the site to even out any discrepancies with the primary station.

STEP 2. DETERMINE VALUE FOR 95TH-PERCENTILE RAINFALL EVENTS E

Using the historical rainfall data collected, calculate the rainfall value for the 95th percentile (in inches or millimeters). This is the precipitation amount that 95 percent of all rainfall events for the period of record do not exceed (see *Further Explanation, Percentile of Rainfall Events*).

STEP 3. CALCULATE RUNOFF VOLUME E

Identify the impervious areas from which water will be treated according to the credit requirements (i.e., the areas to be included in the 25% threshold). Calculate the total volume of runoff (in cubic feet or cubic meters) corresponding to the 95th percentile of rainfall events for those surfaces. This is the amount that the project will need to manage entirely on site through green infrastructure and low-impact development techniques.

- Different methods can be used to calculate the runoff volume. Examples include the modified rational method; Natural Resources Conservation Service method (sometimes called SCS method), as described in Technical Release 55 (TR-55); and the U.S. EPA Rainwater Management Model (SWMM) (see *Further Explanation, Calculations* and *Examples*).
- Runoff volume depends on the specific postdeveloped site conditions of the project, such as amount of paving, permeability of different surfaces, roof area, and vegetated areas.

STEP 4. ASSESS CURRENT SITE CONDITIONS E

If the existing project site already has rainwater management strategies in place that qualify as GI or LID, determine whether they can fully capture and treat runoff from 25% of the impervious areas for the 95th percentile storm event through infiltration, evapotranspiration, and/or capture and reuse.

- Work with a civil engineer, landscape architect, and other contractors or consultants as needed to assess the current site conditions against the credit criteria. This assessment is best performed before site redevelopment activities begin.
- If the current management strategies provide adequate treatment, no further action is necessary to meet the credit requirements.

STEP 5. MODIFY SITE, AS NEEDED, TO INCORPORATE GI AND LID MEASURES E

If the current site conditions or strategies cannot capture and treat the required volume of runoff, or on-site strategies do not currently exist, modify the site such that it can meet the credit requirements.

- Work with rainwater professionals to identify and design the most appropriate GI and LID measures for the site. This process may take several months to several years, depending on the complexity of the site conditions and the GI or LID measures selected.
- The GI or LID measures must be in place by the end of the performance period to satisfy the credit requirements.
- Impervious areas that are removed from the site and replaced with GI or LID measures, such as vegetation or pervious pavement, can contribute to meeting the credit requirements. In this case, the credit requirement is met if the redeveloped site's GI or LID measures can capture and treat the runoff from at least 25% of the baseline impervious area (i.e., before site redevelopment).
- Alternatively, if at least 25% of the site impervious area is replaced by GI or LID measures and those measures can fully contain and treat the rainwater for the 95th percentile storm, the credit requirement is met.

STEP 6. DEVELOP AND IMPLEMENT AN ANNUAL INSPECTION PROGRAM OF ALL RAINWATER MANAGEMENT FACILITIES E P

Regularly evaluate rainwater measures to make sure they are performing properly.

- Inspect measures at least once per year.
- Protect measures from damage from any site modifications or construction activities.
- Inspect the site for changes in landscape contour, areas of erosion, plant health, standing water (for longer than 72 hours), or other problems, and identify maintenance and repair needs.
- Perform necessary maintenance, repairs, or stabilization within 60 days of inspection.
- Maintain records of rainwater inspection activities and repairs.

FURTHER EXPLANATION

CALCULATIONS

The project team may choose the runoff volume calculation methodology most appropriate for the project. Many rainwater software programs include calculation methodologies. Examples include the modified rational method; the Natural Resources Conservation Service method (sometimes called SCS method), as described in Technical Release 55 (TR-55); and the U.S. EPA Rainwater Management Model (SWMM).

Modified rational method

$$Q = C \times I \times A \times APF$$

where

Q = quantity of flow rate (ft^3/second or m^3/second)

C = runoff coefficient

I = rainfall intensity (inches/hour or mm/hour)

A = drainage area (acres or hectares)

APF = antecedent precipitation factor

The TR-55 Natural Resources Conservation Service method includes two equations.

TR-55 graphical peak discharge

$$q_p = q_a \times A_m \times Q \times F_p$$

where

q_p = peak discharge (ft^3/second or m^3/second)

q_a = unit peak discharge (ft^3/second/$mile^2$/inch or m^3/second/km^2/mm)

A_m = drainage area ($mile^2$ or km^2)

Q = runoff (inches or mm)

F_p = pond and swamp adjustment factor

TR-55 tabular hydrograph

$$q = q_t \times A_m \times Q$$

where

q = hydrograph coordinate (ft^3/second or m^3/second) at hydrograph time t

q_t = tabular unit discharge (ft^3/second/$mile^2$/inch or m^3/second/km^2/mm)

A_m = drainage area ($mile^2$ or km^2)

Q = runoff (inches or mm)

PERCENTILE OF RAINFALL EVENTS[1]

A percentile rainfall event represents a precipitation amount that the chosen percent of all rainfall events for the period of record do not exceed. For example, the 95th percentile of rainfall events is the measured precipitation depth accumulated over 24 hours that ranks as the 95th-percent rainfall depth based on the range of all daily event occurrences during the period of record. The 24-hour period is typically defined as 12:00:00 A.M. to 11:59:59 P.M.

Use the following steps to determine the 95th percentile of rainfall events:

1. Obtain a long-term daily precipitation data set for the project location (e.g., for U.S. projects, from the National Climatic Data Center website; for projects outside the U.S., see *International Tips*) . In general, a 30-year period of rainfall record is preferred for the analysis. The raw data are collected by most airports. At least 10 years of data must be included if available.
2. Import the data into the rainfall events calculator provided by USGBC, or another spreadsheet. If using another spreadsheet, organize daily precipitation records in a single column, in any order.
3. Review the records, looking for anomalies, and identify and remove any erroneous or flagged data points.
4. Remove rainfall events of less than 0.1 inch (2.5 mm). The amount of precipitation from these small events generally produces no measurable runoff because of absorption by permeable surfaces and interception and evaporation by impermeable and vegetated surfaces.
5. The USGBC calculator determines the 95th percentile rainfall amounts. If using another spreadsheet software, apply a percentile function (or similar) to obtain results.

GREEN INFRASTRUCTURE AND LOW-IMPACT DEVELOPMENT STRATEGIES

In addition to mimicking natural hydrologic cycle processes, green infrastructure and low-impact development help integrate the site with the surrounding watershed, are appropriate to the local ecosystem and climate, and deliver such other benefits as water reuse, habitat creation, and species diversity. Project teams should consult EPA's National Menu of Stormwater Best Practices and consider the following questions when selecting measures for the project:

- Which GI and LID measures will best mimic natural site hydrology?
- How can multiple measures be used together (in a "treatment train" approach) to manage rainwater?
- What are the infiltration rates and capacities of the most practical measures and how might the site's soil conditions affect their efficiency?

1. *Components adapted from Technical Guidance on Implementing the Stormwater Runoff Requirements for Federal Projects under Section 438 of the Energy Independence and Security Act.*

- What are the types and infiltration rates of existing soil conditions, and what design modifications might need to be made, if any, to the best management practices to satisfy performance goals?
- How effective are the measures at removing contaminants from the rainwater runoff?

EXAMPLES

The project is a 10-story building in a suburban neighborhood in Denver. The total site area is 43,000 square feet (4 000 square meters.) Of the total site area, 25,000 square feet (2 320 square meters) consists of the building footprint and hardscape. A portion of the building has a vegetated roof. Behind the building is an existing pervious patio, and in front is an impervious sidewalk. The current drive aisle and handicap parking are impervious asphalt (most parking is located under the building). There are other existing impervious areas on site, but the project is considering removing them and replacing them with native plantings. The remainder of the site is pervious vegetated area, but the site has no rainwater management facilities. Figure 1 is the proposed plan for the project; arrows indicate the direction of water flow.

Figure 1. Sample site plan for rainwater management

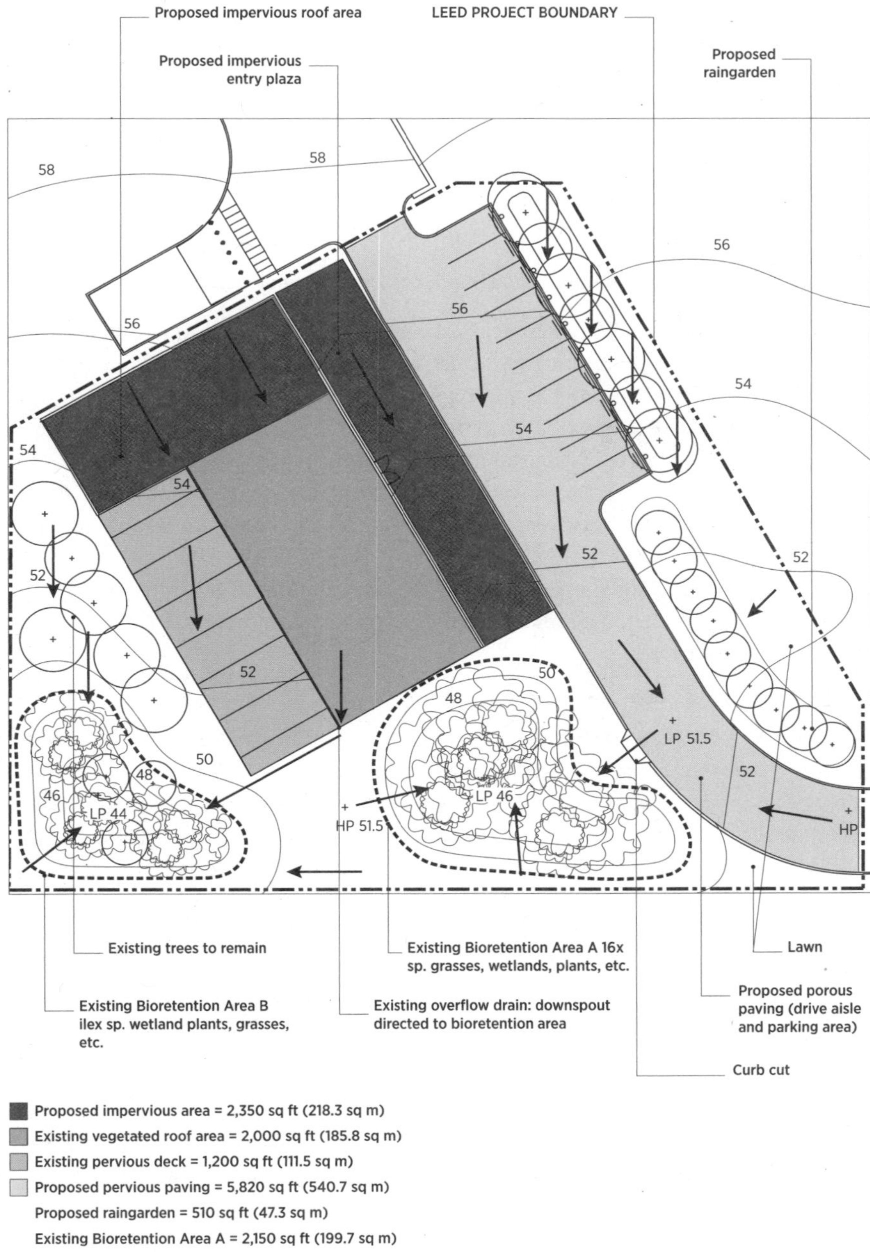

To determine the value for the 95th percentile (Step 2 in *Step-by-Step Guidance*), the project team pulled daily rainfall data from the National Climatic Data Center for the previous 10 years. Based on the historical data, the 95th-percentile storm delivers 1.1 inches (28 millimeters).

TABLE 1. Example percentile of rainfall events

Rainfall	Percentile Storm
1.33 ins. (34 mm)	99
1.29 (33)	98
1.22 (31)	97
1.15 (29)	96
1.1 (28)	95
1.05 (27)	94
1.01 (26)	93
0.96 (24)	92

To calculate the runoff volume from 25% of the impervious surfaces for the 95th percentile of storm events (see *Calculations*), the team notes total site area (43,000 square feet), total impervious area (5,000 square feet), and vegetated roof area (4,000 square feet).

The total impervious area to be managed is 25% of 5,000 square feet, or 1,250 square feet.

Of the impervious areas included in the 25%, the building roof is 3,000 square feet, with a runoff volume of 275 cubic feet; the concrete sidewalk is 2,000 square feet, with a runoff volume of 183.33 cubic feet. Thus, the total runoff volume to be captured and treated on site is 458.33 cubic feet.

The team identifies existing GI and LID features that may contribute toward rainwater management and verifies that they manage the required runoff volume on site (Step 4 in Step-by-Step Guidance). In addition to the existing pervious landscaped areas on the project site, the team will implement additional GI and LID measures: bioretention areas, porous paving, and a rain garden, and pervious decking that captures rainwater diverted from impervious surfaces.

To verify that the designed site manages all the rainwater runoff generated by a 95th percentile storm, the team uses the direct determination method to verify that the area of bioretention required can manage the excess runoff from the developed site.

Sample narrative describing GI and LID measures

The area of bioretention in this project meets the credit criteria by managing rainwater for more than 25% of the impervious surfaces for the 95th percentile of storm events via low-impact development strategies. The bioretention facilities incorporated into the site design are soil- and plant-based filtration systems that receive runoff from the developed site areas. They are located at low points on the site, where rainfall collects (see arrows on site plan). Rainfall runoff infiltrates into a sandy medium that temporarily holds the rainwater, facilitating numerous physical, biological, and chemical processes. Vegetation planted in the bioretention facilities, including Andropogon scoparius, *Iris sp., and* Taxodium distichum, *help filter particles in the runoff, assimilate nutrients and contaminants from the neighboring roadway, degrade engine oil, and oxygenate conditions to promote beneficial microorganisms. Bioretention mimics natural site hydrology by facilitating natural processes such as infiltration and evapotranspiration.*

INTERNATIONAL TIPS

If rainfall data for the project location are not available through the National Climatic Data Center database, the databases of the UN Food and Agriculture Organization (FAO) and Aquastat can be good sources of information for country-level rainwater data. Local rainfall data are best; use country-level data if necessary.

⊕ CAMPUS

Group Approach
All buildings in the group may be documented as one.

Campus Approach
Eligible.

REQUIRED DOCUMENTATION

	Documentation	All projects
E	Rainfall data	X
E	Rainfall events calculator or calculations for 95th percentile storm	X
E	Calculations for runoff volume from 25% of impervious area	X
E	Calculations for volume of rainwater managed by GI or LID strategies	X
E	Plans, details, or cross sections depicting site conditions, GI or LID strategies, topography, direction of water flow, and area of site that each GI or LID measure addresses	X
E	Narrative confirming that measures qualify as GI or LID	X
P	Documents or narrative about inspections and maintenance	X

RELATED CREDIT TIPS

SS Credit Site Improvement Plan. The existing site conditions documentation created for the related credit can be used to assess the project site for rainwater management as well. Investigate adding GI and LID measures to the improvement plan and look for lower-cost opportunities to divert rainwater flows from impervious areas to existing landscape areas for infiltration or evapotranspiration on the site.

SS Credit Site Development—Protect or Restore Habitat. Native and adapted vegetation used in GI and LID approaches also contributes to achieving the related credit.

SS Credit Heat Island Reduction. Vegetated roofs installed for this credit may also meet the requirements of the related credit.

WE Prerequisite and WE Credit Indoor Water Use Reduction. Rainwater collected and treated for this credit may also contribute to the related prerequisite and credit by reducing the potable water demand.

WE Credit Outdoor Water Use Reduction. Rainwater collected and treated for this credit may also contribute to the related prerequsite and credit by reducing the potable water demand.

CHANGES FROM LEED 2009

- Projects must use GI and LID rainwater management techniques on site.
- The metric by which to test compliance is now the total volume of runoff calculated for the 95th percentile of regional or local storm events, rather than the one-year and two-year storm events.

REFERENCED STANDARDS

U.S. EPA Technical Guidance on Implementing the Rainwater Runoff Requirements for Federal Projects under Section 438 of the Energy Independence and Security Act: epa.gov/

EXEMPLARY PERFORMANCE

Use GI and LID practices to capture and treat water from 50% of the impervious surfaces for the 95th percentile storm event.

DEFINITIONS

green infrastructure a soil- and vegetation-based approach to wet weather management that is cost-effective, sustainable, and environmentally friendly. Green infrastructure management approaches and technologies infiltrate, evapotranspire, capture and reuse stormwater to maintain or restore natural hydrologies. (Adapted from U.S. Environmental Protection Agency)

impervious surface an area of ground that development and building have modified in such a way that precipitation cannot infiltrate downward through the soil. Examples of impervious surfaces include roofs, paved roads and parking areas, sidewalks, and soils that have been compacted either by design or by use.

low-impact development (**LID**) an approach to managing rainwater runoff that emphasizes on-site natural features to protect water quality, by replicating the natural land cover hydrologic regime of watersheds, and addressing runoff close to its source. Examples include better site design principles (e.g., minimizing land disturbance, preserving vegetation, minimizing impervious cover), and design practices (e.g., rain gardens, vegetated swales and buffers, permeable pavement, rainwater harvesting, soil amendments). These are engineered practices that may require specialized design assistance.

manage (**rainwater**) **on site** to capture and retain a specified volume of rainfall to mimic natural hydrologic function. Examples of rainwater management include strategies that involve evapotranspiration, infiltration, and capture and reuse.

SUSTAINABLE SITES CREDIT

Heat Island Reduction

This credit applies to:

Existing Buildings (2 points)
Schools (2 points)
Retail (2 points)
Data Centers (2 points)
Hospitality (2 points)
Warehouses and Distribution Centers (2 points)

INTENT

To minimize effects on microclimates and human and wildlife habitats by reducing heat islands.

REQUIREMENTS

Choose one of the following options.

OPTION 1. NONROOF (1 POINT)

ESTABLISHMENT E

Use any combination of the following strategies for a minimum of 50% of the site paving.

- Use the existing plant material or install plants that provide shade over paving areas (including playgrounds) on the site within 10 years of planting. Plants must be in place at the time of certification application.
- Install vegetated planters. Plants must be in place at the time of occupancy permit and cannot include artificial turf.
- Provide shade with structures covered by energy generation systems, such as solar thermal collectors, photovoltaics, and wind turbines.
- Provide shade with architectural devices or structures that have a three-year aged solar reflectance (SR) value of at least 0.28. If three-year aged value information is not available, use materials with an initial SR of at least 0.33 at installation.
- Provide shade with vegetated structures.
- Use paving materials with a three-year aged solar reflectance (SR) value of at least 0.28. If three-year aged value information is not available, use materials with an initial SR of at least 0.33 at installation.
- Use an open-grid pavement system (at least 50% unbound).

PERFORMANCE P

Implement a maintenance program that ensures all high-reflectance paving surfaces are cleaned at least every three years to maintain good reflectance.

OR

OPTION 2. ROOF (1 POINT)

ESTABLISHMENT E

Use either roofing materials with a SRI equal to or greater than the values in Table 1 for a minimum of 75% of the roof area, or a vegetated roof for a minimum of 50% of the roof area, or both. If using both high-reflectance and vegetated roof surfaces, meet the following criterion:

$$\frac{\text{Area of high-reflectance roof}}{0.75} + \frac{\text{Area of vegetated roof}}{0.5} \geq \text{Total roof area}$$

Alternatively, an SRI and SR weighted average approach may be used to calculate compliance.

PERFORMANCE P

Implement a maintenance program that ensures all high-reflectance roof surfaces are cleaned at least every three years to maintain good reflectance, and all vegetated roofs are maintained for plant health and good structural condition.

OPTION 3. NONROOF AND ROOF (2 POINTS)

ESTABLISHMENT E

Meet the following criterion:

$$\frac{\text{Area of nonroof measures}}{0.5} + \frac{\text{Area of high-reflectance roof}}{0.75} + \frac{\text{Area of vegetated roof}}{0.50} \geq \text{Total site paving area} + \text{Total roof area}$$

Alternatively, an SRI and SR weighted average approach may be used to calculate compliance.

Use any combination of the following strategies.

Nonroof Measures
Use the measures listed in Option 1. Plant material must be in place at time of certification application.

High-Reflectance Roof
Use roofing materials that have an SRI equal to or greater than the values in Table 1. Meet the three-year aged SRI value. If three-year aged value information is not available, use materials that meet the initial SRI value.

TABLE 1. Minimum solar reflectance index value, by roof slope

	Slope	Initial SRI	3-year aged SRI
Low-sloped roof	≤ 2:12	82	64
Steep-sloped roof	> 2:12	39	32

Vegetated Roof
Install a vegetated roof.

PERFORMANCE P

Implement a maintenance program that ensures all high-reflectance surfaces are cleaned at least every three years to maintain good reflectance, and all vegetated roofs are maintained for plant health and good structural condition.

OR

OPTION 4. PARKING UNDER COVER (1 POINT)

ESTABLISHMENT E

Place at least 50% of parking spaces under cover. Any roof used to shade or cover parking must (1) have a three-year aged SRI of at least 32 (if three-year aged value information is not available, use materials with an initial SRI of at least 39 at installation), (2) be a vegetated roof, or (3) be covered by energy generation systems, such as solar thermal collectors, photovoltaics, and wind turbines.

PERFORMANCE P

Implement a maintenance program that ensures all SRI surfaces are cleaned at least every three years to maintain good reflectance, and all vegetated roofs are maintained for plant health and good structural condition.

BEHIND THE INTENT

Dark, nonreflective surfaces used for parking, roads, roofs, walkways, and other hardscapes absorb the sun's warmth and radiate heat, creating heat islands. Urban areas can have temperatures 1.8° to 5.4°F (1° to 3°C) warmer than surrounding suburban and undeveloped areas, and as much as 22°F (12°C) warmer in evenings. These heat islands may contribute to regional average warming trends.[1] A study of surface warming resulting from rapid urbanization in east China found urban heat islands responsible for 24.2% of regional warming.[2] Urban heat island effects have numerous negative consequences: plants and animals sensitive to temperature fluctuations may find habitat affected by heat islands inhospitable. Human health may suffer because exposure to ground-level pollution is often worse in places affected by heat islands. Additionally, heat islands increase cooling loads in the summer, necessitating larger, more powerful air-conditioners that use more electricity, in turn increasing cooling costs, producing more greenhouse gases, and generating pollution.

According to a study of the metropolitan areas of Baton Rouge, Chicago, Houston, Sacramento, and Salt Lake City by the Department of Energy's Lawrence Berkeley National Laboratory, the energy savings potential of heat island reduction measures ranges from $4 million to $15 million per year.[3] Efforts to reduce heat islands can have a reasonable payback period when included as part of an integrated systems approach to improving building performance, such as by installing solar panels on shading devices or using a vegetated roof to insulate a building and extend the life of the roof.

The most effective measure of a roofing material's ability to reject solar heat is the solar reflectance index (SRI). However, to measure the solar heat rejection of components that are not roofing materials, or "nonroof"—for example, vegetation, shading devices, and other less reflective components—solar reflectance (SR) is used in this credit instead. SR is a more appropriate way to measure nonroof materials, which have more thermal mass. In addition to a product's initial SRI or SR value, this credit considers a product's three-year-aged SRI or SR values, which measure material performance over time. The credit encourages project teams to adopt a variety of strategies, including reducing hardscape and incorporating high-SRI or high-SR materials such as vegetation and shaded parking, which minimize a project's overall contribution to heat island effects.

STEP-BY-STEP GUIDANCE

STEP 1. IDENTIFY PARKING, HARDSCAPE, AND ROOF AREA

On a site plan or garage plan, identify all vehicle parking spaces, total hardscape area, and total applicable roof area within the project boundary.

- Include motorcycle parking as vehicle parking spaces. Exclude bicycle parking area.
- Hardscape area includes all paved roads, sidewalks, courtyards, and parking lots.
- Applicable roof area excludes roof area covered by mechanical equipment, solar energy panels, skylights, and any other appurtenances.
- The top level of multilevel parking structures is considered nonroof surface if it has parking spaces but roof area if it has no parking spaces.

STEP 2. IDENTIFY AREAS OF EXISTING AND PLANNED HEAT ISLAND MITIGATION MEASURES

Review current conditions and near-term renovation plans to identify the following:

- Area of high-reflectance roofing that meets or exceeds the SRI requirements (Table 1)
- Area of vegetated roofing systems
- Area of planters
- Area of hardscape that meets shading, permeability, or reflectance requirements listed in the credit requirements
- Number of parking spaces under cover that meets credit requirements

1. *U.S Environmental Protection Agency, Heat Island Effect, epa.gov/heatisland/index.htm (accessed May 2013).*
2. *Yang, X., Y. Hou, and B. Chen, Observed Surface Warming Induced by Urbanization in East China. J. Geophys. Res. 116 (2011), D14113, doi:10.1029/2010JD015452.*
3. *U.S Environmental Protection Agency, Heat Island Effect: Urban Heat Island Pilot Project (UHIPP), epa.gov/hiri/pilot/index.html (accessed May 2013).*

STEP 3. SELECT ONE OPTION

Determine which option the project will pursue. Projects may earn points for only one option but are encouraged to incorporate as many heat island reduction strategies as possible.

- Option 1 is for projects with compliant at-grade (i.e., nonroof) strategies and no roof treatments or covered parking.
- Option 2 is for projects with compliant roofs but without compliant at-grade (i.e., nonroof) strategies or covered parking.
- Option 3 is for projects with compliant roofs and at-grade (i.e., nonroof) systems, but no covered parking.
- Option 4 is for projects with only covered or underground parking.

Option 1. Nonroof

STEP 1. EVALUATE COMPLIANCE

Sum the paving area addressed by eligible nonroof measures and confirm that the mitigated area is at least 50% of the site's total hardscape; this is the standard nonroof calculation. Alternatively, use Equation 1 to demonstrate compliance.

- Equation 1 weights the SR for total nonroof area, showing its overall effect on heat island. This equation is useful for projects whose nonroof materials fall both above and below the required SRI values.
- Project teams should first evaluate compliance against the standard nonroof calculation (see *Further Explanation, Example 1*). If the project does not comply with the standard nonroof calculation, move to Equation 1.

EQUATION 1. Weighted nonroof calculation

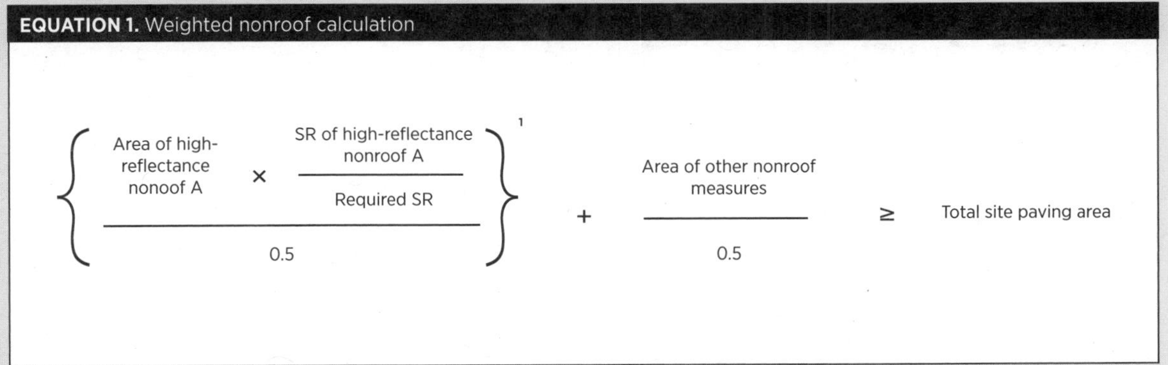

$$\left\{ \frac{\text{Area of high-reflectance nonoof A} \times \dfrac{\text{SR of high-reflectance nonroof A}}{\text{Required SR}}}{0.5} \right\}^{1} + \frac{\text{Area of other nonroof measures}}{0.5} \geq \text{Total site paving area}$$

[1] Summed for all high-reflectance nonroof areas.

STEP 2. INCORPORATE ADDITIONAL MITIGATION STRATEGIES, IF NECESSARY

If the calculation indicates that additional heat island mitigation is necessary to achieve compliance, extend or add nonroof mitigation strategies (see *Further Explanation, Heat Island Mitigation Strategies*). Recalculate to confirm compliance.

- Include performance requirements in the project specifications, or specify particular systems and products that meet the credit requirements.
- Collect manufacturers' documentation of SR and paving permeability, as applicable, to verify compliance.

STEP 3. CREATE AND IMPLEMENT MAINTENANCE PROGRAM

Implement a maintenance program to ensure that all high-reflectance surfaces are cleaned at least once every three years (see *Further Explanation, Maintenance Program*).

Option 2. Roof

STEP 1. EVALUATE COMPLIANCE

Project teams can use several approaches to determine compliance, depending on the nature of the building's roof.

- If the project uses only high-reflectance roofing materials with the minimum required SRI values (Table 1 of the credit requirements), confirm that the total amount of compliant area is at least 50% of the total applicable roof area.
- If the project uses only vegetated roof, confirm that the total amount of compliant area is at least 50% of the total applicable roof area.
- If the project includes a combination of materials, determine credit compliance using Equation 2 (see *Further Explanation, Example 2*). Equation 2 determines the combined compliance of high-reflectance roof and vegetated roof for the whole project. If the project does not comply, move to Equation 3.
- Equation 3 weights the SRI for total roof area, showing its overall effect on heat island. This equation is useful for projects that have multiple roof angles and roof materials that fall both above and below the required SRI values.

EQUATION 2. Standard roof calculation

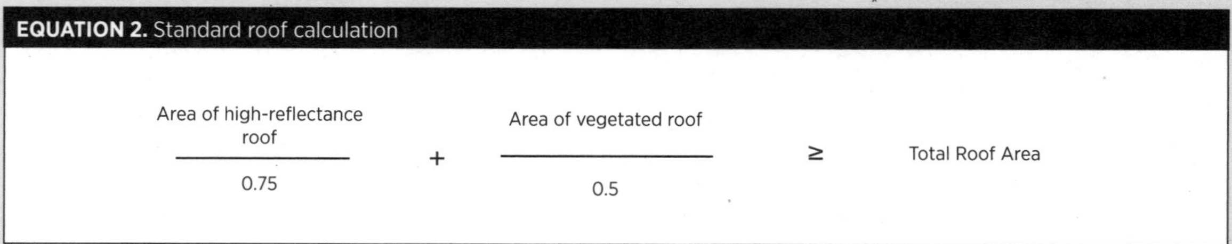

$$\frac{\text{Area of high-reflectance roof}}{0.75} + \frac{\text{Area of vegetated roof}}{0.5} \geq \text{Total Roof Area}$$

EQUATION 3. Weighted roof calculation

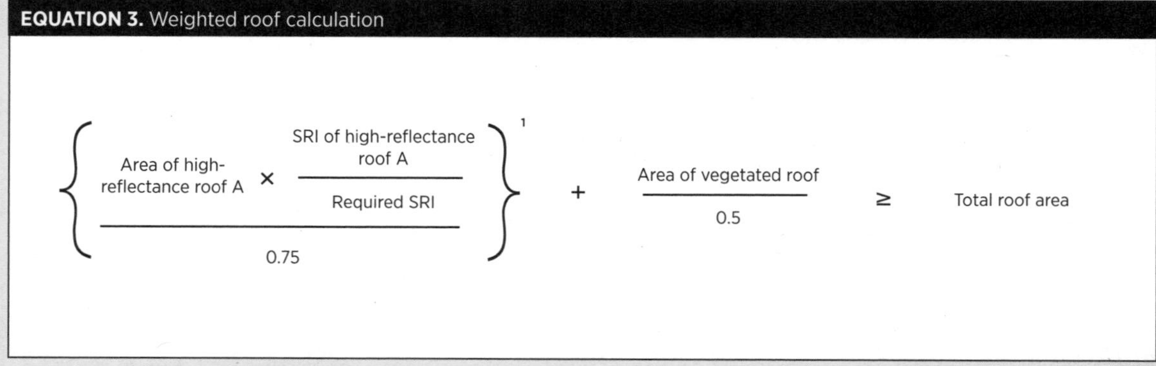

$$\left\{ \frac{\text{Area of high-reflectance roof A} \times \dfrac{\text{SRI of high-reflectance roof A}}{\text{Required SRI}}}{0.75} \right\}^{1} + \frac{\text{Area of vegetated roof}}{0.5} \geq \text{Total roof area}$$

[1] Summed for all high-reflectance roof areas.

STEP 2. INCORPORATE ADDITIONAL MITIGATION STRATEGIES, IF NECESSARY

If the calculation indicates that additional heat island mitigation is necessary to achieve compliance, extend or add high-reflectance or vegetated roof area (see *Further Explanation, Heat Island Mitigation Strategies*). Recalculate to confirm compliance.

- Include performance requirements in the project specifications, or specify particular systems and products that meet the credit requirements.
- Collect manufacturers' documentation of SRI, as applicable, to verify compliance with credit requirements.

STEP 3. CREATE AND IMPLEMENT MAINTENANCE PROGRAM

Implement a maintenance program to ensure that all high-reflectance roof surfaces are cleaned at least once every three years and that all vegetated roofs are maintained for plant health and good structural condition (see *Further Explanation, Maintenance Program*). Ensure that all applicable surfaces are cleaned and maintained during the performance period.

OPTION 3. NONROOF AND ROOF STEP 1. EVALUATE COMPLIANCE

Two equations may be used to demonstrate compliance.

- Project teams should first evaluate compliance using Equation 4, which determines the combined compliance of roof and nonroof measures for the whole project.
- If the project does not comply using Equation 4, move to Equation 5. This equation weights the SR and SRI for total hardscape and roof area, showing its overall effect on heat island; it is useful for projects that have multiple roof angles and nonroof or roof materials that fall both above and below the required SR or SRI values (see *Further Explanation, Example 3*).

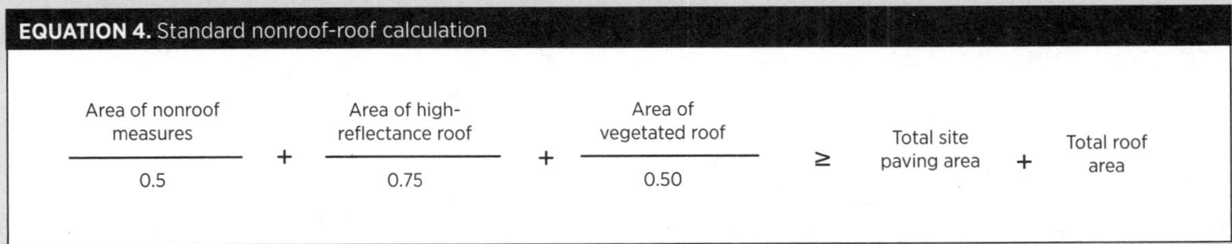

EQUATION 4. Standard nonroof-roof calculation

$$\frac{\text{Area of nonroof measures}}{0.5} + \frac{\text{Area of high-reflectance roof}}{0.75} + \frac{\text{Area of vegetated roof}}{0.50} \geq \text{Total site paving area} + \text{Total roof area}$$

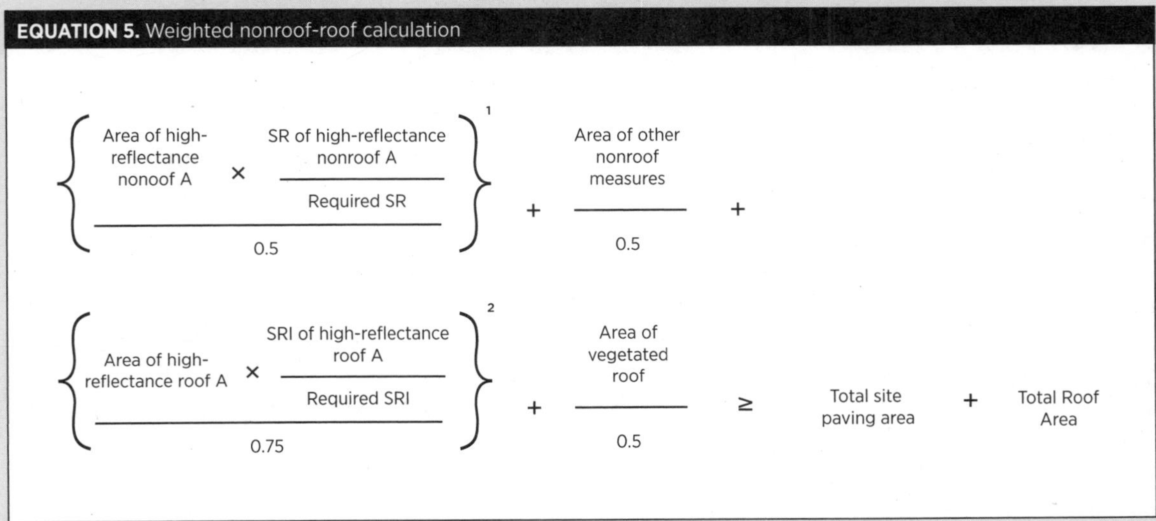

EQUATION 5. Weighted nonroof-roof calculation

$$\left\{\frac{\text{Area of high-reflectance nonroof A} \times \frac{\text{SR of high-reflectance nonroof A}}{\text{Required SR}}}{0.5}\right\}^{1} + \frac{\text{Area of other nonroof measures}}{0.5} + \left\{\frac{\text{Area of high-reflectance roof A} \times \frac{\text{SRI of high-reflectance roof A}}{\text{Required SRI}}}{0.75}\right\}^{2} + \frac{\text{Area of vegetated roof}}{0.5} \geq \text{Total site paving area} + \text{Total Roof Area}$$

[1] Summed for all high-reflectance nonroof areas.

[2] Summed for all high-reflectance roof areas.

STEP 2. INCORPORATE ADDITIONAL MITIGATION STRATEGIES, IF NECESSARY

If the calculation in Step 2 indicates that additional heat island mitigation is necessary to achieve compliance, extend or add nonroof and/or roof mitigation strategies (see *Further Explanation, Heat Island Mitigation Strategies*). Recalculate to confirm compliance.

- Include performance requirements in the project specification sections, or specify particular systems and products that meet the credit requirements.
- Collect manufacturers' documentation of SR, SRI, and paving permeability, as applicable, to verify compliance.

STEP 3. CREATE AND IMPLEMENT MAINTENANCE PROGRAM

Implement a maintenance program to ensure that all high-reflectance surfaces are cleaned at least once every three years and that all vegetated roofs are maintained for plant health and good structural condition (see *Further Explanation, Maintenance Program*). Ensure that all applicable surfaces are cleaned and maintained during the performance period.

Option 4. Parking under Cover

STEP 1. EVALUATE COMPLIANCE

Confirm that at least 50% of parking spaces are located under cover that meets one of the criteria listed in the credit requirements.

- Include motorcycle parking spaces as vehicle parking spaces. Exclude bicycle parking area.
- Count uncovered parking at the top level of a multilevel parking structure as uncovered spaces.
- The top level of a multilevel parking structure is considered nonroof surface if it has parking spaces but roof area if it has no parking spaces. If the latter, it must comply with the criteria for roof area.

STEP 2. INCORPORATE ADDITIONAL PARKING COVER OR MODIFY COVER SURFACE, IF NECESSARY

If additional parking spaces must be covered, or if existing cover does not meet the credit requirements, provide cover that meets one of the requirements listed in the rating system (see *Further Explanation, Heat Island Mitigation Strategies*).

- Include performance requirements in the project specifications, or specify particular systems and products that meet the credit requirements.
- Collect manufacturer's documentation of SRI, as applicable, to verify compliance with the credit requirements.

STEP 3. CREATE AND IMPLEMENT MAINTENANCE PROGRAM, IF APPLICABLE

If any parking cover consists of a high-SRI surface, implement a maintenance program to ensure that the roof surface is cleaned at least once every three years and that all vegetated roofs are maintained for plant health and good structural condition (see *Further Explanation, Maintenance Program*). Ensure that all applicable surfaces are cleaned and maintained during the performance period.

FURTHER EXPLANATION

CALCULATIONS

See calculations in *Step-by-Step Guidance*.

HEAT ISLAND MITIGATION STRATEGIES

TABLE 2. Roof mitigation strategies

Strategy	Rules and tips
High-reflectance roof	Consider glare, which can distress passing vehicles, pedestrians, and occupants of adjacent buildings, especially with steep-sloped roofs.
	Consider maintenance; regular cleaning is required to keep these materials from losing reflectivity over time.
Vegetated roof	Artificial turf grass does not count.
	Plants must be in place at time of certification application.
	Extensive or intensive vegetated roofs are eligible. Roof planters can contribute only if they are part of vegetated roof system.
	Consider maintenance required to keep plants healthy and structure in good condition.

TABLE 3. Nonroof mitigation strategies	
Strategy	**Rules and tips**
Vegetative shading	Plants must be in place at time of certification application. Assume canopy width at noon conditions (i.e., no extending shadows in plan view, regardless of time of year) in year 10 when evaluating shading.
Vegetated planters	Artificial turf grass does not count. Plants must be in place at time of certification application.
Vegetated shading structures	Supports (e.g., trellises) and plants must be in place at time of certification application.
Shading structures with energy generation	Paved area (not roof area) is shaded by energy generation equipment (e.g., solar thermal collectors, photovoltaic panels, wind turbines).
Shading architectural devices or structures	Materials must have 3-year aged SR value of at least 0.28, or initial SR of at least 0.33 at installation.
High reflectance paving	Materials must have 3-year aged SR value of at least 0.28, or an initial SR of at least 0.33 at installation. Consider maintenance (e.g., regular cleaning) required to keep these materials from losing reflectivity over time..
Open-grid paving	Paving must be at least 50% unbound.

TABLE 4. Covered parking strategies	
Strategy	**Rules and tips**
Undercover parking	May be located underground, under deck, under roof, or under building. Stacked parking is considered covered parking. Any roof used to shade or cover parking must meet criteria listed in credit requirements.

MAINTENANCE PROGRAM

Tailor the maintenance program to the specific materials installed. Review manufacturers' recommendations as a starting point for developing the program.

Cleaning activities may be performed in-house or by a contracted vendor. Best practices include using environmentally preferred cleaning products, using electric-powered sweepers and manual tools, and power washing with water only.

Surfaces with higher SRI and SR values after aging usually require less ongoing cleaning and maintenance to maintain their heat island reduction properties. Maintaining the reflectance of light-colored surfaces is especially important in areas that receive a large quantity of direct sunlight.

EXAMPLES

Example 1. Standard nonroof calculation (Option 1)

The project has 3,900 square feet (360 square meters) of hardscape. The following heat island mitigation strategies have been included in the project design:

- 400 square feet (35 square meters) of sidewalks with a three-year aged SR of 0.30
- 650 square feet (60 square meters) of parking with an initial SR of 0.34
- 1,000 square feet (95 square meters) of shading by tree canopy

The total area of nonroof mitigation strategies (2,050 square feet [190 square meters]) is equal to 52.6% of total site hardscape, so the project achieves the credit.

Example 2. Standard roof calculation (Option 2)

The project has 2,450 square feet (230 square meters) of total roof area, of which 200 square feet (20 square meters) is covered by mechanical equipment, making the total applicable roof area 2,250 square feet (210 square meters). The following heat island mitigation strategies have been included in the project design:

- 1,200 square feet (110 square meters) vegetated roof
- 1,050 square feet (100 square meters) of high-reflectance roof with a three-year aged SRI of 90

The project team calculates compliance using Equation 2, as follows:

$$\frac{1{,}050 \text{ ft}^2}{0.75} + \frac{1{,}200 \text{ ft}^2}{0.5} = 2{,}250 \text{ ft}^2$$

The total calculated area of roof mitigation strategies (3,800 square feet [350 square meters]) exceeds the total applicable roof area (2,250 square feet [210 square meters]), so the project achieves the credit.

Example 3. Weighted nonroof-roof calculation (Option 3)

The project has 3,900 square feet (360 square meters) of hardscape. The total roof area is 2,450 square feet (230 square meters), of which 200 square feet (20 square meters) is covered by mechanical equipment, making the total applicable roof area 2,250 square feet (210 square meters). The following heat island mitigation strategies have been included in the project design:

- 400 square feet (35 square meters) of permeable sidewalks that are 55% unbound
- 1,000 square feet (95 square meters) of shading by tree canopy
- 1,200 square feet (110 square meters) vegetated roof
- 400 square feet (35 square meters) of steep-sloped roof with an initial SRI of 42
- 650 square feet (60 square meters) of steep-sloped roof with an initial SRI of 34

The project team calculates compliance using Equation 5, as follows:

$$0 + \frac{400 \text{ ft}^2 + 1{,}000 \text{ ft}^2}{0.5} + \frac{400 \text{ ft}^2 \times \frac{\text{SRI } 42}{\text{SRI } 39} + 650 \text{ ft}^2 \times \frac{\text{SRI } 34}{\text{SRI } 39}}{0.75} + \frac{1{,}200 \text{ ft}^2}{0.50} \geq 3{,}900 \text{ ft}^2 + 2{,}250 \text{ ft}^2$$

The total calculated area of nonroof and roof mitigation strategies (6,529 square feet [600 square meters]) exceeds the sum of total site hardscape and total applicable roof area (6,150 square feet [570 square meters]), so the project achieves the credit.

Example 4. Acceptable site plan

The project team is pursuing Option 3, Nonroof and Roof, and submits the following plan, which has sufficient detail to show compliance.

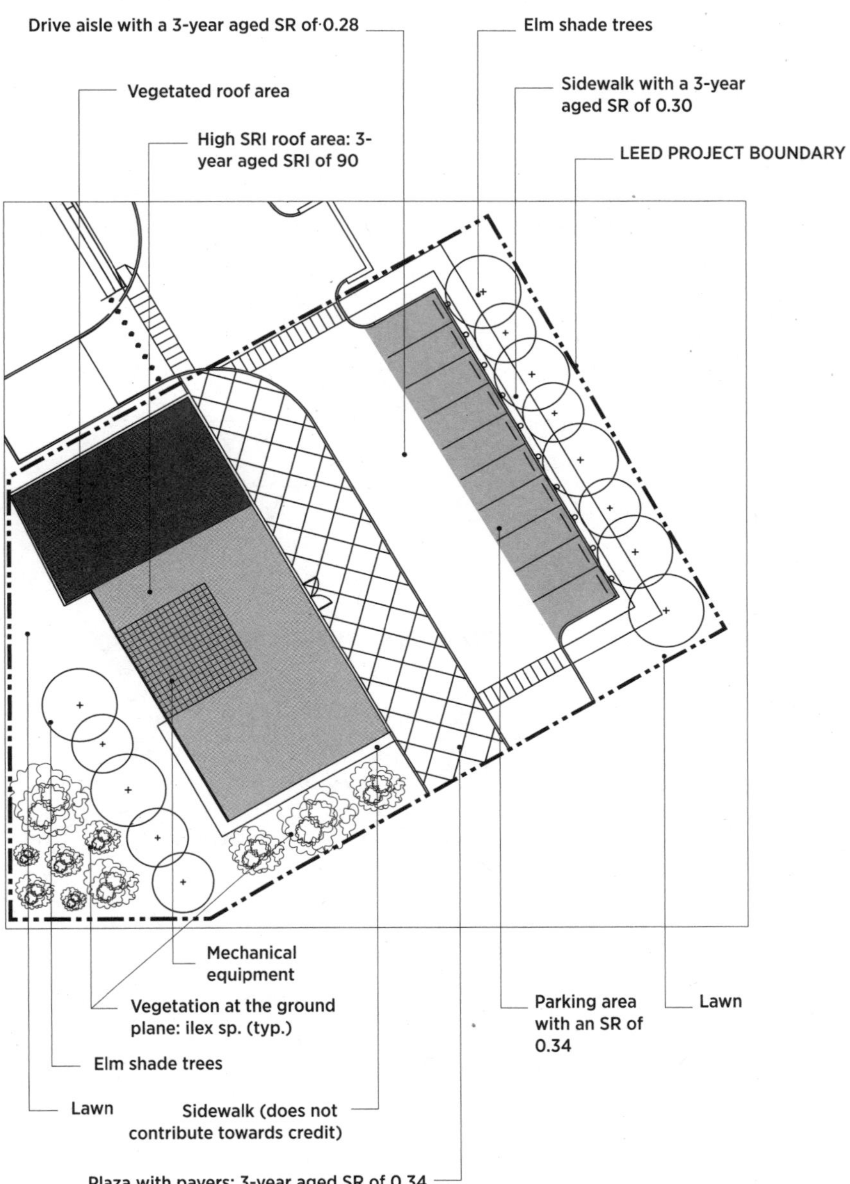

Figure 1. Example site plan

CAMPUS

Group Approach

All buildings in the group may be documented as one.

Campus Approach

Eligible.

REQUIRED DOCUMENTATION

	Documentation	Option 1	Option 2	Option 3	Option 4
E	Nonroof and/or roof area calculations	X	X	X	
E	Site plan indicating LEED project boundary, highlighting nonroof elements and measurements, hardscape area, and area of each nonroof measure	X		X	
E	Parking space calculations				X
E	Plan indicating LEED project boundary and building footprint, highlighting roof elements and measurements, roof area, and area of each roof measure		X	X	
E	Manufacturers' documentation of SRI, SR, and paving permeability	X	X	X	X
P	Description of maintenance program	X	X	X	X

RELATED CREDIT TIPS

SS Credit Site Development—Protect or Restore Habitat. Vegetated roofs installed to mitigate heat island effects can also contribute to the related credit if the plant material are native or adapted species.

SS Credit Site Improvement Plan. The site assessment process can be used to identify opportunities for mitigating heat islands, such as replacing unnecessary hardscape with vegetation.

SS Credit Rainwater Management. Vegetated roofs can contribute to rainwater management, and reducing a site's hardscape area will improve infiltration rates.

EA Prerequisite Minimum Energy Performance and EA Credit Optimize Energy Performance. Vegetated roofs help insulate buildings, and the cooler surrounding microclimate may lower a building's cooling load and improve energy performance. High-reflectance roofs experience less solar heat gain and may therefore lower cooling loads (but increase heating loads in low-rise buildings in cold climates).

CHANGES FROM LEED 2009

- The credit combines the roof and nonroof heat island credits from LEED 2009.
- The minimum frequency for cleaning paving and roof surfaces has been changed to every three years.
- Tree canopy shade area is now calculated after 10 years of growth rather than five years.
- SRI thresholds have been increased and now include both initial SRI and three-year aged SRI.
- Credit compliance for nonroof hardscape is now calculated using SR values instead of SRI values.

REFERENCED STANDARDS

ASTM Standards E903 and E892: astm.org/

Cool Roof Rating Council Standard (CRRC-1): coolroofs.org/

EXEMPLARY PERFORMANCE

Option 1. Install SR-compliant materials and/or open-grid paving, or provide shading within 10 years, for at least 95% of nonroof impervious surfaces.

Option 2. Install a vegetated roof system for at least 95% of the project's roof area (excluding any mechanical equipment, photovoltaic panels, and skylights).

Option 3. Achieve exemplary performance for both Option 1 and Option 2: install SR-compliant materials and/or open-grid paving, or provide shading within 10 years, for at least 95% of nonroof impervious surfaces AND install a vegetated roof system for at least 95% of the project's roof area (excluding any mechanical equipment, photovoltaic panels, and skylights).

Option 4. Locate at least 95% of parking under cover.

DEFINITIONS

appurtenance a built-in, nonstructural portion of a roof system. Examples include skylights, ventilators, mechanical equipment, partitions, and solar energy panels.

heat island effect the thermal absorption by hardscape, such as dark, nonreflective pavement and buildings, and its subsequent radiation to surrounding areas. Other contributing factors may include vehicle exhaust, air-conditioners, and street equipment. Tall buildings and narrow streets reduce airflow and exacerbate the effect.

infrared (thermal) emittance a value between 0 and 1 (or 0% and 100%) that indicates the ability of a material to shed infrared radiation (heat). A cool roof should have a high thermal emittance. The wavelength range for radiant energy is roughly 5 to 40 micrometers. Most building materials (including glass) are opaque in this part of the spectrum and have an emittance of roughly 0.9, or 90%. Clean, bare metals, such as untarnished galvanized steel, have a low emittance and are the most important exceptions to the 0.9 rule. In contrast, aluminum roof coatings have intermediate emittance levels. (Adapted from Lawrence Berkeley National Laboratory)

open-grid pavement system pavements that consist of loose substrates supported by a grid of a more structurally sound grid or webbing. Pervious concrete and porous asphalt are not considered open grid as they are considered bounded materials. Unbounded, loose substrates do not transfer and store heat like bound and compacted materials do.

solar reflectance (SR) the fraction of solar energy that is reflected by a surface on a scale of 0 to 1. Black paint has a solar reflectance of 0; white paint (titanium dioxide) has a solar reflectance of 1. The standard technique for its determination uses spectrophotometric measurements, with an integrating sphere to determine the reflectance at each wavelength. The average reflectance is then determined by an averaging process, using a standard solar spectrum, as documented by ASTM Standards E903 and E892.

solar reflectance index (SRI) a measure of the constructed surface's ability to stay cool in the sun by reflecting solar radiation and emitting thermal radiation. It is defined such that a standard black surface (initial solar reflectance 0.05, initial thermal emittance 0.90) has an initial SRI of 0, and a standard white surface (initial solar reflectance 0.80, initial thermal emittance 0.90) has an initial SRI of 100. To calculate the SRI for a given material, obtain its solar reflectance and thermal emittance via the Cool Roof Rating Council Standard (CRRC-1). SRI is calculated according to ASTM E 1980. Calculation of the aged SRI is based on the aged tested values of solar reflectance and thermal emittance.

solar reflectance and thermal emittance via the Cool Roof Rating Council Standard (CRRC-1). SRI is calculated according to ASTM E 1980. Calculation of the aged SRI is based on the aged tested values of solar reflectance and thermal emittance.

thermal emittance the ratio of the radiant heat flux emitted by a specimen to that emitted by a blackbody radiator at the same temperature (adapted from Cool Roof Rating Council)

three-year aged SR or SRI value a solar reflectance or solar reflectance index rating that is measured after three years of weather exposure

undercover parking vehicle storage that is underground, under deck, under roof, or under a building

SUSTAINABLE SITES CREDIT

Light Pollution Reduction

This credit applies to:

Existing Buildings (1 point)
Schools (1 point)
Retail (1 point)
Data Centers (1 point)
Hospitality (1 point)
Warehouses and Distribution Centers (1 point)

INTENT

To increase night sky access, improve nighttime visibility, and reduce the consequences of development for wildlife and people.

REQUIREMENTS

ESTABLISHMENT E

Meet the requirements of one of the options below:

OPTION 1. FIXTURE SHIELDING

Shield all exterior fixtures (where the sum of the mean lamp lumens for that fixture exceeds 2,500) such that the installed fixtures do not directly emit any light at a vertical angle more than 90 degrees from straight down.

OR

OPTION 2. PERIMETER MEASUREMENTS

Measure the night illumination levels at regularly spaced points on the project boundary, taking the measurements with the building's exterior and site lights both on and off. At least eight measurements are required, at a maximum spacing of 100 feet (30 meters) apart. The illumination level measured with the lights on must not be more than 20% above the level measured with the lights off.

PERFORMANCE P

None.

BEHIND THE INTENT

Artificial exterior lighting not only provides human safety and comfort, it enables us to productively use more hours of the day. If done correctly, exterior lighting offers safety, security, building identification, aesthetics, and way finding. However, poor lighting design causes light pollution.

Light pollution is the misdirection or misuse of light, generally resulting from an inappropriate application of exterior lighting. Backlight creates light trespass onto adjacent sites by directing light in the opposite direction of the area intended to be lighted. Uplight causes artificial sky glow. Glare is caused by high-angle front light.

Light pollution creates an abundance of environmental problems. Wildlife species that hunt or forage at night may be unable to feed. Some flora and fauna are unable to adjust to seasonal variations when exposed to light pollution. Migratory birds that rely on stars to guide them during migration may become disoriented. Even human health can be damaged by misuse of light. Studies have shown that overexposure to artificial lighting, particularly at night, may disrupt our circadian rhythms and melatonin production, impair night vision, and lead to sleep disorders.[1] Finally, light pollution directed into the sky or into areas that do not need illumination is a waste of both energy and money.

This credit addresses two forms of light pollution: uplighting and light trespass. Lamp shielding for luminaires with the highest lamp lumen levels reduces the amount of unwanted light pollution escaping into the night sky. To minimize light trespass, illumination levels at the site boundary should be maintained at specific thresholds.

STEP-BY-STEP GUIDANCE

Select one option for the project.

- Option 1 is appropriate if most of the existing fixtures are shielded already, or if the project team does not have the light measurement tool required for Option 2.
- Option 2 is for projects that have little lighting or have unshielded fixtures that do not spill over the boundary.

The requirements of either option are considered fulfilled, with no further documentation needed, if the project building was previously certified under a LEED Building Design and Construction rating system and earned the Light Pollution Reduction credit.

Option 1. Fixture Shielding

STEP 1. IDENTIFY EXISTING LUMINAIRES ABOVE 2,500 MEAN LUMENS E

Identify all luminaires on the project site that use lamps whose sum for mean lamp lumens exceeds 2,500 (see *Further Explanation, Determining Mean Lamp Lumens*). All such luminaires must comply with the credit requirements.

STEP 2. ASSESS EXISTING LUMINAIRES AGAINST SHIELDING CRITERIA E

Determine whether the luminaires identified in Step 1 already meet the shielding requirements. Existing luminaires are compliant if they do not directly emit any light at a vertical angle more than 90 degrees from straight down.

Compliance with the shielding requirement can be confirmed via manufacturers' technical data sheets. If this information is not available, photographs of the luminaires can be used (see *Further Explanation, Confirming Shielding Requirements*).

1. *American Medical Association, House of Delegates, Report 4 of the Council on Science and Public Health* (A-12), *Light Pollution: Adverse Health Effects of Nighttime Lighting* (2009), *ama-assn.org/resources/doc/csaph/a12-csaph4-lightpollution-summary.pdf* (accessed March 2013)..

STEP 3. ADDRESS NONCOMPLIANT LUMINAIRES E

Investigate options to retrofit or replace noncompliant existing site lighting to meet the credit requirements.

- Shielding to retrofit existing noncompliant luminaires may be available from the manufacturer or may need to be custom designed to work with the luminaire. Shielding that is not designed for the luminaire or does not attach properly may significantly reduce the efficiency of the luminaire, causing both energy and safety issues.
- As an alternative to shielding retrofits, change out the lamps. Noncompliant luminaires whose sum for mean lamp lumens is 2,500 or less meet the credit requirements (see *Further Explanation, Reducing Lamp Lumens*).

Option 2. Perimeter Measurements

STEP 1. IDENTIFY MEASUREMENT POINTS

Identify the points along the project boundary to measure and assess illumination levels against the credit requirements.

- Ensure that there are at least eight measurement points, with a maximum of 100 feet (30 meters) between points.
- Measurement points must be equidistant to fairly represent the illumination levels at all points along the project boundary.

STEP 2. TAKE ILLUMINATION MEASUREMENTS WITH LIGHTS OFF AND LIGHTS ON

With the building's exterior and site lights off, take illumination measurements at each measurement point along the project boundary. Repeat the measurements at the same points with the exterior and site lights on (see *Further Explanation, Example*).

- Measurements may be taken with any light meter capable of measuring illumination at ground level.
- The measurements must be taken on the same date, either after civil twilight in the evening or before civil twilight in the morning. Use U.S. Navy data[2] to determine twilight times for a given location (worldwide) and date.
- The building's interior lights must remain in the same state (either on or off) during both measurements.

STEP 3. COMPARE MEASUREMENTS TO TEST COMPLIANCE

Compare the lights-off and lights-on illumination levels at each measurement point along the project boundary. To meet the credit requirements, at each measurement point, the lights-on illumination must be no more than 20% above the lights-off illumination.

The illumination measurements may not be compared as an average across the project boundary. Rather, each measurement point must be compliant.

2. *aa.usno.navy.mil/data/docs/RS_OneDay.php.*

FURTHER EXPLANATION

DETERMINING MEAN LAMP LUMENS

Mean lumen data are frequently posted in manufacturers' technical data sheets for the lamps used with exterior luminaires. Mean lumens are distinct from initial lumens, which are also frequently listed in technical data sheets. Since lamp lumen output frequently degrades over the life of the lamp, the mean lamp lumen value—the average quantity of light output over the life of the lamp—is a more representative indication than the initial value.

The mean lamp lumen for a given luminaire is determined by summing the mean lamp lumens for all lamps used in the luminaire. For example, if a luminaire uses two identical lamps, each with a mean lamp lumen value of 2,500, the sum of mean lamp lumens for the luminaire is 5,000, and the luminaire must meet the Option 1 requirements for shielding.

CONFIRMING SHIELDING REQUIREMENTS

All luminaires that use lamps whose sum for mean lumens exceeds 2,500 must meet the shielding requirements to comply with Option 1. To be compliant, an individual luminaire must not directly emit any light at a vertical angle more than 90 degrees from straight down (Figure 1).

Figure 1. Compliant and noncompliant light

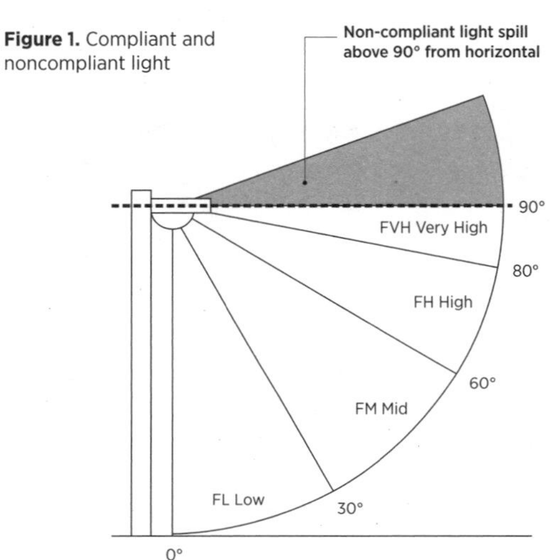

View 1

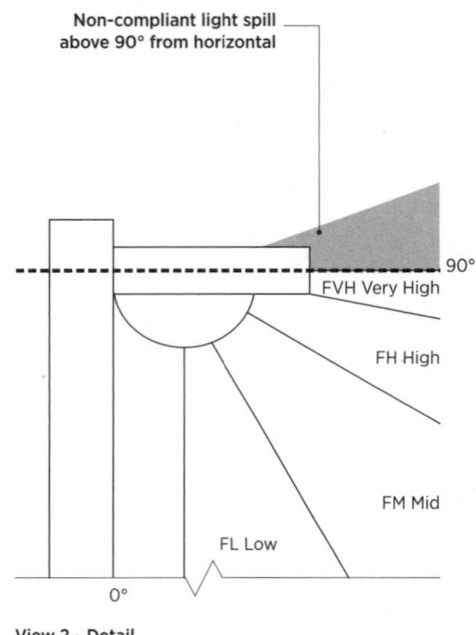

View 2 - Detail

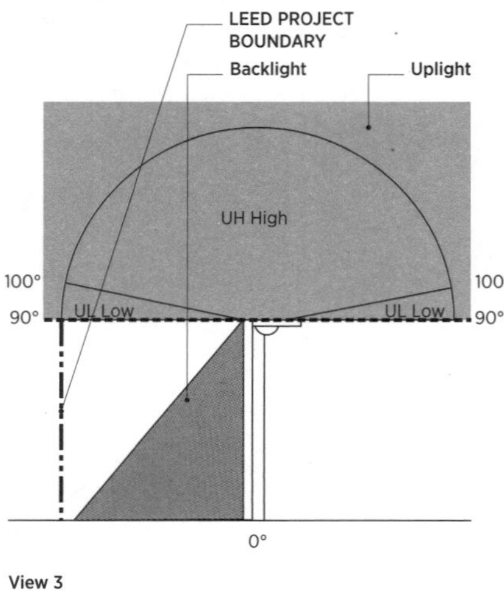

View 3

Non-compliant light

Backlight

REDUCING LAMP LUMENS

For Option 1, reducing the sum for mean lamp lumens of existing noncompliant luminaires is an acceptable strategy to bring luminaires into compliance. Reducing the sum for mean lamp lumens can also reduce energy use and costs for exterior lighting. However, such a strategy has drawbacks, too; teams may need to consult a lighting professional.

Replacing an existing lamp with one that has fewer lumens will reduce brightness. It is recommended that teams maintain the right light levels for safety, security, aesthetics, and visual tasks.

Some fluorescent lamps and all high-intensity discharge lamps (metal halide, high-pressure sodium) require that the ballast be replaced when it is lamp and/or wattage specific. Replacement lamps must be able to fit into the same socket as the existing lamps or the socket will also need to be replaced.

EXAMPLE

A project team is taking illuminance measurements for the project building illustrated in Figure 2. Light trespass measurements were taken on June 14, 2012, beginning at 10:30 P.M. Eastern Standard Time, with an environmental meter. Measurements were taken around the project boundary every 100 feet (30 meters), first with the building exterior lights on, and then at the same points with the exterior lights off.

The west side of the project building abuts the adjacent structure, so measurements were limited to the north, east, and south sides. Eight measurement points were included in the analysis (Table 1). The increase in illuminance with the lights on was no greater than 20% at any measurement point on the project boundary, so the project achieves the credit.

TABLE 1. Illuminance measurements

Measurement	Exterior lights on (fc)	Exterior lights off (fc)	% increase lights on
1	3.1	3.1	0%
2	0.1	0.1	0%
3	0.5	0.5	0%
4	5.3	5.3	0%
5	0.0	0.0	0%
6	0.7	0.6	16.67%
7	0.0	0.0	0.0
8	1.7	1.6	6.25%

fc = footcandles

Figure 2. Site plan with measurement locations

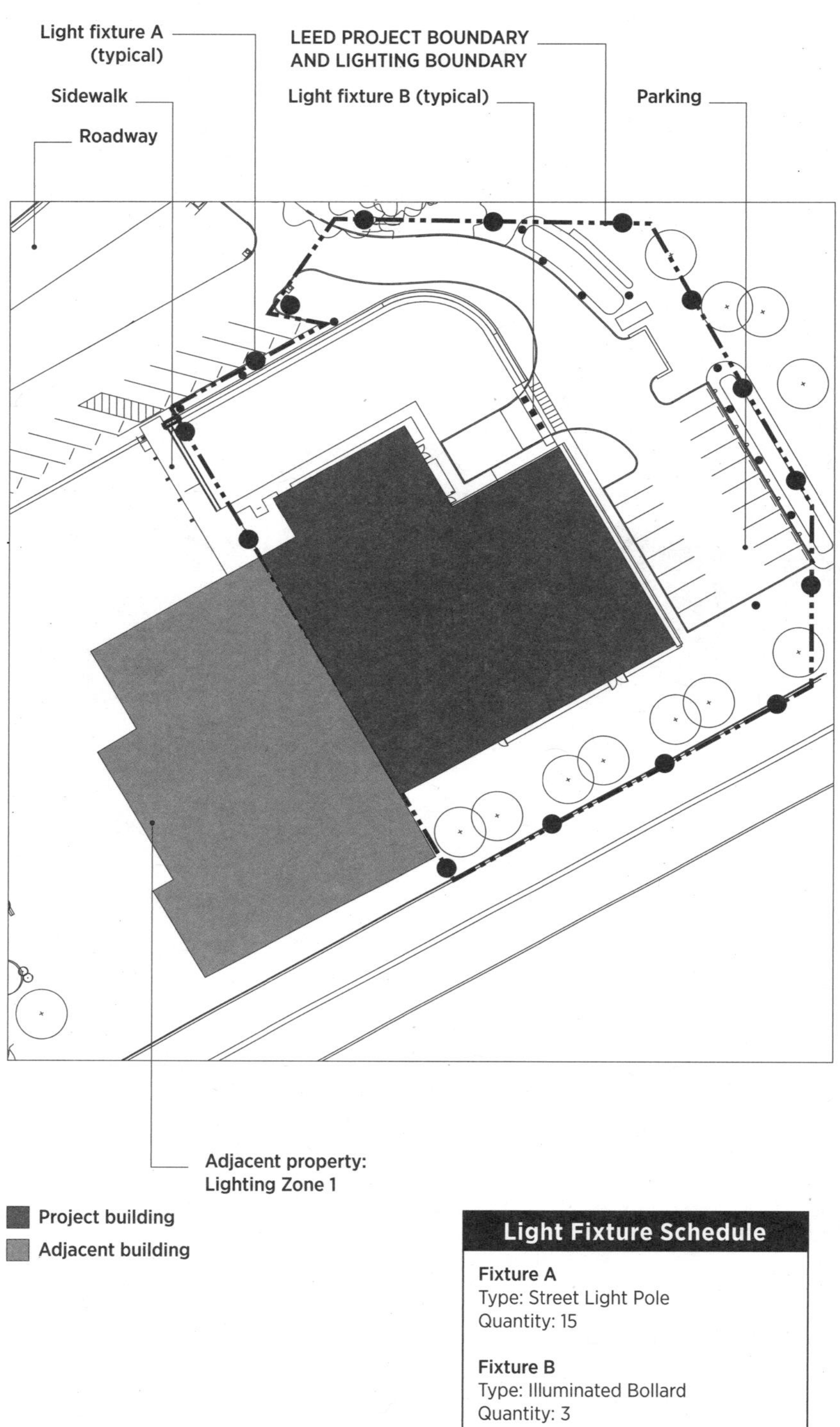

CAMPUS

Group Approach
All buildings in the group may be documented as one.

Campus Approach
Eligible.

REQUIRED DOCUMENTATION

	Documentation	Option 1	Option 2
E	Fixture schedule showing exterior luminaire and lumen information	X	
E	Luminaire shielding information (e.g., typical detail, manufacturers' technical data sheets, or photographs)	X	
E	Site plan showing project boundary, locations of all measurement points, distance between measurement points (maximum 100 feet [30 meters]), existing and proposed light fixtures, and any related site features		X
E	Illumination measurements for each measurement point		X

RELATED CREDIT TIPS

EA Prerequisite Energy Efficiency Best Management Practices and EA Credit Optimize Energy Performance. Meeting the Option 1 requirements of this credit by reducing the sum of mean lamp lumens for exterior luminaires below 2,500 has the added benefit of reducing energy consumption, thus supporting achievement of the related prerequisite and credit.

MR Credit Purchasing—Ongoing. Data collected for the mean lamp lumens for exterior luminaires may also support calculations required to determine the picograms of mercury per lumen-hour for all mercury-containing lamps for the related credit. Ensure that newly purchased exterior lamps meet the related credit's low-mercury lighting plan.

CHANGES FROM LEED 2009

- There are no longer interior lighting requirements associated with the credit.
- The previously available approach for perimeter measurements to demonstrate compliance by meeting maximum footcandle (lux) levels, prescribed by IESNA RP-33, is no longer available.

REFERENCED STANDARDS

None.

EXEMPLARY PERFORMANCE

Not available.

DEFINITIONS

civil twilight the point in time in the morning (dawn) or evening (dusk) when the center of the sun is geometrically 6 degrees below the horizon. Under good weather conditions, civil twilight is the best time to distinguish terrestrial objects clearly. Before civil twilight in the morning and after civil twilight in the evening, artificial illumination normally is required to carry on ordinary outdoor activities.

light pollution waste light from building sites that produces glare, is directed upward to the sky, or is directed off the site. Waste light does not increase nighttime safety, utility, or security and needlessly consumes energy.

light trespass obtrusive illumination that is unwanted because of quantitative, directional, or spectral attributes. Light trespass can cause annoyance, discomfort, distraction, or loss of visibility.

SUSTAINABLE SITES CREDIT

Site Management

This credit applies to:

Existing Buildings (1 point)
Schools (1 point)
Retail (1 point)
Data Centers (1 point)
Hospitality (1 point)
Warehouses and Distribution Centers (1 point)

INTENT

To preserve ecological integrity and encourage environmentally sensitive site management practices that provide a clean, well-maintained, and safe building exterior while supporting high-performance building operations and integration into the surrounding landscape.

REQUIREMENTS

ESTABLISHMENT E

None.

PERFORMANCE P

Demonstrate that the following performance criteria were met:

- Use no calcium chloride or sodium chloride deicers, and/or establish reduced treatment areas equal to 50% of applicable paving area.
- Prevent erosion and sedimentation, and restore any eroded soils.
- Prevent air pollution from construction materials and activities.
- Divert from landfills 100% of plant material waste via low-impact means.
- Prevent the overapplication of nutrients. Use no ammonia-based fertilizers, biosolid-based fertilizers (for continuous application), synthetic quick-release fertilizers, or "weed and feed" formulations. Blanket applications of herbicides are prohibited; turf weeds may be controlled by spot spraying only.
- Monitor irrigation systems manually or with automated systems at least every two weeks during the operating season and correct any leaks, breaks, inappropriate water usage, or incorrect timing.
- Store materials and equipment to prevent air and site contamination.

AND

Meet one of the following options:

OPTION 1. LIMITED TURF AREA

Limit turf to 25% or less of the vegetated area.

Playgrounds and athletic fields in schools or parks are excluded from this option.

OR

OPTION 2. ALL MANUAL OR ELECTRIC-POWERED EQUIPMENT

Use all manual or electric-powered equipment in all site management operations.

OR

OPTION 3. REDUCTION IN EMISSIONS FROM SITE MANAGEMENT EQUIPMENT

Show and maintain a 50% reduction in hydrocarbon (HC) and nitrogen oxide (NO_x) emissions, and a 75% reduction in carbon monoxide (CO) emissions from baseline conditions.

BEHIND THE INTENT

A project team can gain valuable information about the quality of its exterior maintenance program by tracking site management. The goals and objectives identified by the team and established in SS Prerequisite Site Management Policy serve as the foundation of a set of best management practices that, when met or exceeded, can provide excellent results for the property and grounds. Gathering and regularly reviewing documentation will help the team anticipate and avoid problems and identify opportunities for success.

A major component of site management is the type of maintenance equipment used. Gasoline-powered equipment contributes to greenhouse gas emissions and causes noise and air pollution, thereby reducing occupants' health and comfort. For these reasons, gasoline-powered equipment should be eliminated from site management programs whenever possible. Even though electric-powered equipment causes less harm to occupants' health and the environment, it should also be used only as needed, to reduce energy consumption. Manual equipment is greener still but is not a viable alternative for every activity. This credit requires teams to evaluate their projects' needs and find a solution that reduces harm caused by maintenance equipment while still meeting the site's overall goals.

Successful site management depends on using the right equipment, monitoring activities, reporting thresholds, and meeting minimum performance goals. To maintain the highest level of quality site management, teams must regularly review tracking data and work with the building managers to continually improve the site management program.

STEP-BY-STEP GUIDANCE

STEP 1. ALIGN GOALS IN SITE MANAGEMENT POLICY WITH MINIMUM THRESHOLDS FOR CREDIT COMPLIANCE P

Compare the goals outlined in the site management policy completed for SS Prerequisite Site Management Policy with the minimum performance goals required for SS Credit Site Management compliance. Update the site management policy as necessary to meet the minimum thresholds.

STEP 2. IMPLEMENT POLICY P

For the elements identified in the credit, implement and track activities to verify that the performance criteria are met (see *Further Explanation, Site Maintenance Activities for Operational Elements*).

STEP 3. INVENTORY CURRENT EQUIPMENT P

Review the site's current conditions and maintenance equipment. Inventory all equipment used, including any equipment brought to the site by contractors. Identify which items, if any, are powered by gasoline. Vehicles (e.g., trucks for snow removal) are exempt from all three options and do not need to be considered under this credit.

STEP 4. SELECT OPTION FOR REDUCING EMISSIONS FROM MAINTENANCE EQUIPMENT P

Select an option based on the results of the equipment inventory, site conditions, and the equipment that will be used during the performance period. Ensure that the goals and performance metrics defined in the site management policy align with the option chosen.

- Option 1 provides a simple documentation path for projects that have vegetated areas but very little turf grass (and therefore do not need gasoline-powered mowers or other equipment). Because of the minimum vegetation criterion, this option may not apply to urban sites.
- Option 2 provides a simple documentation path for projects that do not rely on any gasoline or propane-powered equipment. The option is appropriate for sites with minimal maintenance needs but can be used by any project, regardless of site size or the absence of vegetated area (e.g., zero lot line buildings).
- Option 3 requires a more complex analysis than Option 1 or 2 but allows a higher degree of flexibility for meeting the criteria. This option is most likely to benefit large project sites with extensive turf grass areas, an array of equipment (including propane-powered equipment), and high maintenance needs.

Complete the steps under the selected option, and then complete the All Projects steps.

Option 1. Limited Turf Area

Calculate turf area as a percentage of the total vegetated area, using Equation 1. Include planter boxes and vegetated roof areas in total vegetated area. Exclude school or park playgrounds and athletic fields from turf area. The turf area must not exceed 25% of the total vegetated area.

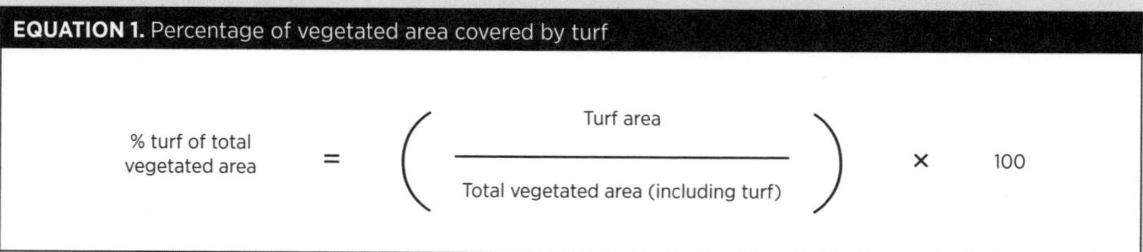

EQUATION 1. Percentage of vegetated area covered by turf

$$\text{\% turf of total vegetated area} = \left(\frac{\text{Turf area}}{\text{Total vegetated area (including turf)}} \right) \times 100$$

Confirm that the turf area is below the limit.

Option 2. All Manual or Electric-Powered Equipment P

Confirm that all maintenance equipment will be manual or electric powered. Use the equipment inventory to determine the fuel source of each piece of equipment used on site.

- All equipment used on site, including equipment owned by vendors and stored on site, must be considered.
- For the project to be eligible for Option 2, no fossil fuel–powered equipment may be used on site.
- Replacing equipment (such as gasoline-powered equipment) may be necessary for compliance.

Option 3. Reduction in Emissions from Site Management Equipment

STEP 1. DETERMINE EMISSIONS BASELINE AND PERCENTAGE REDUCTION P

Use the equipment emissions reduction calculator provided by USGBC to determine annual baseline emissions and calculate the annual percentage reduction (see *Further Explanation, Calculating Equipment Emissions Reductions*).

- To determine the baseline, gather information on all existing maintenance equipment used: equipment type, approximate number and duration of uses or events each year, and approximate usage hours.
- Enter this information into the calculator to get the baseline hydrocarbon (HC), nitrogen oxide (NO_x), and carbon monoxide (CO) emissions.

STEP 2. CHANGE USAGE PATTERNS AND RECALCULATE EMISSIONS TO ACHIEVE REQUIRED REDUCTIONS P

Implement any necessary changes to reduce HC and NO_x by 50% and CO by 75% from the baseline emissions calculated in Step 1.

- The greatest reduction in emissions can generally be achieved by replacing gasoline-powered equipment with manual strategies or electric-powered equipment.
- Reducing equipment runtime by limiting high-maintenance landscaping is another strategy. For example, walkways bordered by turf require lots of edging time, so reducing the amount of this type of landscaping can generate emissions savings.

All Projects

Collect documentation verifying activities during the performance period. **P**

Use the performance metrics established in the site management policy as the basis for tracking and documenting all the activities associated with site management.

- Vendors must supply the project team with activity logs, purchasing records, and other information that confirms proper implementation of the policy and demonstrates compliance.
- Periodically spot-check equipment used during the performance period to ensure that only vetted and approved equipment is actually being used on site. This is particularly important when equipment used by a vendor is stored on site, since vendors may also own and use noncompliant equipment on their other job sites.
- Review documentation on a regular basis (see *Further Explanation, Site Maintenance Activities for Operational Elements* and *Example Equipment Maintenance Tracking Log*).

FURTHER EXPLANATION

CALCULATIONS

See calculations in *Step-by-Step Guidance*.

SITE MAINTENANCE ACTIVITIES FOR OPERATIONAL ELEMENTS

Table 1 lists the operational elements addressed in SS Prerequisite Site Management Policy that must also be tracked during the performance period for this credit. Suggested activities to demonstrate performance are described. Teams are expected to demonstrate full performance of each element listed; partial or incremental adoption is not permitted.

TABLE 1. Example site maintenance activities for operational elements in site management policy	
Operational element	**Example site maintenance activities**
Maintenance equipment	• Demonstrate compliance with selected option for maintenance equipment emissions reduction listed in credit requirements.
Snow and ice removal	• Use environmentally preferred deicers rather than calcium chloride or sodium chloride. Examples include those that contain potassium acetate, potassium chloride, magnesium chloride, or calcium magnesium acetate. • Reduce area treated with calcium chloride or sodium chloride to 50% of total deiced area by discontinuing deicer applications in low-traffic areas or converting some areas to environmentally preferred deicer. • If deicer blend containing calcium chloride or sodium chloride in addition to other compounds is used, demonstrate compliance via reduced treatment area path.
Exterior cleaning	• Not required to be tracked for this credit during performance period
Erosion and sedimentation control	• Perform ongoing erosion and sedimentation control activities, as established in site management policy. • Identify areas where erosion or sedimentation occurs or is likely to occur and implement preventive measures. Restore any eroded areas. • If construction activities occur, follow erosion and sedimentation control measures established in site management policy. Work with general contractor to develop and implement project-specific control measures. • Manage construction materials and activities such that dust does not degrade air quality.
Organic waste management	• Divert all plant material waste generated by on-site landscaping activities by composting or mulching on site or by composting at off-site facility. • Plant material diverted to waste-to-energy facility counts toward diversion quantities. • All plant waste must be diverted from landfills to earn this credit. Invasive and exotic plant species management
Invasive and exotic plant species management	• Not required to be tracked for this credit during performance period.
Fertilizer and herbicide use	• Test soil to establish soil type baseline This testing only needs to occur once, since this soil attribute is unlikely to change without significant human involvement that generally entails removal and replacement of soil. ; retest soil at least every other year for nutrient content and pH. For sites with multiple planting beds, landscape areas, or vegetation types, sample soil in each location. • Use the test results to optimize the type and frequency of nutrient applications. • Use fertilizer derived from animal or vegetable matter, organic or natural fertilizer, and slow-release formulas. • Control exotic species and turf weeds manually or by spot-spraying only.
Irrigation management	• Perform routine leak detection during operating season by either taking irrigation submeter readings at least every two weeks or using automated leak detection systems, such as those that use pressure sensors to detect surges in water pressure. • At least twice per year during operating season, inspect irrigation systems for leaks, breaks, irregularities in water usage, and system time settings. • Perform irrigation management tasks manually or use automated systems. • Correct any deficiencies that are discovered in the irrigation system (e.g., leaks, broken controllers, or incorrect timing).
Storage of materials and equipment	• Store materials and equipment according to manufacturers' recommendations. • Ensure that products and equipment are properly contained and secured to prevent materials and fuels from leaking. • Ventilate storage areas so that chemicals and equipment do not degrade indoor air quality.

CALCULATING EQUIPMENT EMISSIONS REDUCTIONS

Teams may use the equipment emissions reduction calculator provided by USGBC (or a similar tool) to determine the percentage reduction in emissions from the project's baseline conditions and demonstrate compliance with Option 3. Tables 2 and 3 illustrate an example.

TABLE 2. Example existing maintenance equipment plan

Equipment type	Occurences / site visits	Est hrs. / occ.	Est. hrs. / yr.	$HC+NO_x$ (g/hr)	Annual $HC+NO_x$	CO_2 (g/hr)	Annual CO_2
4-stroke 21"–24" push mower	26	2.25	58.50	25	1462.5	2383	139407.2007
4-stroke 48"–54" walk-behind mower	26	0.75	19.50	15	292.5	10940	213335.4534
4-stroke 60"–72" riding mower	26	4.75	123.50	11	1358.5	9938.7	1227430.685
2-stroke line trimmer-edger	26	2.75	71.50	60	4290	2885	206277.5
2-stroke backpack blower	26	3	78.00	50	3900	2980.5	232480.1232
2-stroke line trimmer-edger	13	2.25	29.25	60	1755	2885	84386.25
4-stroke push blower	3	10	30.00	22	660	6783.2	203496.84
2-stroke backpack blower	3	10	30.00	50	1500	2980.5	89415.432
Total hours per year			440				
Total emissions per year in grams					15218.5		2396229.5
Total emissions per year in tons							2.6358524

TABLE 3. Example proposed maintenance equipment plan

Equipment type	Occurences / site visits	Est hrs. / occ.	Est. hrs. / yr.	$HC+NO_x$ (g/hr)	Annual $HC+NO_x$	CO_2 (g/hr)	Annual CO_2
4-stroke 21"–24" push mower	26	2.25	58.50	25	1462.5	2383	139407.2007
4-stroke 48"–54" walk behind mower (lpg)	26	0.75	19.50	9	175.5	1203	23458.5
4-stroke 60"–72" riding mower (lpg)	26	4.75	123.50	11	1358.5	1093	134985.5
Electric line trimmer or edger	26	3	78.00		0		
4-stroke backpack blower	26	3	78.00	15	1170	894	69732
Electric line trimmer or edger	13	3	39.00		0		
4-stroke push blower	3	10	30.00	22	660	6783.2	203496.84
2-stroke backpack blower	3	10	30.00	50	1500	2980.5	89415.432
Total hours per year			457				
Total emissions per year in grams					6326.5		660495.47
Total emissions per year in tons					0.006959		0.726545
Percentage reductions					58.4%		72%

EXAMPLE EQUIPMENT MAINTENANCE TRACKING LOG

Table 4 is a sample entry from a log that tracks recommended maintenance by equipment type.

TABLE 4. Example Tracking Log

Equipment type	Maintenance activity	Completed date	Notes
Leaf blower	Changed filter	11-1-13	Leaf blower is in good condition

CAMPUS

Group Approach
All buildings in the group may be documented as one.

Campus Approach
Eligible.

REQUIRED DOCUMENTATION

	Documentation	All Projects	Option 1	Option 2	Option 3
P	Records of deicer use	X			
P	Erosion and sedimentation prevention logs and photos	X			
P	Air quality protection logs and photos	X			
P	Plant material haul logs	X			
P	Soil test results	X			
P	Fertilizer application logs	X			
P	Biweekly irrigation monitoring logs	X			
P	Turf area calculations		X		
P	Inventory of all current maintenance equipment			X	
P	Calculations for equipment emissions baseline and reduction, or equipment emissions reduction calculator results				X

RELATED CREDIT TIPS

SS Prerequisite Site Management Policy. The site management policy is the primary tool for establishing best practice maintenance procedures. Crafting a policy that clearly establishes strategies, guidelines, and goals will facilitate meeting the requirements of this credit.

SS Credit Site Improvement Plan. Soil testing completed for this credit can be used to inform the long-term objectives of the site improvement plan for the related credit. For example, the result of soil testing can influence selections for the site plant palette. Conversely, site improvements can reduce the need for power maintenance equipment, facilitating achievement of this credit. For example, reducing turf grass areas as part of an improvement plan will also reduce the need for equipment with high emissions. Project teams that review the requirements of both credits in parallel may capture such synergies.

SS Credit Site Development—Protect or Restore Habitat. Naturally vegetated areas that meet the requirements of the related credit are less likely to require the routine use of maintenance equipment. They could also reduce irrigation, nutrient application, and erosion, thereby helping the project meet the requirements of this credit.

MR Credit Purchasing—Ongoing. Maintenance equipment purchases are also tracked in the related credit. Teams may be able to use such logs for both credits.

WE Credit Outdoor Water Use Reduction. Coordinate irrigation system management activities with the irrigation strategy pursued under the related credit. Aligning irrigation strategies between the two credits and monitoring the systems will help projects achieve both credits.

CHANGES FROM LEED 2009

- This credit is derived from two LEED 2009 credits: SS Credit 2 Building Exterior and Hardscape Management Plan, and SS Credit 3 Integrated Pest Management, Erosion Control, and Landscape Management Plan.
- Soil testing and irrigation system monitoring requirements have been added. A new compliance option for reducing emissions from site maintenance equipment has been added.

REFERENCED STANDARDS

None.

EXEMPLARY PERFORMANCE

Not available.

DEFINITIONS

baseline condition before the LEED project was initiated, but not necessarily before any development or disturbance took place. Baseline conditions describe the state of the project site on the date the developer acquired rights to a majority of its buildable land through purchase or option to purchase.

invasive plant nonnative vegetation that has been introduced to an area and that aggressively adapts and reproduces. The plant's vigor combined with a lack of natural enemies often leads to outbreak populations. (Adapted from U.S. Department of Agriculture)

SUSTAINABLE SITES CREDIT

Site Improvement Plan

This credit applies to:

Existing Buildings (1 point)
Schools (1 point)
Retail (1 point)
Data Centers (1 point)
Hospitality (1 point)
Warehouses and Distribution Centers (1 point)

INTENT

To preserve and improve ecological integrity while supporting high-performance building operations.

REQUIREMENTS

ESTABLISHMENT E

Develop a five-year site improvement plan that includes the following:

- documentation of existing site conditions;
- site improvement objectives;
- performance standards to evaluate ongoing progress; and
- monitoring protocols.

The improvement plan must address the following topics.

- **Hydrology**. Protection and improvement of water bodies on-site, rainwater management and reuse opportunities, potable water-use reduction.
- **Vegetation.** Documentation of existing vegetation on-site, turf area reduction, management of native and invasive plants, protection of threatened, endangered or unique species.
- **Soils.** Documentation of general soil structure, preservation of healthy soils, remediation of compacted soils, identification of previously developed area.

The plan must be developed with professionals trained and experienced in the above disciplines.

PERFORMANCE P

Show that at least 5% of the site is vegetated. Implement all no-cost and low-cost measures. Develop a new improvement plan and implement all new no-cost and low-cost measures every five years.

BEHIND THE INTENT

Site improvement plans serve as the foundation for many activities associated with the best management practices of building maintenance. Best-practice activities can create opportunities for projects to achieve additional sustainability goals related to certification. More important, they can reveal opportunities to operate better ecologically.

The purpose of this credit is to outline how site improvement plans can help organize improvements over time. A good site improvement plan requires the team to engage qualified people, follow an established process, map out meaningful improvement initiatives, and work toward implementing identified no- and low-cost measures.

STEP-BY-STEP GUIDANCE

STEP 1. ASSEMBLE SITE PROPERTY TEAM AND INVOLVE TRAINED PROFESSIONALS E

- Industry professionals can assist the property team in gathering and analyzing site information to identify site improvements.
- It is recommended that professionals be involved early in the project planning phase and that team members be selected to meet the unique constraints and opportunities of the site (see *Further Explanation, Integrated Team*).
- Consider involving the team that is developing the site management plan under SS Prerequisite Site Management Policy and SS Credit Site Management.

STEP 2. DETERMINE PROJECT'S CURRENT PERCENTAGE OF VEGETATION E

Use Equation 1 to calculate the total vegetated site area of the property and determine whether the project meets the required minimum percentage of vegetation, 5% of the site.

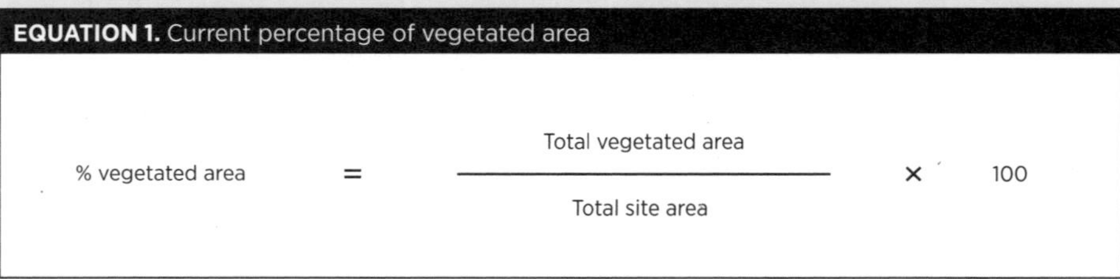

EQUATION 1. Current percentage of vegetated area

$$\text{\% vegetated area} = \frac{\text{Total vegetated area}}{\text{Total site area}} \times 100$$

- If the site meets the minimum threshold of vegetation, include the protection of those vegetated areas in the site improvement plan.
- If the site does not currently meet the vegetated area threshold, include a requirement to increase the vegetated area as a part of the site improvement plan. Increase the vegetated area during the performance period.
- Roof vegetation and planters can be counted toward the vegetation threshold.
- The vegetation threshold must be met before the performance period ends.

STEP 3. PERFORM SITE INVENTORY E P

Gather information and develop an inventory of current site conditions.

- Create a site map that identifies each area on the site and shows the currently vegetated areas. Site plans must include a scale and any other relevant information that would facilitate site improvements.
- Data and information assembled during this step will be used to create the inventory metrics and provide the foundation for determining site improvement goals for the property (see *Further Explanation, Site Inventory*).

STEP 4. ESTABLISH OBJECTIVES E P

Using the inventory and the information gathered by the site team, define site improvement goals and objectives (see *Further Explanation, Establishing Objectives*).

- Address a variety of site concerns, including maintenance activities, watershed quality, soil quality, community congregation areas, plant types and vegetation palette, and exterior design strategies.
- Objectives must take into account the owner's project requirements, budget, and schedule as well as unique opportunities and constraints at the site.
- Teams must establish monitoring activities for each site improvement element that will allow the team to accurately determine whether the objective is being achieved.

STEP 5. IDENTIFY SPECIFIC IMPROVEMENT MEASURES, PERFORMANCE STANDARDS, AND MONITORING PROTOCOLS E

Using the site inventory and objectives, create a list of site improvements. Address each topic area listed in the credit requirements (hydrology, vegetation, and soils) and establish metrics to measure the progress made for each improvement, as well as protocols for monitoring their ongoing operation and condition. Each measure and its associated costs, benefits, and protocols must be summarized in the site improvement plan.

- Site improvements must be categorized as either no-cost measures or low-cost measures (see *Further Explanation, Example*).
- Projects must establish a five-year implementation plan (including a timeline) for all improvement measures.
- It is recommended that the plan include information on the implementation cost, operational savings, maintenance savings, and benefits for occupants and users of each improvement measure.
- Note any measure deemed infeasible and provide the rationale for rejecting it.
- The same performance standards must be used to track progress toward stated goals over time and can either directly or indirectly measure improvement.

STEP 6. IMPLEMENT NO- AND LOW-COST MEASURES P

Implement all no- and low-cost measures established in the improvement plan by the end of the performance period.

- Project teams determine whether a measure is considered a low-cost or a capital measure. However, to be eligible for this credit, teams may not consider all measures to be capital measures. In other words, all projects must include no- and low-cost measures as a part of their improvement plans.
- Some contractors may perform the improvements for free or at a discounted cost because of the potential for future work.
- If a measure was not implemented and there are no plans for future implementation, provide justification for why the measure was rejected.
- Maintain all documentation associated with the implementing no- and low-cost improvements.

STEP 7. REVISE SITE IMPROVEMENT PLAN P

Review and update the site plan every five years to ensure continual improvement and ongoing monitoring.

FURTHER EXPLANATION

CALCULATIONS

See calculations in *Step-by-Step Guidance*.

INTEGRATED TEAM

When assembling a team for this credit, ensure that the members bring a diversity of knowledge, credentials, and responsibility. In addition to the owner and/or property manager, it is recommended that the team include site design professionals with expertise in vegetation, hydrology, soil, landscape ecology, materials, and human health and well-being. Examples may include landscape designers or maintenance firms, landscape architects, civil engineers, restoration ecologists, and hydrologists. To support collaboration, designate specific team members responsible for each task.

Additionally, teams are strongly encouraged to provide training for maintenance staff on changes to the site area and how these changes will affect existing procedures.

Consider involving the team that is developing the site management plan under SS Prerequisite Site Management Policy and SS Credit Site Management to enhance the institutional knowledge on the team. Their participation will be helpful as the team decides on project goals and objectives to review the process implemented for site management and use lessons learned to improve the program.

SITE INVENTORY

Before developing the site improvement plan, gather metrics related to current site conditions. These metrics will be used to establish existing conditions and set specific targets for improvement during ongoing performance evaluation.

Summarize existing information about the site, local resources, and regional context to orient users of the plan and establish a baseline understanding of the current site features. Some examples of areas to include in the description of existing conditions include the following:

Vegetation

- Describe any regional habitat corridors, such as forest, riparian, or other intact ecosystems, used by wildlife.
- Are there currently or historically wildlife corridors on site?
- Are there any sensitive species on or near the site?

Hydrology

- Describe any waterways, water bodies, or wetlands near the site.
- Describe the waterways, water bodies, or wetlands currently or historically on site.
- What are the sources of water entering the site and quality of these sources?
- What water is currently leaving the site and how (surface runoff, groundwater infiltration, etc.)?

Soils

- What are the regional and on-site soil types? What are their characteristics?
- What percentage of the site is intact native ecosystem?
- What percentage of the site is disturbed?

Table 1 illustrates a project site inventory; many of the metrics come from other credits.

TABLE 1. Example site inventory

Item	Metric	Notes
Ecologically appropriate features	Area or percentage of total site area	Area of site that contributes to SS Credit Site Development—Protect or Restore Habitat
Native and/or adapted plants	Area or percentage of total site area	Area of site that contributes to SS Credit Site Development—Protect or Restore Habitat
Total vegetated area	Area or percentage of total site area	Area of all vegetation; vegetated roofs and planters may be included or excluded
Building footprint	Area or percentage of total site area	Area of building footprint (used to determine previously developed area)
Total hardscape	Area or percentage of total site area	Area established in SS Credit Heat Island Reduction; reduce effects of hardscape area or convert it into landscaped and natural features
Degraded land	Area or percentage of total site area	Identify areas of erosion and soil compaction. Target improvements to increase site water quality and decrease need for maintenance
Rainfall	Depth per year	Value established in SS Credit Rainwater Management; may determine feasibility of water reuse
Rainwater collection or retention capacity, and/ or reuse areas	Volume per year	Area of site that contributes to SS Credit Rainwater Management
Water use	Volume per year	Value for both potable and nonpotable water (for irrigation and/ or site cleaning and maintenance) established through submetering or calculations for WE Credit Outdoor Water Use Reduction
Invasive species	Area or percentage of total site area	Area occupied by plant species that are nonnative and invasive to project's region
Annual plantings	Area or percentage of total site area	Area that requires annual plantings, as opposed to horticultural or wild (unmanaged) perennial species
Portion of hardscape runoff into infiltration or rainwater collection	Percentage of total volume	Depends on total rainfall amount and site rainwater management strategies
Quantity of run-off (discharge rate from site)	Volume per second	Volume of runoff from site
Site pervious area	Area or percentage of total site area	Area of site that contributes to SS Credit Rainwater Management
Site impervious area	Area or percentage of total site area	Area of site that contributes to SS Credit Rainwater Management
Total suspended solids (TSS) removal rate	Mg per liter	Provide baseline and after-improvement amounts
Quality of on-site water bodies	Various	Multiple metrics include concentrations of organic and inorganic compounds
Soil test results	Various	Organic matter, nutrient levels
Plant and animal species on site	List	Biodiversity; threatened and endangered species, density of major species

ESTABLISHING OBJECTIVES

Viable objectives are an important element of a quality site improvement plan. Examples of objectives to consider in an improvement plan include the following:

- Increase vegetated areas.
- Transition turf and annual areas toward native perennials.
- Reduce hardscape.
- Improve rainwater management through increasing infiltration or collection opportunities.
- Collect and reuse rainwater.
- Decrease irrigation water consumption.
- Protect or improve water bodies.
- Protect threatened, endangered, native, and keystone species.
- Conserve or restore healthy soils.
- Remediate compacted soils.
- Increase green space and open spaces for public or occupants' use.
- Establish food gardens.
- Reduce site maintenance activities.
- Reduce heat island effect.

The project team can ask its expert consultants whether there are opportunities to support the function of all or a portion of intact ecosystems on site, or to restore areas to their predevelopment conditions of hydrology, vegetation, habitat, or soils.

EXAMPLE

A project team is implementing the site improvement measures illustrated in Figure 1 and tracking costs and schedule using Table 2.

TABLE 2. Example cost and schedule for site improvements

Measure	Estimated cost	Implementation status or target completion
No-cost and low-cost		
Install bracing and plantings to preserve eroding soil	$350	Implemented Q1 2014
Replace 10% of turf area with native plants	$2,500	Implemented Q2 2014
Convert parking wells into bioswales	$4,850	Implemented Q1 2014
Capital expenditure		
Remove small parking lot and convert it to green space	$9,500	Planned for 2016
Vegetate embankment at NW corner of property to prevent runoff	$5,250	Planned for 2015
Improve rainwater infiltration, collection, and irrigation water reuse pond	$26,500	Planned for 2016

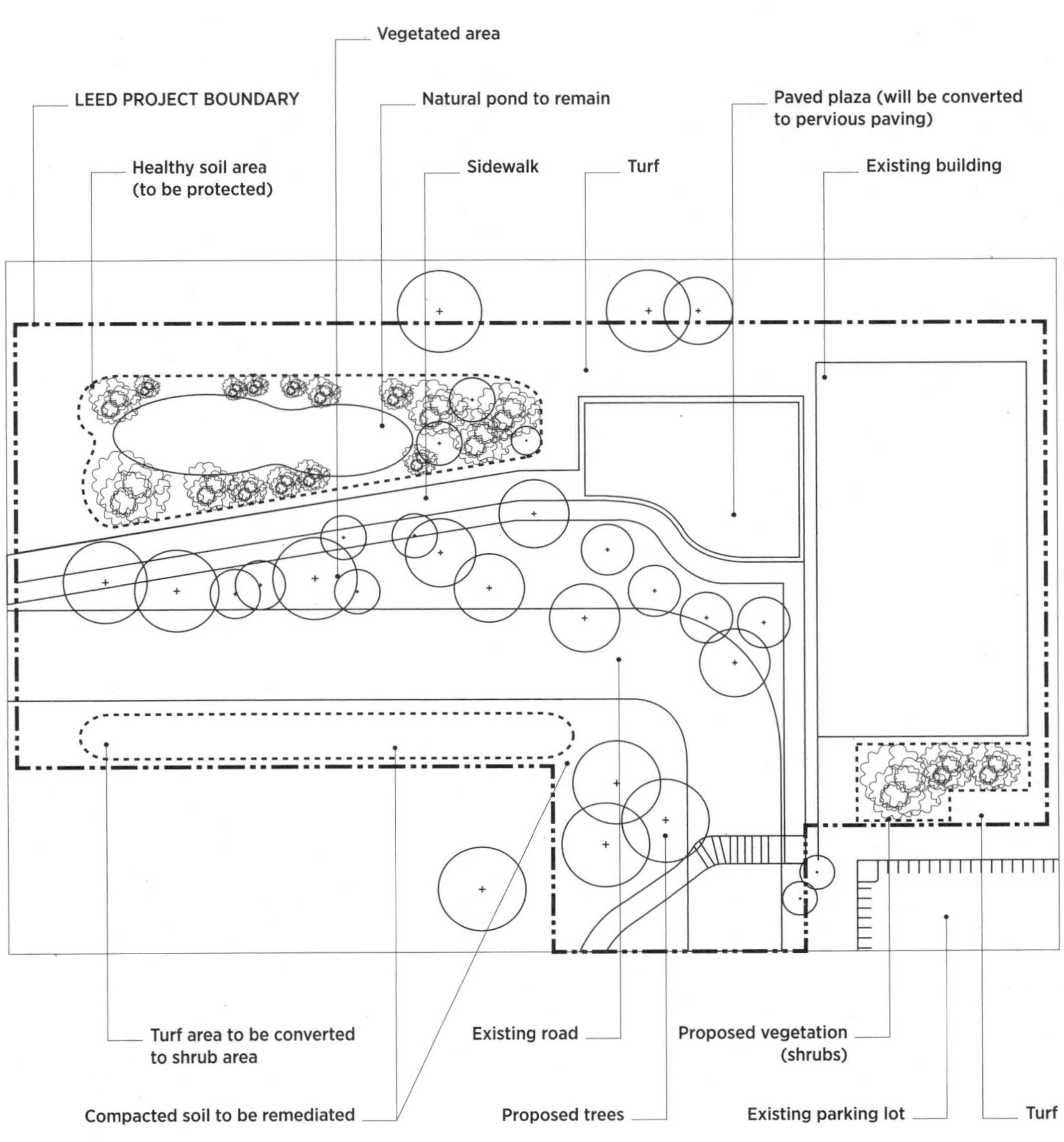

Total site area = 130,680 sq ft (3 ac)
= 12,140 sq m (1.2 ha)

Figure 1. Example site improvement plan

CAMPUS

Group Approach
All buildings in the group may be documented as one.

Campus Approach
Eligible.

REQUIRED DOCUMENTATION

	Documentation	All Projects
E	Site plan noting planned elements and measurements	X
E	Site improvement plan document	X
E	Qualifications of professional consultants	X
P	Description and rationale of no-cost and low-cost site improvement measures	X

RELATED CREDIT TIPS

SS Prerequisite Site Management Policy. Establishing monitoring and maintenance protocols as a part of the site improvement plan will contribute to developing the site management policy.

SS Credit Site Development—Protect or Restore Habitat. Native and adaptive vegetation used as a part of the site improvement plan also contributes to meeting the related credit.

SS Credit Rainwater Management. Site restoration strategies such as increased vegetative areas, rainwater infiltration, and erosion and compaction remediation will contribute to the related credit by decreasing the site's runoff volumes.

SS Credit Site Management. Tracking monitoring and maintenance protocols as a part of the site improvement plan will contribute to achieving the related credit.

WE Credit Outdoor Water Use Reduction. Converting turf, annual plantings, or nonnative vegetation into mixed native vegetation will decreased water consumption for irrigation use. Developing areas of infiltration and collection of water at the site will also contribute to the related credit.

CHANGES FROM LEED 2009

This is a new credit.

REFERENCED STANDARDS

None.

EXEMPLARY PERFORMANCE

Not available.

DEFINITIONS

invasive plant nonnative vegetation that has been introduced to an area and that aggressively adapts and reproduces. The plant's vigor combined with a lack of natural enemies often leads to outbreak populations. (Adapted from U.S. Department of Agriculture)

native vegetation an indigenous species that occurs in a particular region, ecosystem, and habitat without direct or indirect human actions. Native species have evolved to the geography, hydrology, and climate of that region. They also occur in communities; that is, they have evolved together with other species. As a result, these communities provide habitat for a variety of other native wildlife species. Species native to North America are generally recognized as those occurring on the continent prior to European settlement. Also known as native plants.

potable water water that meets or exceeds U.S. Environmental Protection Agency drinking water quality standards (or a local equivalent outside the U.S.) and is approved for human consumption by the state or local authorities having jurisdiction; it may be supplied from wells or municipal water systems

previously developed altered by paving, construction, and/or land use that would typically have required regulatory permitting to have been initiated (alterations may exist now or in the past). Land that is not previously developed and landscapes altered by current or historical clearing or filling, agricultural or forestry use, or preserved natural area use are considered undeveloped land. The date of previous development permit issuance constitutes the date of previous development, but permit issuance in itself does not constitute previous development.

SUSTAINABLE SITES CREDIT

Joint Use of Facilities

This credit applies to: **Schools (1 point)**

INTENT

To integrate the school with the community by sharing the building and its playing fields for nonschool events and functions.

REQUIREMENTS

ESTABLISHMENT E

OPTION 1. MAKE BUILDING SPACE OPEN TO GENERAL PUBLIC (1 POINT)

In collaboration with the school authorities, establish at least three of the following types of spaces as accessible to and available for shared use by the general public:

- auditorium;
- gymnasium;
- cafeteria;
- one or more classrooms;
- playing fields and stadiums; and
- joint parking.

Provide access to toilets in joint-use areas after normal school hours.

OR

OPTION 2. CONTRACT WITH SPECIFIC ORGANIZATIONS TO SHARE BUILDING SPACE (1 POINT)

In collaboration with the school authorities, contract with community or other organizations to provide at least two types of dedicated-use spaces in the building, such as the following:

- commercial office;
- health clinic;
- community service centers (provided by state or local offices);
- police offices;
- library or media center;
- parking lot; and
- one or more commercial businesses.

Provide access to toilets in joint-use areas after normal school hours.

OR

OPTION 3. USE SHARED SPACE OWNED BY OTHER ORGANIZATIONS (1 POINT)

In collaboration with the school authorities, establish at least two of the following six types of spaces (owned by other organizations/agencies) are accessible to students:

- auditorium;
- gymnasium;
- cafeteria;
- one or more classrooms;
- swimming pool; and
- playing fields and stadiums.

Provide direct pedestrian access to these spaces from the school. In addition, provide signed joint-use agreements with the other organizations or agencies that stipulate how these spaces will be shared.

PERFORMANCE P

None.

BEHIND THE INTENT

A joint-use agreement encourages community organizations and businesses to share existing amenity spaces. Doing so brings environmental, economic, and social benefits to the local community; it also may reduce the need for new development, thereby preserving previously undeveloped land and avoiding the financial costs and environmental consequences of new construction.

Local communities benefit most when multiple organizations share the costs of constructing, operating, and maintaining a facility. Joint-use agreements allow buildings and sites that would normally go unused after normal business or operating hours to offer the host community programs, thereby maximizing the useful life of the building. In addition, communities may enjoy new or more convenient services.

STEP-BY-STEP GUIDANCE

STEP 1. ENGAGE SCHOOL AUTHORITIES E

Initiate preliminary discussions with the school authorities, ideally before the performance period begins, to identify the best opportunities for shared use in the school.

School expansion limits, parking capacity limits, resource availability, and the pros and cons of shared spaces are among the points to discuss when meeting with the school authorities.

STEP 2. SELECT ONE OPTION E

- Option 1 is for projects with multiple assembly spaces that could be made accessible to the general public.
- Option 2 is for projects that could be designed to include spaces for external groups or companies.
- Option 3 is for projects that will provide student access to spaces owned by other organizations and located off site.

Option 1. Make Building Space Open to the General Public

STEP 1. ALLOCATE SHARED SPACES E

Work with the school authorities to identify and allocate at least three types of eligible shared spaces within the project that are to be made available to the general community.

- Discuss community needs with the school authorities to determine which types of spaces will be made available.
- Obtain written confirmation from the school authorities that these spaces will be made available to the public.

STEP 2. DESIGNATE FACILITIES FOR SHARED SPACES E

Designate restroom facilities that are accessible to shared-space users after normal school hours.

STEP 3. ESTABLISH TERMS AND CONDITIONS OF USAGE E

Meet with the school authorities to establish terms and conditions surrounding the usage of the shared spaces. Draft a shared-use policy stipulating that at least three types of dedicated-use spaces will be available for public use. Alternatively, demonstrate that an existing policy is in place that meets the criteria. Also describe the specific facilities for use by the general public, and their terms and conditions. Indicate how the availability of the spaces will be communicated to the community. There is no minimum length of contract required. Fees for access to the shared spaces may be determined at the discretion of involved parties (see *Further Explanation, Examples*).

Option 2. Contract with Specific Organizations to Share Building Space

STEP 1. ALLOCATE DEDICATED-USE SHARED SPACES E

Work with school authorities to identify and allocate at least two types of eligible dedicated-use spaces within the project that will be made available to specific outside organizations.

- Together with school authorities, identify community organizations, companies, or government organizations that are in need of assembly space.
- Collaborate with the school authorities and the chosen outside organization(s) to determine which spaces in the project will be shared.

STEP 2. DESIGNATE FACILITIES FOR DEDICATED-USE SHARED SPACES E

Designate restroom facilities that are accessible to shared-space users after normal school hours.

STEP 3. ESTABLISH TERMS AND CONDITIONS OF USAGE E

Meet with the school authorities and the organization(s) that will use the dedicated spaces to establish terms and conditions of usage. Alternatively, demonstrate that an existing policy is in place that meets the criteria. Ensure that a signed contract (joint agreement) is in place between the school authorities and the organization(s); this joint agreement must stipulate that at least two types of dedicated-use spaces will be shared with the organization(s). There is no minimum length of contract required. Fees for access to the shared spaces may be determined at the discretion of involved parties.

Option 3. Use Shared Space Owned by Other Organizations

STEP 1. DETERMINE WHICH SPACES WILL BE ACCESSIBLE TO STUDENTS E

Collaborate with school authorities, neighboring agencies, and outside companies to identify eligible facilities owned by organizations in the community that could be made accessible to students.

- Discuss students' needs and planned school facilities with the school authorities to determine which types of additional spaces would be desirable or necessary. Jointly identify local community groups, companies, or government organizations that may have the desired facilities.
- Collaborate with the school authorities and the identified community organizations to confirm accessibility of at least two types of eligible spaces to students.
- The facilities must be accessible on foot. An example is a park across the street from the school to which students can walk on a continuous sidewalk. Ineligible examples are a park across a busy road without crosswalks, and a pool three miles—an infeasible distance for pedestrians—from the school.

STEP 2. ESTABLISH TERMS AND CONDITIONS OF USAGE E

Meet with the school authorities and community organization(s) providing the shared spaces to establish terms and conditions of usage. Ensure that a signed contract is in place between the school authorities and the outside organization(s). This joint agreement must stipulate that at least two types of dedicated-use spaces will be shared with the students. Describe the accessibility of the shared spaces. There is no minimum length of contract required. Fees for access to the shared spaces may be determined at the discretion of involved parties (see *Further Explanation, Examples*).

FURTHER EXPLANATION

EXAMPLES

Example 1. Sample floor plan for shared-use spaces (Option 1)

Figure 1. Sample floor plan

Example 2. Sample documentation narrative for Option 2

School X has established an agreement with the local land-use planning agency to use specified spaces within the school for meetings and activities. The use of the school by external organizations may not interfere with school programs and must occur after school hours and on weekends. Spaces available for use by community organizations are the Auditorium, Classroom B, Restrooms, and Parking Lot 1. These spaces are identified on the accompanying drawings.

Example 3. Sample documentation narrative for Option 3

School X has established an agreement with the local government to use the gymnasium and swimming pool in the public recreation center. The public recreation center is located approximately 1,000 feet (305 meters) from the school and is accessible by a sidewalk; students will cross one two-lane road at a traffic light that has a walk signal. Use of the recreation spaces will take place before and during normal school operating hours. These spaces are identified on the accompanying site plan as G1 (gymnasium) and S1 (swimming pool).

CAMPUS

Group Approach

Submit separate documentation for each building.

Campus Approach

Ineligible. Each LEED project may pursue the credit individually.

REQUIRED DOCUMENTATION

	Documentation	Option 1	Option 2	Option 3
E	Floor plan highlighting joint-use spaces, restroom facilities, and room names	X	X	
E	Shared use policy describing terms and conditions, and communications to the public	X		
E	Signed agreements between school authorities and occupying organizations		X	
E	Signed agreements stipulating how spaces will be shared with students			X
E	Site plan showing pedestrian access route and distance from school to joint-use spaces			X

RELATED CREDIT TIPS

None.

CHANGES FROM LEED 2009

This is a new credit.

REFERENCED STANDARDS

None.

EXEMPLARY PERFORMANCE

Not available.

DEFINITIONS

None.

Water Efficiency (WE)

OVERVIEW

The Water Efficiency (WE) section addresses water holistically, looking at indoor use, outdoor use, specialized uses, and metering. The section is based on an "efficiency first" approach to water conservation. As a result, each prerequisite looks at water efficiency and reductions in potable water use alone. Then, the WE credits additionally recognize the use of nonpotable and alternative sources of water.

Conservation and the creative reuse of water are important because only 3% of Earth's water is fresh water, and of that, slightly over two-thirds is trapped in glaciers.[1] Typically, most of a building's water cycles through the building and then flows off-site as wastewater. In developed nations, potable water often comes from a public water supply system far from the building site, and wastewater leaving the site must be piped to a processing plant, after which it is discharged into a distant water body. This pass-through system reduces streamflow in rivers and depletes fresh water aquifers, causing water tables to drop and wells to go dry. In 60% of European cities with more than 100,000 people, groundwater is being used faster than it can be replenished.[2]

In addition, the energy required to treat water for drinking, transport it to and from a building, and treat it for disposal represents a significant amount of energy use not captured by a building's utility meter. Research in California shows roughly 19% of all energy used in this U.S. state is consumed by water treatment and pumping.[3]

In the U.S., buildings account for 13.6% of potable water use,[4] the third-largest category, behind thermoelectric power and irrigation. Designers and builders can construct green buildings that use significantly less water than conventional construction by incorporating native landscapes that eliminate the need for irrigation, installing water efficient fixtures, and reusing wastewater for non-potable water needs. The Green Building Market Impact Report 2009 found that LEED projects were responsible for saving an aggregate 1.2 trillion gallons (4.54 trillion liters) of water.[5] LEED's WE credits encourage project teams to take advantage of every opportunity to significantly reduce total water use.

CROSS-CUTTING ISSUES

The WE category comprises three major components: indoor water (used by fixtures, appliances and processes, such as cooling), irrigation water, and water metering. Several kinds of documentation span these components,

1. *U.S. Environmental Protection Agency, Water Trivia Facts, water.epa.gov/learn/kids/drinkingwater/water_trivia_facts.cfm (accessed September 12, 2012).*
2. *Statistics: Graphs & Maps, UN Water, http://www.unwater.org/statistics_use.html (accessed March 8, 2013).*
3. *energy.ca.gov/2005publications/CEC-700-2005-011/CEC-700-2005-011-SF.PDF*
4. *USGBC, Green Building Facts, http://www.usgbc.org/articles/green-building-facts*
5. *Green Outlook 2011, Green Trends Driving Growth (McGraw-Hill Construction, 2010), aiacc.org/wp-content/uploads/2011/06/greenoutlook2011.pdf (accessed September 12, 2012).*

depending on the project's specific water-saving strategies.

Site plans: Plans are used to document the location and size of vegetated areas, and the locations of meters and submeters. Within the building, floorplans show the location of fixtures, appliances, and process water equipment (e.g., cooling towers, evaporative condensers), as well as indoor submeters. The same documentation can be used in credits in the Sustainable Sites category.

Fixture cutsheets: Projects must document their fixtures (and appliances as applicable) using fixture cutsheets or manufacturers' literature. This documentation is used in the Indoor Water Use Reduction prerequisite and credit.

Alternative water sources: A project that includes graywater reuse, rainwater harvesting, municipally supplied wastewater (purple pipe water), or other reused sources, is eligible to earn credit in WE Credit Outdoor Water Use Reduction, WE Credit Indoor Water Use Reduction, WE Credit Cooling Tower Water Use, and WE Credit Water Metering. But the team cannot apply the same water to multiple credits unless the water source has sufficient water volume to cover the demand of all the uses (e.g., irrigation plus toilet-flushing demand).

Occupancy calculations: The Indoor Water Use Reduction prerequisite and credit require projections based on occupant's usage. The Location and Transportation and Sustainable Sites categories also use project occupancy calculations. Review the occupancy section in Getting Started to understand how occupants are classified and counted. Also see WE Prerequisite Indoor Water Use Reduction for additional guidance specific to the WE section.

METERING AND TRACKING

The WE credits have significant synergies between installing water meters and documenting savings. Table 1 details the role of water meters in the WE credits.

TABLE 1. Water metering requirements

WE prerequisite or credit	Metering requirement or option	Reading frequency	Baseline length	Performance period length	Credit requirement	Reporting method
Prerequisite Indoor Water Use Reduction	Option 2, Metered Water Use: at least 80% of fixtures and fittings	Monthly summaries	12 months	12 months	No increase in water usage from baseline	Form
Prerequisite Building Level Water Metering	Whole building and associated grounds	Monthly summaries			Install meter, report data	Third-party data tool, USGBC-approved template
Credit Outdoor Water Use Reduction	Option 3, Irrigation Meter Installed	Monthly summaries	At least 3 years	12 months	Show 30% reduction from baseline	Form
Credit Indoor Water Use Reduction	Option 2, Metered Water Use: at least 80% of fixtures and fittings	Monthly summaries	12 months	12 months	Show reduction from baseline	Form
Credit Cooling Tower Water Use	None; cooling towers can be metered for points under WE Credit Water Metering					
Credit Water Metering	Irrigation, indoor plumbing fixtures and fittings, cooling towers, domestic hot water, reclaimed water, other process water	Weekly, including whole-building meter			Install meters; record data at least weekly and report; analyze time trends	Third-party data tool, USGBC-approved template, form

WATER EFFICIENCY PREREQUISITE

Indoor Water Use Reduction

This prerequisite applies to:

Existing Buildings
Schools
Retail
Data Centers
Hospitality
Warehouses and Distribution Centers

INTENT

To reduce indoor water consumption.

REQUIREMENTS

OPTION 1. CALCULATED WATER USE

ESTABLISHMENT E

For the indoor plumbing fixtures and fittings listed in Table 1, reduce water consumption to or below the LEED v4 for Existing Buildings baseline, calculated assuming 100% of the building's indoor plumbing fixtures and fittings meet the flush and flow rates listed in Table 1.

The LEED v4 for Existing Buildings water use baseline is set depending on the year of building's occupancy, as follows:

- For a building with a certificate of occupancy dated 1995 or later, the baseline is 120% of the water use that would result if all fixtures met the code requirements in Table 1.
- For a building with a certificate of occupancy dated before 1995, the baseline is 150% of the water use that would result if all fixtures met the code requirements in Table 1.

TABLE 1. Fixture and fitting code requirements

Fixture or fitting	Baseline (IP units)	Baseline (SI units)
Toilet (water closet)*	1.6 gpf	6 lpf
Urinal*	1.0 gpf	3.8 lpf
Public lavatory (restroom) faucet	0.5 gpm at 60 psi** all others except private applications	1.9 lpm at 415 kPa, all others except private applications
Private lavatory faucet*	2.2 gpm at 60 psi	8.3 lpm at 415 kPa
Kitchen faucet (excluding faucets used exclusively for filling operations)	2.2 gpm at 60 psi	8.3 lpm at 415 kPa
Showerhead*	2.5 gpm at 80 psi per shower stall	9.5 lpm at 550 kPa per shower stall

*WaterSense label available for this product type
gpf = gallons per flush gpm = gallons per minute psi = pounds per square inch
lpf = liters per flush lpm = liters per minute kPa = kilopascals

If indoor plumbing systems were renovated after initial occupancy of the building, set a whole-building average baseline by prorating the above limits, based on the proportion of plumbing fixtures installed during the plumbing renovations in each period. Pre-1995 buildings that have had only minor fixture retrofits (e.g., aerators, showerheads, flushing valves) but no plumbing renovations in or after 1995 may use the 150% baseline for the whole building.

Calculate fixture and fitting performance to compare the water use of the as-installed fixtures and fittings with the use of Uniform Plumbing Code or International Plumbing Code-compliant (baseline) fixtures and fittings.

Inspect all existing fittings or fixtures to ensure they are operating properly. Make any repairs needed to bring all fixtures into good working order or permanently turn off water supply to nonfunctional units.

Implement a fixture and fitting replacement and retrofit policy specifying that all newly installed toilets, urinals, private lavatory faucets, and showerheads that are eligible for labeling be WaterSense labeled (or a local equivalent for projects outside the U.S.).

RETAIL, HOSPITALITY AND SCHOOLS ONLY

Have in place a process and appliance water equipment purchasing policy for the building and site addressing the products listed in Table 2. The policy must cover at least those products purchased within the building and site management's control.

TABLE 2. Standards for appliances

Appliance	Requirement
Residential clothes washer	ENERGY STAR or performance equivalent
Commercial clothes washer	CEE Tier 3A
Residential dishwasher, standard or compact	ENERGY STAR or performance equivalent
Prerinse spray valve	≤ 1.3 gpm (4.9 lpm)
Ice machine	ENERGY STAR or performance equivalent, and use either air-cooled or closed-loop cooling, such as chilled or condenser water system
Kitchen faucet (excluding faucets used exclusively for filling operations)	2.2 gpm at 60 psi
Showerhead	2.5 gpm at 80 psi per shower stall

gpm = gallons per minute lpm = liters per minute

PERFORMANCE P

For building water use, confirm that calculations are up to date. Demonstrate that all applicable purchases made during the performance period meet the requirements of the fixture and fitting replacement and retrofit policy.

For appliances, demonstrate that appliances purchased and installed within the building meet the requirements listed in Table 2. Appliances not listed are not subject to any additional requirements.

OPTION 2. METERED WATER USE

ESTABLISHMENT E

Meter fixtures and fittings and record metered data for one year to establish a water-use baseline.

PERFORMANCE P

For projects with at least 80% of fixtures and fittings metered, show that the water-use baseline has been maintained.

BEHIND THE INTENT

Potable water usage in buildings constitutes a large portion of freshwater consumption. Strategies to reduce potable water use in buildings entail the selection of efficient plumbing fittings, fixtures, and equipment. Fixtures that use 20% to 50% less water than code-required levels are now widely available. The WaterSense label was developed by the U.S. Environmental Protection Agency to identify these efficient fixtures and ensure that higher efficiency does not come at the cost of performance. The WaterSense label has been incorporated as a requirement for this credit to ensure that any new fixtures in a LEED building are both water efficient and high performing.

In some buildings, intensive appliance and process water use can exceed water use from fixtures and landscape combined. This is especially true for buildings with cooling towers or evaporative condensers. Appliance and process water use is therefore addressed specifically with a separate set of requirements.

Because the WE section is designed around an "efficiency first" model, the prerequisite deals only with the efficiency of fixtures and fittings; alternative or nonpotable water sources that offset potable water demand are also addressed in the corresponding credit.

STEP-BY-STEP GUIDANCE

During the establishment period, select the appropriate option, based on preference and water meter data availability, as described in the prerequisite requirements.

- Option 1 is for projects that do not separately meter at least 80% of fixtures (as a percentage of total fixture count) or cannot isolate fixtures by subtracting all other building water systems, based on submeter data.
- Option 2 is for projects that separately meter at least 80% of fixtures (as a percentage of total fixture count) or can isolate fixtures by subtracting all other building water systems, based on submeter data.

Complete the steps below for the chosen option and then complete the steps under All Projects.

Option 1. Calculated Water Use E

STEP 1. DETERMINE BASELINE E

Use the indoor water use calculator provided by USGBC to determine the building's water-use baseline according to the credit requirements.

- Sinks can be defined as public, private, kitchen, or process, depending on use and location (see *Further Explanation, Excluded Water-Using Equipment* and *Public versus Private Lavatories*).
- Kitchen sinks include all sinks in public or private buildings that are used with patterns and purposes similar to residential kitchen sinks. Hotel or motel kitchenette sinks, office kitchenette sinks, staff lounge sinks, pantry or nutrition station sinks, school classroom sinks (if used similarly to residential kitchen sinks), and commercial (food service) kitchen hand sinks that do not pass through a grease interceptor are considered kitchen sinks.
- For buildings built before 1995 but renovated after initial occupancy in 1995 or later, use Equation 1 to determine the baseline multiplier (a value between 120% and 150%).

EQUATION 1. Baseline multiplier

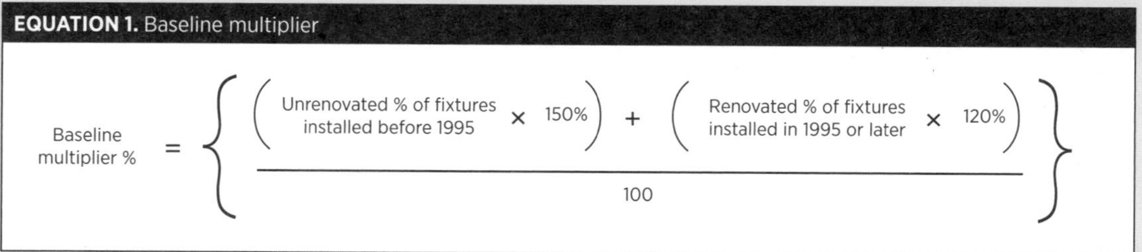

$$\text{Baseline multiplier \%} = \left\{ \frac{\left(\text{Unrenovated \% of fixtures installed before 1995} \times 150\%\right) + \left(\text{Renovated \% of fixtures installed in 1995 or later} \times 120\%\right)}{100} \right\}$$

STEP 2. GATHER INFORMATION FOR CALCULATOR

The indoor water use calculator requires the following information:

- **Project occupancy.** Count occupants consistently across all LEED credits (see *Further Explanation, Occupant Types*).
    - If the project has different sets of fixtures for different parts of the building, create a separate table for each subset. If fixtures are uniform across the project and restroom access is unrestricted, multiple calculations are not necessary; one calculation can cover all building fixtures and occupants.
    - A separate calculation to accommodate visitors is not necessary because the calculator automatically assigns them a lower daily usage rate. For example, it assumes that visitors do not use kitchen faucets.
- **Gender ratio.** The default gender mix is half male and half female. Assumptions that differ from the default must be supported by a narrative and supporting data (see *Further Explanation, Gender Ratio*).
- **Days of operation.** The default number of days of operation per year is 365.
    - If the project is in use for only a portion of the year or closes on specific days, the days of operation can be reduced.
    - The same number of days of operation must be applied to both the baseline and the design cases.
    - Ensure that the number of days of operation is consistent with the building's operating schedule and prepare supporting documentation.
- **Fixture types used in the project.**

STEP 3. COMPLETE CALCULATIONS

Complete the calculations for the design case (installed) flush and flow fixtures. The following information is required:

- Fixture type
- Flush or flow rate
- Fixture manufacturer and model (which should match cutsheets)
- Percentage of occupants using each fixture model. The total for all fixtures of each type must total 100% of occupants for standard fixture types.

The calculator determines annual baseline water consumption, annual design case water consumption, and percentage savings between baseline and design case, based on Equation 1 (see *Further Explanation, Calculations* and *Default Durations and Uses*).

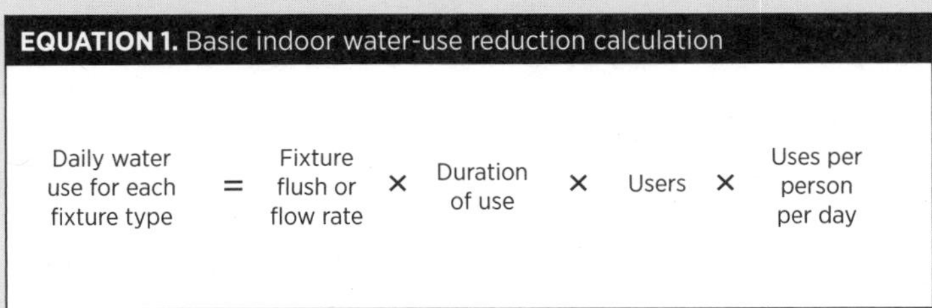

EQUATION 1. Basic indoor water-use reduction calculation

- The duration of use, number of users, and uses per person per day must be the same in both the baseline and the design cases.
- Dual-flush toilet flush rates must be calculated as the average using a 1:2 (high flush:low flush) ratio.
- Metering faucets measured in gallons (liters) per cycle (gpc, lpc) and cycle duration in manufacturer's documentation must be converted to a flow rate in gallons (liters) per minute (gpm, lpm). Use Equation 2 to perform the conversion.

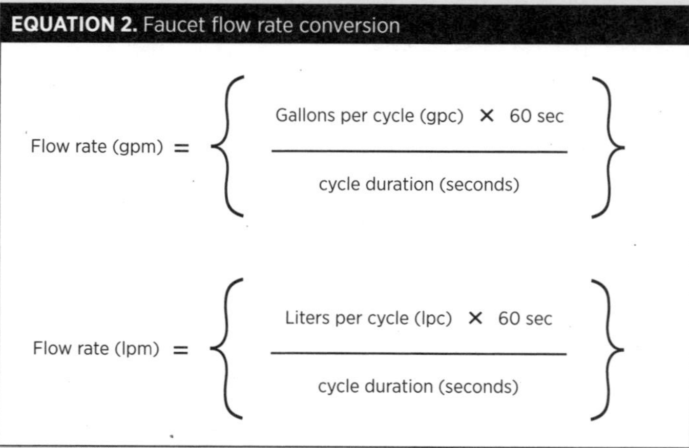
EQUATION 2. Faucet flow rate conversion

$$\text{Flow rate (gpm)} = \left\{ \frac{\text{Gallons per cycle (gpc)} \times 60 \text{ sec}}{\text{cycle duration (seconds)}} \right\}$$

$$\text{Flow rate (lpm)} = \left\{ \frac{\text{Liters per cycle (lpc)} \times 60 \text{ sec}}{\text{cycle duration (seconds)}} \right\}$$

For example, convert a 0.2 gpc metering faucet with a 12-second cycle duration as follows:

(0.2 gpc × 60 sec) / 12 sec = 1 gpm

Likewise, convert a 0.76 lpc metering faucet with a 12-second cycle duration as follows:

(0.76 lpc × 60 sec) / 12 sec = 3.8 lpm

Convert a 0.083 gpc metering faucet with a 10-second cycle duration as follows:

(0.083 gpc × 60 sec) / 10 sec = 0.5 gpm

Likewise, convert a 0.314 lpc metering faucet with a 10-second cycle duration as follows:

(0.314 lpc × 60 sec) / 10 sec = 1.9 lpm

Provide manufacturer's documentation to confirm the flow rate conversion.

Option 2. Metered Water Use E P

STEP 1. DETERMINE BASELINE E

Determine the baseline water use for one year, based on the building's water meter data.

- If submeters do not exist or the project does not have 12 months of data, the project team may choose to install submeters for 80% of fixtures or begin recording data.
- Alternative water sources can be separately metered or metered along with fixtures' potable water use, provided the metering is done uniformly for both the baseline and the performance periods.

STEP 2. ANALYZE CURRENT PRACTICES AND DESIGN E

Examine current fixtures and fittings to determine where improvements may be made.

- Look for older fixtures with especially high flush and flow rates, fixtures in high-use areas, and fixtures with known maintenance issues. Determine which repairs or retrofits would yield the most water savings.
- Also consider drainage problems and tenants' complaints and determine the most feasible solution.

STEP 3. MAKE IMPROVEMENTS E

Install new fittings or fixtures or use alternative water sources to increase the percentage reduction from baseline. Alternatives to potable water include municipally supplied reclaimed water, graywater, rainwater, and stormwater.

STEP 4. MEASURE WATER USAGE DURING PERFORMANCE PERIOD P

Collect water usage data during the entire performance period, a 12-month minimum.

STEP 5. CALCULATE PERCENTAGE IMPROVEMENT USING PERFORMANCE PERIOD DATA P

Compare the baseline data with the performance period data to determine the percentage reduction. If building occupancy has changed from the baseline to the performance, control for the change and show calculations.

All Projects

STEP 1. INSPECT AND REPAIR ALL EXISTING FIXTURES AND FITTINGS E

Make any repairs needed to bring all fixtures and fittings into good working order. Permanently turn off the water supply to any nonfunctional units.

STEP 2. CREATE FIXTURE AND FITTING REPLACEMENT AND RETROFIT POLICY E

Develop and implement a policy specifying that all newly installed toilets, urinals, private lavatory faucets, and showerheads that are eligible for labeling be WaterSense labeled (or a local equivalent for projects outside the U.S.).

- If plumbing capacity is insufficient to support WaterSense fixtures, include a narrative explaining why WaterSense fixtures would not perform well.
- Schools, Retail, and Hospitality projects must include applicable appliances in the building and under site management's control.

STEP 3. DOCUMENT NEW PURCHASES AND INSTALLATIONS P

Document any new purchases and installations of fixtures, fittings, and appliances to demonstrate compliance.

- Demonstrate that all applicable fixture and/or fitting purchases made during the performance period meet the requirements of the fixture and fitting replacement and retrofit policy.
- For Schools, Retail, and Hospitality projects, demonstrate that all applicable appliances purchased during the performance period meet the prerequisite requirements and replacement and retrofit policy.

STEP 4. CONFIRM CALCULATIONS P

Confirm that the calculations reflect the building's current water use and recalculate as necessary.

FURTHER EXPLANATION

CALCULATIONS

See equations in *Step-by-Step Guidance*. Calculations are built into the indoor water use calculator; the following information is provided for reference.

The usage-based calculation for the project is the difference between the calculated design case and a baseline case. The percentage is determined by dividing the design case reduction by the baseline reduction. In traditional plumbing design, calculations are based on fixture counts; the methodology under this prerequisite calculates water use according to fixture consumption rates and estimated use. Occupants' estimated use is determined by counting full-time-equivalent and transient occupants and applying appropriate fixture use rates to each. The calculator estimates the percentage reduction of potable water use, compared with the baseline, using the following equation (see *Further Explanation, Default Durations and Uses* for more about this equation's variables).

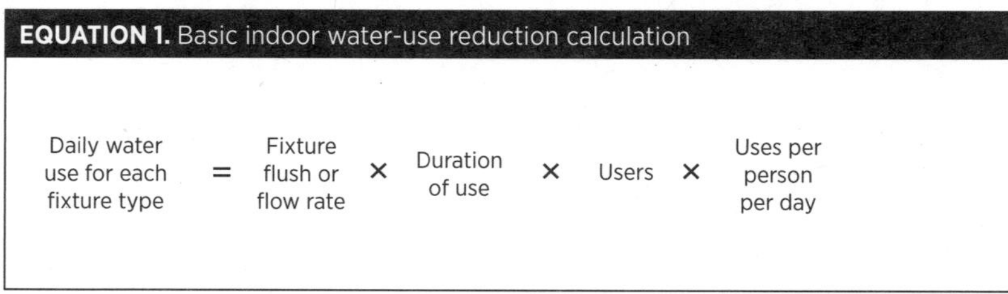

The calculator produces the following:

- Annual baseline water consumption (gallons or liters per year)
- Annual design case water consumption (gallons or liters per year)
- Percentage savings between baseline and design cases

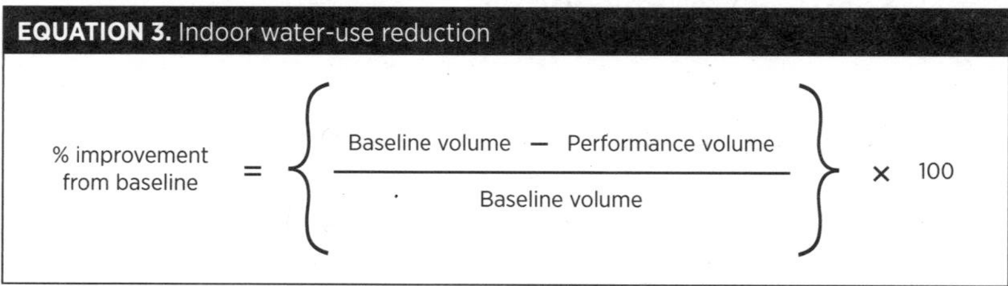

This prerequisite deals only with the water efficiency of fittings and fixtures, appliances, and processes that use potable water. Water derived from alternative sources, such as captured rainwater, is not considered under this prerequisite but can be used to document additional savings in WE Credit Indoor Water Use Reduction.

EXCLUDED WATER-USING EQUIPMENT

Appliances and equipment that use water on materials intended for human consumption may be excluded. For example, bread and produce misters, soda machines, coffee-making machines, and fixtures used to fill sinks for washing produce are excluded.

Fixtures whose flow rates are regulated by health codes may be excluded from the calculation. For example, regulated medical equipment is considered a process water user and is excluded from fixture calculations.

Process water sinks are excluded from the fixture water-use reduction calculations.

The following list provides examples of process water sink fixtures that are excluded.

Specialized

- Janitor sinks
- Laboratory sinks regulated for medical or industrial purposes

Commercial kitchens (food service)

- Commercial kitchen (food service) sinks and prep sinks, including pot filling sinks, wash-down, and cleaning sinks

Healthcare

- Surgical scrub sinks
- Exam or procedure room sinks for clinical use
- Medication room sinks

General

- Janitor closet sinks
- Soiled utility room flushing rim sinks
- Soiled utility room hand-washing sinks
- Clean utility room hand-washing sinks

PUBLIC VERSUS PRIVATE LAVATORIES

Lavatory faucets must be classified as public or private. The Uniform Plumbing Code, International Plumbing Code, and the National Standard Plumbing Code each define private as those fixtures in residences, hotel or motel guest rooms, and private rooms in hospitals. All other applications are deemed to be public.

Fixtures used by residential occupants and fixtures used by residential-type occupants who use the building for sleeping accommodations fall into the private classification. Resident bathrooms in dormitories, patient bathrooms in hospital and nursing homes, and prisoner bathrooms are considered private use.

If it is unclear whether the classification should be public or private, default to public use flow rates in performing the calculations.

Lavatory faucets are intended for hand washing (Table 3). Private lavatory faucets are subject to the federal standard of 2.2 gallons per minute at 60 pounds per square inch (8.3 liters per minute at 415 kilopascals). Public lavatory faucets are subject to the federal standard of 0.5 gallons per minute at 60 pounds per square inch (1.9 liters per minute at 415 kilopascals).

TABLE 3. Typical public and private lavatory faucet applications

Lavatory faucet	Classification
Restroom sink School classroom sinks (if used primarily for hand washing)	Public (baseline: 0.5 gpm, 1.9 lpm)
Residential bathroom sink Hotel or motel bathroom sink Dormitory bathroom sink Patient room sink Patient bathroom sink in hospital or nursing home	Private (baseline: 2.2 gpm, 8.3 lpm)

gpm = gallons per minute   lpm = liters per minute

OCCUPANT TYPES

Identify the daily average number of building users by type (see *Getting Started, Occupancy*). The indoor water use calculator requires total occupant counts in the following categories:

- Employees and staff, expressed as full-time-equivalent (FTE) employees.
- Residents
  - Determine the number of residents—residential occupants in dormitories, hospital in-patients, prisoners, hotel guests, and any other people who use the building for sleeping accommodations. For apartments or multifamily residences where resident occupancy is unknown, estimate the default resident number as the total number of bedrooms + 1 for each residential unit. For example, assume two residents per one-bedroom unit, three residents per two-bedroom unit, and so forth, unless a different assumption is warranted.
  - Include inpatients at health care facilities with residents.
  - Include hotel guests with residents. Calculate the number of overnight hotel guests based on the number and size of units in the project. Assume 1.5 occupants per guest room and multiply the resulting total by 60% (average hotel occupancy, per American Hotel and Lodging Association).
- K–12 students. See *Rating System Variations*.

- Retail customers
- Visitors (excluding retail customers)
  - Include outpatients and higher education students.
  - Report visitors as a daily average total.

If occupancy is known, use the actual occupant counts for calculating occupancy. Use occupancy numbers that are a representative daily average over the course of the year. If the occupancy is not known, use Appendix 2, Default Occupancy Counts, to calculate the default occupancy. (For project types not listed in that appendix, use code occupancy.)

Tables 4 and 5 (see *Default Duration and Uses*) provide default fixture use values for different occupancy types. These values should be used in the calculations unless special circumstances warrant modifications (see *Further Explanation, Rating System Variations*).

GENDER RATIO

The default gender ratio for full-time-equivalent occupants is 50:50. In special circumstances, where an alternative ratio may be justified, provide a narrative and supporting documentation. Modifications to the 50:50 ratio must be shown to apply for the life of the building.

Acceptable special circumstances include projects specifically designed for an alternative gender ratio—for example, a single-gender educational facility. Such projects must show that flush and flow fixtures have been distributed to account for the modified ratio. Project teams must provide documentation of the code-required plumbing fixture counts per gender so that the review team can verify that the flush-fixture ratio installed in the project supports the alternative gender ratio.

Gender ratio affects water usage only when urinals are installed. If the project does not include urinals, a 50:50 or 0:100 male:female ratio should yield the same usage results.

REDUCED OCCUPANCY

To determine the annual usage of each plumbing fixture type, use the following rules:

- For floors or separate tenant spaces that are fully occupied or partially occupied during some portion of the performance period, use the normal procedures for this prerequisite. Assume any partial-year numbers apply on an annual basis as well unless circumstances justify an adjustment.
- For floors or separate tenant spaces that are completely vacant or unused throughout the entire performance period, use the default values for occupancy listed in ASHRAE Standard 62.1–2010 for the given space type; maintain consistency with EQ Prerequisite Minimum Indoor Air Quality Performance. Apportion the default occupants reasonably to the various fixture types present in the building. Create usage groups in this prerequisite's calculator to account for the vacant areas.

These rules apply both to base building or core fixtures and to tenant space fixtures. If fixture upgrades are required to achieve compliance, project teams may consider focusing first on base building or core fixtures.

UNIQUE OR NONSTANDARD WATER CLOSETS

For unique or nonstandard toilets and fixtures, the following may apply:

- **Toilets with flush valve control and separate bowls.** The flush rates should be based on installed flush valve. Confirm that bowl and flush valve rates are compatible to ensure performance.
- **Prison fixtures.** Flow rates and flushing mechanisms must conform to the same design standards as commercial toilets.
- **Children's toilets.** Flow rates and flushing mechanisms must conform to the same design standards as commercial toilets. Confirm that the flush rates of the flush valves are compatible with the bowl sizes to ensure performance.
- **Squat (floor-mounted) toilets.** Flow rates and flushing mechanisms must conform to the same design standards as commercial toilets.

DEFAULT DURATIONS AND USES

Duration of use and uses per day are calculated using defaults (Tables 4 and 5).

TABLE 4. Nonresidential default fixture uses

Fixture type	Duration (sec)	Uses per day			
		Employees (FTE)	Visitors	Retail customers	Students
Water closet (female)	n/a	3	0.5	0.2	3
Water closet (male)	n/a	1	0.1	0.1	1
Urinal (female)	n/a	0	0	0	0
Urinal (male)	n/a	2	0.4	0.1	2
Public lavatory faucet	30	3	0.5	0.2	3
Shower	300	0.1	0	0	0
Kitchen sink	15	1	0	0	0

TABLE 5. Residential default fixture uses

Fixture type	Duration (sec)	Uses per day
Water closet (female)	n/a	5
Water closet (male)	n/a	5
Private lavatory Faucet	60	5
Shower	480	1
Kitchen sink	60	4

For residents, hospital inpatients, hotel guests, prisoners, or any other residential occupants who use the building for sleeping accommodations, use the default residential fixture usage assumptions.

RATING SYSTEM VARIATIONS

Schools

For K–12 schools that close on weekends, holidays, and for eight weeks of school vacation, assume 195 days of operation.

PROJECT TYPE VARIATIONS

Mixed-Use Projects

If a mixed-use project uses the same fixtures throughout the building, complete one calculation for building water use. If the spaces use different fixtures or have dramatically different occupant patterns, complete the indoor water use calculator separately for each space type.

INTERNATIONAL TIPS

For fixtures that require the WaterSense label in countries where the label is unavailable, look up acceptable WaterSense substitutes at usgbc.org. Projects in unlisted countries must comply with the 20%-below-baseline requirement but have no additional performance requirements.

For appliances that require the ENERGY STAR label, a project outside the U.S. may install products that are not labeled under the ENERGY STAR program if they meet the ENERGY STAR product specifications, available on the ENERGY STAR website. All products must meet the standards of the current version of ENERGY STAR as of the date of their purchase.

For appliances that require the Consortium for Energy Efficiency (CEE) label, a project outside the U.S. may purchase products that have not been qualified or labeled by CEE if they meet the CEE product criteria for efficiency.

CAMPUS

Group Approach

Submit separate documentation for each building.

Campus Approach

Ineligible. Each LEED project may pursue the credit individually.

REQUIRED DOCUMENTATION

	Documentation	Fixtures	Appliances
E P	Cutsheets, manufacturers' information	X	X
E P	Indoor water use calculator	X	
E P	Purchasing policy	X	X

RELATED CREDIT TIPS

WE Prerequisite Building-Level Water Metering. Metering of potable water usage will allow facilities management staff to monitor changes in water usage as efficiency measures are implemented.

WE Credit Water Metering. Additional submetering of water-using systems will give facilities management staff actual performance data on specific water efficiency measures so that they can make adjustments to reduce water consumption.

CHANGES FROM LEED 2009

- The year for the baseline multiplier cutoff has changed from 1994 to 1995.
- The multiplier for projects built and occupied before 1995 has changed from 160% to 150% of UPC/IPC.
- Duration-based savings from autocontrol faucets with automatic fixture sensors or metering controls are no longer allowed in the design case. Studies have shown that autocontrol faucets do not result in savings, because users frequently reactivate the faucet after initial use or stop washing before the cycle ends.
- Applying nonpotable water is no longer allowed as an alternative compliance path in the prerequisite. An alternative water source can, however, earn points in the corresponding credit.

REFERENCED STANDARDS

The Energy Policy Act (EPAct) of 1992 and as amended: eere.energy.gov/femp/regulations/epact1992.html

EPAct 2005: eere.energy.gov/femp/regulations/epact2005.html

International Association of Plumbing and Mechanical Officials Publication IAPMO / ANSI UPC 1-2006, Uniform Plumbing Code 2006, Section 402.0, Water-Conserving Fixtures and Fittings: iapmo.org

International Code Council, International Plumbing Code 2006, Section 604, Design of Building Water Distribution System: iccsafe.org

ENERGY STAR: energystar.gov

Consortium for Energy Efficiency: cee1.org

WaterSense: epa.gov/watersense

IgCC/ASHRAE 189.1 – cooling tower and evaporative condenser requirements: ashrae.org/resources--publications/bookstore/standard-189-1

EXEMPLARY PERFORMANCE

Not available.

DEFINITIONS

nonpotable water water that does not meet drinking water standards

potable water water that meets or exceeds U.S. Environmental Protection Agency drinking water quality standards (or a local equivalent outside the U.S.) and is approved for human consumption by the state or local authorities having jurisdiction; it may be supplied from wells or municipal water systems

process water water that is used for industrial processes and building systems, such as cooling towers, boilers, and chillers. It can also refer to water used in operational processes, such as dishwashing, clothes washing, and ice making.

WATER EFFICIENCY PREREQUISITE

Building-Level Water Metering

This prerequisite applies to:

Existing Buildings
Schools
Retail
Data Centers
Hospitality
Warehouses and Distribution Centers

INTENT

To support water management and identify opportunities for additional water savings by tracking water consumption.

REQUIREMENTS

ESTABLISHMENT E

Have permanently installed water meters that measure the total potable water use for the building and associated grounds. Metering of any gray or reclaimed water supplied to the building is encouraged but not required.

PERFORMANCE P

Record meter data on a monthly basis and compile; meter readings can be manual or automated.

Commit to sharing with USGBC the resulting whole-project water usage data for a five-year period beginning on the date the project accepts LEED certification or typical occupancy, whichever comes first.

This commitment must carry forward for five years or until the building changes ownership or lessee.

BEHIND THE INTENT

In order to ensure that water consumption is optimized at a building level, which includes both the project building and grounds, monitoring and measurement strategies should be implemented, and water meters must be installed. Disparities often exist between how buildings are designed to operate and how they actually perform. Even green buildings experience this gap between projected and actual performance. Numerous factors can explain the incongruity—flaws with energy modeling, inadequate commissioning, inaccurate assumptions regarding occupant behavior, lack of coordination during the transition from construction to operations, or the everyday operation of the building systems.

Project teams are encouraged to establish comprehensive plans so that water efficiency strategies can be measured. Instituting informational and competitive programs may encourage occupants to use less water and malfunctioning systems or leaks can be identified quickly to save potable water and money.

STEP-BY-STEP GUIDANCE

STEP 1. IDENTIFY ALL POTABLE WATER END USES E

Determine all end uses of potable water in the project building and on the grounds. These could include plumbing fixtures, cooling towers and evaporative condensers, laundering, dishwashing, indoor and outdoor water features, irrigation, exterior cleaning, and manufacturing processes.

STEP 2. IDENTIFY ALL POTABLE WATER SOURCES THAT SERVE PROJECT E

All potable water sources must be metered so that operations staff can track water consumption over time. Examples of potable water sources that must be metered include the following:

- Public water supply
- On-site well
- On-site potable water treatment system

STEP 3. DETERMINE ATTRIBUTES OF PUBLIC WATER SUPPLY METERS E

If all water comes from a public water supply and the utility's water meter provides monthly consumption data, that system's meter meets the prerequisite requirements.

If the public water supplier restricts access to the meter or uses proprietary remote reporting technology, the project team may meet the prerequisite requirements by tracking water usage through monthly billing. To collect more frequent or accurate data, the team may elect to install a private meter downstream from the public water supply meter.

STEP 4. DETERMINE NUMBER, LOCATION, AND TYPE OF ALL METERS E

If the project is not served by a public water supply, or if the project uses multiple sources of potable water, two or more meters may be required. A single meter installed downstream of multiple potable water supply systems may be used if it is upstream of all project water uses.

- In some cases, projects may elect to use multiple meters to gain additional information on water use.
- Select locations with easy access for reading and maintenance. There are no requirements for the type of meters except that they be permanent.
- If rainwater, graywater, or municipally reclaimed water is used in the building, consider metering those volumes individually as well.
- Additional meters may be needed to satisfy the requirements for WE Credit Water Metering (see *Related Credit Tips*).

STEP 5. TRACK WATER CONSUMPTION P

Begin tracking water consumption during the performance period. Although monthly tracking is required, weekly or daily readings provide quicker information about spikes in consumption and may help identify ways to capture additional savings. Review the water-use data in the context of building operations; consider tracking building occupancy changes and maintenance activities concurrently. This additional information may explain fluctuations in usage.

STEP 6. SHARE WATER CONSUMPTION DATA WITH USGBC P

Commit to sharing with USGBC the whole-project water usage data acquired from permanent meters installed in accordance with the prerequisite requirements. The project owner must commit to sharing water use data with USGBC for five years in one of two ways:

- USGBC-approved data template
- Third-party data source

To see the most recent list of data sharing pathways, visit USGBC's credit library, at usgbc.org/credits.

FURTHER EXPLANATION

PROJECT TYPE VARIATIONS

Multifamily Residential

Either use a whole-building meter or, provided all potable water uses are accounted for and included, aggregate data from submeters for each unit and common spaces.

Additions

A single meter that covers both old and new portions of the building may be installed, but submetering for the addition is encouraged.

CAMPUS

Group Approach

Submit separate documentation for each building. Potable water used for landscape irrigation must be tracked in any of three ways: by including it with a single building, by installing a dedicated meter, or by installing multiple meters.

Campus Approach

Ineligible. Each LEED project may pursue the credit individually.

REQUIRED DOCUMENTATION

	Documentation	All projects
E	Meter declaration	X
E	Sharing commitment	X
P	Consumption data	X

RELATED CREDIT TIPS

WE Prerequisite Indoor Water Use Reduction. The related prerequisite requires separate water submeters for cooling tower makeup and blowdown and for evaporative condensers.

WE Credit Water Metering. This credit encourages project teams to install submeters on certain systems serving the building.

EA Prerequisite Building-Level Energy Metering. Water meters may be tracked by a building automation system (BAS) that also records energy consumption. Data sharing for both this and the related prerequisite can be achieved through ENERGY STAR's Portfolio Manager.

CHANGES FROM LEED 2009

This is a new prerequisite.

REFERENCED STANDARDS

None.

EXEMPLARY PERFORMANCE

Not available.

DEFINITIONS

potable water water that meets or exceeds U.S. Environmental Protection Agency drinking water quality standards (or a local equivalent outside the U.S.) and is approved for human consumption by the state or local authorities having jurisdiction; it may be supplied from wells or municipal water systems

private meter a device that measures water flow and is installed downstream from the public water supply meter or as part of an on-site water system maintained by the building management team

public water supply (PWS) a system for the provision to the public of water for human consumption through pipes or other constructed conveyances. To be considered public, such system must have at least 15 service connections or regularly serve at least 25 individuals. (Adapted from U.S. Environmental Protection Agency)

WATER EFFICIENCY CREDIT

Outdoor Water Use Reduction

This credit applies to:

Existing Buildings (1–2 points)
Schools (1–2 points)
Retail (1–2 points)
Data Centers (1–2 points)
Hospitality (1–2 points)
Warehouses and Distribution Centers (1–2 points)

INTENT

To reduce outdoor water consumption.

REQUIREMENTS

Reduce outdoor water use through one of the following options. Nonvegetated surfaces, such as permeable or impermeable pavement, should be excluded from landscape area calculations. Athletic fields and playgrounds (if vegetated) and food gardens may be included or excluded at the project team's discretion.

If landscape irrigation is not submetered, use Option 2.

ESTABLISHMENT E

OPTION 1. NO IRRIGATION REQUIRED (2 POINTS)

Show that the landscape does not require irrigation beyond a maximum two-year plant establishment period.

OPTION 2. NO IRRIGATION METER INSTALLED: CALCULATED WATER BUDGET (1–2 POINTS)

Use the existing landscape to calculate the landscape water requirement using the EPA WaterSense Water Budget Tool.

Install an irrigation meter.

OPTION 3. IRRIGATION METER INSTALLED (1–2 POINTS)

The baseline is established using the annual average of at least 3 years of consecutive data out of the last 5 years.

PERFORMANCE P

OPTION 1. NO IRRIGATION REQUIRED (2 POINTS)

None.

OPTION 2. NO IRRIGATION METER: CALCULATED WATER BUDGET (1–2 POINTS)

Points are earned according to Table 1.

OPTION 3. IRRIGATION METER INSTALLED (1–2 POINTS)

Demonstrate a reduction in outdoor water use over the most recent 12 months compared with the established baseline. Points are earned according to Table 1.

TABLE 1. Points for reducing irrigation water

Percentage reduction from baseline	Points
30%	1
40%	2

BEHIND THE INTENT

Landscape irrigation practices consume large quantities of potable water, sometimes accounting for 30% to 70% of the water consumed in nonagricultural use.[1] Potable water is a precious resource globally. For example, in many European cities, groundwater is being used at a faster rate than it can be replenished, according to the World Business Council for Sustainable Development.[2] Good landscape design and use of native, adapted, and drought-tolerant plants can dramatically reduce and even eliminate the need for irrigation while better integrating the building site into its surroundings and attracting native wildlife. Native plants also tend to require less fertilizer and fewer chemical pesticides, which degrade water quality when carried away in stormwater runoff.

The landscape water requirement (LWR) can be estimated by developing a water budget that allows landscape professionals to consider the effects of the many variables, such as plant types, planting density, and irrigation system elements. Using a water budget optimizes water use in landscape designs. Potable water consumption may also be reduced by reusing potable water and using nonpotable water sources.

STEP-BY-STEP GUIDANCE

For U.S. projects, the WaterSense Water Budget Tool automatically derives rainfall and evapotranspiration from the project's zip code. Skip Step 1 and go to Step 2.

STEP 1. PROJECTS OUTSIDE U.S. ONLY: OBTAIN PRECIPITATION AND EVAPOTRANSPIRATION DATA E

Gather average monthly precipitation data and evapotranspiration rates (ET_o) for the project area to determine the site's potential irrigation needs. Precipitation data and ET_o can be found for most locations around the world.

- An Excel version of the WaterSense Water Budget Tool is available under the Resources tab for this credit, at usgbc.org/credits. Complete the tool using IP (inches, pounds) rather than SI units; see the conversion calculator, also under the Resources tab.
- See *Further Explanation, International Tips*, for information on rainfall and evapotranspiration statistics outside the U.S.

STEP 2. DETERMINE VEGETATED AREAS E

On a map, indicate all areas on the project site that are or will be vegetated.

- Do not include hardscapes (whether pervious or impervious) or unvegetated softscapes, such as mulched paths and playground areas.
- The following landscape types may be included or excluded from landscape calculations: vegetated playgrounds, athletic fields, food gardens, and urban agricultural areas.

STEP 3. SELECT PLANT TYPES AND COVERAGE E

Identify plant types and coverage that will balance water use efficiency with the area's intended function.

- Reserve grass for play fields or other activities that require turf; using turf for groundcover will make it very difficult to meet the credit thresholds.
- Once established, native and drought-tolerant plants generally require little to no irrigation.

STEP 4. SELECT ONE OPTION E

Select the appropriate option for the project's irrigation needs.

- Option 1 is for projects that do not require irrigation, based on the location and landscape design. Projects that have no landscape area automatically earn this credit.
- Option 2 is for projects that require irrigation but do not have an irrigation meter installed or do not have meter data for at least three years.
- Option 3 is for projects that require irrigation, have an irrigation meter installed, and have meter data for at least three years. This is also the appropriate option for recertification of projects that have at least 12 months of water baseline tracking, followed by 12 months of performance data.

1. *U.S. EPA*
2. *unwater.org/statistics_use.html.*

Option 1. No Irrigation Required E

Develop the plant species and water requirement narrative.

- Describe the plantings and explain why they will not require irrigation beyond their specified establishment periods. Indicate why average rainfall will be sufficient.
- A landscaping plan showing native plants may be provided to confirm that irrigation will not be required, based on local rainfall and plants' water demands.

Option 2. No Irrigation Meter Installed E

STEP 1. REDUCE IRRIGATION NEEDS BY ALTERING DESIGN

Project teams can dramatically alter irrigation demand by selecting plants that are appropriate for their intended uses.

- Reserve grass for play fields or other activities that require turf; using turf for groundcover will make it very difficult to meet prerequisite and credit thresholds.
- Restore or plant native species to replace areas requiring intensive irrigation.

STEP 2. CONSIDER ALTERNATIVE WATER SOURCES

Consider using alternative sources of water collected on site or treated wastewater provided by a municipal agency to offset potable water for irrigation (see *Further Explanation, Alternative Water Sources*).

STEP 3. CONSIDER SMART IRRIGATION CONTROLS

Consider including smart-sensor technology irrigation controls for additional water savings.

STEP 4. CALCULATE LANDSCAPE WATER BUDGET

Calculate water use as a percentage of total irrigation and peak month irrigation demand using the WaterSense Water Budget Tool (see *Further Explanation, About WaterSense* and *International Tips*).

- Use the tool for vegetated areas only. Do not include hardscapes (whether pervious or impervious) or unvegetated softscapes, such as mulched paths and playgrounds.
- Resolve uncertainties about plants' water requirements by referring to local resources such as plant guides, the state agricultural extension service, or nurseries to classify each plant type as a low, medium, or high water user.
- Projects may not enter zero landscape water consumption for any landscaped area.
- If only part of the lot is irrigated, complete the calculation twice—once for the irrigated section, and again for the unirrigated area—and sum the results.

STEP 5. CALCULATE ADJUSTED LANDSCAPE WATER REQUIREMENT

Determine the landscape requirement (LWR) using Equations 1 and 2. The volume of water obtained from any alternative sources can be determined from historical data or, for municipally supplied treated wastewater, from utility bills.

EQUATION 1. Adjusted monthly landscape water requirement (LWR)

Adjusted LWR (volume/month) = LWR (volume/month) − Alternative water quantity (volume/month)

STEP 6. CALCULATE ADDITIONAL REDUCTION FROM BASELINE FOR SMART IRRIGATION CONTROLS

Count only irrigation controls whose smart-sensor technology meets the WaterSense criteria. These controls result in an additional 15% reduction that project teams can take from the baseline.

EQUATION 2. Landscape water requirement for smart irrigation controls

Final LWR = LWR or Adjusted LWR − (0.15 × LWR or Adjusted LWR)

STEP 7. INSTALL IRRIGATION WATER METER

For initial certification of a project that previously had no irrigation water meter, or a project lacking at least three years of irrigation data, the team must install a meter and begin tracking irrigation water use.

Option 3. Irrigation Meter Installed

STEP 1. ESTABLISH IRRIGATION WATER USAGE BASELINE E

Establish the baseline irrigation water usage by taking the annual average of at least three years of consecutive data from the past five years. The baseline must be established using data from years before the performance period.

For future recertification, the original baseline can be used for 10 years. After 10 years, reset the baseline following the instructions above. The baseline content should be drawn from the immediate five years before the performance period year.

STEP 2. ANALYZE CURRENT PRACTICES AND DESIGN E

Analyze current irrigation practices and landscape design to determine where improvements may be made. Consider plant species selection, planting density, and location of plants relative to sunlight, shade, water access, and topography.

STEP 3. IMPLEMENT IMPROVEMENTS E

Use alternative water sources and controls with smart-sensor technology to increase the percentage reduction from baseline.

- Use site-derived alternative water sources or treated wastewater provided by the municipality to offset potable water used for irrigation (see *Further Explanation, Alternative Water Sources*).
- Irrigation controls that use smart-sensor technology can provide additional water savings.

STEP 4. MEASURE WATER USAGE DURING PERFORMANCE PERIOD P

Measure the irrigation water usage during the entire performance period. For the most recent 12 months of the performance period, compare data with the baseline. This option requires a 12-month performance period.

- For future recertification, reanalyze irrigation practices and landscape design to see whether additional improvements can be made.
- Look for changes in water use over time. An increase could indicate a leak in the irrigation system, a change in landscaping, or climatic variations over years. Take these factors into consideration when planning improvements.

STEP 5. CALCULATE PERCENTAGE IMPROVEMENT USING PERFORMANCE PERIOD DATA P

Calculate the percentage improvement over the baseline annual average using Equation 3 (see *Further Explanation, Examples*).

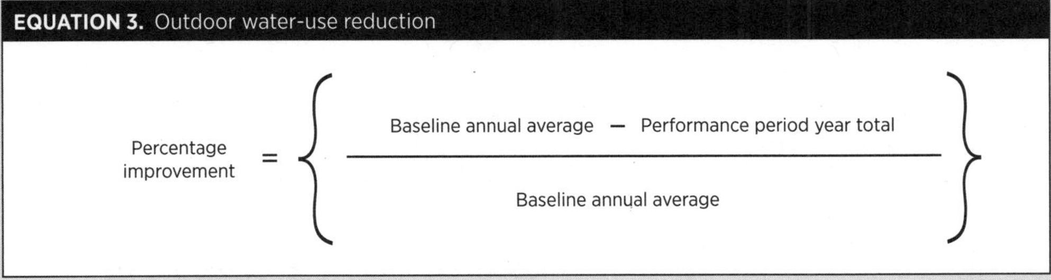

EQUATION 3. Outdoor water-use reduction

$$\text{Percentage improvement} = \left\{ \frac{\text{Baseline annual average} - \text{Performance period year total}}{\text{Baseline annual average}} \right\}$$

FURTHER EXPLANATION

CALCULATIONS

See calculations in *Step-by-Step Guidance*.

ABOUT WATERSENSE

EPA's WaterSense website includes this reference for native vegetation in various parts of the U.S.: epa.gov/watersense/outdoor/what_to_plant.html.

Use the WaterSense Water Budget Data Finder to estimate the evapotranspiration rate (ET_o) in inches per month for the critical month of the year, based on a project's zip code. ET_o, a measurement of water lost from a well-maintained expanse of average-height green grass and the surrounding soil, varies with a location's sunshine, wind, humidity, and temperature. Hot, dry, and windy locations have higher ET_o values than cool, humid locations. Data for these variables are based on 30-year historical averages. Data for projects outside the U.S. are not included in this tool.

The WaterSense Water Budget Tool (epa.gov/watersense/water_budget/) calculates a baseline landscape water requirement of a typical landscape, as described above. Different plant species and their arrangement in the landscape can be entered, and the tool estimates the effect of these design variables on LWR. Projects outside the U.S. may use this tool with local data.

Design decisions about the different components of irrigation water delivery systems also factor into the estimates the tool provides.

WaterSense irrigation controller specifications (epa.gov/WaterSense/products/controltech.html) outline the requirements for weather-based irrigation controller systems. These systems earn projects a standard 15% reduction in landscape water requirement for WE Credit Outdoor Water Use Reduction.

ALTERNATIVE WATER SOURCES

Alternative water sources include reclaimed wastewater, graywater, swimming pool backwash filter, refrigeration system condensate, captured rainwater, stormwater and foundation drain water, steam system condensate, fluid cooler discharge, food steamer discharge, combination oven discharge, industrial process water, fire pump test water, municipally supplied treated wastewater, and ice machine condensate.

Testing site-derived alternative water to confirm its suitability for irrigation uses is recommended. Salinity is one concern. Irrigation with saline water in an arid environment causes salt buildup in the soil, eventually degrading it. Condensate and cooling tower blowdown in particular may have salinity levels precluding use for irrigation. A second concern is that alternative water supplies must be stored until needed for irrigation; the timing and reliability of the supply must be assessed.

When calculating alternative water source annual projections, follow these guidelines:

- Depending on supply timing and availability, monthly water budget calculations may be necessary to show how much potable water may be replaced. Calculate irrigation water demand during each month of the irrigation season.
- Assume that alternative water will be used for irrigation as it is available. The contribution of alternative water to the peak month irrigation demand must be based on having excess alternative water available and stored before the peak month.

If the project team is attempting a 100% reduction in outdoor water use by harvesting rainwater, ensure that the water needed in the peak month can be stored on site. Use Equations 1 and 2 to help in sizing rainwater cisterns.

EQUATION 1. Rainwater harvesting

Gallons per 1 inch of rain = Roof area in ft^2 × 0.6

EQUATION 2. Monthly harvested rainwater volume

Amount available = gallons per 1 inch of rain × Average inches rain per month

EXAMPLES

A location's rainfall and evapotranspiration levels determine how much water a project needs. Consider two projects using Option 2, each with a fairly water-efficient landscape around an office building, one in Livingston, New Jersey, and one in Palo Alto, California (Figure 1).

Example 1. Livingston, New Jersey

The location is a typical suburban community in northern New Jersey. The team uses the EPA WaterSense Water Budget Data finder:

- Enter Zip Code: 07039
- Peak Month: Jun
- ET_o Value: 6.30 inches/month
- Rainfall: 3.40 inches/month

Figure 1. Example Site Plan

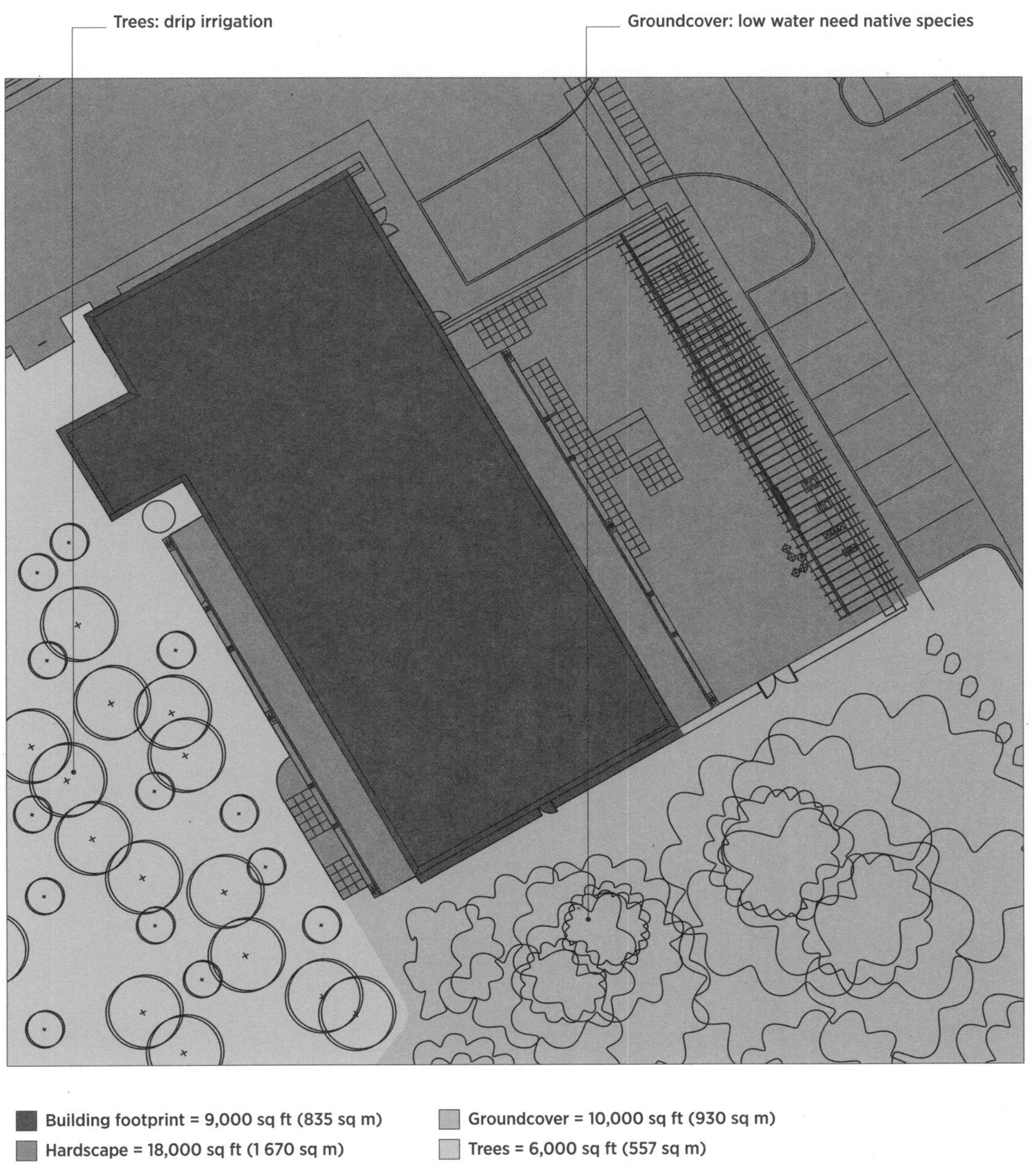

Building footprint = 9,000 sq ft (835 sq m)
Hardscape = 18,000 sq ft (1 670 sq m)
Groundcover = 10,000 sq ft (930 sq m)
Trees = 6,000 sq ft (557 sq m)

When landscape area is entered, the tool offers these results (Figure 2):

- Total: 16,000 sq ft
- 10,000 sq ft of groundcover—low water need, native species, drip irrigation
- 6,000 sq ft of trees—medium water need, drip irrigation

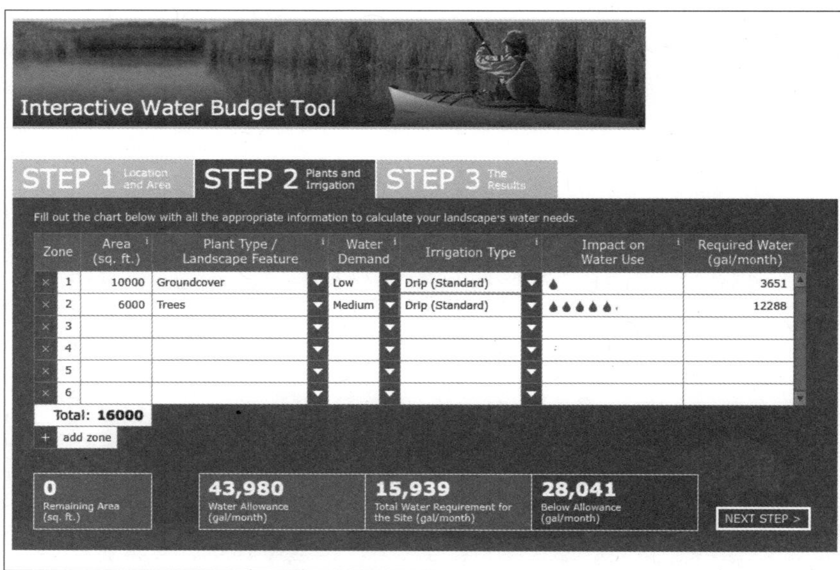

Figure 2. Water Budget Calculation for Livingston, NJ Location. Screenshot taken from http://www.epa.gov/watersense

The landscape water allowance (30% below baseline minimum) equals 43,980 gallons a month. The landscape water requirement for this design in this location is 15,939 gallons a month. The total savings without alternative water sources equals 75%. The project achieves the credit and earns 1 point.

The team has determined that rainwater harvested from the building's roof will supply all the project's outdoor water needs. Given the average monthly rainfall in this location and the roof's area, average monthly rainwater available for harvesting is 21,217 gallons per month. The team installs a rainwater cistern capable of holding 20,000 gallons of rainwater for irrigation. The rainwater cistern would be full during the peak watering month. With an adjusted landscape water requirement of 15,939 gallons a month minus 20,000 gallons a month available for harvesting, the project uses—4,061 gallons a month (i.e., it has a rainwater surplus). The total savings is 100%, for 2 points.

Example 2. Palo Alto, California

Palo Alto is in a fairly dry region of the country. The team uses the EPA WaterSense Water Budget Data Finder (Figure 3):

- Enter Zip Code: 94301
- Peak Month: Jul
- ET_o Value: 6.00 inches/month
- Rainfall: 0.00 inches/month

Figure 3. Water Budget Calculation for Palo Alto, CA Location. Screenshot taken from http://www.epa.gov/watersense/

With a total landscape area of 16,000 square feet—10,000 square feet of groundcover (low water need, native species, drip irrigation) and 6,000 square feet of trees (medium water need, drip irrigation)—the tool now calculates a landscape water allowance of 41,886 gallons a month, or 30% below the baseline minimum. Compared with the New Jersey example above, the landscape water requirement for this design has increased to 26,713 gallons a month. The total savings is now 55%, for 2 points.

Example 3. Metered Data
The project team is using Option 3 and creates a table to compare water savings in 2012 with the baseline, which is an average of irrigation volumes in previous years.

TABLE 2. Monthly irrigation (volume)

	2008	2009	2010	2011	Baseline averages	2012
January	10	10	10	10	10	6
February	20	20	20	20	20	12
March	30	30	30	30	30	18
April	50	50	50	50	50	29
May	70	60	82	70	71	45
June	100	100	100	100	100	81
July	110	123	98	140	120	89
August	100	111	118	132	120	88
September	70	70	70	70	70	57
October	50	52	45	60	52	29
November	30	30	30	30	30	17
December	20	20	20	20	20	7
Total	660	676	673	732	693	478
		Baseline years selected				Performance period

Percentage improvement = (693 − 478) / 693 = 31.02%

This project earns 1 point for a 30% reduction.

INTERNATIONAL TIPS

Project teams outside the U.S. may obtain monthly average rainfall and reference evapotranspiration data from the Food and Agriculture Organization of the United Nations. If the data are unavailable, teams must provide estimates. Monthly rainfall should be an average value based on data from a reliable source, such as the World Meteorological Organization.

Reference evapotranspiration may be calculated from weather data. REF-ET software uses a variety of algorithms based on monthly average weather data to calculate reference evapotranspiration.

The month with the largest deficit between reference evapotranspiration and rainfall is the peak month. These estimates may then be used in the EPA WaterSense Water Budget Tool to calculate the landscape water requirement for the site.

CAMPUS

Group Approach
All buildings in the group may be documented as one. Use the total landscaped area on the entire campus. The results of the Water Budget Tool apply to all buildings in the group.

Campus Approach

Option 1. Eligible.

Option 2. Eligible. May be documented for the total landscape area, but irrigation meters must be installed at the individual building level.

Option 3. Ineligible. Each LEED project may pursue the credit individually.

REQUIRED DOCUMENTATION

	Documentation	Option 1	Option 2	Option 3
E P	Site plan		X	
E P	Narrative for plant species and water requirements	X		
E P	Alternative water supply calculations		X	X
E P	Water Budget Tool report		X	
E P	Irrigation meter report (monthly summaries)			X

RELATED CREDIT TIPS

WE Prerequisite Indoor Water Use Reduction. Graywater is a potential source for reducing outdoor potable water use.

WE Credit Cooling Tower Water Use. Cooling tower blowdown water and other cooling tower process water are potential alternative water sources for meeting outdoor water demand.

WE Building-Level Water Metering. The landscape may be metered separately or with the whole building. Separate metering will help project teams achieve both this credit and the related metering prerequisite.

WE Credit Water Metering. Metering irrigation water (Option 3 in this credit) contributes to achieving the related credit.

CHANGES FROM LEED 2009

- This is a new credit.
- The WaterSense Water Budget Tool is now listed as the referenced calculation tool.

REFERENCED STANDARDS

None.

EXEMPLARY PERFORMANCE

Not available.

DEFINITIONS

adapted plant vegetation that is not native to a particular region but that has characteristics that allow it to live in the area. Adapted plants do not pose the same problems as invasive species.

combination oven discharge water released from an oven that includes a steam cycle or option

conventional irrigation a region's most common system for providing water to plants by nonnatural means. A conventional irrigation system commonly uses pressure to deliver water and distributes it through sprinkler heads above the ground.

cooling tower blowdown the water discharged from a cooling tower typically because increased salinity or alkalinity has caused scaling. Cooling tower blowdown may be too saline for use in landscape irrigation.

evapotranspiration the combination of evaporation and plant transpiration into the atmosphere. Evaporation occurs when liquid water from soil, plant surfaces, or water bodies becomes vapor. Transpiration is the movement of water through a plant and the subsequent loss of water vapor.

foundation drain the water discharged from a subsurface drainage system. If a building foundation is below the water table, a sump pump may be required. Discharge from the sump may be stored and used for irrigation.

graywater "untreated household waste water which has not come into contact with toilet waste. Graywater includes used water from bathtubs, showers, bathroom wash basins, and water from clothes-washers and laundry tubs. It must not include waste water from kitchen sinks or dishwashers" (Uniform Plumbing Code, Appendix G, Gray Water Systems for Single-Family Dwellings); "waste water discharged from lavatories, bathtubs, showers, clothes washers and laundry sinks" (International Plumbing Code, Appendix C, Gray Water Recycling Systems). Some states and local authorities allow kitchen sink wastewater to be included in graywater. Other differences can likely be found in state and local codes. Project teams should comply with the graywater definition established by the authority having jurisdiction in the project area.

hardscape the inanimate elements of the building landscaping. It includes pavement, roadways, stonewalls, wood and synthetic decking, concrete paths and sidewalks, and concrete, brick, and tile patios.

hydrozone a group of plantings with similar water needs

industrial process water any water discharged from a factory setting. Before this water can be used for irrigation, its quality needs to be checked. Saline or corrosive water should not be used for irrigation.

native vegetation an indigenous species that occurs in a particular region, ecosystem, and habitat without direct or indirect human actions. Native species have evolved to the geography, hydrology, and climate of that region. They also occur in communities; that is, they have evolved together with other species. As a result, these communities provide habitat for a variety of other native wildlife species. Species native to North America are generally recognized as those occurring on the continent prior to European settlement. Also known as native plants.

peak watering month the month with the greatest deficit between evapotranspiration and rainfall. This is the month when the plants in the site's region potentially require the most supplemental water typically a mid-summer month. (Sustainable Sites Initiative)

potable water water that meets or exceeds U.S. Environmental Protection Agency drinking water quality standards (or a local equivalent outside the U.S.) and is approved for human consumption by the state or local authorities having jurisdiction; it may be supplied from wells or municipal water systems

rainwater harvesting the capture, diversion, and storage of rain for future beneficial use. Typically, a rain barrel or cistern stores the water; other components include the catchment surface and conveyance system. The harvested rainwater can be used for irrigation.

reclaimed water wastewater that has been treated and purified for reuse

reference evapotranspiration rate the amount of water lost from a specific vegetated surface with no moisture limitation. Turf grass with height of 120 mm is the reference vegetation.

softscape the elements of a landscape that consist of live, horticultural elements

xeriscaping landscaping that does not require routine irrigation

WATER EFFICIENCY CREDIT

Indoor Water Use Reduction

This credit applies to:

Existing Buildings (1–5 points)
Schools (1–5 points)
Retail (1–5 points)
Data Centers (1–4 points)
Hospitality (1–5 points)
Warehouses and Distribution Centers (1–5 points)

INTENT

To reduce indoor water consumption.

REQUIREMENTS

OPTION 1. CALCULATED WATER USE (1–5 POINTS EXCEPT DATA CENTERS, 1–4 POINTS DATA CENTERS)

ESTABLISHMENT E

None.

PERFORMANCE P

Have fixtures that use less water than the baseline calculated in WE Prerequisite Indoor Water-Use Reduction. Points are awarded according to Table 1.

TABLE 1. Points for reducing calculated water use beyond the prerequisite level

Additional percentage reduction	Points (except Data Centers)	Points (Data Centers)
10%	1	1
15%	2	2
20%	3	3
25%	4	4
30%	5	

Confirm that calculations are up to date. Demonstrate that all purchases made since the end of the performance period meet the design performance requirements.

OR

OPTION 2. METERED WATER USE (1–5 POINTS EXCEPT DATA CENTERS, 1–4 POINTS DATA CENTERS)

ESTABLISHMENT E

Meter fixtures and fittings, and record meter data for one year to establish a water-use baseline.

PERFORMANCE P

For projects with at least 80% of fixtures and fittings metered, show a reduction from the baseline year of meter data.

TABLE 2. Points for reducing metered water use

Additional percentage reduction	Points (except Data Centers)	Points (Data Centers)
<5%	1	1
5%	2	2
10%	3	3
15%	4	4
20%	5	

BEHIND THE INTENT

See *Behind the Intent* in WE Prerequisite Indoor Water Use Reduction.

STEP-BY-STEP GUIDANCE

During the establishment period, select the appropriate option, based on preference and water meter data availability, as described in the credit requirements.

- Option 1 is for projects that do not separately meter at least 80% of fixtures (as a percentage of total fixture count) or cannot isolate fixtures by subtracting all other building water systems, based on submeter data.
- Option 2 is for projects that separately meter at least 80% of fixtures (as a percentage of total fixture count) or can isolate fixtures by subtracting all other building water systems, based on submeter data.

Option 1. Calculated Water Use E

Follow the instructions in WE Prerequisite Indoor Water Use Reduction to determine additional savings beyond the prerequisite requirement.

Option 2. Metered Water Use E P

Use the project's water use data from WE Prerequisite Indoor Water Use Reduction to demonstrate additional savings beyond the prerequisite requirement.

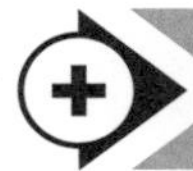

FURTHER EXPLANATION

CALCULATIONS

See WE Prerequisite Indoor Water Use Reduction and use the indoor water use calculator provided by USGBC.

REDUCED OCCUPANCY

To determine the annual usage of each plumbing fixture type, use the following rules:

- For floors or separate tenant spaces that are fully occupied or partially occupied during some portion of the performance period, use the normal procedures for this credit. Assume any partial-year numbers apply on an annual basis as well unless circumstances justify an adjustment.
- For floors or separate tenant spaces that are completely vacant or unused throughout the entire performance period, see *Getting Started, Occupancy*). Apportion the default occupants reasonably to the various fixture types present in the building. Create usage groups in this prerequisite's calculator to account for the vacant areas.

These rules apply both to base building or core fixtures and to tenant space fixtures. If fixture upgrades are required to achieve compliance, project teams may consider focusing first on base building or core fixtures.

RATING SYSTEM VARIATIONS

Schools

For K–12 schools that close on weekends, holidays, and for eight weeks of school vacation, assume 195 days of operation.

PROJECT TYPE VARIATIONS

Mixed-Use Projects

If a mixed-use project uses the same fixtures throughout the building, complete one calculation for building water use. If the spaces use different fixtures or have dramatically different patterns of occupancy, complete the indoor water use calculator separately for each space type.

INTERNATIONAL TIPS

For fixtures that require the WaterSense label in countries where the label is unavailable, look up acceptable WaterSense substitutes at usgbc.org. Projects in unlisted countries must comply with the 20%-below-baseline requirement but have no additional performance requirements.

For appliances that require the ENERGY STAR label, a project outside the U.S. may install products that are not labeled under the ENERGY STAR program if they meet the ENERGY STAR product specifications, available on the ENERGY STAR website. All products must meet the standards of the current version of ENERGY STAR as of the date of their purchase.

CAMPUS

Group Approach

Submit separate documentation for each building. If nonpotable water systems will be shared by multiple projects, ensure adequate supply to meet the demands of all projects using nonpotable water. The nonpotable water may not be double-counted among projects.

Campus Approach

Ineligible. Each LEED project may pursue the credit individually.

REQUIRED DOCUMENTATION

	Documentation	Fixtures
E P	Meter data	X
E P	Indoor water use calculator	X
E P	Alternative water source calculations (if applicable)	X

RELATED CREDIT TIPS

WE Prerequisite Building-Level Water Metering. Metering of potable water usage allows facilities management staff to monitor changes as efficiency measures are implemented.

WE Credit Water Metering. Submetering of water-using systems provides water efficiency performance data so that facilities operators can optimize water consumption.

CHANGES FROM LEED 2009

A second option has been added for metered water use.

REFERENCED STANDARDS

The Energy Policy Act (EPAct) of 1992 and as amended: eere.energy.gov/femp/regulations/epact1992.html

EPAct 2005: eere.energy.gov/femp/regulations/epact2005.html

International Association of Plumbing and Mechanical Officials Publication IAPMO / ANSI UPC 1-2006, Uniform Plumbing Code 2006, Section 402.0, Water-Conserving Fixtures and Fittings: iapmo.org

International Code Council, International Plumbing Code 2006, Section 604, Design of Building Water Distribution System: iccsafe.org

ENERGY STAR: energystar.gov

Consortium for Energy Efficiency: cee1.org

WaterSense: epa.gov/watersense

IgCC/ASHRAE 189.1 – cooling tower and evaporative condenser requirements: ashrae.org/resources--publications/bookstore/standard-189-1

EXEMPLARY PERFORMANCE

One exemplary performance point is available for achieving either a minimum reduction of 35% using Option 1 or a minimum reduction of 25% using Option 2.

DEFINITIONS

None.

WATER EFFICIENCY CREDIT

Cooling Tower Water Use

This credit applies to:

Existing Buildings (2–3 points)
Schools (2–3 points)
Retail (2–3 points)
Data Centers (2–4 points)
Hospitality (2–3 points)
Warehouses and Distribution Centers (2–3 points)

INTENT

To conserve water used for cooling tower makeup while controlling microbes, corrosion, and scale in the condenser water system.

REQUIREMENTS

ESTABLISHMENT E

For cooling towers and evaporative condensers, conduct a potable water analysis within five years of submission for certification, measuring at least the five control parameters listed in Table 1.

TABLE 1. Maximum concentrations for parameters in condenser water

Parameter	Maximum level
Ca (as $CaCO_3$)	1,000 ppm
Total alkalinity	1,000 ppm
SiO_2	100 ppm
Cl^-	250 ppm
Conductivity	2000 μS/cm

ppm = parts per million
μS/cm = micro siemens per centimeter

Calculate the number of cooling tower cycles by dividing the maximum allowed concentration level of each parameter by the actual concentration level of each parameter found in the potable makeup water. Limit cooling tower cycles to avoid exceeding maximum values for any of these parameters.

TABLE 2. Points for cooling tower cycles		
Cooling tower cycles	**Points (except Data Centers)**	**Points (Data Centers)**
Maximum number of cycles achieved without exceeding any filtration levels or affecting operation of condenser water system (up to maximum of 10 cycles)	2	2
Achieve a minimum 10 cycles by increasing the level of treatment in condenser or make-up water **OR** Meet the minimum number of cycles to earn 1 point and use a minimum 20% recycled nonpotable water	3	4

PERFORMANCE P

None.

BEHIND THE INTENT

Refrigeration systems remove heat, usually from air, to cool interior building spaces. This heat is expelled into either the atmosphere or another medium. A cooling tower or evaporative condenser removes heat in part by evaporating water; as the water absorbs heat, it changes from a liquid to a vapor. As the water evaporates, however, dissolved solids become more concentrated in the remaining water and eventually begin to deposit scale on cooling tower or evaporative condenser elements, making such systems less efficient. To prevent buildup of deposits, cooling tower and evaporative condenser systems remove a portion of the water through a process called blowdown. Makeup water is then added to replace evaporative losses and blowdown volume. Cooling towers can therefore account for large portions of a building's total water use.

To significantly reduce makeup water inputs, it is important to achieve target cycles of concentration (see *Further Explanation, Cycles of Concentration*). Cooling tower or evaporative condenser water efficiency is measured in the number of recirculation cycles before water must be removed by blowdown.

Increasing the number of cycles can save thousands of gallons of potable water during a building's peak cooling periods. Chemically analyzing makeup water allows for calculation of optimal cycles. Cycles can also be increased by treating water to remove or sequester dissolved solids rather than relying only on blowdown and input of fresh makeup water.

STEP-BY-STEP GUIDANCE

Only projects served by cooling towers or evaporative condensers are eligible for this credit.

STEP 1. OBTAIN WATER ANALYSIS E

Whether the project uses 100% potable water or 100% nonpotable water for cooling, the first step is to obtain a chemical analysis.

- Engage a water treatment professional to perform the analysis. If a potable water analysis has already been completed, it must be no more than five years old.
- At a minimum, the analysis must measure the concentration parameters identified in the credit requirements. Highlight each parameter in the documentation.
- Describe the analysis. The narrative must identify the source of the makeup water and the process for analysis.

STEP 2. CALCULATE CYCLES OF CONCENTRATION E

Determine how many times the cooling tower or evaporative condenser water can circulate through the system without creating performance or operational problems by using Equation 1, based on the maximum concentrations indicated in the credit requirements.

EQUATION 1. Cycles of concentration

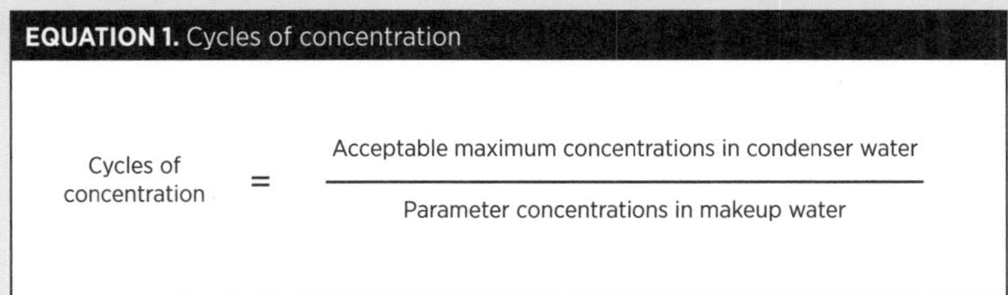

$$\text{Cycles of concentration} = \frac{\text{Acceptable maximum concentrations in condenser water}}{\text{Parameter concentrations in makeup water}}$$

STEP 3. IDENTIFY LIMITING FACTOR E

Identify which concentration parameter has the fewest calculated cycles before it exceeds the maximum concentration. That parameter's number of cycles, the limiting factor, will determine the maximum number of cycles for the cooling tower or evaporative condenser.

STEP 4. SET COOLING TOWER OR EVAPORATIVE CONDENSER CYCLES E

Adjust the cooling tower or evaporative condenser settings for the maximum number of cycles without exceeding concentration levels or affecting condenser operation.

STEP 5. INCREASE SYSTEM PERFORMANCE E

For 1 additional point, use further treatment, filtration, or nonpotable water to increase the number of cycles.

- Evaluate whether greater potable water efficiency could be achieved by treating makeup water to reduce or sequester some of the dissolved solids.
- Nonpotable water derived from the site can offset a portion of the potable water used for makeup (see *Further Explanation, Selecting Nonpotable Sources*).

STEP 6. CONFIRM SYSTEM PERFORMANCE P

Verify that the cooling tower or evaporative condenser settings are consistent with the number of cooling tower or evaporative condenser cycles. Prepare a narrative detailing the settings and other performance characteristics.

FURTHER EXPLANATION

CALCULATIONS

See calculations in *Step-by-Step Guidance*.

CYCLES OF CONCENTRATION

Cycles of concentration are the number of times that a volume of water can circulate through a cooling tower system before dissolved minerals become so concentrated (as water is lost to evaporation) that they precipitate and cause scaling—deposits that reduce the efficiency of the cooling system. To dilute the concentration of minerals, some water must be removed (blowdown) and replaced with fresh makeup water, or the water must be chemically treated, or both. The number of times water can cycle through the system before scaling becomes a problem depends on the amount of total dissolved solids (TDS) in the original water and the temperature of the water and heat exchange surfaces. Low-temperature water with low initial TDS levels can be circulated through more cycles than very hot, mineral-laden ("hard") water.

More technically, a cycle of concentration is defined as the ratio of TDS levels in makeup water to TDS levels in water removed through blowdown, evaporative loss, and drift (windage). A higher number of cycles indicates better water efficiency because less makeup water is required.

Building maintenance staff can monitor cycles of concentration by comparing the amount of soluble chloride ions (measured in parts per million, ppm) in makeup water with that in the recirculating water. A test kit is typically available through the cooling tower or evaporative condenser manufacturer or the service contractor responsible for maintaining makeup water chemistry. The minimum number of cycles would be a once-through system that runs the makeup water through the heat exchange media once, without recirculating it. For obvious reasons, this wasteful use of water is discouraged. Yet as cycles increase, the amount of TDS also increases, resulting in potential fouling of the system. Optimizing the number of cycles avoids both of these scenarios.

SELECTING NONPOTABLE SOURCES

When selecting a nonpotable source, consider the factors that affect makeup water quality. Acceptable sources should have relatively low levels of dissolved solids. Stormwater runoff from the ground surface or graywater may contain contaminants, including dissolved chlorides that may need treatment. In contrast, air-conditioning condensate and rainwater collected from building roofs have relatively low mineral content.

Good nonpotable water sources include the following:

- Air-conditioner condensate
- Rainwater
- Steam system condensate
- Food steamer discharge water
- Fire pump test water
- Ice machine condensate

Other factors to consider are ease of transport to the cooling tower and required volume of makeup water.

EXAMPLE

Analysis of the makeup water for a cooling tower or evaporative condenser at an office building reveals the following concentrations:

TABLE 3. Analysis of makeup water

Parameter	Maximum allowable concentrations	Makeup water concentrations
Calcium (as $CaCO_3$)	1,000 ppm	100 ppm
Alkalinity	1,000 ppm	200 ppm
SiO_2	100 ppm	20 ppm
Chloride	250 ppm	50 ppm
Conductivity	2,000 μS/cm	300 μS/cm

The cycles of concentration based on each of these parameters are as follows:

TABLE 4. Cycles of concentration

$CaCO_3$: 1,000 / 100 = 10 cycles
Alkalinity: 1,000 / 200 = 5 cycles
SiO_2: 100 / 20 = 5 cycles
Chloride: 250 / 50 = 5 cycles
Conductivity: 2,000 / 300 = 6.7 cycles

The lowest number—five cycles—is therefore the maximum cycles of concentration for this makeup water.

CAMPUS

Group Approach

All buildings in the group project may be documented as one.

Campus Approach

Eligible.

REQUIRED DOCUMENTATION

	Documentation	2 points	3 points (4 points for Data Centers)
E	Potable water analysis results	X	X
E	Potable water analysis narrative	X	X
E	Cycles of concentration calculations	X	X
E	Nonpotable water calculations		X
E	Water treatment calculations		X
P	System performance narrative	X	X

RELATED CREDIT TIPS

WE Prerequisite Indoor Water Use Reduction. The related prerequisite requires makeup meters, conductivity controllers and overflow alarms, and efficient drift eliminators that reduce drift to a maximum of 0.002% of recirculated water volume for counterflow towers, 0.005% of recirculated water flow for cross-flow towers. These performance and tracking measures allow for better ongoing maintenance of efficient cooling tower or evaporative condenser systems.

WE Credit Water Metering. Subsystem meters to measure cooling tower or evaporative condenser makeup water can assist in water management and can help optimize cycles of concentration.

CHANGES FROM LEED 2009

The cooling tower credit structure has been modified to highlight appropriate cycling based on the concentrations of dissolved solids on the project site.

REFERENCED STANDARDS

None.

EXEMPLARY PERFORMANCE

Not available.

DEFINITIONS

blowdown the removal of makeup water from a cooling tower or evaporative condenser recirculation system to reduce concentrations of dissolved solids

makeup water water that is fed into a cooling tower system or evaporative condenser to replace water lost through evaporation, drift, bleed-off, or other causes

WATER EFFICIENCY CREDIT

Water Metering

This credit applies to:

Existing Buildings (1–2 points)
Schools (1–2 points)
Retail (1–2 points)
Data Centers (1–2 points)
Hospitality (1–2 points)
Warehouses and Distribution Centers (1–2 points)

INTENT

To support water management and identify opportunities for additional water savings by tracking water consumption.

REQUIREMENTS

ESTABLISHMENT E

Establish permanently installed meters; 1 point for two water subsystems, 2 points for four or more water subsystems:

- **Irrigation.** Meter water systems serving at least 80% of the irrigated landscaped area. Calculate the percentage of irrigated landscape area as the total metered irrigated landscape area divided by the total irrigated landscape area. Landscape areas fully covered with xeriscaping or native vegetation that requires no routine irrigation may be excluded from the calculation.
- **Indoor plumbing fixtures and fittings.** Meter water systems serving at least 80% of the indoor plumbing fixtures and fittings listed in WE Prerequisite Indoor Water-Use Reduction, either directly or by deducting all other measured water use from the measured total water consumption of the building and grounds.
- **Cooling towers.** Meter replacement water use of all cooling towers serving the facility.
- **Domestic hot water.** Meter water use of at least 80% of the installed domestic hot water heating capacity (including both tanks and on-demand heaters).
- **Reclaimed water.** Meter reclaimed water, regardless of rate. A reclaimed water system with a makeup water connection must also be metered so that the true reclaimed water component can be determined.
- **Other process water.** Meter at least 80% of expected daily water consumption for process end uses, such as humidifiers, dishwashers, clothes washers, and pools.

PERFORMANCE P

All meters, including whole-building meters, must be recorded at least weekly and used in a regular analysis of time trends.

Meters must be calibrated within the manufacturer's recommended interval if the building owner, management organization, or tenant owns the meter. Meters owned by third parties (e.g., utilities or governments) are exempt.

Commit to sharing with USGBC the resulting water usage data for a five-year period beginning on the date the project accepts LEED certification or typical occupancy, whichever comes first.

BEHIND THE INTENT

Metering water usage by subsystem helps facilities managers better gauge a building's water efficiency. Submetering the major building water systems provides a way to formulate independent system baselines, track usage against those baselines, isolate and identify potential sources of waste, and take corrective action. Moreover, submetering helps track periodic changes in water usage and provides the data necessary to calculate opportunities for water savings at a systemwide level.

This credit expands on Prerequisite Building-Level Water Metering, which requires a main water meter to measure the total quantity of water entering the building.

STEP-BY-STEP GUIDANCE

STEP 1. IDENTIFY CANDIDATE SYSTEMS FOR SUBMETERING

Identify all systems serving the project building and grounds. These subsystems may include irrigation, indoor plumbing fixtures, domestic hot water, process water, reclaimed water, and boiler water. Cooling tower submeters are addressed separately, under WE Prerequisite Indoor Water Use Reduction.

- Consider those subsystems that consume the most water, are the most expensive to operate, or most closely align with the goals of the building management. A variety of factors will affect the decision.
- Consider not only the number, types, and sizes of meters but also the effort required to take meter readings.
- The cost of a wet meter (a meter installed in the pipe) increases with pipe size; many external, clamp-on meters are adaptable to a range of pipe sizes. Clamp-on meters are more costly on small-diameter pipes, but initial cost differences are reduced for larger pipes.
- The higher cost of a larger meter may be offset by reduced operations and maintenance costs if facilities staff will be making manual readings.
- Automatic data logging also adds to initial cost, but it may be cost-effective if it reduces the effort of obtaining and recording readings.

STEP 2. DETERMINE SCOPE OF SUBMETERING

Identify which subsystems are most appropriate to submeter based on the project objectives.

- As noted in WE Prerequisite Building-Level Water Metering, consider location and accessibility when placing submeters, particularly for taking manual readings.
- If the project team is claiming credit for irrigation, indoor plumbing fixtures, domestic hot water, or other process water submeters, at least 80% of water distribution must be submetered. If 100% of the water used by a subsystem is metered, no calculation is necessary.
- Determine how much of the total water system will be submetered by comparing the submetered portions with total landscape area, number of indoor fixtures, domestic water heating units, or process use quantities, as follows:

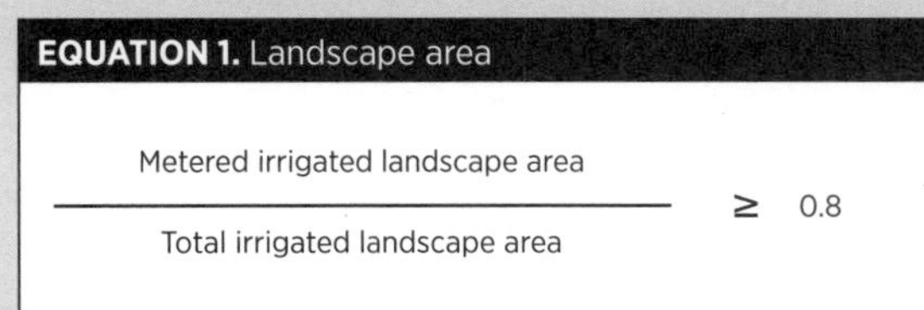

EQUATION 1. Landscape area

$$\frac{\text{Metered irrigated landscape area}}{\text{Total irrigated landscape area}} \geq 0.8$$

Unirrigated landscape areas should not be included in either the numerator or denominator of this equation.

EQUATION 2. Fixtures

$$\frac{\text{Number of metered indoor fixtures and fittings}}{\text{Total number of indoor fixtures}} \geq 0.8$$

EQUATION 3. Domestic hot water

$$\frac{\text{Heating capacity of metered domestic water heating units}}{\text{Total heating capacity of all domestic water heating units}} \geq 0.8$$

EQUATION 4. Other process water

$$\frac{\text{Daily metered gallons (or liters) for process-type end uses}}{\text{Total expected daily gallons (or liters) for process-type end uses}} \geq 0.8$$

- If the team is using reclaimed water for irrigation, 100% of this water must be submetered. The meter for reclaimed water may also be the same meter that is counted for irrigation, fixtures, or process water. If reclaimed water is used in multiple applications in the project (e.g., for irrigation, flush fixtures, or process water), then all reclaimed water use must be metered; the team may report data from multiple submeters, as applicable.
- Discuss water efficiency goals with the building operations and maintenance team to ensure that the metered systems reflect needs.

STEP 3. SELECT METERING EQUIPMENT, AS REQUIRED E

Choose a submeter type if no existing meters are present or if existing meters need replacing.

- Submeters may be manually read or connected to a building information system. The meters may be equipped with data logging capability independent of a building information system.
- If meters are to be read manually, consider digital indicators, which may reduce errors in recording.
- Wet meters will likely be the most cost-effective approach. However, clamp-on meters may be simpler to install.

Prepare a narrative describing the subsystems metered, including the location and model of each installed submeter.

STEP 4. COLLECT METER DATA P

Collect meter data for each subsystem at least weekly during the performance period.

- Calibrate meters in accordance with the manufacturer's recommendation. If the manufacturer does not recommend recalibration within 10 years of installation, recalibrate or replace meters every 10 years.
- Compile data into monthly and annual summaries for each subsystem. Describe the method and process for meter reading in the summaries and indicate the frequency of readings.
- Although data collection is only required on a weekly basis, more frequent (daily or continuous) recording allows project teams to quickly identify leaks and other operational problems and provides valuable feedback on occupants' usage.

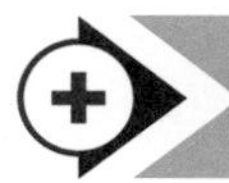

FURTHER EXPLANATION

CALCULATIONS

See calculations in *Step-by-Step Guidance*.

PROJECT TYPE VARIATIONS

Multifamily

Metering in residential units may be included or excluded, but should be done uniformly. Multifamily projects still need to meter full subsystems (for common areas or the whole building) to earn credit.

Additions or Renovations

For additions to existing buildings, the submetered systems must include both the addition and the original building.

In projects where part of the building is being renovated, submeters must include the entire subsystem being affected, regardless of whether that subsystem is in the renovated or original part of the building. (For example, a project with a new cooling tower and new cooling tower submeter can earn the credit even if the original building has not been altered.) However, a project that has renovated and submetered 30% of the building's plumbing fixtures cannot earn credit unless an additional 50% of fixtures can also be submetered (for a total of 80% of total fixtures).

CAMPUS

Group Approach

Submit separate documentation for each building. Each building in the group must have an individual whole-building water meter. Each individual building in the group must meet the credit requirements for submetering of indoor plumbing fixtures and fittings, domestic hot water, and other process water. All buildings in the group can be served the same submeter for irrigation systems, boilers, and reclaimed water, provided all the water used by the group is captured.

Campus Approach

Ineligible. Each LEED project may pursue the credit individually.

REQUIRED DOCUMENTATION

	Documentation	All projects
E	Water metering strategy narrative	X
E	Weekly meter log	X
P	Monthly and annual summaries of meter data	X

RELATED CREDIT TIPS

WE Credit Outdoor Water Use Reduction. If a meter is installed to pursue Option 3 of the related credit, the data can be used for this credit.

WE Credit Indoor Water Use Reduction. If a meter is installed to pursue Option 2 of the related credit, the data can be used for this credit.

CHANGES FROM LEED 2009

Option 1, Whole Building Metering, from LEED 2009 has been moved to the prerequisite level in version 4. The credit is now comparable to Option 2, Submetering, in LEED 2009.

REFERENCED STANDARDS

None.

EXEMPLARY PERFORMANCE

Not available.

DEFINITIONS

external meter a device installed on the outside of a water pipe to record the volume of water passing through it. Also known as a clamp-on meter.

Energy and Atmosphere (EA)

OVERVIEW

The Energy and Atmosphere (EA) category approaches energy from a holistic perspective, addressing energy use reduction, energy-efficient design strategies, and renewable energy sources.

The current worldwide mix of energy resources is weighted heavily toward oil, coal, and natural gas.[1] In addition to emitting greenhouse gases, these resources are nonrenewable: their quantities are limited or they cannot be replaced as fast as they are consumed.[2] Though estimates regarding the remaining quantity of these resources vary, it is clear that the current reliance on nonrenewable energy sources is not sustainable and involves increasingly destructive extraction processes, uncertain supplies, escalating market prices, and national security vulnerability. Accounting for approximately 40% of the total energy used today,[3] buildings are significant contributors to these problems.

A well-run facility is not only more energy efficient but also more healthful and comfortable for its occupants. In existing buildings, the focus is on improving building operations. Through the auditing or commissioning process, inefficiencies and opportunities for improvement are identified and prioritized, generally according to cost and benefit. The many no- and low-cost items often uncovered during this process can generate savings and efficiencies without significant capital investment. In an operationally effective and efficient building, the staff understands what systems are installed and how they function. Metering and ongoing commissioning allow staff to track energy use and identify issues on a consistent basis. Staff must have training, both initially and on a continuing basis, so that they can learn new methods for optimizing system performance.

Existing building commissioning is generally a set of discrete tasks that include monitoring system performance, executing functional tests, and verifying equipment operation. The timeline of these activities can extend anywhere from six to 18 months, depending on staff time, seasonal variations, and identified issues. Ongoing commissioning organizes those tasks into a repeating cycle of 24 months or less over the lifetime of the building. Some aspects of monitoring-based commissioning, including submetering, point trending, and energy analysis, can be incorporated into an ongoing commissioning program to help improve the process and identify issues in real time.

1. *iea.org/publications/freepublications/publication/kwes.pdf*
2. *cnx.org/content/m16730/latest/*
3. *unep.org/sbci/pdfs/SBCI-BCCSummary.pdf*

The commissioning process is focused on making the project building run as efficiently and use as little energy as possible; supplying that remaining energy use from renewables on the project site or purchased green power goes a step beyond. Nonfossil fuel energy helps balance the demand on traditional sources and reduce greenhouse gas emissions.

The EA category recognizes that the reduction of fossil fuel use extends far beyond the walls of the building. Projects can contribute to increasing the electricity grid's efficiency by enrolling in a demand response program. Demand response allows utilities to call on buildings to decrease their electricity use during peak times, reducing the strain on the grid and the need to operate more power plants, thus potentially avoiding the costs of constructing new plants. Permanent peak loading shifting addresses many of the same issues as demand response but results in demand reduction on a continuous basis, rather than just when an event is called.

The American Physical Society has found that if current and emerging cost-effective energy efficiency measures are employed in new buildings and in existing buildings as their heating, cooling, lighting, and other equipment is replaced, the growth in energy demand by the building sector could fall from a projected 30% increase to zero between now and 2030.[4] The EA section supports the goal of reduced energy demand through credits related to reducing usage, designing for efficiency, and supplementing the energy supply with renewables.

4. *Energy Future: Think Efficiency, Chapter 3, Buildings* (American Physical Society, September 2008), *aps.org/energyefficiencyreport/report/energy-bldgs.pdf* (accessed September 13, 2012).

ENERGY AND ATMOSPHERE PREREQUISITE

Energy Efficiency Best Management Practices

This prerequisite applies to:

Existing Buildings
Schools
Retail
Data Centers
Hospitality
Warehouses and Distribution Centers

INTENT

To promote continuity of information to ensure that energy-efficient operating strategies are maintained and provide a foundation for training and system analysis.

REQUIREMENTS

ESTABLISHMENT E

EXISTING BUILDINGS, SCHOOLS, RETAIL, HOSPITALITY, WAREHOUSES AND DISTRIBUTION CENTERS

Conduct an energy audit that meets both the requirements of the ASHRAE preliminary energy use analysis and an ASHRAE Level 1 walk-through assessment identified in the ASHRAE Procedures for Commercial Building Energy Audits or equivalent.

Prepare and maintain a current facilities requirements and operations and maintenance plan that contains the information necessary to operate the building efficiently. The plan must include the following:

- a current sequence of operations for the building;
- the building occupancy schedule;
- equipment run-time schedules;
- setpoints for all HVAC equipment;
- setpoints for lighting levels throughout the building;
- minimum outside air requirements;
- any changes in schedules or setpoints for different seasons, days of the week, and times of day;
- a systems narrative describing the mechanical and electrical systems and equipment in the building; and
- a preventive maintenance plan for building equipment described in the systems narrative.

DATA CENTERS

Use the U.S. Department of Energy's DC PRO Profiling Tool to perform a preliminary assessment of energy consumption in data center spaces for critical systems.

PERFORMANCE P

None.

BEHIND THE INTENT

This prerequisite provides a foundation for establishing energy-efficient operating strategies and training staff in system maintenance, monitoring, and evaluation over the life of the building. By developing an operations and maintenance plan and updating the current facility requirements, operators can see how the building's current use relates to its original design and analyze actual and intended operations. These two documents are intended to be living records of building systems, operations, and maintenance procedures. Regularly recording any changes in systems, operation, and usage ensures that knowledge can be easily passed from operator to operator and is also available to support future upgrades, audits, or commissioning activities.

The prerequisite requires an energy audit that complies with the standards outlined in the ASHRAE Procedures for Commercial Building Energy Audits. An energy auditor gathers energy consumption data for the entire building so that facilities teams can develop performance indicators and identify no-cost and low-cost energy conservation measures to improve overall energy performance.

STEP-BY-STEP GUIDANCE

STEP 1. DOCUMENT CURRENT FACILITY REQUIREMENTS AND OPERATIONS AND MAINTENANCE PLANS E

Review current facility requirements (CFR) and available operations and maintenance (O&M) plans and manuals and determine the current operations for the facility.

- Documenting, updating, and confirming the operations will create an overall facility building operating plan (see *Further Explanation, Example 1*).
- Current plans may include functional space requirements, operational space requirements, building plans, system narratives, sequences of operations, and preventive maintenance activities (see *Further Explanation, Current Facility Requirements and O&M Plans* and *Example 2*).

STEP 2. REVIEW ASHRAE PROCEDURES FOR COMMERCIAL BUILDING ENERGY AUDITS E

Read the ASHRAE procedures to prepare for a preliminary energy use analysis and an ASHRAE Level 1 walk-through assessment.

STEP 3. IDENTIFY THE ASHRAE LEVEL 1 ENERGY AUDIT TEAM E

Determine whether the ASHRAE Level 1 energy audit will be conducted by in-house staff or by a third-party auditor (see *Further Explanation, In-House versus Third-Party Audit*).

The energy audit team is likely to have the following members:

- Owner
- General manager or property manager
- Building engineering staff
- Energy auditor
- Controls contractor (if necessary)

Optional team members include mechanical, electrical, and plumbing service providers, plus a testing and balancing contractor and other maintenance staff.

STEP 4. CREATE IMPLEMENTATION PLAN FOR ENERGY AUDIT E

Determine the schedule for the energy audit, including the preliminary energy use analysis and the walk-through assessment, and outline the activities necessary to complete the process (see *Further Explanation, ASHRAE Energy Audit and Walk-Through Assessment*). The plan should include these major activities:

- On-site survey of the building to observe any special problems or needs and the functions of each space
- Review of the current CFR and O&M plans

STEP 5. PERFORM ASHRAE ENERGY USE ANALYSIS E

Using the implementation plan and the expertise of the audit team, complete a preliminary energy use analysis to establish a baseline for building performance (see *Further Explanation, Energy Use Analysis*). Follow the preliminary energy use analysis section of the ASHRAE Procedures for Commercial Building Energy Audits to complete this analysis.

- Collect at least one but ideally three years of utility bills.
- Examine average and peak utility costs.
- Develop an energy cost index, energy demand index, and energy use index for each fuel or demand type, and their combined total, including all fuel types and district energy systems, if applicable (see *Further Explanation, Project Type Modifications*).

STEP 6. PERFORM ASHRAE LEVEL 1 WALK-THROUGH ASSESSMENT E

Use the ASHRAE Procedures for Commercial Building Energy Audits to conduct the audit. This standard provides guidance on preparing, conducting, and documenting an ASHRAE Level 1 energy audit. The procedures and forms are standardized for use in a variety of building types but can be tailored to suit particular projects.

Identify no- and low-cost improvement opportunities that will improve operations and save energy (see *Further Explanation, No-Cost and Low-Cost Measures*).

STEP 7. PREPARE ASHRAE LEVEL 1 REPORT E

Using the information from the ASHRAE Level 1 energy audit, write a report that describes the current operational parameters and systems, as well as the findings of the analysis. The report must include the following information, at minimum:

- Comparison of project building with similar building types
- Current energy cost index, energy demand index, energy use index, and reduction goals
- Energy use breakdown by major system types or end uses
- Financial assessment (e.g., return on investment, payback) and maintenance implications of no-cost and low-cost improvement opportunities.

STEP 8. MODIFY BUILDING PLANS AS NECESSARY E

Revisit the CFR and O&M plans and document any changes that were identified during the energy audit so that the building's operating documents are accurate and current.

FURTHER EXPLANATION

CURRENT FACILITY REQUIREMENTS AND OPERATIONS AND MAINTENANCE PLANS

Building operators who perform daily operational and preventive maintenance procedures know what systems are installed in their buildings. However, in many buildings, the CFR and O&M plans are either out-of-date or not formalized. Project teams must create or maintain the occupancy schedule and system operations information in standard operating procedures and basic building documentation.

For current facility requirements, prepare and/or maintain the following documents and information:

- Functional space requirements
    - Building functions by space type
    - Occupancy schedules (by space type as necessary)
    - Cleaning schedules
- Operational space requirements
    - Required temperature setpoints for occupied spaces
    - Required temperature setpoints for process spaces
    - Lighting levels
    - Humidity setpoints (if applicable)

- Building drawings, where available
  - As-built drawings
  - Tenant drawings
  - Mechanical schedule
  - Electrical schedule
  - Plumbing schedule

For operations and maintenance plans, maintain the following documents and information:

- **Systems narrative.** This summary of building systems and equipment provides a high-level understanding of the mechanical, electrical, plumbing, and controls design and status of equipment. Include information about system-specific setpoints, flows, and capacities. This will help the energy auditor complete the required audit and also help verify outside airflow rates for EQ Prerequisite Minimum Indoor Air Quality.
- **Description of building systems.** Include modifications that have been made since the original building design and describe the current state of systems. Cover all major building systems and associated controls, including the following:
  - HVAC
  - Electrical (power and exterior/interior lighting plumbing
  - Building automation system (BAS)
  - Process equipment
  - Heating and cooling systems for process equipment
  - Supplemental heating and cooling systems
- **Building operating plan.** This document summarizes the intended operation of each system described in the systems narrative. The plan must address schedules, the mode of operation, and the desired indoor conditions, such as temperature and humidity setpoints for each schedule or mode. The plan must account for any differences in needs or desired conditions for different portions of the project building, as well as any seasonal variations in operations. Include the following items in the plan. All the monitored space conditions used to control the base systems, such as the following:
  - Building occupancy schedule
  - Equipment run-time schedule
  - Setpoints for HVAC and lighting
  - Unoccupied setpoints
  - Vacant-space setpoints
  - Minimum outside air requirements
  - Temperature requirements
  - Humidity requirements
  - CO_2 level requirements
  - Seasonal, day of week, and time of day differences

The time-of-day schedules for each system must address each of the eight day types: Monday through Sunday plus holidays and must account for seasonal variations, where applicable. The mode of operation must address each system when it is running (e.g., occupied versus unoccupied, day versus night). For the desired indoor conditions, note differences in setpoints and schedules for spaces with special operating conditions, including vacant spaces.

- **Sequences of operations.** Also known as the controls sequences, these are the prescribed processes by which building systems respond to external conditions (e.g., temperature, humidity) and commands (e.g., on, off, modulate). These sequences are typically available in buildings with building automation systems and may be documented in one or more of the following formats:
  - Narrative and/or controls drawings created by the original design engineer
  - Narrative and/or controls drawings created by the current building controls contractor
  - Code contained in the BAS programming

- **Preventive maintenance plan.** This is a schedule of preventive maintenance activities for all building systems and equipment described in the systems narrative. The plan must provide detail regarding the tasks associated with each activity. It may also list responsible parties and discuss the following:
  - Daily, weekly, monthly, quarterly, and annual tasks, based on manufacturers' specifications, vendor requirements, industry knowledge, or an automated work order system
  - Commonly overlooked systems like tenant lighting, domestic hot water, and building automation systems
  - Building systems that are maintained by a third party and the current status of the maintenance contracts

IN-HOUSE VERSUS THIRD-PARTY AUDIT

A Level 1 energy audit is commonly performed by a qualified third-party consultant; however, knowledgeable in-house staff can also conduct the audit. Determine whether staff have the interest, knowledge, and time to complete the audit. If an auditor will be used, ask for work samples from similar project types and determine whether his or her experience meets the goals and intent of the energy audit team. Table 1 lists benefits and drawbacks for each approach.

If the analysis will be performed in-house, closely review the ASHRAE Procedures for Commercial Building Energy Audits to ensure that staff collects the correct data during the building walk-through. The checklists in this document guide users through the auditing process but do not provide a complete ASHRAE Level 1 analysis report.

TABLE 1. In-house staff versus third-party auditor

	Benefits	Drawbacks
In-house staff	• Is aware of age and condition of building equipment • Understands operation of building systems • Knows building operational issues • Is likely less expensive	• May be distracted from normal duties and responsibilities • May lack ability to objectively and critically review system operations • May not have proper measurement and assessment tools for required energy and cost analysis • May lack experience with ASHRAE Level 1 energy audits
Third-party auditor	• Should have proven experience with completing ASHRAE Level 1 energy audits • Can objectively and critically review system operations • May have broader range of experience in reviewing system operation and making energy conservation measure recommendations • Has proper measurement and assessment tools for required energy and cost analysis	• Is likely more expensive than in-house staff • Will require some in-house staff time for walk-through and survey • Does not have experience with project building

Regardless of who performs the energy audit, interview building operators before the audit to gain insights that management staff or owners may not have. The role of the energy auditor is to act as an owner's advocate and reduce energy consumption. Engaging with building engineering staff is an important part of meeting these objectives.

Once the audit is complete, discuss the report's details with the operating staff, particularly if the audit was conducted by a third party auditor who would not necessarily know the details of the building. Discussing the audit findings with building operating staff helps ensure that building systems and operations are adequately and accurately assessed.

ASHRAE LEVEL 1 ENERGY AUDIT AND WALK-THROUGH ASSESSMENT

The ASHRAE Level 1 energy audit involves examining utility records and mechanical, electrical (including lighting), and plumbing systems to identify opportunities to reduce building energy consumption and operating costs. It also involves evaluating a building's energy performance and energy consumption by analyzing building energy bills and conducting a brief visual survey.

Understanding and visually inspecting the facility by undertaking a walk-through is important to gaining a full understanding of the property and what operational items need to be addressed. In conjunction with the walk-through, the team should review facility design, operations, and function (or document these items as part of the building operating conditions or basis of operation and systems narrative) and take note of the following:

- Building age
- Building upgrades
- Space usage types and locations
- Age and type of HVAC equipment, electrical, and plumbing systems
- Quantity and size of HVAC equipment, electrical, and plumbing systems
- Nontypical HVAC, electrical, and plumbing systems
- Control or automation system age and functionality
- Differences between the HVAC, electrical, and occupancy schedules
- Location of HVAC equipment, electrical, and plumbing systems

The final outcome of the walk-through is a list of improvement measures to be implemented. Simply by compiling the basic building information and developing the O&M plans, teams may discover many no- and low-cost opportunities. These should be included in the improvement opportunities list.

Although it is not required for prerequisite documentation, this list of potential capital improvements can be analyzed to estimate potential costs and savings. This step, if applicable, may require the assistance of an energy engineer or local utility provider (see EA Credit Existing Building Commissioning—Analysis). The referenced document also provides guidance.

Completing the audit early in the LEED project schedule is recommended, to allow enough time for implementing any energy improvements and capturing their energy savings. Ideally, at least 12 months of improved energy consumption data should be collected to determine the energy savings associated with the improvements.

Take photos during the walk-through to document current conditions and opportunities for upgrades to mechanical equipment. Including these photos in the audit report may help make the case to building owners and operators to implement improvements. See EA Credit Existing Building Commissioning—Implementation.

Research opportunities for rebates or incentives to perform energy audits at the project building. Power utilities often offer rebate programs for companies that improve energy efficiency. However, the reports associated with these types of audits may not meet the minimum documentation requirements outlined in this prerequisite.

If an ASHRAE Level 1 audit has been conducted within the past five years, there is no need to repeat the procedure during the performance period. Submit an updated audit report that describes any significant changes in operating procedures or building systems, as well as any new energy conservation measures observed during the walk-through.

ENERGY USE ANALYSIS

Energy use analysis, an important step in preparing for the energy audit, will affect the validity of the audit results. The energy auditor should manage this process and obtain information and details from the audit team.

If the building is eligible for ENERGY STAR, this program's Portfolio Manager can be used to compare it with similar buildings. ENERGY STAR scores buildings on an energy efficiency scale of 1 to 100. See EA Prerequisite Minimum Energy Performance for more information on using the Portfolio Manager tool.

If the project building is not ENERGY STAR eligible because of its space type, use an alternative comparison for the required assessment. The Commercial Buildings Energy Consumption Survey (CBECS) and Labs21 can be used where applicable.

Establish target indices related to energy and cost reduction goals with the owner and operating staff. These goals can be used in conjunction with the recommendations that come from the audit process. The energy use intensity (EUI) tool of ENERGY STAR's Portfolio Manager can help teams establish target goals, regardless of the project building's ENERGY STAR eligibility.

Determine the approximate breakdown of energy use for major end-use categories. This breakdown must include all fuel sources. Examples of common end-use categories include heating, cooling, ventilation, lighting, plug loads, and miscellaneous sources; tailor the list to the project building and its systems.

Use engineering calculations, installed submeters, and spot submetering to determine the breakdown. Teams can also use CBECS values for a typical breakdown according to space types, if building-specific information cannot be obtained. The breakdown provides a direction for energy conservation recommendations. EA Credit Existing Building Commissioning—Analysis requires a more precise breakdown of energy use that may be used to document compliance with this prerequisite.

EXAMPLES

Example 1. Example building operating plan

TABLE 2. Sample building operating plan

Requirements	Typical for building	Typical building AHUs	Building lobby	Building atrium	Conference rooms	Computer, data rooms	Notes
Air temperature requirements for cooling and heating seasons							
Humidity							
Dehumidification							
Pressure relationship							
Filtration							
Ventilation							
Outside air							
Sound and noise level							
Weekly operating hours (occupied)							
Weekend schedule							
Holiday schedule							
Process and office equipment status during evening and night hours							
Process and office equipment status during holiday hours							
Process and office equipment status during scheduled maintenance shutdowns							
Cleaning schedule							
Lighting levels							
Other: parking garage lighting							

Example 2. Sequence of operations

Temperature-Controlled Exhaust Fan

System Description

- Individual constant-volume fan

- Normally closed, spring return, exhaust air motorized damper
- Electronic actuator with travel switch
- Wall-mount temperature sensor

System Setpoints

- Space temperature set point: 75°F [23.9°C] (adjustable)
- Alarm generation: 5°F [2.8°C] above setpoint (adjustable)

Sequence of Operation

- Fan start-stop. Fan shall be cycled on and off by BAS to maintain space temperature setpoint.
- Start. Motorized damper shall open when space temperature rises 1°F [0.5°C] (adjustable) above space temperature setpoint. Fan shall start when damper travel switch reaches 50% open.
- Stop. Stop fan when space temperature drops 2°F [1.1°C] (adjustable) below setpoint. Close motorized damper.

Alarms

- Monitor space temperature and generate alarm when temperature is 5°F [3°C] (adjustable) above setpoint.
- Fan failure alarm shall be generated at operator workstation (OWS) whenever run status of fan does not match current command state. Failure alarm shall occur when run status of fan shows no operation and fan has been commanded to be on.
- Advisory alarm shall occur when run status of fan shows operation and fan has been commanded to be off.
- Each alarm shall be recorded in alarm event log. Each alarm shall require operator acknowledgment at OWS. Provide time delay (5 seconds, adjustable) before generating alarm.
- Each alarm shall automatically return to normal when status and command conditions match. Return to normal status shall be recorded in alarm event log. No operator acknowledgment shall be required on return to normal.

NO-COST AND LOW-COST MEASURES

The ASHRAE Level 1 report must include a list of no-cost and low-cost improvement opportunities. Table 3 is an example, and the listed costs should not be considered to define low cost for project teams. Project teams and owners will need to determine their own cost constraints (see EA Credit Existing Building Commissioning—Implementation, *Further Explanation, No- and Low-Cost Measures*).

TABLE 3. Example summary of no- and low-cost measures

Measure	Implementation cost ($)	Total annual savings ($)	Simply payback period (years)	Complete?
No-cost or low-cost (less than $7,500)				
Modify fan controls	$2,400	$7,797	0.3	Complete
Add pipe insulation	$650	$1,173	0.6	Complete
Install LEDs on all exit signs	$2,500	$1,175	2.1	Complete
Chiller maintenance	$0	$5,528	0.0	Complete
Pump balancing	$0	$1,848	0.0	Complete
Pump maintenance	$7,400	$2,503	3.0	Complete
Install light occupancy sensors in mechanical rooms and lobby	$3,150	$5,649	0.6	Complete
AHU sensor calibration issues	$600	$6,174	0.1	Complete
AHU damper, economizer cycle issues	$2,800	$3,638	0.8	Complete
Adjust tenant lighting controls	$7,200	$10,471	0.7	Complete
Total	**$26,700**	**$45,956**	**0.6**	

RATING SYSTEM VARIATIONS

Data Centers

A preliminary assessment using the web-based DC Pro Profiling Tool is required. Specific to data centers, this tool helps identify potential energy savings using basic inputs, such as utility bills and system characteristics, and is the basis for further assessment in EA Credit Existing Building Commissioning—Analysis.

PROJECT TYPE VARIATIONS

District Energy Systems

If all or part of the energy used by the facility comes from a district energy system (DES), ensure that the documentation adequately addresses applicable building systems. Specifically, all downstream equipment is included in the scope of this prerequisite. Downstream equipment includes heat exchangers, steam pressure reduction stations, pumps, valves, pipes, building electrical services, and controls. All upstream equipment is excluded.

CAMPUS

Group Approach

All buildings in the group may be documented as one.

Campus Approach

Ineligible. Each LEED project may pursue the credit individually.

REQUIRED DOCUMENTATION

	Documentation	All projects (except Data Centers)	Data Centers
E	Summary of ASHRAE preliminary energy use analysis	X	
E	Summary of results of ASHRAE Level 1 walk-through	X	
E	Output from DC Pro Profiling Tool		X
E	Current facility requirements and operations and maintenance plan	X	

RELATED CREDIT TIPS

EA Credit Existing Building Commissioning—Analysis. The same team may undertake the Level 1 analysis for this prerequisite and the Level 2 analysis for the related credit simultaneously. The ASHRAE Level 1 report for this prerequisite may include a list of potential energy conservation measures that could be evaluated in more detail in the related credit.

EA Credit Existing Building Commissioning—Implementation. Recommendations arising from the ASHRAE Level 1 audit (for this prerequisite) and either the Level 2 audit or the retrocommissioning process (for EA Credit Existing Building Commissioning—Analysis) will be implemented under the related credit.

EA Credit Ongoing Commissioning. Teams that pursue the related credit should review the credit requirements while preparing the documentation for this prerequisite to ensure that all necessary elements are present and the foundation is set for credit achievement.

EA Prerequisite Minimum Energy Performance. Recommendations from the energy audit can produce savings that support achievement of the related prerequisite.

EA Credit Demand Response. Use the Level 1 audit done for this prerequisite as an opportunity to undertake a parallel evaluation of demand response opportunities. Consider how equipment and controls must be incorporated into the development of the operations and maintenance plan.

CHANGES FROM LEED 2009

Specific requirements for Data Center projects are now included.

REFERENCED STANDARDS

ASHRAE Procedures for Commercial Building Energy Audits, 2nd edition: ashrae.org

EXEMPLARY PERFORMANCE

Not available.

DEFINITIONS

current facilities requirements (**CFR**) the implementation of the owner's project requirements, developed to confirm the owner's current operational needs and requirements

operations and maintenance (**O&M**) plan a plan that specifies major system operating parameters and limits, maintenance procedures and schedules, and documentation methods necessary to demonstrate proper operation and maintenance of an approved emissions control device or system

ENERGY AND ATMOSPHERE PREREQUISITE

Minimum Energy Performance

This prerequisite applies to:

Existing Buildings
Schools
Retail
Data Centers
Hospitality
Warehouses and Distribution Centers

INTENT

To reduce the environmental and economic harms associated with excessive energy use by establishing a minimum level of operating energy performance.

REQUIREMENTS

ESTABLISHMENT E

Calibrate meters within the manufacturer's recommended interval if the building owner, management organization, or tenant owns the meter. Meters owned by third parties (e.g., utilities or governments) are exempt.

PERFORMANCE P

Meter the building's energy use for a full 12 months of continuous operation and achieve the levels of efficiency set forth in the options below. Each building's energy performance must be based on actual metered energy consumption for both the LEED project building(s) and all comparable buildings used for the benchmark.

Case 1. ENERGY STAR Rating

For buildings eligible to receive an energy performance rating using the Environmental Protection Agency (EPA) ENERGY STAR® Portfolio Manager tool, achieve an energy performance rating of at least 75. For projects outside the U.S., consult ASHRAE/ASHRAE/IESNA Standard 90.1–2010, Appendixes B and D, to determine the appropriate climate zone.

Case 2. Projects Not Eligible for ENERGY STAR Rating

Projects not eligible to use EPA's rating system may compare their buildings' energy performance with that of comparable buildings, using national averages or actual buildings, or with the previous performance of the project building.

OPTION 1. BENCHMARK AGAINST TYPICAL BUILDINGS

Path 1. National Average Data Available
Demonstrate energy efficiency performance that is 25% better than the median energy performance of similar buildings by benchmarking against the national source energy data provided in the Portfolio Manager tool.

Path 2. National Average Data Not Available
If national average source energy data are unavailable for buildings of similar type, benchmark against the building site energy data of at least three similar buildings, normalized for climate, building use, and occupancy. Demonstrate a 25% improvement.

OR

OPTION 2. BENCHMARK AGAINST HISTORICAL DATA

If national average source energy data are unavailable, compare the building's site energy data for the previous 12 months with the data from three contiguous years of the previous five, normalized for climate, building use, and occupancy. Demonstrate a 25% improvement.

BEHIND THE INTENT

Energy-efficient buildings will realize environmental and operational benefits. To encourage exceptional energy efficiency, this prerequisite requires benchmarking the project building's energy performance against comparable buildings with similar space use, occupancy, operations, and location.

Projects that are eligible for an ENERGY STAR rating are required to benchmark their buildings' energy performance using Portfolio Manager. This tool, managed by the U.S. Environmental Protection Agency (EPA), ensures consistency in benchmarking and allows teams to compare their buildings' energy efficiency with that of similar buildings based on the annual energy use and such operating characteristics as occupancy and gross building floor area.

Teams whose buildings are not eligible for ENERGY STAR can use alternative methods for benchmarking, such as comparisons with national source energy data for similar buildings or the project building's historical energy use.

STEP-BY-STEP GUIDANCE

STEP 1. CONFIRM REQUIRED METERING SETUP E

Determine whether the building has the appropriate metering for energy benchmarking.

- Each building must be individually metered. Install whole-building energy meters if they are not currently in place (see EA Prerequisite Whole-Building Energy Metering).
- Buildings with district energy must have meters that track the consumption from these systems (see *Further Explanation, Project Type Variations*).
- Data centers require submetering for specific space parameters (see *Further Explanation, Data Centers in ENERGY STAR's Portfolio Manager Tool*).

Before the performance period begins, calibrate any building-owned meters according to the manufacturer's recommended interval.

- Meters owned by third parties (e.g., utility companies) do not need to be calibrated by the building management team (see *Further Explanation, Meter Calibration*).
- Meters own by tenants must be included and should be calibrated before the performance period.

STEP 2. SET UP ENERGY STAR PORTFOLIO MANAGER PROFILE E

Establish an ENERGY STAR Portfolio Manager profile (see *Further Explanation, Setting up an ENERGY STAR Profile*).

- All projects, regardless of building type or ENERGY STAR eligibility, are required to establish a profile.
- Enter energy consumption data, building space types, and usage patterns into Portfolio Manager. All projects must follow the minimum occupancy requirements defined by EPA's ENERGY STAR for Buildings program.
- Share access to this account with USGBC.

STEP 3. ESTABLISH PERFORMANCE PERIOD E

Determine the start of the performance period such that 12 continuous months of metered energy data can be collected before the end of the performance period. The performance period must end within 30 days of that for all other prerequisites and credits, unless the project is pursuing the streamlined path.

It is recommended that teams conduct a preliminary benchmarking exercise before the performance period to evaluate performance.

- If 12 months' worth of metered data is already available, conduct a preliminary benchmarking exercise using the data to assess whether building performance could be improved.
- If no previous metered data exist (because new meters are installed or energy conservation measures have been implemented), it is recommended that teams collect new data for the preliminary benchmarking exercise.

This collection period allows teams the opportunity to implement any equipment upgrades and/or other efficiency measures before the performance period. If initial benchmarking shows the building does not meet the minimum requirements, consider the following as next steps:

- Review utility bills for irregularities, such as months of high consumption because of unusual weather.
- Review maintenance logs to see whether major equipment was malfunctioning.
- Perform a basic energy use analysis and a walk-through audit, and consider an advanced audit or commissioning process to identify further savings opportunities.
- See EA Prerequisite Energy Best Management Practices, EA Credit Enhanced Building Commissioning, and *Further Explanation, Improving Performance*.

Implement upgrades and operational changes as early as possible, since it will be a full 12 months from initiation of improvements before the associated energy savings are fully reflected in the benchmarking

STEP 4. DETERMINE APPLICABLE CASE AND SELECT OPTION IF APPLICABLE E

Follow Case 1 or Case 2 based on the building's ENERGY STAR rating eligibility (Figure 1; also see *Further Explanation, Determining Case and Option*). For projects with multiple buildings, each building must meet the prerequisite requirements individually.

- Case 1 is required for building types eligible for EPA's ENERGY STAR rating, as listed on the ENERGY STAR website.
- Case 2 is for project types that do not meet the ENERGY STAR eligibility requirements. Teams may select either Option 1 or Option 2.
  - Option 1 requires comparing the project building's energy use intensity (EUI) with either national average data (Path 1) or similar comparable buildings as described in the credit requirements (Path 2). Using national average data for similar building types avoids the effort of finding and normalizing comparable buildings. For unique and complex facilities, it may be advantageous to find comparables. Pursuing Path 2 alone limits the number of points that can be earned under EA Credit Optimize Energy Performance. For projects that do not clearly fit one path or the other, submit justification for the choice.
  - Option 2 allows projects to demonstrate improvement by comparing the project buildings' current and historical EUI. Projects do not need to find comparable buildings but must have historical data. Pursuing Option 2 alone limits the number of points that can be earned under EA Credit Optimize Energy Performance.
  - Option 3 (see EA Credit Optimize Energy Performance) involves benchmarking against a combination baseline of Case 2, Option 1, Path 2 (comparables) and Case 2, Option 2 (historical data). Project teams that want to pursue additional points under EA Credit Optimize Energy Performance may consider this option, but it is not necessary to combine baselines for achievement of this prerequisite.

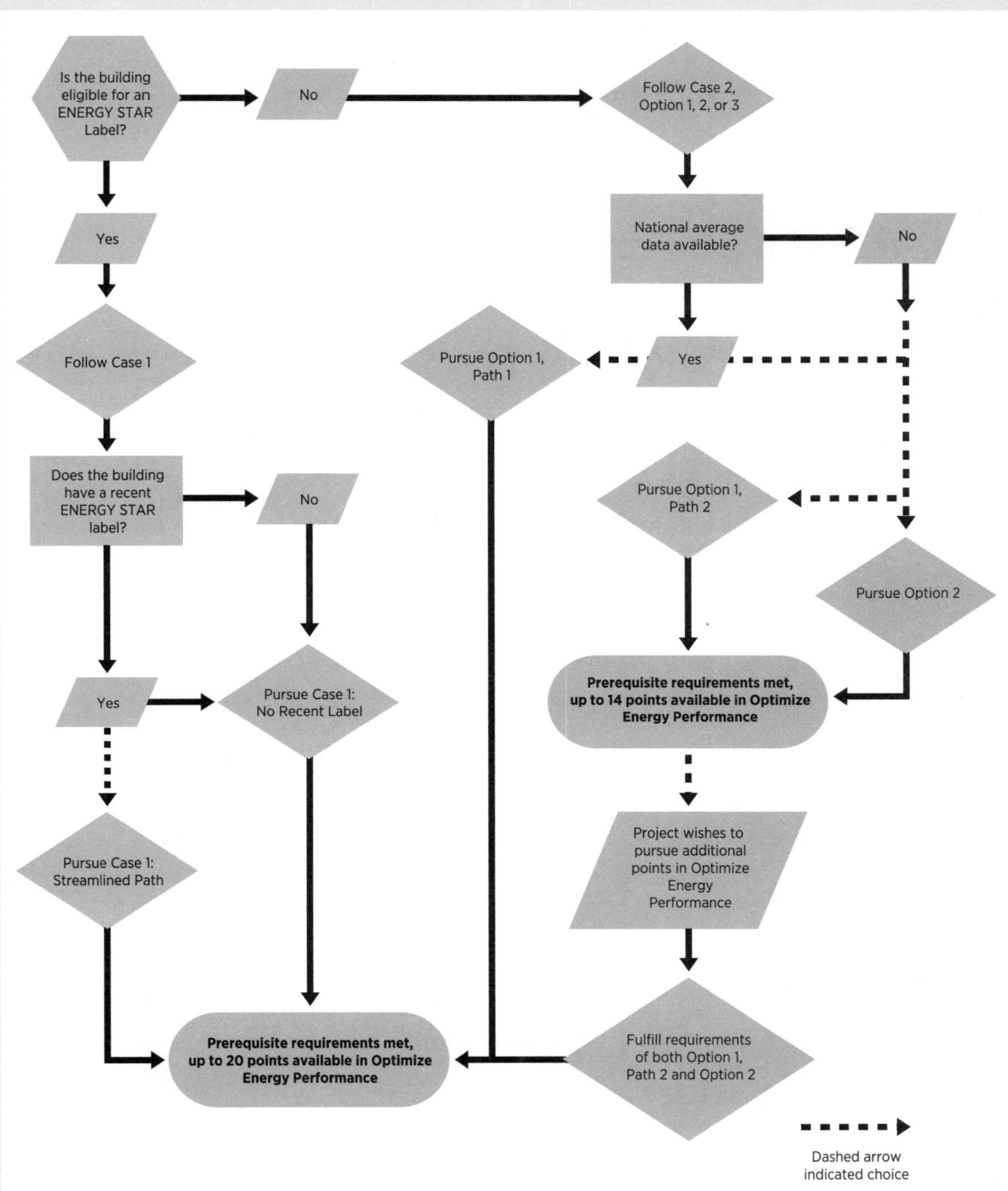

Figure 1. Determining case and choosing an option

STEP 5. OBTAIN METERED ENERGY CONSUMPTION DATA P

Energy consumption data must be obtained for the full performance period and must be based on actual metered data. Update Portfolio Manager with compiled energy data.

- It is recommended that projects update the Portfolio Manager profile and energy consumption data on a regular basis throughout the performance period (e.g., monthly).
- Both the dates of the service period and the energy consumption values entered into Portfolio Manager must be consistent with the metered data.
- It is recommended that meters be monitored during the performance period to ensure that they are functioning properly (see *Further Explanation, Meter Calibration*).

STEP 6. BENCHMARK BUILDING ACCORDING TO CASE 1 OR CASE 2 P

Confirm that the building's current performance meets the prerequisite requirements for Case 1 or Case 2 (see *Further Explanation, Normalizing Data*).

- **Case 1.** Determine the building's score using the ENERGY STAR Portfolio Manager tool.
- **Case 2.** Use Portfolio Manager to benchmark the building's current performance. This requires historical EUI data for the building and/or the energy use and building characteristics for a set of similar buildings.
- **Case 2, Option 1, Path 1.** Benchmark against typical buildings using national median data. Teams can compare their weather-normalized source EUI with the national median data in Portfolio Manager, which incorporates CBECS data. Laboratory projects may use the Labs21 tool. Labs21 may be used for comparison only for projects with a net lab area of at least 10% of gross area (see *Further Explanation, Labs21 Benchmarking Tool Guidance*). Projects outside the U.S. may use their country's national median data.
- **Case 2, Option 1, Path 2.** If national median data are not available, benchmark against comparable buildings. Create ENERGY STAR Portfolio Manager profiles for at least three similar buildings and justify the appropriateness of the comparables. If applicable, account for normalization (for factors besides floor area) when entering data for comparable buildings into Portfolio Manager. Both actual and normalized data must be retained. If data have been normalized, provide the normalization methodology.
- **Case 2, Option 2.** Benchmark against historical data for the project building. Enter at least three consecutive years of energy use data into Portfolio Manager, in addition to the current year's data from the performance period. The three years must fall within five years of the beginning of the performance period. As appropriate, project teams may further normalize the data for operating hours, number of occupants and computers, vacant space, and other factors. Provide the normalization methodology.

STEP 7. UPDATE BUILDING BENCHMARKING DATA ROUTINELY P

Update the ENERGY STAR Portfolio Manager profile regularly. The following information must be kept up-to-date throughout the performance period:

- **Energy consumption for all energy sources.** Update as data become available.
- **Number of occupants and vacant spaces.** As tenants add or lose staff and as spaces turn over, make adjustments in Portfolio Manager. For accurate benchmarking, note the exact dates of such changes.
- **Space type changes.** As renovations or new fit-outs occur, add or adust space types in Portfolio Manager.

For Case 2, Option 2 or 3, revise the historical baseline every five years. Project teams pursuing recertification must add at least one year from the most recent five years to the baseline from the previous certification; do not add data more than five years old.

FURTHER EXPLANATION

DATA CENTERS IN ENERGY STAR'S PORTFOLIO MANAGER TOOL

Data center spaces are often misclassified by project teams using Portfolio Manager. This space type is limited to spaces intentionally designed to be data centers and high-computing processing areas. The design may include server racks, raised-floor computing space, uninterruptible power supplies, and dedicated cooling systems. Data center spaces often have a distinct operating schedule, commonly remaining on at all times. A whole building may be considered a data center if it meets these requirements. However, often data centers are within a larger building, making the distinction of these space types important for accurate benchmarking. Most small server closets are not classified as data centers by ENERGY STAR.

The total gross floor area of a data center must be measured from the exterior of the space wall and include the entire data center. Its energy consumption must be separately metered and entered into ENERGY STAR Portfolio Manager. For more information on the data center metering requirements and the data center space type, see the ENERGY STAR website.

For office buildings, server rooms that do not meet the definition of a data center but have separate cooling systems and operating hours that differ from the rest of the building must be entered as a separate space in Portfolio Manager, using the office space type. Enter weekly operating hours, zero workers, and number of PCs to approximate the number of servers in the space.

METER CALIBRATION

Teams are required to calibrate meters owned by the project building according to the manufacturer's recommended calibration interval.

If the manufacturer does not provide recommended calibration intervals, the project team may establish a reasonable interval, preferably no longer than five years. Teams must demonstrate that meters have been calibrated or replaced within the established timeframe and confirm that the manufacturer does not recommend a calibration interval.

IMPROVING PERFORMANCE

Once a building is benchmarked, the project team can begin improving performance and increasing the overall score. Careful planning and early implementation are necessary so that the improvements are fully reflected in the results.

Improving energy performance might involve implementing major efficiency upgrades or, for lower capital outlays, adjusting or optimizing equipment and enhancing operations for energy efficiency. Use the results of the energy audit performed for EA Prerequisite Energy Efficiency Best Management Practices to determine the areas of greatest opportunity based on the breakdown of energy consumption by end-use category. Consider using an advanced energy audit or commissioning existing equipment to ensure that installed systems are working as intended and identify strategies for optimization (see EA Credit Existing Building Commissioning—Analysis).

The following four fundamental strategies can increase energy performance.

- **Demand reduction** includes reducing internal loads through shell and lighting improvements and setting operating schedules appropriately. Demand reduction involves no- or low-cost measures and is typically considered first.
- **Harvesting site energy** includes using free resources, such as daylight, ventilation cooling, solar heating, solar power, and wind energy, to satisfy needs for space conditioning, service water heating, and power generation.
- **Increasing efficiency** can be accomplished with more efficient envelope, lighting, and HVAC systems and by appropriately sizing HVAC systems. More efficient systems reduce energy demand and energy use.
- **Recovering waste energy** can be accomplished through exhaust air energy recovery systems, graywater heat recovery systems, and cogeneration.

SETTING UP AN ENERGY STAR PROFILE

All project teams are required to use EPA's ENERGY STAR Portfolio Manager to track a minimum 12 months of data for all energy consumption. This is a preliminary step even for projects not eligible for an ENERGY STAR rating, though most buildings will ultimately benchmark through ENERGY STAR and follow Case 1.

Projects not eligible for an Energy Star rating must use summary data generated in Portfolio Manager in conjunction with protocols provided by USGBC to complete benchmarking calculations and document compliance under Case 2.

An ENERGY STAR Portfolio Manager profile can be set up by the internal project team, perhaps with the help of an energy engineer, consultant, or auditor. Follow the rules and guidelines set by ENERGY STAR to generate the profile and rating. If questions arise regarding benchmarking inputs, review ENERGY STAR technical guidance documents and contact ENERGY STAR customer service.

ENERGY STAR protocols are subject to change, and project teams must follow the program's current guidance. Basic considerations follow.

Setup. If the project does not already have an account, create a Portfolio Manager account and a specific profile for each building by entering a new facility. Follow the prompts and guidance in Portfolio Manager, entering specific information for different space types. Common examples include offices, laboratories, data centers, retail areas, banking institutions, warehouses, and congregation areas. For information on mixed-use facilities, see Portfolio Manager, Guidance for Benchmarking Mixed-Use Properties.

Area. Determine the gross areas of each space type, using floor area as measured to the exterior wall. The total area must include the floor area for all supporting functions, such as lobbies, stairways, rest rooms, storage areas, elevator shafts, and mechanical rooms. These supporting spaces are included under the square footage (square meters) of the building's main space function. This floor area must be consistent across all other documentation for LEED. Parking area may be included or excluded, based on the rules established by ENERGY STAR.

Energy sources. Input data for building's energy use from all energy sources and for a full 12 months of continuous operation. The energy use data must include all energy consumed at the project building (e.g., electricity, natural gas, fuel oil, diesel fuel, district steam or hot water, district chilled water, propane, liquid propane, photovoltaics, wind, wood). Renewable energy consumption must be separately metered and reported. It is not acceptable to enter a net meter reading. Include process energy that might be used directly by tenants, such as commercial kitchen natural gas, fuel, and wood.

Exclusions for LEED. Up to 10% of the floor area and its associated energy consumption may be excluded from this prerequisite. However the energy associated with the excluded areas must be separately metered, be under separate management, and not support the typical operations of the remaining portions of the building.

Computers. Portfolio Manager requires an input for the number of computers for various space types. Collect accurate information on the total number of personal computers and servers in operation in the office space. The number of monitors in the building does not affect the number of computers entered into Portfolio Manager.

Hours. For some building types, Portfolio Manager requires operating hours. Input these hours according the program's directions and definition of operating hours. The value must be for time when at least 75% of the regular building occupants are present; exclude time when the facility is occupied only by cleaning, maintenance, security, or other support personnel.

Office building occupancy. For office buildings only, if the vacant space is greater than 10% of the building area, use the following guidance: Enter completely vacant or unused space separately from fully occupied or partially occupied space: enter zero workers, zero operation hours (even if the space is conditioned), and zero personal computers. Enter partially occupied spaces using normal procedures. If occupancy conditions change during the performance period, edit the space inputs and link the adjustments to the date they took effect.

DETERMINING CASE AND OPTION

Determine which case applies to the project building and then select the option and submittal path. All projects are required to use Portfolio Manager to calculate site- and weather-normalized source energy use for this prerequisite.

Case 1. The project is eligible for an ENERGY STAR rating.

All buildings that are eligible to receive an ENERGY STAR rating based on their space types must follow Case 1.

Many projects, even projects outside the U.S., fall under Case 1 because most buildings are eligible for an ENERGY STAR rating. To determine eligibility, enter all information into Portfolio Manager, which automatically determines whether the building is eligible to receive an ENERGY STAR rating. If the building is not eligible, Portfolio Manager will list the rating as "N/A" and display the reason the facility is ineligible (e.g., "Because more than 50% of your building is classified as 'Other,' this building is not eligible for an energy performance rating").

TABLE 1. Case 1—ENERGY STAR label

Description	Procedure	Considerations
Project building must earn official label within 12 months before performance period ends.	• Engage professional engineer or licensed architect to review project's energy inputs and stamp statement of energy performance. • To find licensed professionals, see ENERGY STAR website (energystar.gov). • Submit validated inputs in ENERGY STAR application.	• Label allows team to lock in its energy rating for 12 months, even if building's performance fluctuates or if changes to ENERGY STAR algorithm affect benchmark. • Engaging required professional entails cost. • Documentation for this approach is streamlined: team submits stamped statement of energy performance and shows proof of its ENERGY STAR label.

TABLE 2. Case 1—No ENERGY STAR label

Description	Procedure	Considerations
If project building has label older than one year or cannot obtain label because it is outside U.S, it must achieve ENERGY STAR score of 75 or better for 12-month period coinciding with end of performance period.	• Enter project information into Portfolio Manager. • Use ENERGY STAR rating from end of performance period even if higher rating was earned earlier.	• This approach may be advantageous if building's rating is rising and older label showed lower rating. • It avoids costs associated with obtaining label. • It entails additional documentation, including submission of detailed information on all energy inputs.

Case 2. The project type is not eligible for an ENERGY STAR rating.

Not all building types are eligible for an ENERGY STAR rating. Common reasons for ineligibility are related to space types:

- The predominant space type is not listed by ENERGY STAR.
- The floor area for "other" space type is greater than 10% of total floor space. Portfolio Manager cannot compute an energy performance rating if more than 10% of gross floor area consists of a space type designated "other."
- The floor area for multifamily spaces is greater than 10% of the gross floor area. Portfolio Manager cannot compute an energy performance rating if more than 10% of gross floor area consists of multifamily housing.

The following four approaches are available to such projects. For each, the project team must normalize energy use intensity (EUI) data for weather and convert site energy use to source energy, using Portfolio Manager, then enter the data.

TABLE 3. Case 2, Option 1, Path 1—Benchmark against typical buildings using national averages

Description	Procedure	Special types
If national energy use data are available, project must use this approach. Project building must be more efficient than 75% of similar buildings based on national averages. If national energy use data are not available, choose Option 1, Path 2; Option 2; or Option 3.	• Enter weather-normalized source EUI information, taken from project's Portfolio Manager profile, into form.	• For buildings with net laboratory area of at least 10% of gross area, use Labs21 Energy Benchmarking Tool to complete benchmarking. • For buildings with multiple space types, transfer space type information, originally entered into Portfolio Manager, into form.

TABLE 4. Case 2, Option 1, Path 2— Benchmark against typical buildings using comparables

Description	Procedure	Considerations
If national energy use data are not available or not applicable, project team must obtain energy use data from three or more similar buildings and demonstrate energy efficiency at least 25% better.	• Identify similar buildings that are representative of entire group of comparable buildings. • Comparables must have similar space types, functions, activities, and schedules. Explain basis for comparability. • Normalize data for weather and convert site energy use to source energy, using Portfolio Manager. • Normalize data for operating parameters (e.g., energy use for manufacturing based on relative production of each building) if necessary. • Enter information for project building and each comparable building into form.	• This approach applies to unique space configurations or process loads that make building's energy use difficult to compare with national average consumption data. • It requires project team to obtain data from other building owners and property managers. • Getting information on energy performance of similar buildings may not be feasible.

TABLE 5. Case 2, Option 2—Benchmark against historical data

Description	Procedure	Considerations
If national energy use data are not available or not applicable, or if comparables are not available, project must compare its current energy efficiency against its historical performance and demonstrate a 25% or better improvement from historical baseline.	• Choose historical baseline. Baseline is average of three consecutive years within five-year period that immediately precedes performance period (e.g., if performance period is calendar year 2012, baseline is any three consecutive years between January 1, 2007, and December 31, 2011). • Team may select optimum three-year period (i.e., period with highest energy consumption). • Normalize baseline average and performance period data for weather and convert site energy use to source energy, using Portfolio Manager. To update baseline for recertification, every five years, add at least one year from most recent five years to baseline. Do not add data more than five years old.	• Buildings that have insufficient metering or have been built or changed ownership recently may not have three years of historical data. • Buildings that have been operating efficiently for preceding five years are at disadvantage and may find it difficult to show required savings. • Underperforming facilities will benefit from cost-effective efficiency measures installed between historical baseline and performance period.

TABLE 6. Case 2, Option 3— Benchmark against a baseline that combines comparables and historical data

Description	Procedure	Considerations
Eligibility is same as for Case 2, Option 1, Path 2; or Case 2, Option 2.	• Follow procedures for Option 1, Path 2 (comparables), and Option 2 (historical baseline) to obtain necessary information. Submit information for project's performance period, comparable buildings, and historical baseline.	• This approach enables projects to earn up to 20 points under EA Credit Optimize Energy Performance.

NORMALIZING DATA

For Case 2 projects, teams may be required to normalize comparable benchmarking data before calculating the energy use intensities. Normalization is intended to account for any unusual location- or activity-related differences among the buildings (not including efficiency features and measures). It may be appropriate to adjust energy use for differences or changes in schedules or the level of energy-intensive occupant activities.

Weather normalization may also be required, depending on the compliance path selected, to account for the actual temperatures of the performance year compared with historical average temperatures for the same area or for comparable buildings in different areas.

LABS21 BENCHMARKING TOOL GUIDANCE

If the project has a net lab area of at least 10% of gross area and is following Case 2, Option 1, Path 1, the building must be registered in the Labs21 tool. The Labs21 dataset must then be filtered based on lab area ratio, lab type, occupancy hours, and climatic region to obtain a comparable average source energy use intensity. The resulting dataset must have enough buildings and the filters must be applied appropriately according to the Guidance on Using Labs21 Benchmarking Tool for LEED- O&M (http://labs21benchmarking.lbl.gov/).

PROJECT TYPE VARIATIONS

District Energy Systems

Any energy use from district energy systems (DES) serving the project building must be incorporated into the benchmarking. The energy used by the individual project building must therefore be metered. Teams can account for DES in either of two ways.

The team may enter the output from the DES delivered to the project building into the Portfolio Manager tool as site energy from a district system (e.g., district chilled water); Portfolio Manager then converts it to source energy based on ENERGY STAR's standard methodology.

Alternatively, the team may include the energy consumed by the DES and attributable to the project building in the energy use data. This typically requires knowing the portion of DES output delivered to the project building, as well as the total energy inputs into the DES.

To prorate the DES energy consumption to the building, multiply the thermal energy measured at the building by the ratio of the DES energy inputs to the DES energy generated. Account for thermal losses by multiplying this total by (1 + Thermal distribution losses) to determine the total energy consumption to be entered into Portfolio Manager. Ensure the units are consistent for the building-level chilled water consumption and the DES plant chilled water consumption:

- **Chilled water electricity allocation.** Multiply the building level chilled water consumption (CHW_B) " by the ratio of the total annual electric energy associated with DES chilled water generation ($ELEC_{CHW}$) to the total annual DES chilled water generated (CHW_P). Multiply this total by (1 + Thermal distribution losses) ($1+ L_{CHW}$).

$$(CHW_B) \times \frac{(ELEC_{CHW})}{(CHW_P)} \times (1 + L_{CHW})$$

- **Chilled water fuel allocation (if applicable).** Multiply the building level chilled water consumption (CHW_B) by ratio of the total annual fuel energy associated with DES chilled water generation ($FUEL_{CHW}$) to the total annual DES chilled water generated (CHW_P). Multiply this total by (1 + Thermal distribution losses) ($1+ L_{CHW}$).

$$(CHW_B) \times \frac{(FUEL_{CHW})}{(CHW_P)} \times (1 + L_{CHW})$$

- **Hot water (or steam or DHW) fuel allocation.** For each DES fuel source, multiply the building-level hot water (steam, DHW water) consumption ($HEAT_B$) by ratio of the total annual fuel energy associated with DES hot water (steam, DHW) generation ($FUEL_{HEAT}$) to the total annual DES hot water (steam, DHW) generated ($HEAT_P$). Multiply this total by (1 + Thermal distribution losses) ($1+ L_{HEAT}$). If a separate loop is provided for domestic hot water, perform a separate calculation for the domestic hot water loop.

$$(HEAT_B) \times \frac{(FUEL_{HEAT})}{(HEAT_P)} \times (1 + L_{HEAT})$$

- **Hot water (or steam or DHW) electricity allocation.** Multiply the building-level hot water (steam, DHW) water consumption ($HEAT_B$) by the ratio of the total annual electric energy associated with DES hot water (steam, DHW) generation ($ELEC_{HEAT}$) to the total annual DES hot water (steam, DHW) generated ($HEAT_P$). Multiply this total by (1 + Thermal distribution losses) ($1+ L_{HEAT}$). If a separate loop is provided for domestic hot water, perform a separate calculation for the domestic hot water loop.

$$(HEAT_B) \times \frac{(ELEC_{HEAT})}{(HEAT_P)} \times (1 + L_{HEAT})$$

Calculate the combined building and prorated DES monthly energy use based on the metered data:

$$(ELEC_{B2}) = (ELEC_B) + \left[(CHW_B) \times \frac{(ELEC_{CHW})}{(CHW_P)} \times (1 + L_{CHW}) \right] + \left[(HEAT_B) \times \frac{(ELEC_{HEAT})}{(HEAT_P)} \times (1 + L_{HEAT}) \right]$$

$$(FUEL_{B2}) = (FUEL_B) + \left[(CHW_B) \times \frac{(FUEL_{CHW})}{(CHW_P)} \times (1 + L_{CHW}) \right] + \left[(HEAT_B) \times \frac{(FUEL_{HEAT})}{(HEAT_P)} \times (1 + L_{HEAT}) \right]$$

- Use thermal distribution losses consistent with those required by ENERGY STAR or provide documentation to justify alternative losses:
  - L_{CHW}: chilled water, 2.5%
  - L_{STEAM}: steam, 7.5%
  - L_{HW}: district hot water, 2.5%
  - L_{CHP}: combined heat and power, 7.5%
- At the building level, chilled water consumption, hot water consumption, and domestic hot water consumption may be calculated based on the building-level DES flow rates and the building's supply and return water DES temperatures. This method would require building-level flow sensors and building-level supply and return water temperature sensors.
- At the district level, chilled water energy generated, hot water energy generated, and domestic hot water energy generated may be calculated based on the flow rates through the chillers or boilers and the chiller's or boiler's entering and leaving water temperatures.
- In the absence of metered data for heating hot water or steam pumps, trend data for pump speed may be used along with data for the pump brake horsepower and motor efficiency to calculate the annual energy use.

Combined Heat and Power (CHP)
Use production efficiency for conventional steam and electricity generation to determine the building-level energy consumption associated with steam and electricity generation using the campus cogeneration plant. The following efficiencies are from ENERGY STAR Performance Ratings Methodology for Incorporating Source Energy Use:

$$\eta_{HEAT,\,T} = \text{Production efficiency} - \text{Conventional heating} = 80\%$$

$$\eta_{E,\,T} = \text{Production efficiency} - \text{Conventional electricity} = 32\%$$

Calculate the effective delivered efficiency for the heating ($\eta_{HEAT,\,CHP}$), electricity ($\eta_{E,\,CHP}$), and chilled water ($\eta_{CHW,\,CHP}$) as follows. Ensure the units are consistent for the electricity, chilled water consumption, and hot water consumption, and represent site energy (not source energy values):

$$\eta_{HEAT,\,CHP} = \frac{\left(\frac{HEAT_P}{FUEL_P}\right) \times \left[\left(\frac{HEAT_P}{\eta_{HEAT,\,T}}\right) + \left(\frac{ELEC_{PG}}{\eta_{E,\,T}}\right)\right]}{\left(\frac{HEAT_P}{\eta_{HEAT,\,T}}\right)} \times (1 - L_{CHP})$$

$$\eta_{E,\,CHP} = \frac{\left(\frac{ELEC_{PG}}{FUEL_P}\right) \times \left(\frac{HEAT_P}{\eta_{HEAT,\,T}} + \frac{ELEC_{PG}}{\eta_{E,\,T}}\right)}{\left(\frac{ELEC_{PG}}{\eta_{E,\,T}}\right)} \times (1 - L_{COGEN})$$

$$\eta_{CHW,\,CHP} = \frac{(CHW_P)}{\left(\frac{HEAT_{CHW}}{\eta_{HEAT,\,CHP}}\right) + \left(\frac{ELEC_{CHW}}{\eta_{E,\,CHP}}\right) + FUEL_{CHW}} \times (1 - L_{CHW})$$

Calculate the monthly energy prorated to the building based on the monthly metered data as follows:

$$ELEC_{B2} = \frac{ELEC_B \times ELEC_{PC} + \dfrac{(CHW_B) \times (ELEC_{CHW})}{(CHW_P)} + \dfrac{(HEAT_B) \times (ELEC_{HEAT})}{(HEAT_P)}}{ELEC_{PG} + ELEC_{PC}}$$

$$FUEL_{B2} = FUEL_B + \frac{(ELEC_B)}{(\eta_{E,\,CHP})} + \frac{(CHW_B)}{(\eta_{CHW,\,CHP})} + \frac{(HEAT_B)}{(\eta_{HEAT,\,CHP})}$$

where

$ELEC_{PC}$ = total campus purchased electricity consumption for electric energy crossing the curb into the campus

L_{COGEN} = total cogeneration parasitic losses as a percentage of total electricity generated (e.g., cooling of intake air). Assume 5% of the total cogeneration electrical generation if not metered.

$FUEL_P$ = plant fuel consumption, for fuel energy crossing the curb into the plant, with the exception of energy fuel that is directly used to generate chilled water

$ELEC_{CHW}$ = total electric energy consumption associated with chilled water generation, including energy for chillers, cooling towers, and pumps

$HEAT_{CHW}$ = campus plant steam or hot water consumption for chilled water generation energy outputs

$FUEL_{CHW}$ = total fuel energy input for chillers, if applicable (e.g., for absorption or engine-driven chillers). This does not include any fuel required to generate steam to drive the chillers.

$ELEC_{HEAT}$ = total electric energy consumption associated with hot water or steam generation and distribution (i.e., pumps)

$ELEC_{PG}$ = plant electricity generated by cogeneration

CHW_P = total chilled water energy generated

$HEAT_P$ = total hot water or steam energy generated by fuel boilers or recovered as waste heat from cogeneration. If a separate distribution loop at the district plant level distributes domestic water heating, meter the DHW heating energy generated for that loop separately, and include it in the total.

Prorate the energy costs associated with the CHP energy to the building using the virtual electric rate and virtual fuel rate at the building level (or at the campus level if the fuel or electricity is centrally billed).

INTERNATIONAL TIPS

Cities in many countries are listed in Portfolio Manager. For an unlisted city, use ASHRAE 90.1–2010, Appendixes B and D, to identify a climatologically similar city. If the project team's city is not listed in ASHRAE 90.1, find a climate zone based on heating degree-days and provide a narrative to support the selection.

CAMPUS

Group Approach

Submit separate documentation for each building; however, K-12 schools, hospitals, hotels, resorts, and resort properties with multiple structures, as defined by ENERGY STAR, may submit one ENERGY STAR score.

Campus Approach

Ineligible. Each LEED project may pursue the credit individually.

REQUIRED DOCUMENTATION

	Documentation	Case 1, streamlined	Case 1	Case 2, Option 1, Path 1	Case 2, Option 1, Path 2	Case 2, Option 2
E	Meter calibration report, as applicable	X	X	X	X	X
E	Access to ENERGY STAR Portfolio Manager account (see Further Explanation, Sharing Access)	X	X	X	X	X
P	Statement of energy performance stamped by professional engineer or licensed architect	X				
P	Letter from ENERGY STAR, copy of ENERGY STAR recognition certificate, or screenshot of ENERGY STAR website	X				
P	Data verification checklist		X	X	X	X
P	Copies of utility bill summary pages or cover pages for 3 months of performance period for each fuel source		X	X	X	X
P	Weather-normalized source EUI			X	X	X
P	Weather-normalized source EUI from 3 similar buildings				X	
P	Descriptions of 3 similar buildings and comparability to project building				X	
P	Weather-normalized source EUI from 3 recent years					X
P	Calculations supporting additional normalization (if applicable)			X	X	X

RELATED CREDIT TIPS

EA Credit Optimize Energy Performance. The path chosen in this prerequisite determines the path in the credit. Review the requirements for the related credit to determine the number of points available for various options.

EA Prerequisite Energy Efficiency Best Management Practices. Building operating plan information must be consistent with the information entered into Portfolio Manager. Conducting the ASHRAE Level 1 audit will provide opportunities for energy improvement, which will assist with achieving the minimum energy efficiency performance threshold.

EA Credit Existing Building Commissioning—Analysis. The commissioning process may uncover energy efficiency opportunities that will help teams achieve this prerequisite.

CHANGES FROM LEED 2009

The minimum ENERGY STAR score has been increased to 75.

REFERENCED STANDARDS

Environmental Protection Agency (EPA) ENERGY STAR Portfolio Manager tool: energystar.gov/benchmark

ASHRAE Standard 90.1-2010, Appendices B and D: ashrae.org

EXEMPLARY PERFORMANCE

Not available.

DEFINITIONS

district energy system (**DES**) a central energy conversion plant and transmission and distribution system that provides thermal energy to a group of buildings (e.g., a central cooling plant on a university campus). It does not include central energy systems that provide only electricity.

downstream equipment the heating and cooling systems, equipment, and controls located in the project building or on the project site and associated with transporting the thermal energy of the district energy system (DES) into heated and cooled spaces. Downstream equipment includes the thermal connection or interface with the DES, secondary distribution systems in the building, and terminal units.

upstream equipment a heating or cooling system or control associated with the district energy system (DES) but not part of the thermal connection or interface with the DES. Upstream equipment includes the thermal energy conversion plant and all the transmission and distribution equipment associated with transporting the thermal energy to the project building or site.

ENERGY AND ATMOSPHERE PREREQUISITE

Building-Level Energy Metering

This prerequisite applies to:

Existing Buildings
Schools
Retail
Data Centers
Hospitality
Warehouses and Distribution Centers

INTENT

To support energy management and identify opportunities for additional energy savings by tracking building-level energy use.

REQUIREMENTS

ESTABLISHMENT E

Install new or use existing building-level energy meters or submeters that can be aggregated to provide building-level data representing total building energy consumption (electricity, natural gas, chilled water, steam, fuel oil, propane, etc). Utility-owned meters capable of aggregating building-level resource use are acceptable.

PERFORMANCE P

Compile meter data into monthly and annual summaries; meter readings can be manual or automated.

Commit to sharing with USGBC the resulting energy consumption data and electrical demand data (if metered) for a five-year period beginning on the date the project accepts LEED certification or typical occupancy, whichever comes first. At a minimum, energy consumption must be tracked at one-month intervals.

This commitment must carry forward for five years or until the building changes ownership or lessee.

BEHIND THE INTENT

Whole-building metering lets building operators track energy consumption over time, illustrating variations in usage patterns that can be used to develop energy conservation measures over the lifetime of the building. Once such conservation measures are in place, metering then allows staff to track energy savings and justify additional investments with calculable payback periods. Building operators gain detailed feedback, enabling them to precisely calibrate operational parameters, depending on the needs of changing occupancy groups, while continuing to operate building systems efficiently.

Disparities between how buildings are designed to operate and how they actually perform are common. Even green buildings exhibit this gap between projected and actual performance. Numerous factors can explain the incongruity: flaws with energy modeling, inadequate commissioning, inaccurate assumptions regarding occupants' behavior, lack of coordination during the transition from construction to operations, or the everyday operation of the building systems. To reduce such disparities, USGBC collects and analyzes performance data, comparing building performance across the LEED portfolio to identify common traits among high and low performers, then shares the findings to help LEED registrants improve their buildings' performance.

STEP-BY-STEP GUIDANCE

STEP 1. IDENTIFY ALL ENERGY SOURCES THAT SERVE BUILDING E

Identify all sources of energy delivered to the building. Sources of energy that must be metered include all energy supplied by a utility company or campus central plant, such as the following:

- Electricity
- Natural gas, synthetic natural gas, propane, fuel oil, diesel fuel, other fossil fuels
- Biofuels
- District chilled water, steam, and hot water

This prerequisite does not require metering of locally generated sources of energy that are dedicated to the project building, such as the following:

- Solar photovoltaic–generated electricity
- Wind-generated electricity
- Solar hot water generation for domestic hot water or heating hot water

STEP 2. DETERMINE SCOPE OF UTILITY COMPANY METERING E

If all energy provided to the building is supplied by one or more utility companies and the utility meters provide monthly consumption data, those meters meet the prerequisite requirements. However, the project team may have little influence on the location and function of utility company meters. If the utility company restricts access to the meter or uses proprietary remote reporting technology, the project team may meet the prerequisite requirements by tracking energy usage through monthly billing. To collect more frequent or accurate data, the team may elect to install a private meter downstream of the utility company meter.

STEP 3. DETERMINE NUMBER, TYPE AND LOCATION OF ALL METERS E

If the project is not served by a utility company, or if the project uses multiple sources of energy, additional meters may be required. Identify the location of primary building-level meters for each energy source. If the project shares utility meters with other buildings or includes energy sources that are not metered by the supplier, install submeters that will provide the required data.

- Projects may use a single meter at the utility entrance or multiple submeters that account for whole building energy use in aggregate (see *Further Explanation, Examples*).
- Areas within the project boundary that are served by separate utility feeds, such as parking garages, must also be metered.
- Some projects may elect to use multiple submeters to gain more insight into energy uses.
- Select locations with easy access for reading and maintenance.

- There are no requirements for the type of meters except that they be permanent (see *Further Explanation, Meter Selection*).
- Additional meters and meter capabilities will be needed if the project team pursues EA Credit Advanced Energy Metering (see *Related Credit Tips*).
- Meters installed by the owner must be maintained and calibrated per the manufacturer's recommendations.

STEP 4. TRACK ENERGY CONSUMPTION DATA P

Track energy use monthly, beginning at least 12 months before the final day of the building's initial LEED O+M performance period. Monthly data are required for the ENERGY STAR rating under EA Prerequisite Minimum Energy Performance.

- Energy consumption must be measured and recorded on at least a monthly basis (see *Further Explanation, Measurement Interval*).
- Consider tracking building occupancy, use, and maintenance concurrently to help place energy use data in context and understand anomalies in usage patterns.

STEP 5. SHARE WHOLE-BUILDING ENERGY CONSUMPTION P

Commit to sharing with USGBC the whole-project energy usage data acquired from permanent installed meters in accordance with the prerequisite requirements. The project owner must commit to sharing energy use data with USGBC for five years in one of two ways:

- USGBC-approved data template
- Third-party data source

To see the most recent list of data-sharing pathways, visit USGBC's credit library, at usgbc.org/credits.

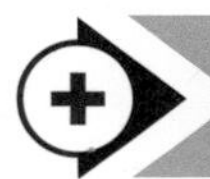

FURTHER EXPLANATION

EXAMPLES

Example 1. An office building within an office park is directly served by the local electrical utility, which has installed a meter. The building receives monthly bills for the electrical energy consumed. The project meets the requirements for electrical energy.

Example 2. The same office building receives chilled water from a central utility plant, which is owned and operated by the office park management company. The office building pays a flat fee for chilled water, included as part of the lease. The management company does not meter or invoice for actual chilled water consumption. To meet the requirements for chilled water, the building must install a chilled water meter at each service point.

Example 3. A stand-alone data center building on a corporate campus receives electricity from a campus central utility plant, and there are no meters at the electrical service entrances. The data center includes a sophisticated real-time advanced energy monitoring and reporting system, comprising submeters on all end devices downstream of a whole-building uninterruptable power supply (UPS) system backed up by diesel generators. The project meets the requirements for electrical energy.

Example 4. An office building in the central business district of a large city shares a boiler system with another building across the street. The building housing the boiler system sells steam to the other building, which pays for the associated energy on a square-foot-prorated basis. To meet the requirements for steam, the building must install a steam meter at each service point.

METER SELECTION

Utility-provided meters are typically regulated by code or law to establish their accuracy. Utility meters are often called "revenue-grade" because their measurement results directly in a charge to the customer. However, the accuracy of commercial meters and submeters available to building owners varies, and incorrect meter application or installation can further affect measurement accuracy. Meter selection is an important component of this prerequisite for owners to consider because of its implications for data quality.

Standards and regulations vary by location, and there is no single standard for revenue-grade accuracy (see *Referenced Standards*). For building-level meters located at the fuel source point of entry, projects should aim to provide meters that conform to one of the referenced resources or to a local law or regulation governing revenue-grade metering, or are otherwise defensible as sufficiently accurate. For more information regarding system submeters, see EA Credit Advanced Energy Metering.

METER LOCATION

For projects served by a utility, the utility generally owns the meter, so all energy required to power the building is accounted for. If the meter is owned by the building, the its best location for the purposes of determining building-level energy consumption is generally at the point where energy enters the building.

The location of the meter affects whether conversion losses are included. Ideally, building-level measurement will include losses from conversion and distribution of power within the building via transformer or heat exchangers. For example, in a data center, the UPS is a point of power conversion, meaning the energy consumption metered at the UPS output does not include conversion losses; therefore the meter should be located upstream of the UPS.

MEASUREMENT INTERVALS

Projects with utility-owned energy meters may meet the monthly measurement requirement through one of two strategies: either the utility provides monthly energy consumption data in the form of invoices or online reporting tools, or building staff can read monthly cumulative energy usage directly from the meter.

Projects with owner-provided energy meters may meet the monthly measurement requirement through one of two strategies: either data are collected through the building automation system or other energy-reporting software on a monthly basis, or building staff can read monthly cumulative energy usage directly from the meter.

PROJECT TYPE VARIATIONS

District Energy Systems (DES)

This prerequisite is not applicable to upstream equipment. However, it is applicable to the energy source entering the building produced by upstream equipment. Building-level metering does not need to account for inefficiencies of the central plant or energy delivery methods.

Additions

If the original building has building-level meters and the addition's energy use is fully covered by those meters, the requirements of the prerequisite are met. If the original building is not metered, the project needs to install meters to cover only the entirety of the addition's energy use to meet the prerequisite requirements.

CAMPUS

Group Approach

Submit separate documentation for each building.

Campus Approach

Ineligible. Each LEED project may pursue the credit individually.

REQUIRED DOCUMENTATION

	Documentation	All projects
E	Confirmation of permanently installed meters	X
E	Letter of commitment	X
E	Confirmation of data sharing source	X

RELATED CREDIT TIPS

EA Credit Advanced Energy Metering. The related credit builds on this prerequisite by requiring advanced metering capabilities and submetering. An early decision on whether to pursue the related credit credit will help inform prerequisite compliance.

EA Prerequisite Energy Efficiency Best Management Practices. The ASHRAE Level 1 energy audit, conducted for the related prerequisite, requires 12 months of whole-building energy consumption data.

EA Prerequisite Minimum Energy Performance. The related prerequisite requires 12 months of whole-building energy consumption data.

CHANGES FROM LEED 2009

- This prerequisite is new.
- The ongoing energy tracking and reporting components were previously required under Minimum Program Requirement #6 for LEED 2009 projects.

REFERENCED STANDARDS

Electricity: American National Standards Institute, ANSI C12.20, Class 0.2 (±0.2): ansi.org

Natural gas: American National Standards Institute, ANSI B109: ansi.org

Thermal energy (Btu meter or heat meter), EN Standard, EN-1434: cen.eu

EXEMPLARY PERFORMANCE

Not available.

DEFINITIONS

revenue-grade meter a measurement tool designed to meet strict accuracy standards required by code or law. Utility meters are often called revenue grade because their measurement directly results in a charge to the customer.

ENERGY AND ATMOSPHERE PREREQUISITE

Fundamental Refrigerant Management

This prerequisite applies to:

Existing Buildings
Schools
Retail
Data Centers
Hospitality
Warehouses and Distribution Centers

INTENT

To reduce stratospheric ozone depletion.

REQUIREMENTS

ESTABLISHMENT E

Do not use chlorofluorocarbon (CFC)-based refrigerants in heating, ventilating, air-conditioning, and refrigeration (HVAC&R) systems unless a third-party audit shows that system replacement or conversion is not economically feasible or unless a phase-out plan for CFC-based refrigerants is in place. Phase-out plans should be scheduled for completion within 10 years. The replacement or conversion of HVAC&R equipment is considered not economically feasible if the simple payback of the replacement or conversion is greater than 10 years. Perform the following economic analysis:

$$\text{Simple payback} = \frac{\text{Cost of replacement or conversion}}{\text{Resulting annual energy cost difference} + \text{Resulting annual maintenance and refrigerant cost difference}} > 10$$

If CFC-based refrigerants are maintained in the building, reduce annual leakage to 5% or less using the procedures in the Clean Air Act, Title VI, Rule 608, governing refrigerant management and reporting (or a local equivalent for projects outside the U.S.), and reduce the total leakage over the remaining life of the unit to less than 30% of its refrigerant charge.

Small HVAC&R units (defined as containing less than 0.5 pound [225 grams] of refrigerant), standard refrigerators, small water coolers, and any other cooling equipment that contains less than 0.5 pound (225 grams) of refrigerant are exempt.

PERFORMANCE P

None.

BEHIND THE INTENT

Chlorofluorocarbons (CFCs) and other refrigerants contribute to the depletion of the stratospheric ozone layer. The thinning of this ozone layer is linked to many human health problems, such as skin cancer, to ecological effects, such as reduced crop yields, and to damage to the marine food chain.[1] To address these issues, the 1987 Montreal Protocol established an international agreement to phase out use of the most harmful ozone-depleting substances, including CFCs.

Production of CFCs was phased out in industrialized nations that signed the Montreal Protocol before December 1995 and in most other countries by 2010. Accordingly, new construction projects cannot install new CFC-based refrigeration. However, CFCs may still be used in previously installed HVAC equipment.

CFCs must be phased out when replacement or conversion has a simple payback of less than 10 years. Though both hydrochlorofluorocarbons (HCFCs) and CFCs contribute to ozone depletion, only CFCs must be addressed to meet this prerequisite.

STEP-BY-STEP GUIDANCE

STEP 1. IDENTIFY CFC-BASED EQUIPMENT E

Identify all HVAC&R equipment in the building and determine whether any existing HVAC&R equipment uses CFCs.

- All equipment with 0.5 pound (225 grams) or more of refrigerant must be assessed Include supplemental cooling equipment and commercial refrigeration equipment.
- Existing small equipment with less than 0.5 pound (225 grams) of refrigerant is exempt from the prerequisite requirements.
- No new equipment, regardless of size, may contain CFCs.
- If no CFCs are identified, proceed to Step 6.

STEP 2. DETERMINE WHETHER FEASIBILITY ANALYSIS IS REQUIRED E

Determine whether the owner has plans to replace CFC-based HVAC&R equipment. If CFC phase out is planned and scheduled to begin within five years, an economic feasibility analysis is not required; however a CFC phase out plan must be prepared and signed by the owner.

STEP 3. DETERMINE ECONOMIC FEASIBILITY OF CFC PHASE-OUT E

Retain a third party to determine whether it is economically feasible to replace or convert existing CFC-based equipment. This step is required if CFC-based equipment has not been scheduled for replacement in less than five years. Replacement or conversion is considered economically feasible if the simple payback is less than 10 years (see *Further Explanation, Economic Analysis* and *Example Economic Analysis for Chiller Replacement or Conversion*).

- If replacement or conversion is not economically feasible, the project team must still meet the refrigerant leakage requirements, as described in *Further Explanation, Minimizing Refrigerant Leakage*.
- Even if replacement or conversion does not meet the economic criteria, the owner may still want to consider scheduling replacement or conversion if other work is being conducted in the same time frame.

STEP 4. DEVELOP AND IMPLEMENT CFC PHASE-OUT PLAN E

Develop and implement a CFC phase-out plan if the economic analysis demonstrates feasibility or if existing equipment was scheduled for replacement or conversion. The plan must contain a commitment to phase out CFC-based refrigerants within 10 years.

Projects that retain CFCs, even if a phase-out plan is in progress, are ineligible for EA Credit Enhanced Refrigerant Management. Account for all refrigerants present at time of application except those in existing small equipment with less than 0.5 pound (225 grams) of refrigerant.

1. *Questions and Answers about the Environmental Effects of the Ozone Layer Depletion and Climate Change: 2010 Update, http://ozone.unep.org/Assessment_Panels/EEAP/eeap-report2010-FAQ.pdf.*

STEP 5. DEVELOP PLAN TO MINIMIZE REFRIGERANT LEAKAGE IN ALL CFC-CONTAINING EQUIPMENT E

Develop a plan that addresses the best practices as outlined in the referenced standard. All buildings that continue to use CFC-based refrigerants after the performance period ends must address refrigerant leakage (see *Further Explanation, Minimizing Refrigerant Leakage*). The plan must be implemented on all equipment that contains CFC-based refrigerants even if the equipment will be phased out or converted within five years.

STEP 6. SELECT NEW EQUIPMENT THAT CONTAINS NO CFC REFRIGERANTS

If adding or replacing HVAC&R equipment, confirm that CFC refrigerants are not used. Older or retrofit equipment with higher efficiency ratings are the most likely to have CFCs, but it is important to check the refrigerant type for all new equipment.

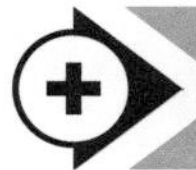

FURTHER EXPLANATION

ECONOMIC ANALYSIS

The economic analysis used to determine the feasibility of replacing or converting CFC-based equipment must include the following variables:

Equipment and installation or conversion cost. For existing equipment, include any work that would be required to use an alternative refrigerant (e.g., piping, seal replacement). Include all installation costs for new equipment, including demolition or removal of existing equipment, if required. For remaining equipment, also consider the costs for additional leak detection equipment, if required.

Equipment life. Account for the expected life of both new and existing equipment.

Energy cost. Include the energy cost savings of operating new equipment. For existing refrigeration equipment, also include the energy requirements for operating the equipment with different refrigerants. Because older refrigerants were selected for their superior energy performance, replacing the refrigerant may increase energy costs.

Maintenance cost. For conversion or equipment replacement, consider changes in maintenance frequency and scope and account for any new or different demands on building staff.

Refrigerant cost savings. Account for the difference in cost of refrigerants. Use historical annual leakage rates for existing equipment, a default annual rate of 2%, or actual manufacturer's data for replacement equipment. Additionally, consider that the costs of CFC refrigerants may increase as their availability becomes more limited.

It is recommended that the economic analysis also include assessment of the changes to the system design capacity, improved plant capabilities, and system level efficiency.

EXAMPLE

A project team is considering replacing a chiller that uses R-22 and conducts the following economic analysis.

EQUATION 1. Simple payback for equipment replacement or conversion

$$\text{Simple payback} = \frac{\text{Cost of replacement or conversion}}{\text{Resulting annual energy cost difference} + \text{Resulting annual maintenance and refrigerant cost difference}} > 10$$

TABLE 1. Example economic feasibility comparison, replacement versus conversion

	Replacement	Conversion
Equipment, installation	$500,000	—
Conversion	N/A	$89,737
Annual energy savings	$24,930	($8,000)
Maintenance savings	$1,200	N/A
Annual refrigerant savings	$2,058	$2,058
Equipment life	23 years	10 years
Payback period	17.74 years	—

The simple payback period for chiller replacement is greater than 10 years. Conversion is also not economically feasible because the conversion increases operating costs. Since neither replacement nor conversion is feasible, a CFC phase-out plan is not required.

MINIMIZING REFRIGERANT LEAKAGE

When CFC-containing equipment is retained, project teams must adhere to the U.S. Clean Air Act, Title VI, Section 608 (or a local equivalent for projects outside the U.S.), to minimize leakage. Apply the following best practices in addition to the requirements of Section 608:

- Require that the maximum amount of ozone-depleting compounds (including both CFCs and HCFCs) be recycled during the servicing and disposal of air-conditioning and refrigeration equipment.
- Require that recycling and recovery equipment and technicians be certified, and prohibit the sale of refrigerants to uncertified technicians. Require the technicians to confirm with the U.S. Environmental Protection Agency (or the authority having jurisdiction for projects outside the U.S.) that they have acquired recycling or recovery equipment and are complying with the requirements of the rule.
- Require the repair of substantial leaks in air-conditioning and refrigeration equipment with a charge of greater than 50 pounds (23 kilograms).
- Establish safe disposal requirements to ensure removal of refrigerants from goods that enter the waste stream with the charge intact (e.g., refrigerators, room air-conditioners).
- Prohibit individuals from knowingly venting ozone-depleting compounds that are used as refrigerants (generally CFCs and HCFCs) into the atmosphere while maintaining, servicing, repairing, or disposing of air-conditioning or refrigeration equipment (including appliances).

PROJECT TYPE VARIATIONS

District Energy Systems (DES)

All upstream and downstream equipment owned by the project building must meet the prerequisite requirements. Upstream equipment owned by a third party is excluded.

CAMPUS

Group Approach

Submit separate documentation for each building.

Campus Approach

Eligible.

REQUIRED DOCUMENTATION

	Documentation	All projects	Phase-out plan	Economic feasibility
E	Equipment type	X	X	X
E	Refrigerant type	X	X	X
E	Installation date	X	X	X
E	CFC conversion and replacement plan		X	
E	Refrigerant leakage rate or quantity		X	X
E	Phase-out completion date		X	
E	Leakage reduction plan		X	X
E	New equipment or conversion cost			X
E	Predicted savings			X

RELATED CREDIT TIPS

EA Credit Enhanced Refrigerant Management. Selecting equipment that has low ozone depletion potential (ODP) and global warming potential (GWP), as well as no CFCs, will assist with achievement of the related credit.

EA Credit Optimize Energy Performance. Alternative refrigerants, such as HFC-410A, have lower refrigerant impacts than CFCs and HCFCs but may use more energy use. Conversely, some energy-efficient systems, like variable refrigerant flow (VRF), may increase the overall refrigerant impact because they require a higher amount of refrigerants.

CHANGES FROM LEED 2009

None.

REFERENCED STANDARDS

U.S. EPA Clean Air Act, Title VI, Section 608, Refrigerant Recycling Rule: epa.gov/air/caa/

EXEMPLARY PERFORMANCE

Not available.

DEFINITIONS

chlorofluorocarbon (CFC)-based refrigerant a fluid, containing hydrocarbons, that absorbs heat from a reservoir at low temperatures and rejects heat at higher temperatures. When emitted into the atmosphere, CFCs cause depletion of the stratospheric ozone layer.

ENERGY AND ATMOSPHERE CREDIT

Existing Building Commissioning—Analysis

This credit applies to:

Existing Buildings (2 points)
Schools (2 points)
Retail (2 points)
Data Centers (2 points)
Hospitality (2 points)
Warehouses and Distribution Centers (2 points)

INTENT

To use the existing building commissioning process to improve building operations, energy, and resource efficiency.

REQUIREMENTS

ESTABLISHMENT E

Evaluate the current performance of the project building against the performance specifications in the current facilities requirements and the operations and maintenance plan.

Identify the systems and components in the facility to be investigated and analyzed as part of the existing building commissioning or energy auditing process. Provide a breakdown of estimated resource use for each of these systems.

OPTION 1. EXISTING BUILDING COMMISSIONING

Develop an existing building commissioning plan to effectively inventory and evaluate specific opportunities within the systems being analyzed. The commissioning plan must include the following:

- updated current facilities requirements;
- the commissioning team members and their roles and responsibilities during the commissioning process;
- a description of the approach for identifying and analyzing facility improvement opportunities;
- the process for reviewing and prioritizing identified opportunities with the owner and developing an implementation plan;
- the format and content of the eventual deliverables from the commissioning process; and
- the proposed schedule.

OPTION 2. ENERGY AUDIT

Develop an energy audit plan following the requirements of ASHRAE Level 2, Energy Survey and Analysis, to evaluate efficiency opportunities. The audit plan must include the following:

- the audit team members and their roles and responsibilities during the audit process;
- a description of the approach for identifying and analyzing facility improvement opportunities;
- the process for reviewing and prioritizing identified opportunities with the owner and developing an implementation plan;
- the format and content of the eventual deliverables from the audit process; and
- the proposed schedule.

PERFORMANCE P

Apply the requirements below to all direct energy-consuming or energy-producing systems, including lighting, process loads, HVAC&R, domestic water heating, and renewable energy.

Update the systems and components to be addressed as part of the existing building commissioning or energy auditing process. Provide a breakdown of estimated resource use for each of these systems.

OPTION 1. EXISTING BUILDING COMMISSIONING

Update and execute the existing building commissioning plan.

OPTION 2. ENERGY AUDIT

Update and execute the energy audit plan following the requirements of ASHRAE Level 2, Energy Survey and Analysis.

For each opportunity, describe the potential improvement, estimated implementation costs, and anticipated savings.

DATA CENTERS ONLY

In addition to the requirements above, data centers must use the Department of Energy's Save Energy Now Program's on-line DC Pro Energy Assessment Tools for data center critical systems.

BEHIND THE INTENT

Commissioning (Cx) of an existing building helps ensure that its operations align with owners' and occupants' requirements and allows facilities staff to identify areas where the building is not performing optimally. Existing building commissioning relies on a process of dynamically testing equipment according to their sequences of operation to determine that the system operation meets the owner's current facility requirements.

Energy audits also aim to improve building performance but are generally focused on energy improvement opportunities and savings. An ASHRAE Level 2 energy audit is an accounting assessment of equipment age and efficiency as well as operating procedures.

Beyond the baseline assessment and plan developed in EA Prerequisite Energy Efficiency Best Management Practices, existing building commissioning and energy auditing can enhance understanding of how the building uses energy, identify additional opportunities to improve performance, quantify energy and cost savings for energy conservation measures (ECMs), and ensure that the operational and comfort needs of building occupants are met. Both activities will identify potential energy conservation opportunities through equipment upgrades or retrofits, as well as operational changes that could improve the operating efficiency of the building's equipment and systems.

STEP-BY-STEP GUIDANCE

STEP 1. SELECT ONE OPTION E

Review the project's goals and desired outcome, the status of original design documents, and the state of existing building systems. Select the preferred option.

- Option 1 is appropriate if the focus will be on controls, proper system operations, and efficiency improvements, if the existing documentation is current, and if the control systems are functional. This option also lays the foundation for future commissioning activities under EA Credit Ongoing Commissioning.
- Option 2 is appropriate if the owner wishes to make major upgrades to the building envelope or mechanical, electrical, or controls systems to reduce the building's energy use, or if documentation is not up-to-date.

These two options are available to all buildings regardless of age or history of upgrades, commissioning and energy auditing; however, well-documented and up-to-date as-built drawings, schedules, operations and maintenance plan, and sequences of operation will facilitate the commissioning process (see *Further Explanation, Choosing an Appropriate Energy Analysis Program*).

STEP 2. IDENTIFY PROJECT TEAM E

Assemble a team to work on the necessary assessment and planning for commissioning or an energy audit (See *Further Explanation, Existing Building Commissioning or Energy Audit Team Members*). A typical team includes the following people and roles:

- Owner, to define current facility requirements
- General manager or property manager, to facilitate and support the commissioning or auditing process, review and approve the activities coordinated by the commissioning authority (CxA) or energy auditor, and assist in developing the current facility requirements for the CxA or auditor
- Building engineering staff, to lead development of the building operating plan and assisting in resolving problems
- Commissioning authority or energy auditor, to coordinate the process and ensure that the required activities are implemented professionally and in compliance (see *Further Explanation, Choosing the Appropriate Commissioning Authority or Energy Auditor*).
- Controls contractor (if necessary), to perform the activities defined in the functional performance test procedures and demonstrate that controls logic and sequences comply with current sequences of operation and current facility requirements

STEP 3. REVIEW PERFORMANCE SPECIFICATIONS IN CURRENT FACILITIES REQUIREMENTS AND OPERATIONS AND MAINTENANCE PLAN E

Review the performance specifications established and documented under EA Prerequisite Energy Efficiency Best Management Practices.

- Ensure that the CFR and O&M documents accurately interpret the desired building operations to meet the energy, cost, schedule, and comfort requirements of the occupants and the owner.
- Use these specifications as the basis against which to compare the current building performance.

STEP 4. IDENTIFY SYSTEMS TO BE EVALUATED AND ESTIMATE THEIR RESOURCE CONSUMPTION E

Identify and become familiar with all energy-using and energy-producing systems and equipment that are under the management's control. Estimate or measure the resource consumption for all major energy end uses. Examine energy consumption by major end use to help the project team determine which equipment and systems should be targeted for energy reduction (see *Further Explanation, Determining Major Energy End Uses*).

STEP 5. DEVELOP COMMISSIONING PLAN OR ENERGY AUDIT PLAN E

Depending on the option selected, develop an existing building commissioning or energy audit plan that outlines the scope of activities, roles and responsibilities of all participants, schedule of commissioning or auditing activities, and method for documenting and prioritizing improvement opportunities.

For projects pursuing Option 1, consider the credit requirements of EA Credit Ongoing Commissioning while preparing the commissioning plan; the plan will become the basis for the final commissioning report (see *Further Explanation, Existing Building Commissioning Plan*).

STEP 6. DEVELOP EXISTING BUILDING COMMISSIONING OR ENERGY AUDITING SCHEDULE AND TIMELINE E

Once the equipment has been identified and the team assembled, coordinate the schedule and timeline with all team members. Consider the following factors:

- Availability of operating staff and all other team members
- Total length of the performance period
- Amount of time required to complete each task and functional performance testing procedures
- Seasonal operating schedules (e.g., chillers that are not operated in winter, boilers that are not operated in summer)

Option 1. Existing Building Commissioning

STEP 1. DEVELOP TESTING PROCEDURES AND DECIDE ON REPORTING FORMAT E

Develop a set of testing procedures to assess building systems' operation, including sensor and equipment checks, functional testing, and alarms. The functional performance testing procedures should be based on the available information and aligned with the owner's CFR.

- Testing the operation of the systems against the sequences of operation allows the CxA to identify dynamic operational errors that may waste energy.
- Testing equipment by using the sequences of operation allows the CxA to identify additional efficiency opportunities.

Decide how to present the test results in the Cx report and what information is most important to convey to the owner (see *Further Explanation, Tests and Procedures* and *Functional Testing and Reporting*).

STEP 2. DETERMINE CRITERIA FOR EVALUATING AND PRIORITIZING OPPORTUNITIES AND ISSUES E

Issues identified during the commissioning process can be considered opportunities for improved operational and energy efficiency. The following kinds of issues may be identified:

- Equipment sensors are not calibrated.
- Equipment does not respond to building automation system (BAS) or controller input.
- Equipment malfunctions.

- Equipment is unable to maintain setpoint.
- Equipment has unstable operation and/or hunts.
- Equipment does not respond according to the sequence of operation.
- Equipment does not respond or incorrectly responds to alarm conditions.
- Sequence of operation is not appropriate for the CFR.

Decide on a method for evaluating which issues should be dealt with first, using such criteria as cost, occupants' comfort, and ease of resolution (see *Further Explanation, Determining Criteria for Project Implementation*).

STEP 3. EXECUTE COMMISSIONING PLAN AND DOCUMENT RESULTS P

Use a log to record any issues or opportunities identified during the testing.

- Note the date, type and location of equipment, and the identified issue or opportunity for improvement.
- The CxA and building staff are responsible for determining the costs associated for correcting each issue or implementing each opportunity.
- See *Further Explanation, Functional Testing and Reporting.*

STEP 4. DOCUMENT CHANGES TO CFR AND O&M PLAN P

If changes were implemented as part of the commissioning process, update the CFR and the O&M plan to reflect building's current status.

Option 2. Energy Audit

STEP 1. DETERMINE APPROACH FOR ANALYZING FACILITY AND DEVELOP REPORTING FORMAT E

Follow the guidance in ASHRAE's Procedures for Commercial Building Energy Audits and the requirements of EA Prerequisite Energy Efficiency Best Management Practices for identifying and analyzing improvement opportunities. Based on these references, develop a format for reporting issues and recommendations to the owner.

The ASHRAE Level 2 audit builds on the procedures and methods developed as part of the Level 1 audit. Project teams pursuing this option may wish to perform both the Level 1 and Level 2 audits together.

STEP 2. PERFORM ENERGY AUDIT AND DOCUMENT RESULTS P

Implement the ASHRAE Level 2 analysis, following ASHRAE's Procedures for Commercial Building Energy Audits.

- The energy auditor must document all ECMs in a report and share these results with the building owner.
- The energy auditor must associate each potential facility improvement with predicted energy use, energy demand, energy cost, and maintenance cost savings.
- If planned, the ASHRAE Level 2 analysis—including in-depth review of existing design drawings, operating procedures, installed condition of equipment, and maintenance methods—can occur concurrently with the ASHRAE Level 1 walk-through analysis undertaken for EA Prerequisite Energy Efficiency Best Management Practices.
- An energy audit may uncover operating deficiencies, but its focus is on upgrades to systems to reduce energy use while maintaining the CFR.

STEP 3. DOCUMENT CHANGES TO CFR AND O&M PLAN P

If changes were implemented as part of the auditing process, work with building staff to update the CFR and the O&M plan to reflect the building's current status.

FURTHER EXPLANATION

CALCULATIONS

Simple Payback Period

The simple payback period is the length of time required to recoup the initial investment from an operational improvement or capital investment. This calculation reveals when the investment will effectively pay for itself and begin to generate actual net savings. Use Equation 1.

EQUATION 1. Simple payback period

$$\text{Simple payback (years)} = \left\{ \frac{\text{Project cost (\$)}}{\text{Annual operating savings (\$)}} \right\}$$

For example, an equipment upgrade costing $1,200 will generate total annual savings (energy consumption + energy peak demand + maintenance labor and materials) of $600. The simple payback period is $1,200 divided by $600, or 2 years. Beginning in the third year, the upgrade will be generating net savings for the building operating budget.

Rate of Return

Rate of return, or return on investment (ROI), is the ratio of cost savings generated by an improvement or upgrade relative to the amount of money invested to perform the improvement. Knowing the rate of return helps determine the profitability of investments that may be undertaken now or in the future. Although a $100,000 improvement that saves $1,000 per year delivers a larger annual savings, a $1,000 improvement that saves $100 per year has a much higher rate of return. Use Equation 2.

EQUATION 2. Return on investment

$$\text{ROI (\%)} = \left\{ \frac{\text{Annual savings (\$)}}{\text{Project cost (\$)}} \right\}$$

For example, installing time clocks to control ventilation fan operation in a building parking garage requires an initial investment of $5,000. By reducing ventilation fan run-time, the clocks cut energy costs for the building by $250 per year. The rate of return for this investment is 5%.

Cost-Benefit Ratio

The cost-benefit ratio determines the total financial return for each dollar invested in operational improvements and upgrades. The cost-benefit ratio indicates the effectiveness of each dollar invested in generating operational cost savings. The cost-benefit ratio is used to determine the effectiveness of a project over its lifetime, rather than annual savings. Use Equation 3.

EQUATION 3. Cost-benefit ratio

$$\text{Cost-benefit ratio} = \left\{ \frac{\text{Total operating savings (\$)}}{\text{Project cost (\$)}} \right\}$$

For example, replacement of a conventional water heater with an on-demand system costs \$1,500 and generates \$200 per year in energy cost savings. The cost-benefit ratio for the project over the 15-year anticipated lifetime of the system is \$3,000 divided by \$1,500, or 2. For every \$1 invested in the new water heating system, a savings of \$2 is expected.

EXISTING BUILDING COMMISSIONING OR ENERGY AUDIT TEAM MEMBERS

Assembling the right team is important to the success of existing building commissioning or an energy audit. In-house team members and even third-party experts may not be able to perform all the necessary activities. Consider the goals, schedule, and desired outcome and determine whether team members in addition to those listed in Step 2 are needed. Depending on what the tests reveal, other team members may include the following:

- Mechanical, electrical, and plumbing service providers, if equipment needs to be repaired, replaced or upgraded
- Testing and balancing contractor, if air systems are not correctly balanced
- Cooling tower chemical maintenance contractor, if cooling tower efficiency or water usage has been affected by the chemical composition of the condenser water
- Other maintenance staff

CHOOSING AN APPROPRIATE ENERGY ANALYSIS PROGRAM

The choice between existing building commissioning and the ASHRAE Level 2 audit depends on the owner's desired outcome of the analysis as well as the status of original and updated design documents and the state of the existing systems.

- Existing building commissioning may be better suited for buildings that are relatively new or have been recently retrofitted, have an up-to-date sequence of operation, and are seeking improved operational efficiency.
- Energy auditing may be more useful for older buildings that have not been recently retrofitted or are missing original and updated design documents, and whose owner is evaluating capital upgrades to improve energy consumption.

The following matrix, offered only as guidance, may be helpful in deciding between existing building commissioning and an ASHRAE Level 2 audit. The appropriate option should be determined by the project team based on their knowledge of the project building.

TABLE 1. Determining Appropriateness of ASHRAE Level 2 Audit

Evaluation criteria	Existing building Cx	ASHRAE Level 2 energy audit
Owner wishes to evaluate upgrades to building envelope		X
Owner wishes to evaluate upgrades to mechanical, electrical or plumbing systems		X
Owner wishes to evaluate upgrades to controls systems	X	X
Energy consumption is higher than expected	X	X
Owner wishes to improve energy efficiency	X	X
Building equipment exhibits persistent failure	X	X
Occupants' complaints are frequent	X	
Owner is planning capital investment		X
Sequence of operations is up-to-date	X	
Sequence of operations is not up-to-date		X
As-built drawings are available and up-to-date	X	
As-built drawings are not available and/or are not up-to-date		X
Building or building retrofit is less than 5 years old	X	
Building or building retrofit is more than 5 years old		X
Building function or use has changed since original design	X	X

CHOOSING THE APPROPRIATE COMMISSIONING AUTHORITY OR ENERGY AUDITOR

Existing building commissioning activities can be conducted either by in-house operations staff or by a third-party CxA who is responsible for all testing and issues reporting. In-house staff may be capable of conducting the functional performance tests, and doing so may further their understanding of the building operations. However, as the facility requirements change or as systems are retrofitted over the lifetime of the building, a CxA may need to be retained to ensure that all test scripts and procedures are up-to-date and properly documented.

Energy auditing activities can be completed by a third-party consultant or qualified in-house staff. Determine whether the current staff has the interest, knowledge, and perhaps most importantly, time to complete the audit. If the analysis will be performed in-house, closely review the ASHRAE Procedures for Commercial Building Energy Audits to ensure that staff collect the proper data during the building walk-through.

See EA Prerequisite Energy Efficiency Best Management Practices, *Further Explanation, In-House versus Third-Party Audit,* regarding the pros and cons of using an outside consultant versus in-house staff.

DETERMINING MAJOR ENERGY END USES

Identify and become familiar with all energy-using systems and equipment that are under the management's control. The major end uses can be estimated by one of the following methods:

- Submetering specific systems and equipment, using either permanently installed meters or temporary data collectors
- Engineering analysis, such as energy modeling or manual calculations

Examples of major energy end users in commercial buildings include the following:

- Interior lighting
- Exterior lighting
- Space heating
- Space cooling
- Pumps
- Heat rejection

- Fans
- Domestic hot water
- Receptacle equipment

The building engineer, CxA, or energy auditor may assess energy end uses by studying the building's utility panels and meter layout.

The energy auditor can create a calibrated energy model to estimate energy end uses as well as assess recommended energy conservation measures and operational opportunities uncovered during the ASHRAE Level 2 energy audit. Most energy modeling software produces an energy end-use report.

The ASHRAE Procedures for Commercial Building Energy Audits provides additional guidance for determining energy end uses. Resources for estimating common energy end uses include the Commercial Building Energy Consumption Survey (2003), End-Use Consumption Tables for Non-Mall Buildings, and End-Use Consumption Tables for All Buildings. However, the final breakdown of estimated energy end uses must be specific to the project building.

EXISTING BUILDING COMMISSIONING PLAN

The CxA develops the existing building commissioning plan with input from the project team. The Cx plan should contain, at minimum, the following elements.

Cx program overview

- Goals and objectives
- General project information, including updated CFR, sequences of operation, and O&M plan
- Systems to be commissioned
- Schedule of commissioning activities

Cx team

- Team members, roles, and responsibilities
- Communication protocol, coordination, meetings, and management

Cx process activities

- Reviewing the CFR
- Reviewing the O&M plan
- Conducting a site inventory
- Developing systems functional test procedures
- Determining data logging procedures
- Verifying system performance
- Reporting and prioritizing issues and opportunities to the owner
- Developing a resolution process and implementation plan for identified deficiencies and opportunities

Commissioning Tests and Procedures

The following tests and procedures are often used in conjunction and can be used to assess whether building systems are operating correctly.

- Sensor checks verify the location and calibration of sensors. Sensors are monitoring devices within a system that measure equipment's operational conditions, such as temperature, cfm, and relative humidity.
- Device checks verify the equipment's ability to respond correctly to a signal sent by the associated controller (whether a BAS or a local switch). For example, when a damper is commanded to modulate via the BAS, the field observation should match the open or close signal that is sent to the damper actuator.
- Functional or operational testing follows verification that the controller or BAS is communicating correctly with the equipment. It confirms that equipment responds correctly to inputs as specified by the up-to-date sequence of operations. For example, if the temperature reading at a thermostat falls below the setpoint for that space, the sequence of operation may call for the zone fan-powered box to modulate its damper to the minimum position and energize a stage of electric heat until the zone space temperature increases and the thermostat setpoint is satisfied.

- Alarm testing follows verification that the controller or BAS is communicating correctly with equipment. It confirms that equipment responds appropriately during emergency conditions. Alarms are generally programmed into the sequence of operation to preserve equipment during nondesign operating conditions or during life-safety events, such as a fire.
- Point trending, available with most BAS systems, involves monitoring and recording operating setpoints and system output parameters over time. It tracks the long-term dynamic behavior of a system during actual operating conditions. To gain the most from point trending, the BAS should be able to monitor and record trend data at least one-hour intervals and store at least one week's worth of data for all points monitored. Issues that may be identified when trending system performance include the following:
  - Over- and then undershooting a system setpoint over time ("hunting")
  - Inability to make setpoint (because of constant over- or undershooting)
  - Incorrect response to signal input
- Metering is similar to point trending but measures actual energy consumption directly. Metering may involve a main meter at the building entrance, permanent submeters located at the system or equipment level, or temporary spot meters located at the system or equipment level.

DETERMINING CRITERIA FOR PROJECT IMPLEMENTATION

Determining the criteria for prioritization gives the project team a standard process for evaluation. Basic criteria for determining which issues warrant priority resolution may include the following:

- **Human health concerns.** Conditions that could harm occupants' health or cause discomfort should be a priority.
- **Low- or no-cost improvements.** A problem with controls or similar issues with low or no cost (as defined by the owner or project team) can be resolved quickly and inexpensively by in-house staff or the controls contractor.
- **Capital project, acceptable payback period.** An improvement that is capital intensive (as defined by the owner) but significantly reduces the building's energy consumption may have a payback period that is acceptable to the owner.
- **Capital project, unacceptable payback period.** A capital-intensive improvement may significantly reduce the building's energy consumption but have a payback period that extends beyond the owner's acceptable timeframe.

During the existing building commissioning and energy audit, the expert and team will likely identify opportunities to save energy that cannot be implemented without requesting additional budget. A return-on-investment or simple payback calculation can be run to determine whether the upgrade is a worthwhile investment that will pay for itself over a specified time. Although the initial cost may be high, the ultimate reduction in energy costs can make it more attractive.

FUNCTIONAL TESTING AND REPORTING

Commissioning of existing buildings consists of the following activities.

Developing functional test scripts

The CxA must create functional testing scripts that follow the most up-to-date sequences of operation. The functional performance tests typically have the following sections:

- **Date and time of test**
- **Individuals present during testing**
- **Visual inspection observations.** Before testing, the CxA should perform a visual inspection and document any issues or observations.
- **Sensor checks.** The sensors are checked individually to make sure they are reading properly and are in the correct locations, per the design and controls documents.
- **Device checks.** Each device is checked to verify it can open, close, modulate, start, stop, energize in stages, etc.

- **Operating mode tests.** A system is run through each type of operating mode, such as startup, shutdown, capacity modulation, emergency and failure modes, alarm scenarios, occupied mode and unoccupied mode, and interlocks with other equipment.
- **Results.** The Cx indicates whether the system passed, failed, or requires retesting.

The CxA shares the functional tests with the building engineers and managers before testing so that they can review the scripts, verify proper operating modes, and comment on modifications to match actual operation, if different.

Executing functional testing

Functional testing begins only after all system components are installed, energized, programmed, balanced, and otherwise ready for operation under partial- and full-load conditions. Any systems that require deferred or seasonal testing or verification to verify proper operation in each mode must be noted in the commissioning report. A report addendum can then be issued to discuss the seasonal testing results.

The CxA typically oversees the testing, but the building engineers execute the testing. Sampling may be appropriate for multiples of the same type of equipment with the same components and sequences. In certain cases, the CxA and owner can choose sampling as a method to control costs while still testing a representative population of the building's equipment. If major deficiencies are uncovered during testing, the sampling rate may need to be increased to determine whether the identified deficiency is endemic to the equipment type being tested. A typical minimum sampling rate is "10 or 10%, whichever is greater" for large quantities of identical equipment. However, the responsibility of choosing a reasonable sampling rate is left up to the CxA, building staff, and owner, who may wish to exceed the minimum. Including the building engineer or owner in the testing execution provides training for future operation of the systems.

Documenting issues and opportunities

As the functional testing is executed, the CxA logs the results, recording any deficiency or potential improvement discovered and responsible party for subsequent action. The CxA is responsible for maintaining the log to track the status of issues. Correction of problems may fall to multiple responsible parties.

Preparing the Cx report

The CxA reports on all components of the commissioning process and prepares a document with the following sections:

- Executive summary of commissioning process and results, system deficiencies identified and resolution, and outstanding issues
- Project team directory
- Cx process overview
- Current facility requirements
- Operations and maintenance plan
- List of systems commissioned
- Installation verification checklists (required only if equipment is retrofitted)
- Functional performance tests
- Issues log, noting open and closed issues

RATING SYSTEM VARIATIONS

Data Centers

In addition to the requirements above, data centers must use the U.S. Department of Energy's Save Energy Now Program's online DC Pro Energy Assessment Tools for data center critical systems. The DC Pro Tool Suite is available online through the Department of Energy website as either a web-based application or a downloadable version. Using a description of the data center, utility bill data, and equipment information, it provides a depiction of the data center's overall energy use and efficiency and potential areas for improvement.

PROJECT TYPE VARIATIONS

District Energy Systems (DES)

All downstream equipment is included in the scope of this credit. Such equipment includes heat exchangers, steam pressure reduction stations, pumps, valves, pipes, building electrical services, and controls.

All upstream equipment associated with serving the project building is included in the scope if the project building is taking credit for the efficiency of the DES under EA Credit Optimize Energy Performance; otherwise, upstream equipment is excluded.

Commissioning or auditing applies only to the DES services the project building is using. For example, if the building is using only the heating services of a district heating and cooling plant, then only the heating systems of the DES must be included in the scope; however, commissioning or auditing of upstream equipment applies to the entire portion of the DES, including both the central plant and the transmission and distribution systems.

CAMPUS

Group Approach

All buildings in the group may be documented as one. If so, each building in the group must use the same compliance option to meet the credit requirements.

Campus Approach

Ineligible. Each LEED project may pursue the credit individually.

REQUIRED DOCUMENTATION

	Documentation	Option 1	Option 2
E	Existing building commissioning plan	X	
E	Level 2 energy audit plan		X
E	Updated CFR	X	
E	Team members, roles, responsibilities	X	X
E	Schedule	X	X
P	Energy use breakdown	X	X
P	List of issues found and planned resolution	X	
P	List of planned facility improvements	X	X
P	Confirmation that significant upgrades and revisions have been added to CFR and O&M plan		X

RELATED CREDIT TIPS

EA Prerequisite Energy Efficiency Best Management Practices. The ASHRAE Level 2 energy analysis undertaken as part of this credit may be performed simultaneously with the ASHRAE Level 1 analysis required by the related prerequisite. The plan developed for the related prerequisite may serve as the foundation for the commissioning plan prepared this credit.

EA Prerequisite Minimum Energy Performance. The activities conducted through commissioning or an energy audit, as required by this credit, provide opportunities to reduce energy consumption and can therefore improve performance that will contribute to achievement of the related prerequisite.

EA Credit Existing Building Commissioning—Implementation. Low- and no-cost energy conservation measures found through this credit must be implemented under the related credit. The requirements of this credit must be met to earn the related credit.

EA Credit Ongoing Commissioning. The requirements of this credit and EA Credit Existing Building Commissioning—Implementation must be met to earn the related credit. The existing building commissioning plan can be the basis for the ongoing commissioning plan, but projects that pursue the ASHRAE Level 2 energy analysis (Option 2 of this credit) may need to do additional work to achieve the ongoing commissioning credit.

CHANGES FROM LEED 2009

For DES, building-owned systems are treated the same as third-party systems.

REFERENCED STANDARDS

ASHRAE Procedures for Commercial Building Energy Audits, 2nd edition: ashrae.org

EXEMPLARY PERFORMANCE

Not available.

DEFINITIONS

commissioning (Cx) the process of verifying and documenting that a building and all of its systems and assemblies are planned, designed, installed, tested, operated, and maintained to meet the owner's project requirements

current facilities requirements (CFR) the implementation of the owner's project requirements, developed to confirm the owner's current operational needs and requirements

district energy system (DES) a central energy conversion plant and transmission and distribution system that provides thermal energy to a group of buildings (e.g., a central cooling plant on a university campus). It does not include central energy systems that provide only electricity.

operations and maintenance (O&M) plan a plan that specifies major system operating parameters and limits, maintenance procedures and schedules, and documentation methods necessary to demonstrate proper operation and maintenance of an approved emissions control device or system

ENERGY AND ATMOSPHERE CREDIT

Existing Building Commissioning—Implementation

This credit applies to:

Existing Buildings (2 points)
Schools (2 points)
Retail (2 points)
Data Centers (2 points)
Hospitality (2 points)
Warehouses and Distribution Centers (2 points)

INTENT

To use the existing building commissioning process to improve building operations, energy and resource efficiency.

REQUIREMENTS

ESTABLISHMENT E

Meet the requirements of EA Credit Existing Building Commissioning—Analysis.

PERFORMANCE P

Apply the requirements below to all direct energy-consuming or energy-producing systems, including lighting, process loads, HVAC&R, domestic water heating, and renewable energy.

Implement no- or low-cost operational improvements and develop a five-year plan for equipment replacement and major modifications or upgrades based on the analysis phase.

Confirm training of building operations staff so that they can efficiently operate all new or substantially altered building equipment or systems.

Develop a tracking and verification program for all projects implemented as part of the existing building commissioning process. Note factors such as effectiveness, financial costs and benefits, and observed or estimated environmental and human health and comfort benefits.

Update the operations and maintenance plan and the current facilities requirements to incorporate the newly implemented improvements.

BEHIND THE INTENT

EA Prerequisite Energy Efficiency Best Management Practices and EA Credit Existing Building Commissioning—Analysis set the path for implementation, in the form of a list of energy conservation measures (ECMs) (from the energy audit) or an issues log (from commissioning).

The ECMs should be organized by category, such as no-and-low-cost items and capital projects that, if properly implemented, will save the project energy and reduce operating costs to pay for themselves over time. The implementation of ECMs demonstrates a commitment to energy usage reduction and continual improvement.

Like the ECMs, the issues documented should be characterized by cost, as no- and low-cost items or capital projects, to help determine priority. Other factors include effects on other systems and on occupants.

The implementation program should include a mechanism for verifying energy savings. Verification allows project teams to correct any errors that may have occurred during implementation and quantify the benefits of the program. Comparing the predicted and actual energy savings will support teams as they continue to assess future options for energy savings.

STEP-BY-STEP GUIDANCE

STEP 1. CONFIRM ANTICIPATED ACHIEVEMENT OF EA CREDIT EXISTING BUILDING COMMISSIONING—ANALYSIS E

Projects that do not comply with the analysis credit cannot earn this implementation credit, which requires that energy conservation opportunities found through the commissioning or auditing analysis be implemented.

STEP 2. CREATE PLAN TO IMPLEMENT NO- AND LOW-COST MEASURES P

Develop an implementation plan for the identified no- and low-cost measures that includes the following activities:

- Review the list of opportunities identified in EA Credit Existing Building Commissioning—Analysis.
- Classify all measures either as low- or no-cost or as capital intensive, according to the established criteria.
- Prepare an implementation schedule for all low- and no-cost measures.
- Determine whether the measures can be implemented by current building staff or must be contracted.
- Determine who will be responsible for implementation. If outside contractors or groups are required, the person identified as responsible will coordinate the work.

STEP 3. IMPLEMENT NO- AND LOW-COST MEASURES P

Using the implementation plan, complete the implementation of no- and low-cost measures (see *Further Explanation, Implementing Identified No- and Low-Cost Measures*). Maintain records to demonstrate that all indicated improvements were completed. Examples include invoices, the names and titles of those involved, the time each spent working on the measure, photos, emails, operational logs, and other evidence of completion.

STEP 4. DEVELOP FIVE-YEAR PLAN AND BUDGET FOR CAPITAL IMPROVEMENTS P

Review the list of identified building upgrades that have capital costs and create a five-year implementation plan (see *Further Explanation, Developing a Five-Year Implementation Plan for Capital Improvements*).

- Determine the best order for implementation of the future improvements and determine how each improvement will be implemented.
- Verify the process for budgeting the capital improvements.
- Assign a responsible persons or persons to each improvement and determine the steps that need to be taken to meet the schedule.

STEP 5. PROVIDE TRAINING FOR BUILDING OPERATIONS STAFF P

Organize and provide the necessary training for building staff and operators (see *Further Explanation, Training Building Operations Staff*).

- Create a training outline and provide any other documents that may be helpful for staff.
- Bring in experts as needed to train staff properly.
- Ask staff attending the training to sign an attendance sheet to demonstrate training was provided.

STEP 6. DEVELOP FORMAL TRACKING AND VERIFICATION PROGRAM FOR IMPLEMENTED ECMS P

Develop a detailed and viable tracking and verification program to monitor the results of the ECMs (see *Further Explanation, Developing a Formal Measurement and Verification Program*). This allows project teams to assess the actual energy savings for each ECM. The tracking and verification program must include the follow components:

- Verification of effectiveness
- Documentation of observed costs and operational benefits
- Observed or estimated environmental benefits
- Observed or estimated benefits to human health and comfort

STEP 7. UPDATE CURRENT FACILITY REQUIREMENTS AND OPERATIONS AND MAINTENANCE PLAN P

Update the current facility requirements to reflect the implementation of the no- and low-cost ECMs.

- Include the installation of new equipment and recalibration of existing equipment.
- Update the O&M plan outline.
- Update or write a sequence of operation for new and recalibrated equipment.

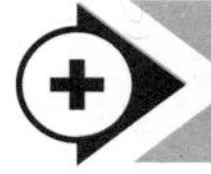

FURTHER EXPLANATION

IMPLEMENTING IDENTIFIED NO- AND LOW-COST MEASURES

The recommended no- and low-cost measures can be implemented in any of the following three basic approaches (from the ENERGY STAR® Building Manual).

- **Turnkey implementation.** The third-party commissioning or retro-commissioning agent or energy management consultant performs the service if the building in-house staff is not available or able to implement the measures.
- **In-house staff under expert direction.** ECMs are implemented by in-house staff with guidance from the third-party CxA or energy auditor, who oversees the implementation but does not directly complete the majority of the work. Involving building operators gives staff valuable training and insight into the operation of the building. Implementation by in-house staff may also be cheaper and faster. Skilled building operations staff can streamline the process and increase the effectiveness of the consultant's time by undertaking the following activities:
    - Collecting all building documentation and data
    - Performing preventive maintenance tasks before starting the implementation
    - Assisting with diagnostic trending and testing
    - Installing and removing temporary monitors
- **Owner-led implementation.** Either a highly qualified in-house engineer or a trusted service contractor can implement and verify the existing building commissioning measures.

All no- and low-cost measures must be implemented before the performance period ends but can be staged for budgetary reasons. To maximize savings, staff time, and project momentum, consider implementing all or most of the measures at one time.

DEVELOPING A FIVE-YEAR IMPLEMENTATION PLAN FOR CAPITAL IMPROVEMENTS

Advance planning helps ensure that all the information needed for future equipment replacements and major modifications or upgrades will be available. The five-year plan will also facilitate budgeting and scheduling.

A typical five-year plan lists anticipated major modifications, equipment replacement, and major upgrade tasks, with a schedule for performing them and their associated cost. A checklist can be kept for each piece of equipment and be updated after maintenance tasks are performed.

Projects that cannot be reasonably accommodated within a five-year period should be noted and tracked for future consideration.

TRAINING BUILDING OPERATIONS STAFF

Building operations staff must have thorough knowledge of how to operate new or significantly altered equipment. Training is typically provided by a third party or the commissioning authority, and sometimes by the equipment manufacturer or the general contractor.

Include all new HVAC&R, controls, and other systems improvements and cover all operating scenarios to help the building engineering team understand the most effective and efficient way to operate the building.

A training session can involve a classroom workshop with some hands-on demonstrations on the building equipment. Suggested topics for training sessions include the following (from California Commissioning Guide: Existing Buildings):

- Energy usage analysis
- Operating schedules and requirements
- Methods for identifying problems and deficiencies
- Description of project findings and measures that were implemented
- Improvements expected as a result of the commissioning or energy audit
- Operations and maintenance procedures needed to ensure that benefits are maintained
- Staff role in helping maintain savings

DEVELOPING A FORMAL TRACKING AND VERIFICATION PROGRAM

As energy conservation measures are implemented, it is important to verify the results. Tracking and verification ensure that the work was completed correctly and also establishes a new baseline for performance and allows for updated cost savings estimates. This program is ideally developed and deployed before implementation of ECMs. Building operations staff track the measures to ensure that systems continue to work properly and have lasting benefits. Best practices for a measurement and verification program include the following:

- **Verification of effectiveness.** Retest equipment to ensure the ECMs are working as expected. Document before-and-after energy use data to determine efficiency improvements. Also document any improvements to the overall facility's operation (e.g., number of maintenance calls).
- **Documentation of financial costs and benefits.** Document anticipated versus actual return on investment for each ECM to inform the analysis of future improvements. Include the benefits from longer equipment life, reduced maintenance, savings from change orders and warranty claims, and increased productivity and safety.
- **Observation or estimation of environmental and human benefits.** Document the number and type of occupants' complaints about thermal comfort, lighting quality, and indoor air quality before and after implementation.

An annual report is useful for evaluating and tracking long-term savings and benefits and will become a resource for current and future operators. It is recommended that a tracking and verification report be part of the O&M plan. Refer to the International Performance Measurement and Verification Protocol for additional guidance on developing an effective measurement and verification plan.

EXAMPLE NO- AND LOW-COST MEASURES

Significant energy efficiency improvements can be found in simple control changes or low-cost maintenance repairs that can be funded within the building's established maintenance budget.

- Isolate control of outside air to a separate control point on the energy management system and reprogram to run only during occupancy.
- Replace manual thermostats with programmable thermostats.
- Optimize start and stop times for air-handling units.
- Change the sequence of operation for chillers to better match cooling demand.
- Install optimization controllers on all refrigerated beverage machines.
- Repair the motorized damper motor for outside air intake.
- Repair or replace any nonfunctioning temperature and humidity sensors.
- Repair duct leaks.
- Reprogram DDC controls to prevent simultaneous heating and cooling.
- Reprogram timer switches for all domestic water heaters to match usage patterns.
- Adjust operating schedules to reflect daylight saving time.
- Replace lighting fixtures with more efficient ones.
- Recalibrate occupancy sensors, timers, and photocells to restore correct operation.
- Clean lighting fixtures to boost light output.

PROJECT TYPE VARIATIONS

District Energy Systems (DES)

All downstream equipment is included in the scope of this credit. Such equipment includes heat exchangers, steam pressure reduction stations, pumps, valves, pipes, building electrical services, and controls.

All upstream equipment associated with serving the project building is included in the scope if the project building is seeking credit for the efficiency of the DES under EA Credit Optimize Energy Performance; otherwise, upstream equipment is excluded.

Implementation of ECMs and planned upgrades applies only to the DES services the project building is using. For example, if the building is using only the heating services of a district heating and cooling plant, then only the heating systems of the DES must be included in the scope; however, commissioning or auditing of upstream equipment applies to that entire portion of the DES, including both the central plant and the transmission and distribution systems.

Show that all operational improvements and planned upgrades have been included in a formal tracking and verification program for all relevant DES equipment and that these improvements were implemented within the past three years.

CAMPUS

Group Approach

All buildings in the group may be documented as one.

Campus Approach

Ineligible. Each LEED project may pursue the credit individually.

REQUIRED DOCUMENTATION

	Documentation	All projects
P	List of all no- and low-cost measures implemented and their benefits	X
P	Summary of capital plan for major retrofits, upgrades	X
P	Description of management staff training program	X
P	Revisions to CFR and O&M plan	X

RELATED CREDIT TIPS

EA Credit Ongoing Commissioning. Projects must earn this implementation credit to earn the related credit.

EA Prerequisite Minimum Energy Performance and EA Credit Optimized Energy Performance. ECMs implemented under this credit will improve energy performance and can provide significant energy savings, supporting achievement of the related prerequisite and credit.

CHANGES FROM LEED 2009

- The capital plan required for major retrofits and upgrades is now specified as a five-year plan.
- A formal tracking and verification plan is now required for the implemented energy conservation measures.

REFERENCED STANDARDS

ENERGY STAR Building Manual—Retrocomissioning: energystar.gov/ia/business/EPA_BUM_CH5_RetroComm.pdf?ef1f-1a58

California Commissioning Guide: Existing Buildings: cacx.org/resources/documents/CA_Commissioning_Guide_Existing.pdf

Building Operator Certification: theboc.info/

International Performance Measurement and Verification Protocol—Concepts and Options for Determining Energy and Water Savings—Volume I: nrel.gov/

ENERGY STAR Guidelines for Energy Management: energystar.gov/index.cfm?c=guidelines.guidelines_index

EXEMPLARY PERFORMANCE

Not available.

DEFINITIONS

current facilities requirements (CFR) the implementation of the owner's project requirements, developed to confirm the owner's current operational needs and requirements

district energy system (**DES**) a central energy conversion plant and transmission and distribution system that provides thermal energy to a group of buildings (e.g., a central cooling plant on a university campus). It does not include central energy systems that provide only electricity.

low-cost improvement an operational improvement, such as a repair, upgrade, or staff training or retraining. In LEED, the project team determines the reasonable upper limit for low-cost improvements based on facility resources and operating budgets.

operations and maintenance (**O&M**) **plan** a plan that specifies major system operating parameters and limits, maintenance procedures and schedules, and documentation methods necessary to demonstrate proper operation and maintenance of an approved emissions control device or system

ENERGY AND ATMOSPHERE CREDIT

Ongoing Commissioning

This credit applies to:

Existing Buildings (3 points)
Schools (3 points)
Retail (3 points)
Data Centers (3 points)
Hospitality (3 points)
Warehouses and Distribution Centers (3 points)

INTENT

To use the existing building commissioning process to improve building operations, energy, and resource efficiency.

REQUIREMENTS

ESTABLISHMENT E

Meet the requirements of EA Credit Existing Building Commissioning–Analysis and EA Credit Existing Building Commissioning–Implementation.

Establish an ongoing commissioning process that includes planning, point monitoring, system testing, performance verification, corrective action response, ongoing measurement, and documentation to proactively address operating problems in the systems being commissioned.

Develop an on-going commissioning plan that defines the following:

- roles and responsibilities;
- measurement requirements (meters, points, metering systems, data access);
- the points to be tracked, with frequency and duration for trend monitoring;
- the limits of acceptable values for tracked points and metered values;
- the review process that will be used to evaluate performance;
- an action plan for identifying and correcting operational errors and deficiencies
- planning for repairs needed to maintain performance;
- the frequency of analyses in the first year (at least quarterly); and
- the subsequent analysis cycle (at least every 24 months).

PERFORMANCE P

Apply the requirements below to all direct energy-consuming or energy-producing systems, including lighting, process loads, HVAC&R, domestic water heating, and renewable energy.

- Update the systems manual with any modifications or new settings, and give the reason for any modifications from the original design. Define methods for improving operations and maintenance.
- Include quarterly reports during the first year of implementation and annual reports on the performance of building systems.

Continue to update the facility's operating and maintenance plan and current facilities requirements to reflect actual conditions and issue annual revisions of these documents.

Only activities associated with ongoing commissioning completed within two years of the LEED application may be included to show progress.

BEHIND THE INTENT

Ongoing commissioning builds on energy analyses and implementation of energy conservation measures (ECMs). The defining characteristic of an ongoing commissioning program is that the activities are on a continual, 24-month cycle. This helps ensure that the building operations are regularly reviewed and updated to address changing operational needs, and that new energy reduction opportunities are identified, implemented, and verified.

Ongoing commissioning and existing building commissioning have the same goal—improving building operations—but whereas existing building commissioning corrects operational issues, identifies no- and low-cost operational improvements, and updates the current facility requirements and operations and maintenance plan, ongoing commissioning ensures that the building continues to meet or exceed expectations for performance.

In addition to finding savings opportunities, ongoing commissioning programs help building operators locate operational or functional issues before they cause occupant discomfort or become costly to fix. The value of ongoing commissioning is based on performance improvements through measurement and assessment, and therefore elements of monitoring-based commissioning—such as submetering, point trending, ongoing data collection, and energy analytics—can be used to identify issues in real time. Ongoing commissioning demands commitment but delivers measurable returns.

STEP-BY-STEP GUIDANCE

STEP 1. CONFIRM COMPLIANCE WITH EA CREDIT EXISTING BUILDING COMMISSIONING—ANALYSIS AND EA CREDIT EXISTING BUILDING COMMISSIONING—IMPLEMENTATION E

Verify that all no- and low-cost ECMs identified in the commissioning analysis have been or will be implemented before the performance period ends.

- Confirm that the current facility requirements (CFR) and operations and maintenance (O&M) plan are up to date.
- Confirm that the CFR and associated documents are appropriate to generate testing and monitoring procedures.

STEP 2. CREATE ONGOING COMMISSIONING PLAN E

The existing building commissioning plan (see EA Credit Existing Building Commissioning—Analysis) can be easily modified to include the requirements of ongoing commissioning (see *Further Explanation, Ongoing Commissioning Basics*).

- For projects that completed EA Credit Existing Building Commissioning—Analysis Option 1, use the existing building commissioning as the foundation of the ongoing commissioning plan.
- For projects that completed EA Credit Existing Building Commissioning—Analysis Option 2, ASHRAE Level 2 energy audit, review the existing building commissioning requirements and the audit plan to see where they overlap and where more work may be required.

STEP 3. ASSIGN ROLES AND RESPONSIBILITIES E

Review the roles and responsibilities identified during the ASHRAE Level 2 energy audit or existing building commissioning activities (see *Further Explanation, Ongoing Commissioning Team Setup*).

- When possible, maintain the same roles throughout ongoing commissioning cycles.
- Determine whether outside vendors, such as the controls contractor, will be team members and seek their commitment to ongoing commissioning for the duration of their contract.
- Third-party consultants or contractors may be retained to perform commissioning activities at the discretion of the building owner but are not necessarily part of the ongoing commissioning team.
- Review the ongoing commissioning requirements to ensure that each required action is assigned to a responsible person or persons.

STEP 4. DEVELOP ONGOING FUNCTIONAL PERFORMANCE TESTING PROCEDURES E

Review, update as needed, and use the functional testing process created for the existing building commissioning tests outlined in EA Credit Existing Building Commissioning—Analysis, Option 1. For projects that pursued Option 2, write and/or review the necessary functional performance testing procedures based on the available information. Refer to the guidance under Option 1 of EA Credit Existing Building Commissioning—Analysis for additional information.

Working with the commissioning team and any outside vendor or contractor, determine the best order for testing procedures. Functional testing procedures include the following:

- Device checks
- Sensor checks
- Functional or operational testing
- Alarm testing
- Point trending
- Metering

STEP 5. SET TIMELINE FOR FREQUENCY OF ANALYSIS AND ANALYSIS CYCLE E

Determine a schedule for performing ongoing commissioning and incorporate it into the building staff's normal schedule (see *Further Explanation, Example—Ongoing Commissioning Schedule*).

- Commissioning activities must occur at least quarterly, and all building systems must be commissioned within a two-year cycle.
- Quarterly reports are required for the first year of the ongoing commissioning cycle; after the first year, follow an annual schedule.

STEP 6. DETERMINE MEASUREMENT REQUIREMENTS E

Review the existing building automation system (BAS) and system-level submeters to determine which systems will be monitored and trended. Verify the data storage capacity of the BAS and determine points to be tracked, with frequency and duration for trend monitoring (see *Further Explanation, Examples of BAS Trend Points*).

- Confirm that the points being monitored and trended correlate with the systems being evaluated according to the commissioning schedule.
- It is recommended that data be collected at 15-minute (or shorter) intervals for at least a week and stored such that the information can be viewed via the BAS or third-party energy management software or exported to a spreadsheet program for analysis.
- Work with the team and commissioning authority (CxA) to ensure that the monitoring and trending are addressing targeted operational issues.

Though not required for the credit, a BAS will facilitate tracking and monitoring. Projects may use a manual or hybrid approach, provided the data and trends are still being captured.

STEP 7. DEVELOP ACTION PLAN E

Develop an action plan for identifying and correcting operational errors and deficiencies and devise a process to evaluate performance. Add them to the tracking and verification program established under EA Credit Existing Building Commissioning—Implementation.

Indicators to evaluate performance include the following:

- Conflicts between systems, such as simultaneous heating and cooling
- Out-of-sequence operation of systems components
- Unexpected energy and water usage profiles
- Recurring system alarms

An action plan to correct identified problems should have the following elements:

- Ongoing documentation in a log
- A process for prioritizing issues based on their effects on the building and its occupants
- Ongoing training to prevent errors and enhance operators' and occupants' understanding of the building's systems

STEP 8. UPDATE CURRENT FACILITY REQUIREMENTS AND OPERATIONS AND MAINTENANCE PLAN P

Establish a process for updating the CFR and O&M plan. Confirm that a team member has responsibility and that the documents are being revised regularly.

STEP 9. DEVELOP QUARTERLY AND ANNUAL REPORT FORMAT P

Using the ongoing commissioning plan, create an ongoing commissioning report template that includes the following:

- Building system performance information
- Corrective action taken and status of open issues
- Energy and water consumption data and assessment
- Occupants' comfort data
- Updated CFR and O&M documentation

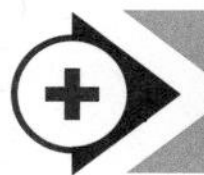

FURTHER EXPLANATION

ONGOING COMMISSIONING BASICS

Ongoing Cx is essentially a repetition of the functional performance testing and reporting procedures that occurred during the initial existing building commissioning. Ongoing testing is required to ensure that the performance of the building is maintained according to the CFR and O&M plan. The commissioning activities must be scheduled to occur in a two-year cycle. The individuals conducting the Cx activities should use the functional performance tests and issues log templates provided as part of the original Cx report.

Ongoing Cx activities can be conducted either by in-house staff, in addition to their normal maintenance activities, or by a third-party CxA who is responsible for all testing and issues reporting. In-house staff may be capable of conducting the functional performance tests, and doing so may further their understanding of the building operations. However, as the facility requirements change or as systems become retro-fitted over the lifetime of the building, a CxA may need to be retained to ensure that all test scripts and procedures are up-to-date and properly documented.

ONGOING COMMISSIONING TEAM SETUP

Commissioning teams are typically composed of the following individuals:

- Owner
- General manager or property manager
- Building engineering staff
- Commissioning agent
- Controls contractor
- Mechanical, electrical, and plumbing service providers
- Testing and balancing contractor
- Other maintenance staff

EXAMPLES

Ongoing Commissioning Schedule Example

The following is an example of a two-year commissioning testing schedule:

TABLE 1. Example schedule

Q1_YR	Q2_YR	Q3_YR	Q4_YR	Q5_YR	Q6_YR	Q7_YR	Q8_YR
AHUs 1-4	Sample of VAV terminal units served by AHUs 1-4	Chillers and associated pumps	Sample of interior lighting system	Domestic water heaters and pumps	Renewable energy systems	AHUs 5-8	Rest room and general exhaust fans
Boilers and associated pumps		Cooling towers and associated pumps				Sample of VAV terminal units served by AHUs 5-8	

Sampling of substantially similar components is allowed; however, the minimum rate should be 10 or 10%, whichever is greater. Sampling must be random, but the equipment tested in a previous commissioning cycle should not be tested again until all other similar equipment has been tested. For example, if the sampling rate for VAV terminal units is 10%, then by the completion of 10 cycles of the commissioning plan, every terminal should have been commissioned once.

Examples of BAS Trend Points

The following list illustrates the trend points that might be required to accurately evaluate system performance and identify trends.

Air-handling units

- Supply air temperature
- Mixed air temperature
- Return air temperature
- OA temperature
- OA humidity
- OA damper position
- RA damper position
- Exhaust damper position
- Supply static
- Supply and return fan VFD status
- Chilled water coil valve position
- Hot water coil valve position
- Representative room temperatures

Chilled water system

- Chiller status
- Chilled water supply temperature
- Chilled water return temperature
- Chilled water pump status
- Chilled water pump speed

Condenser water system

- Cooling tower status
- Condenser water supply temperature
- Condenser water return temperature
- Condenser water pumps status
- Condenser water pumps speed

Hot water system

- Boiler status
- Hot water supply temperature
- Hot water return temperature
- Hot water pump status
- Hot water pump speed

PROJECT TYPE VARIATIONS

District Energy Systems (DES)

All downstream equipment is included in the scope of this credit. Such equipment includes heat exchangers, steam pressure reduction stations, pumps, valves, pipes, building electrical services, and controls.

All upstream equipment associated with serving the project building is included in the scope if the project building is seeking credit for the efficiency of the DES under EA Credit Optimize Energy Performance; otherwise, upstream equipment is excluded.

Commissioning applies only to the DES services the project building is using. For example, if the building is using only the heating services of a district heating and cooling plant, then only the heating systems of the DES must be included in the scope; however, commissioning or auditing of upstream equipment applies to that entire portion of the DES, including both the central plant and the transmission and distribution systems.

Show all relevant DES equipment has been commissioned and that preventive and corrective maintenance and efficiency monitoring programs have been implemented within the past three years.

CAMPUS

Group Approach

All buildings in the group may be documented as one.

Campus Approach

Ineligible. Each LEED project may pursue the credit individually.

REQUIRED DOCUMENTATION

	Documentation	All projects
E	Ongoing commissioning plan	X
P	Confirmation that systems manual has been updated	X
P	Confirmation that CFR and O&M plan have been updated to reflect actual conditions	X
P	List of activities and tasks implemented as part of ongoing Cx	X

RELATED CREDIT TIPS

EA Prerequisite Energy Efficiency Best Management Practices. The related prerequisite creates a foundation for projects to identify ongoing energy conservation measures and activities. The CFR and O&M plan developed for the prerequisite will form the basis for the ongoing Cx plan.

EA Credit Existing Building Commissioning—Analysis. The requirements of the commissioning analysis credit must be met to earn the ongoing commissioning credit. The existing building commissioning plan can be the basis for the ongoing commissioning plan, but projects that pursue the ASHRAE Level 2 energy analysis (Option 2 of the related credit) may need to do additional work to achieve this credit.

EA Credit Existing Building Commissioning—Implementation. The requirements of the implementation credit must be met to earn the ongoing commissioning credit.

EA Credit Advanced Energy Metering. When developing the ongoing commissioning plan, consider the data that can be supplied by the metering installed to comply with the requirements of the related credit.

CHANGES FROM LEED 2009

None.

REFERENCED STANDARDS

None.

EXEMPLARY PERFORMANCE

Not available.

DEFINITIONS

current facilities requirements (**CFR**) the implementation of the owner's project requirements, developed to confirm the owner's current operational needs and requirements

district energy system (**DES**) a central energy conversion plant and transmission and distribution system that provides thermal energy to a group of buildings (e.g., a central cooling plant on a university campus). It does not include central energy systems that provide only electricity.

operations and maintenance (**O&M**) **plan** a plan that specifies major system operating parameters and limits, maintenance procedures and schedules, and documentation methods necessary to demonstrate proper operation and maintenance of an approved emissions control device or system

ENERGY AND ATMOSPHERE CREDIT

Optimize Energy Performance

This credit applies to:

Existing Buildings (1–20 points)
Schools (1–20 points)
Retail (1–20 points)
Data Centers (1–20 points)
Hospitality (1–20 points)
Warehouses and Distribution Centers (1–20 points)

INTENT

To reduce environmental and economic harms associated with excessive energy use by achieving higher levels of operating energy performance.

REQUIREMENTS

ESTABLISHMENT E

None.

PERFORMANCE P

Demonstrate increased energy efficiency or efficiency improvement beyond EA Prerequisite Minimum Energy Performance as described below. Each building must provide actual metered energy data. A full 12 months of continuous energy data is required.

Case 1. ENERGY STAR Rating (3–20 points)

For buildings eligible to receive an energy performance rating using the EPA ENERGY STAR's Portfolio Manager tool, points are awarded for ENERGY STAR scores above 75, according to Table 1. For projects outside the U.S., consult ASHRAE/ASHRAE/IESNA Standard 90.1–2010, Appendixes B and D, to determine the appropriate climate zone.

TABLE 1. Points for ENERGY STAR performance ratings	
ENERGY STAR rating	Points
76	3
77	4
78	5
79	6
80	7
81	8
82	9
83	10
84	11
85	12
86	13
87	14
88	15
89	16
90	17
91	18
93	19
95	20

Case 2. Projects Not Eligible for ENERGY STAR Rating

Projects not eligible to use EPA's rating system may compare their buildings' energy performance with that of comparable buildings, using national averages or actual buildings, or with the previous performance of the project building.

OPTION 1. BENCHMARK AGAINST TYPICAL BUILDINGS (1–20 POINTS)

Path 1. National Average Data Available (1–20 **points**)
Demonstrate energy efficiency performance that is at least 26% better than the median energy performance for typical buildings of similar type by benchmarking against national average source energy data provided in the Portfolio Manager tool. Points are awarded according to Table 2.

TABLE 2. Points for percentage improvement over national average (Option 1, Path 1) or comparable buildings and historical data (Option 3)	
Percentage improvement	Points
26	1
27	2
28	3
29	4
30	5
31	6
32	7

TABLE 2 (CONTINUED). Points for percentage improvement over national average (Option 1, Path 1) or comparable buildings and historical data (Option 3)	
Percentage improvement	**Points**
33	8
34	9
35	10
36	11
37	12
38	13
39	14
40	15
41	16
42	17
43	18
44	19
45	20

Path 2. National Average Data Not Available (2–14 points)
If national average source energy data are unavailable for buildings of similar type, benchmark against the building site energy data of at least three similar buildings, normalized for climate, building use, and occupancy. Points are awarded according to Table 3.

OR

OPTION 2. BENCHMARK AGAINST HISTORICAL DATA

If national average source energy data are unavailable, compare the building's site energy data for the previous 12 months with the data from three contiguous years of the previous five, normalized for climate, building use, and occupancy. Use Table 3 to determine points.

TABLE 3. Points for percentage improvement over comparable buildings (Option 1, Path 2) or historical data (Option 2)	
Percentage improvement	**Points**
27	2
30	4
33	6
36	8
39	10
42	12
45	14

OR

OPTION 3. BENCHMARK AGAINST BOTH SIMILAR BUILDINGS AND HISTORICAL DATA

Follow the requirements of both Option 1, Path 2, and Option 2 to benchmark against the site energy data for the three similar buildings and the building's historic data. Use Table 2 to determine points.

BEHIND THE INTENT

See EA Prerequisite Minimum Energy Performance, *Behind the Intent.*

STEP-BY-STEP GUIDANCE

STEP 1. CONFIRM REQUIRED METERING AND ALL PREREQUISITE REQUIREMENTS E

This credit's requirements follow directly from those of the related prerequisite. Careful consideration of the prerequisite will set project teams up for successful credit achievement.

STEP 2. VERIFY PERFORMANCE PERIOD AND DESIRED UPGRADES E

The performance period must end within 30 days of that of all other prerequisites and credits, unless the project is pursuing the streamlined path.

It is recommended that teams conduct a preliminary benchmarking exercise before the performance period to evaluate performance (see EA Prerequisite Minimum Energy Performance, *Further Explanation, Improving Performance*).

- If the project team is pursuing a higher score than for benchmarking, install any equipment upgrades or other efficiency measures before the performance period begins.
- Implement upgrades and operational changes as early as possible, since it will be a full 12 months from initiation of improvements before the associated energy savings are fully reflected in the benchmarking.

STEP 3. DETERMINE POINTS AVAILABLE WITH SELECTED OPTION E

Under Case 2, two approaches—Option 1, Path 2; and Option 2—limit the number of points that can be achieved. Three approaches—Case 1; Case 2, Option 1, Path 1; and Option 3—all allow pursuit of the maximum number of points (see *Further Explanation, Considerations for Case 2, Option 3*).

STEP 4. OBTAIN METERED ENERGY CONSUMPTION DATA P

Energy consumption data must be obtained for the full performance period and must be based on actual metered data. Update Portfolio Manager with compiled energy data.

STEP 5. BENCHMARK BUILDING ACCORDING TO CASE 1 OR CASE 2 E P

Confirm that the building's current performance meets the credit requirements for Case 1 or Case 2.

STEP 6. UPDATE BUILDING BENCHMARKING DATA ROUTINELY P

Update the ENERGY STAR Portfolio Manager profile regularly. The following information must be kept up-to-date throughout the performance period:

- **Energy consumption for all energy sources.** Update as data become available.
- **Number of occupants and vacant spaces.** As tenants add or lose staff and as spaces turn over, make adjustments in Portfolio Manager. For accurate benchmarking, note the exact dates of such changes.
- **Space type changes.** As renovations or new fit-outs occur, add or adjust space types in Portfolio Manager.

FURTHER EXPLANATION

CONSIDERATIONS FOR CASE 2, OPTION 3

This option combines a building's historical data and comparable building's data to establish a baseline. It requires that the team have historical data for the project building and obtain data from at least three comparable buildings.

Review the sections on historical data and comparables in EA Prerequisite Minimum Energy Performance. Normalize the data and enter the building information and source EUI data into the Case 2 calculator for the project building's performance period year, the project building's historical baseline years, and the comparable buildings.

Project teams that fall under Case 2 but are not eligible for Path 1 of Option 1 have three choices: Path 2 of Option 1, Option 2, or Option 3. See EA Prerequisite Minimum Energy Performance for a description of the other options and paths.

PROJECT TYPE VARIATIONS

District Energy Systems (DES)

See EA Prerequisite Minimum Energy Performance.

CAMPUS

Group Approach

All buildings in the group may be documented as one.

Campus Approach

Ineligible. Each LEED project may pursue the credit individually.

REQUIRED DOCUMENTATION

	Documentation	Case 1, streamlined	Case 1	Case 2, Option 1, Path 1	Case 2, Option 1, Path 2	Case 2, Option 2	Case 2, Option 3
E	Meter calibration report, as applicable	X	X	X	X	X	X
E P	Access to ENERGY STAR Portfolio Manager account (see Further Explanation, Sharing Access)	X	X	X	X	X	X
E P	Statement of energy performance stamped by professional engineer or licensed architect	X					
E P	Letter from ENERGY STAR, copy of ENERGY STAR recognition certificate, or screenshot of ENERGY STAR website	X					
E P	Data verification checklist		X	X	X	X	X
E P	Copies of utility bill summary pages or cover pages for 3 months of performance period for each fuel source		X	X	X	X	X
E P	Weather-normalized source EUI			X	X	X	X
E P	Weather-normalized source EUI from 3 similar buildings				X		X
E	Descriptions of 3 similar buildings and comparability to project building				X		X
E P	Weather-normalized source EUI from 3 recent years					X	X
E P	Calculations supporting additional normalization (if applicable)			X	X	X	X

RELATED CREDIT TIPS

EA Prerequisite Minimum Energy Performance. The path chosen in the related prerequisite determines the path in this credit. Review the prerequisite requirements before pursuing the credit.

EA Prerequisite Energy Efficiency Best Management Practices. Building operating plan information developed for the related prerequisite must be consistent with the information entered into ENERGY STAR Portfolio Manager for this credit. Conducting the ASHRAE Level 1 Audit provides opportunities for energy improvement, which will assist with achieving the minimum energy efficiency performance threshold.

EA Credit Existing Building Commissioning—Analysis. The activities conducted under the related credit uncover opportunities for energy efficiency measures that will reduce energy consumption.

CHANGES FROM LEED 2009

The minimum ENERGY STAR score has been increased to 75.

REFERENCED STANDARDS

Environmental Protection Agency (EPA) ENERGY STAR Portfolio Manager tool: energystar.gov/benchmark

ASHRAE Standard 90.1–2010, Appendices B and D: ashrae.org

EXEMPLARY PERFORMANCE

Case 1. Achieve a threshold of 97%.

Case 2, Option 3. Achieve a threshold of 47%.

DEFINITIONS

district energy system (DES) a central energy conversion plant and transmission and distribution system that provides thermal energy to a group of buildings (e.g., a central cooling plant on a university campus). It does not include central energy systems that provide only electricity.

downstream equipment the heating and cooling systems, equipment, and controls located in the project building or on the project site and associated with transporting the thermal energy of the district energy system (DES) into heated and cooled spaces. Downstream equipment includes the thermal connection or interface with the DES, secondary distribution systems in the building, and terminal units.

upstream equipment a heating or cooling system or control associated with the district energy system (DES) but not part of the thermal connection or interface with the DES. Upstream equipment includes the thermal energy conversion plant and all the transmission and distribution equipment associated with transporting the thermal energy to the project building or site.

ENERGY AND ATMOSPHERE CREDIT

Advanced Energy Metering

This credit applies to:

Existing Buildings (2 points)
Schools (2 points)
Retail (2 points)
Data Centers (2 points)
Hospitality (2 points)
Warehouses and Distribution Centers (2 points)

INTENT

To support energy management and identify opportunities for additional energy savings by tracking building-level and system-level energy use.

REQUIREMENTS

ESTABLISHMENT E

Install advanced energy metering for the following:

- all whole-building energy sources used by the building; and
- major end uses that represent 20% or more of the total annual consumption of the building minus plug load use.

The advanced energy metering must have the following characteristics.

- Meters must be permanently installed, record at intervals of one hour or less, and transmit data to a remote location.
- Electricity meters must record both consumption and demand. Whole-building electricity meters should record the power factor, if appropriate.
- The data collection system must use a local area network, building automation system, wireless network, or comparable communication infrastructure.
- The system must be capable of storing all meter data for at least 36 months.
- The data must be remotely accessible.
- All meters in the system must be capable of reporting hourly, daily, monthly, and annual energy use.

PERFORMANCE P

Program the facility's energy management system to set an alarm whenever the energy consumption and peak demand rise above the anticipated amount by more than 5%. The anticipated consumption and peak should be determined by analyzing historical facility performance and weather and operating conditions and should be set on at least monthly, preferably daily.

Demand measurements must be taken in time increments no longer than the increments used for utility billing or in one-hour increments, whichever is less time.

On at least a monthly basis, report the facility's utility peak demand and total consumption and compare it with the data for the previous month and the same month from the previous year.

BEHIND THE INTENT

See EA Prerequisite Building-Level Energy Metering, *Behind the Intent.*

STEP-BY-STEP GUIDANCE

STEP 1. IDENTIFY ENERGY SOURCES THAT SERVE PROJECT BUILDING E

Determine all energy sources that serve the project.

- Whole-building energy sources delivered to the building by an external provider, such as a utility company or campus central plant, include sources owned by the building owner that cross an exterior wall between the point of generation and point of use (see EA Prerequisite Building-Level Metering).
- Count both renewable and nonrenewable sources of on-site energy generation.
- Renewable sources include wind turbines, photovoltaic panels, solar thermal panels, and geothermal.
- Nonrenewable sources include fossil fuel–burning generators and microturbines. Both inputs and outputs of nonrenewable sources, including fuel input, electricity output, and recovered heat (if applicable), must be metered.

STEP 2. IDENTIFY ENERGY END USES THAT REQUIRE ADVANCED ENERGY METERING E

Identify each end use that represents 20% or more of total annual building energy consumption, not including plug loads (see *Further Explanation, Determining Major End Uses*).

- Use energy measurements from utility meters, the building automation system (BAS), or temporary spot metering to determine which end uses must be permanently metered. Large end uses may already be submetered by the utility or segregated by electrical panel.
- If end-use energy data are not available, use the results of the ASHRAE Level 1 walk-through analysis, completed for EA Prerequisite Energy Efficiency Best Management Practices, to help determine which end uses to meter.

STEP 3. IMPLEMENT ADVANCED METERING SYSTEM E

Install an advanced metering system based on the credit requirements for type of equipment, measurement frequency, communication protocols, and data storage (see *Further Explanation, Meter Selection* and *Electricity-Metering Strategies*).

STEP 4. CONFIRM ENERGY MANAGEMENT SOFTWARE CAPABILITIES E

Install or upgrade energy management software, if necessary. The software must have the following capabilities:

- Ability to generate an alarm when demand or consumption over a set time interval exceeds anticipated levels by more than 5%
- Ability to generate electricity demand and energy consumption reports for each advanced meter

STEP 5. ESTABLISH BASELINES P

Determine an energy consumption and demand baseline for each fuel source used in the building (see *Further Explanation, Determining Baseline Consumption and Demand*). Baseline consumption and demand data can be determined using either of the following:

- 12 months of historical energy and demand measurements
- A calibrated energy model

STEP 6. PROGRAM ENERGY MANAGEMENT SOFTWARE P

Use the baseline data to establish alarm setpoints. Program the building's energy management software to generate an alarm whenever consumption or demand exceeds the setpoint by more than 5%.

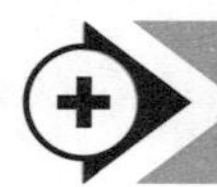

FURTHER EXPLANATION

DETERMINING MAJOR ENERGY END USES

Defining appropriate energy end uses is crucial to the success of an advanced energy metering program and energy management plan. Low data granularity, such as with whole-building energy data, will not help a building operator understand or identify sources of anomalies in energy consumption and does not meet the intent of this credit.

Extreme granularity, achieved by metering every piece of equipment in a building, may be cost prohibitive because of the quantity of equipment and the data storage capacity required. In addition, too much information may overwhelm an energy manager and may hamper the effectiveness of an energy management program.

Identifying major energy end uses is the first step in choosing what to meter. Often, in large commercial or industrial buildings, end uses are classified as systems composed of discrete pieces of equipment that can be metered together. For example,

- Chilled water system: chillers, chilled water pumps
- Condenser water system: cooling tower, condenser water pumps
- Hot water system (natural gas): boilers
- Hot water system (electricity): hot water pumps
- Air-handling system: supply fan, return fan, damper motors

Smaller buildings may not have large systems that are easily segregated by function. A common example is a rooftop unit (RTU), a single packaged piece of equipment that can provide the cooling, heating, and air handling but is cost and space prohibitive to submeter. Therefore, metering the entire RTU (or metering each fuel supplying the RTU, if there is more than one) is an acceptable way to achieve this credit. Even though metering the energy usage of each system component of a packaged system is not practical, the performance of each system component should be monitored by the BAS.

The metering strategy for systems that serve the same basic function, such as multiple built-up air-handling units serving a 1,000,000-square-foot (92 900-square-meter) multitenant office building, or multiple RTUs serving a 25,000-square-foot (2 325-square-meter) physician's office, is left to the discretion of the project team. Examples of options for submetering these systems include the following:

- Meter all similar systems together. This strategy is appropriate for multiple systems that serve the same type of occupant and operate according to the same schedule.
- Meter all similar systems separately. This strategy is appropriate if each system serves a different type of occupancy group or has a different operating schedule.
- Meter similar systems by grouped occupancy type or operating schedule. This strategy is a combination of the above.

Choosing what equipment and components to group requires a balance between keeping the project costs on budget while ensuring that robust data are available for future decision making.

The ASHRAE Level 1 energy auditor may assess energy end uses either by studying the building's utility panels and meter layout or by creating an energy model to assess recommended energy conservation measures. Most energy modeling software produces a report of energy consumption for a standard set of end uses, and some programs also allow the user to virtually meter additional end uses.

Additional resources for estimating common energy end uses include the Commercial Building Energy Consumption Survey (2003) End-Use Consumption Tables for Non-Mall Buildings or End-Use Consumption Tables for All Buildings.

Examples of typical end uses for a commercial office building that may require advanced metering include the following:

- Interior lighting
- Space cooling
- Space heating
- Fans

- Pumps
- Heat rejection
- Exterior lighting
- Service water heating
- Receptacle equipment

End uses can be grouped by occupancy type, building section, or building level. This type of consolidation can be useful for buildings with different usage types, such as a commercial office with an industrial test kitchen, since it allows building operators and energy managers to separately monitor different space types and account for different energy usage patterns.

METER SELECTION

The accuracy of available commercial meters and submeters varies widely. Select meters based on the level of accuracy required for energy management purposes.

It is recommended that submeters that may be used for revenue purposes conform to the applicable revenue-grade accuracy (see EA Prerequisite Building-Level Metering, *Further Explanation, Meter Selection*).

When locating meters, consider any physical installation requirements (e.g., straight lengths of piping). Incorrect application or installation of a meter can reduce measurement accuracy.

Ensure that staff responsible for installing and maintaining equipment and using the data have input into the meter selection.

The owner is responsible for maintaining and calibrating meters per the manufacturer's recommendations.

Existing equipment may already have energy-metering capabilities, such as a variable frequency drive that tracks instantaneous demand in kW and consumption in kWh. Metering of this type is acceptable and avoids the cost of installing new submeters.

ELECTRICITY-METERING STRATEGIES

The number and location of electricity meters depend on the layout of a project's electrical panels.

If major energy-using systems are segregated by panel, energy consumption can be measured at the panel level and fewer submeters will be required (Figure 1). Individual branch circuit meters can be avoided if more than 80% of the panel's power is directed to a single end use. For example, if a panel is shared by the air-handling system and mechanical room but the lighting accounts for less than 20% of the power load of the panel, then the individual lighting branch circuits do not need to be metered.

If multiple diverse end uses are connected to the same panel, individual branch circuits must be metered to extract the individual energy consumption of each (Figure 2). Submetering individual branch circuits will be an additional cost.

If the majority of a panel serves one system type, subtraction metering may be used. This strategy requires metering of the entire panel as well the individual branch circuits for minority end uses. The energy consumption of the majority end use is then determined by subtracting the minority end uses from the total panel consumption (Equation 1, Figure 3).

EQUATION 1. Example subtraction metering

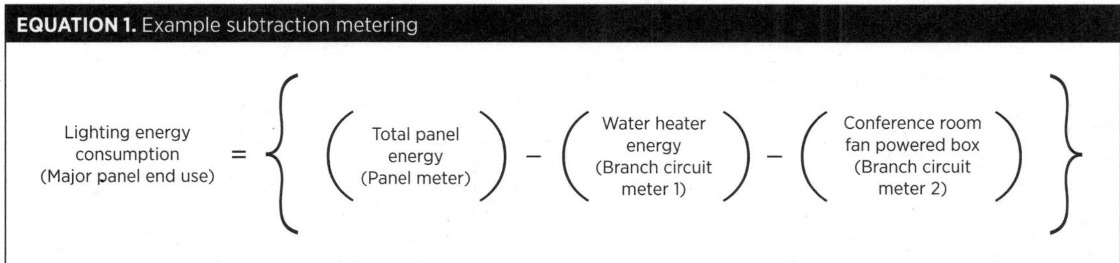

Figure 1. Power panel that serves single end use: single submeter

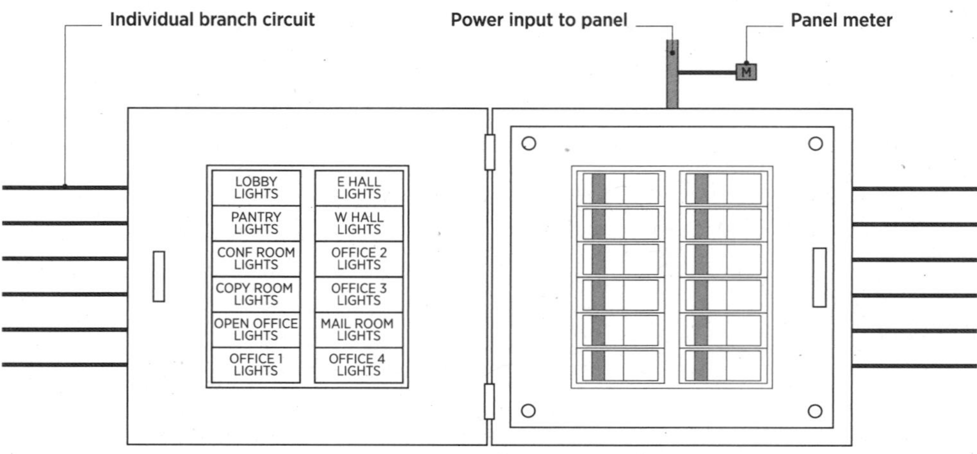

Figure 2. Panel that serves diverse end uses: one submeter for each branch circuit

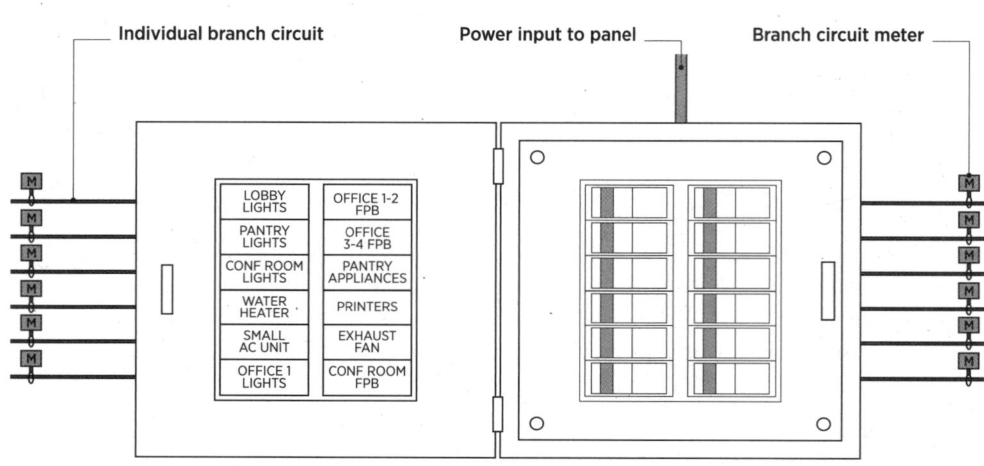

Figure 3. Panel that serves one majority use: one meter for panel and one meter for branch circuits for minority uses

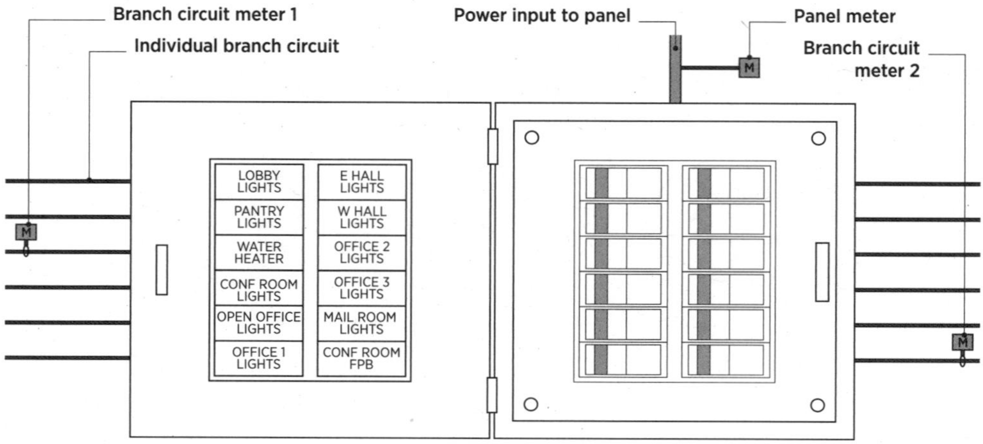

DETERMINING BASELINE ENERGY CONSUMPTION AND DEMAND

Baseline consumption and demand data are a point of reference for both maintaining and improving energy efficiency.

For buildings in operation for 12 or more months, the baseline can be derived from advanced metering system data or utility bills, weather data, and occupancy records. Using this information, building operators implement a controls sequence in the BAS or energy management system that predicts the expected energy consumption and peak demand for different temperatures in occupied and unoccupied conditions. If the real energy use or demand is more than 5% above the predicted level, the BAS or energy management system generates an alarm.

An energy performance baseline can also be created through an energy model, which an energy auditor may use to test the effectiveness of energy conservation measures during an ASHRAE Level 1 or 2 energy audit. If the project initially earned LEED BD&C certification, refer to the energy model created for EA Prerequisite Minimum Energy Performance. In either case, the energy model will need to be calibrated to the actual operational conditions of the building.

A calibrated energy model includes actual (as opposed to historical or assumed) weather data, operational schedules, and equipment setpoints. Calibration of an energy model requires thorough examination of how the building operates at the time of the assessment. Information regarding mechanical, electrical, and plumbing systems can be obtained from an as-built set of drawings or from a survey of new, existing and retrofitted equipment.

To understand the how the building is used by its occupants and operated by its engineers, the energy modeler must collect the current facility requirements and operations and maintenance plan, required for EA Prerequisite Energy Efficiency Best Management Practices.

Detailed documentation of operating schedules may be available from building security systems or BAS trending of signals from occupant-sensing controls and their known sequence of operation. If such automated tracking systems are lacking, project teams may need to observe occupants' behavior and develop operating schedules.

The building operator can use a calibrated energy model to develop a controls sequence in the energy management system that predicts the consumption and peak demand for given weather and occupancy conditions.

UNUSUAL ENERGY CONSUMPTION, PEAK DEMAND, AND SYSTEM DRIFT

Each building system, even if integrated with other systems in the building, will have its own strengths and weaknesses. For example, how a chiller performs today is not how it will perform five years from now, since mechanical parts may degrade over time. Additionally, programming and setpoints may be adjusted incorrectly by well-intentioned operators. Metering that permits monitoring and analysis of systems performance over time against a baseline can detect and correct for the slow slide from efficient to inefficient operation.

The software that serves the advanced metering system will assist the building operation staff in determining unusual energy and demand consumption patterns, using accumulated weekly, monthly, or yearly data. This information can be also used to obtain an ENERGY STAR rating.

RATING SYSTEM VARIATIONS

Data Centers

IT energy consumption, as measured from an uninterruptible power supply (UPS) output meter, should be metered separately from non-IT equipment, such as HVAC, plug loads, and lighting. If the UPS system supports non-IT loads that amount to more than 20% of its total load, the non-IT load should also be submetered. This guidance is derived from ENERGY STAR and applies to data center buildings as well as commercial buildings that contain large data centers.

CAMPUS

Group Approach

Submit separate documentation for each building.

Campus Approach

Ineligible. Each LEED project may pursue the credit individually.

REQUIRED DOCUMENTATION

	Documentation	All Projects
E	List of all advanced meters to be installed, including type and energy source metered	X
E	Manufacturers' cutsheets	X
P	Confirm facility's energy management system alarm programming	X
P	Confirm project has monthly and annual summaries of energy consumption and monthly peak demand data	X

RELATED CREDIT TIPS

EA Prerequisite Minimum Energy Performance. Installation of an advanced metering system will help a project team increase the efficiency of the building's systems and operation, thereby decreasing overall energy consumption and operating costs.

EA Prerequisite Building-Level Metering. An advanced metering system meets the requirements of the related prerequisite; additional whole-building metering is not required.

EA Credit Existing Building Commissioning—Analysis. Advanced metering system data will support the commissioning agent's evaluation of energy and water performance under Option 1 of the related credit. The identification of major energy end uses completed during the ASHRAE Level 2 audit and analysis (Option 2 of the related credit) will help the building staff and third-party consultants determine what end uses must be metered to comply with this credit.

EA Credit Existing Building Commissioning—Implementation. Installation of an advanced metering system will help quantify energy and cost savings due to implemented energy conservation measures.

EA Credit Ongoing Commissioning. Advanced metering system data will support the commissioning agent's evaluation of energy and water performance on an ongoing basis. The advanced metering system will make implementing the monitoring requirements of the related credit easier to achieve.

CHANGES FROM LEED 2009

System-level metering and building automation systems were included in LEED 2009 as Minimum Program Requirement 6 and as EA Credit Performance Measurement—Building Automation System. Both topics are combined into this credit.

REFERENCED STANDARDS

None.

EXEMPLARY PERFORMANCE

Not available.

DEFINITIONS

None.

ENERGY AND ATMOSPHERE CREDIT

Demand Response

This credit applies to:

Existing Buildings (1–3 points)
Schools (1–3 points)
Retail (1–3 points)
Data Centers (1–3 points)
Hospitality (1–3 points)
Warehouses and Distribution Centers (1–3 points)

INTENT

To increase participation in demand response technologies and programs that make energy generation and distribution systems more efficient, increase grid reliability, and reduce greenhouse gas emissions.

REQUIREMENTS

ESTABLISHMENT E

Evaluate building systems and equipment for participation in a demand response program. On-site electricity generation does not meet the intent of this credit.

Case 1. Demand Response Program Available (3 points)

Participate in an existing demand response (DR) program and complete the following activities.

- Have in place a system with the capability for real-time, fully automated DR based on external initiation by a DR program provider. Semi-automated DR may be utilized in practice.
- Enroll in a minimum one-year DR participation amount contractual commitment with a qualified DR program provider, with the intention of multiyear renewal, for at least 10% of the annual peak electricity demand. Peak demand is based on electric utility bills.
- Develop a comprehensive plan for meeting the contractual commitment during a Demand Response event.
- Include the DR processes in the current facilities requirements and operations and maintenance plan.
- Initiate at least one full test of the DR plan.

Case 2. Demand Response Program Not Available (1 point)

- Have infrastructure in place to take advantage of future demand response programs or dynamic, real-time pricing programs and complete the following activities. Develop a comprehensive plan for shed at least 10% of the annual peak electricity demand. Peak demand is based on electric utility bills.
- Include the DR processes in the current facilities requirements and operations and maintenance plan.

- Initiate at least one full test of the DR plan.
- Contact local utility representatives to discuss participation in future DR programs.

Case 3. Permanent Load Shifting (2 points)

Implement electrical load shifting measures with the following requirements:

- Have in place during the performance period a system which permanently transfers electricity demand from peak hours to off-peak hours as defined by the local utility provider.
- Demonstrate that the facility is successfully reducing peak demand by 10% during the performance period as compared to peak electrical demand by:
  - Identifying all load shifting measures and their intended peak electrical load shift
  - Verifying a corresponding peak electrical load reduction for each measure
  - Verifying a corresponding off-peak electrical load increase for each measure
- Include the load shifting measures in the Current Facilities Requirements and Operations and Maintenance Plan.

PERFORMANCE P

None.

BEHIND THE INTENT

When temperatures rise or fall dramatically, use of air-conditioning or heating increases. The electricity grid must respond quickly, especially in urban areas and places where commercial buildings or industrial operations are clustered. Utilities work to keep the system operating in balance, reliably, and at reasonable cost.

Demand response (DR) strategies encourage electricity customers to reduce their usage during peak demand times, helping utilities optimize their supply-side energy generation and delivery systems. One strategy is tiered demand electricity pricing. Another is incentive programs that reward commercial consumers who agree to change their usage patterns when the utility company sends an alert (to the building's operator or the building automation system) announcing a DR event (also known as a curtailment event). DR programs set a maximum number of events that can be announced and specify the time frames in which they may occur.

By reducing overall demand for electricity, DR helps utilities avoid building additional power generation facilities, transmission lines, and distribution stations, thereby avoiding some of the environmental effects of energy infrastructure and consumption. DR also helps balance the contribution of renewable energy sources. For example, on calm days or at night, when renewable sources such as wind and solar are less available, grid operators must either find additional generation sources or persuade energy users to lower demand. DR achieves the latter, balancing system-wide usage and reducing the need for nonrenewable backup generation.

Permanent peak load shifting also reduces demand on the grid during peak service times but occurs even if no event is called. Permanent load shifting then provides a constant, reliable reduction for utilities and buildings.

Whether pursuing demand response or permanent peak load shifting, project teams should weigh the size and cost requirements of installing these systems with the energy and cost savings. For automated demand response, the utility or a third-party demand response vendor may help cover the upfront costs of enhanced controls technology.

STEP-BY-STEP GUIDANCE

STEP 1. CONTACT LOCAL UTILITY E

Contact the utilities serving the project site to determine peak and off-peak hours. Peak hours may vary regionally and seasonally (see *Further Explanation, Demand Response Program Availability*).

Ask whether demand response programs are available.

STEP 2. SELECT ONE OPTION E

Select the more appropriate option for the project.

- Option 1 is feasible for projects in areas where demand response programs are operating or planned.
- Option 2 is appropriate for projects that have load-shifting systems already installed or have the space and capital to install them.

STEP 3. DETERMINE PEAK DEMAND REDUCTION REQUIREMENT E

Obtain peak demand estimates from utility bill data or, if this information is not available, 15-minute interval data from an interval meter. Peak demand is based on a minimum of one year's worth of utility bills or metered data to capture seasonal variances; however, teams pursuing Option 1 should verify the program period with the DR program provider. Use Equation 1 to determine the minimum peak demand reduction required.

EQUATION 1. Minimum reduction in peak electricity demand

$$\text{Minimum reduction} = \left\{ 10\% \times \text{Peak demand} \right\}$$

STEP 4. DEVELOP STRATEGIES FOR PEAK DEMAND REDUCTION E

Identify strategies that will allow the project to meet or exceed the minimum demand reduction target (see *Further Explanation, Strategies to Reduce Demand*).

- Many utilities and third-party energy providers can work with project teams to review local demand response options and make design and implementation suggestions.
- Evaluate systems in place or determine feasibility of installing a system that is capable of temporarily reducing demand (Option 1) or permanently shifting load from peak to off-peak hours (Option 2).

STEP 5. INCLUDE DEMAND RESPONSE IN CURRENT FACILITY REQUIREMENTS AND OPERATIONS AND MAINTENANCE PLAN E

Include all systems setpoints and procedures associated with the demand response plan or load-shifting system in the current facilities requirements and operations and maintenance plan. See EA Prerequisite Energy Efficiency Best Management Practices.

Option 1. Demand Response Program

STEP 1. DETERMINE WHICH CASE APPLIES TO THE PROJECT E

Based on the team's communication with the local utility or independent service provider, select the appropriate case for Option 1. See *Further Explanation, Demand Response Program Availability*.

- Case 1 is for projects in locations that have DR programs. Participation is required to achieve the credit.
- Case 2 requires the project team to design a system to accommodate future DR programs.

STEP 2. IMPLEMENT AUTOMATIC SYSTEM RESPONSE TO UTILITY SIGNAL E

Confirm that the current system has the capability to allow the project to participate in a demand response program. If not, explore upgrades. Systems must be capable of acting on an external signal, but their actual operation may be either fully or semi-automated (see *Further Explanation, Demand Response Event Management*).

STEP 3. PREPARE PLAN FOR PEAK DEMAND REDUCTION E

Generate a plan that provides clear direction for implementing the identified demand reduction strategies. Include activities, responsible parties, and anticipated reduction for each measure (see *Further Explanation, Developing the Action Plan*). The training plan and objectives for those employees directly responsible for executing the demand response action plan should address the following activities:

- Individual assignments
- Event signals
- Communication protocols
- Recovery
- Reporting
- Clear status

Ensure that the DR operations team members, which may include the DR coordinator, facilities manager, and DR action plan manager, agree with the content of the plan, since they will be implementing it (see *Further Explanation, Demand Response Operations Team*). The building's DR coordinator and team members should be well trained in mitigating any potential problems.

STEP 4. TEST DR PLAN E

Perform at least one test of the full DR plan to verify that all equipment responds as planned and that all responsible parties understand their roles.

Option 1, Case 1. Demand Response Program Available

STEP 1. ENROLL IN DEMAND RESPONSE PROGRAM E

Select a DR program and enroll in a minimum one-year contract (see *Further Explanation, Demand Response Program Types*).

- Participation in a DR program requires engaging a DR provider and entering into an agreement to provide curtailment of building energy demand upon notification of a DR event, or to participate in other DR strategies, such as ancillary services.
- Retain a copy of the DR program enrollment contract or verification issued by the independent system operator, regional transmission organization, or energy provider.
- Typical contracts specify the physical address of the building(s), authorized agents for event notification, utility account numbers, terms for earning revenue, terms for revenue sharing, number and duration of events, notification processes, monitoring requirements, enrollment periods, minimum size, performance and consequences for nonperformance, penalties, and renewal options. Not all elements listed will be applicable to all project types.

Option 1, Case 2. Demand Response Program Not Available

STEP 1. CONTACT LOCAL UTILITY E

Contact the local utility or service provider to express interest in a future program. Utilities and service providers may want to start a demand response program but not know about facilities that can and would participate. Indicating the project's capability and willingness to take part in a program may encourage them to proceed.

Option 2. Permanent Peak Load Shifting

STEP 1. MAINTAIN OR INSTALL SYSTEMS FOR PEAK LOAD SHIFTING E

Maintain any existing systems or implement the selected strategies that contribute to the desired load shifting goal (see *Further Explanation, Permanent Load-Shifting Systems*).

STEP 2. DEMONSTRATE CAPABILITY OF SYSTEM TO MEET MINIMUM LOAD TRANSFER REQUIREMENTS E

Verify that the system is capable of permanently shifting at least 10% of the measured or calculated peak load, as indicated in the credit requirements.

To calculate the peak load, project teams may use records (e.g., utility bills) from before system installation or from a time when the system was not in operation, provided no major operational or occupancy changes have occurred. Projects may also calculate the peak load based on the corresponding off-peak load increase.

FURTHER EXPLANATION

CALCULATIONS

See calculations in *Step-by-Step Guidance*.

DEMAND RESPONSE PROGRAM AVAILABILITY

Energy supply and demand vary widely on a regional and national basis and are determined in part by local market conditions and regulatory frameworks. Participation in demand response is often encouraged by state regulatory agencies or state legislatures. Information on state demand response programs can often be found on the public utility commission's website.

In the U.S., the Federal Energy Regulatory Commission has developed the National Action Plan on Demand Response, with the goal of achieving greater demand response consistent with the requirements of the Energy Independence and Security Act of 2007.

STRATEGIES TO REDUCE DEMAND

Project teams may reduce peak demand by modifying consumption from various end-use systems, such as HVAC and lighting.

- Global temperature adjustments increase cooling setpoints (or decrease heating setpoints) for an entire facility for a given period. Facilities managers may find that some occupants prefer the temperatures under DR events, indicating the possibility of making permanent changes to the setpoints.
- Turning off decorative features, like fountains and video displays, reduces energy consumption without affecting worker productivity.
- Hospitality and health care facilities may be able to reschedule housekeeping activities, such as dishwashing and laundry.

DEMAND RESPONSE EVENT MANAGEMENT

When a DR event is called, the DR program provider sends a signal as specified in the program enrollment contract. The signal may be based on price, reliability, or supply and demand.

Demand response signals are received and acted on manually or through an energy management control system, which may include a building automation system (BAS), a building management system, and a programmable load control.

TABLE 1. Demand response management

Level	Energy management control system	Response to DR event	Eligible for credit
Manual demand response	No	Building operator or occupants manually turn off end-use systems (e.g., lights, HVAC, other equipment)	No
Semiautomated demand response	Yes	DR coordinator or other person initiates control strategy programmed into BAS	Yes
Fully automated demand response	Yes	BAS control sequence initiates strategy, without human intervention	Yes

Source: Based on Kiliccote and Piette, Lawrence Berkeley National Laboratory, 2005.
Used with permission from Lawrence Berkeley National Laboratory.

Figure 1. Demand response progression. Used with permission from Lawrence Berkeley National Laboratory.

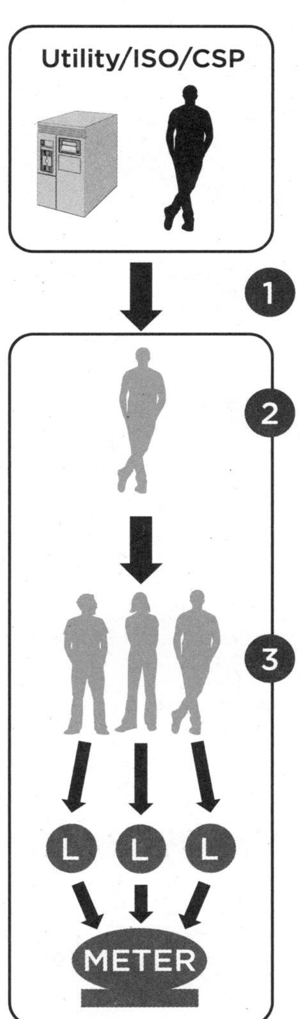

1. DR Event notice sent via text, e-mail or phone call
2. Decision to participate is made by a person
3. DR measures are initiated by people on-site and limited to manually adjustable components such as light switches, thermostats etc

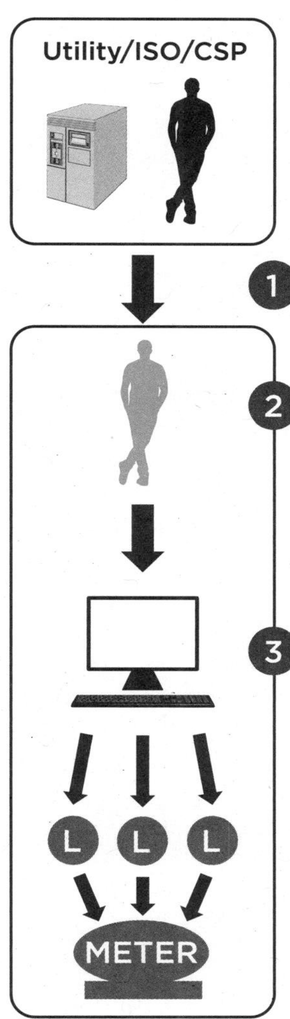

1. DR Event notice sent via text, e-mail or phone call
2. Decision to participate is made by a person
3. Pre-programmed DR measures are initiated by a person at a workstation

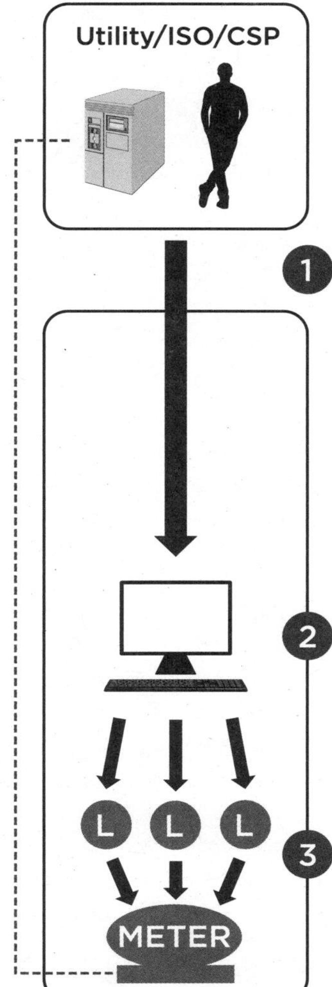

1. DR Event notice sent over the internet or private networkl
2. Pre-programmed DR measures are initiated automatically
3. In some case the meter feedback is provided

ISO = Independent System Operator CSP = Curtainment Service Provider L = Load

DEMAND RESPONSE OPERATIONS TEAM

Participating in DR requires careful evaluation, planning, and execution of curtailment strategies. A project team member may fill one or more of the following roles:

- DR project coordinator
- Facilities manager
- DR action plan (curtailment) manager
- DR credit project manager
- DR integration service provider, or energy services company
- DR provider account manager (e.g., utility, independent system operator, curtailment service provider employee)

The demand response provider or curtailment service provider can recommend qualified outside contractors for help with system analysis and demand response planning.

DEVELOPING THE ACTION PLAN

Projects must develop a comprehensive action plan to address roles, responsibilities, and expectations for a demand response event. The plan should address at least the following:

- Potential for demand response participation, such as curtailment of peak demand, and the elected demand response value, or schedule of values, in kWs, to be registered with the DR provider
- Event notification process for demand response events, such as a phone call, an alarm with countdown clock, or a signal to a BAS console, depending on the degree of program automation (i.e., semi-automated or automated).
- Detailed procedures and responses to execute the program measures consistent with the demand response contract
- Contract and the registered demand response participation amount, including the notification method, specific actions, order of execution, load-monitoring process, and postevent recovery process
- Energy management team responsible for coordinating with the program provider, the facilities department, and internal risk management, including event notification and response, revenue settlements, contract administration, assessments, action fulfillment, employee awareness training, readiness drills, and energy management reporting
- Description of end-use systems that will be affected, such as HVAC or lighting, on a stand-alone or integrated basis, during participation in demand response events.

DEMAND RESPONSE PROGRAM TYPES

DR programs vary regionally in the number and timing of events called. One factor that affects the type and number of DR programs is weather: regions with hot weather may have more summer-peaking programs, and regions with cool weather may have more winter-peaking programs. Congestion (transmission constraints) is another: regions that have congestion may have more interruptible load and emergency DR programs. Some program types may be better suited to certain building use categories.

PERMANENT LOAD-SHIFTING SYSTEMS

Measures to permanently shift load to off-peak hours may include hot water storage, ice- or chilled-water storage, battery storage, and EV charging stations. These systems may take up significant space or require significant investment; however, if the project is in an area with high demand charges, the return on investment may be attractive.

CAMPUS

Group Approach

All buildings in the group may be documented as one.

Campus Approach

Ineligible. Each LEED project may pursue the credit individually.

REQUIRED DOCUMENTATION

	Documentation	Option 1 Case 1	Option 1 Case 2	Option 2
E	Proof of enrollment in DR program	X		
E	Evidence of ability to shed 10% of peak demand	X	X	X
E	Inclusion of DR or load shifting in CFR and O&M plan	X	X	X
E	Comprehensive action plan	X	X	
E	Performance of one full test of DR plan	X	X	
E	Description of system for load shifting			X

RELATED CREDIT TIPS

EA Prerequisite Energy Efficiency Best Management Practices. Include the DR processes in the current facility requirements and operations and maintenance plan. Energy audits, baseline energy use, and building operating plans will be especially useful for developing DR metrics.

EA Prerequisite Minimum Energy Efficiency Performance, EA Credit Optimize Energy Performance, and EA Credit Existing Building Commissioning—Analysis. Commissioning teams and energy auditors may be able to combine energy efficiency analysis efforts with demand response program documentation.

CHANGES FROM LEED 2009

This is a new credit.

REFERENCED STANDARDS

None.

EXEMPLARY PERFORMANCE

Not available.

DEFINITIONS

demand response (DR) a change in electricity use by demand-side resources from their normal consumption patterns in response to changes in the price of electricity or to incentive payments designed to induce lower electricity use at times of high wholesale market prices or when system reliability is jeopardized

demand response (DR) event a specific period of time when the utility or independent service operator calls for a change in the pattern or level of use in grid-based electricity from its program participants. Also known as a curtailment event.

load shedding an intentional action by a utility to reduce the load on the system. Load shedding is usually conducted during emergency periods, such as capacity shortages, system instability, or voltage control.

peak demand the maximum electricity load at a specific point in time or over a period of time

permanent peak load shifting the transfer of energy consumption to off-peak hours, when demand for power is lower and energy is therefore less expensive

ENERGY AND ATMOSPHERE CREDIT

Renewable Energy and Carbon Offsets

This credit applies to:

Existing Buildings (1–5 points)
Schools (1–5 points)
Retail (1–5 points)
Data Centers (1–5 points)
Hospitality (1–5 points)
Warehouses and Distribution Centers (1–5 points)

INTENT

To encourage the reduction of greenhouse gas emissions through the use of local and grid-source renewable energy technologies and carbon mitigation projects.

REQUIREMENTS

ESTABLISHMENT E

Demonstrate one or both of the following for at least a portion of the building's total energy use.

- Total energy use is met directly with renewable energy systems.
- A minimum two-year contract is in place, with the commitment to renew on an ongoing basis, to purchase qualified resources that will be delivered at least annually. Resources must have come online after January 1, 2005.

PERFORMANCE P

Meet at least some of the building's total energy use directly with renewable energy systems, or engage in a contract to purchase green power, carbon offsets, or Renewable Energy Certificates (RECs).

Green power and RECs must be Green-e Energy Certified or the equivalent. RECs can be used only to mitigate the effects of Scope 2, electricity use.

Carbon offsets may be used to mitigate Scope 1 or Scope 2 emissions on a metric ton of carbon dioxide–equivalent basis and must be Green-e Climate certified, or the equivalent.

For U.S. projects, the offsets must come from greenhouse gas emissions reduction projects within the U.S.

Use the following equation to calculate credit, up to the 5-point limit:

$$\text{(Points)} = \frac{\text{Renewable energy generated \%}}{1.5\%} + \frac{\text{Energy purchased/offset \% (not to exceed 100\%)}}{25\%}$$

BEHIND THE INTENT

Because options for reducing energy consumption in existing buildings are generally limited to improving windows and insulation, retrofitting mechanical systems, and modifying building operations, renewable energy systems and carbon mitigation strategies can be attractive. Renewable energy systems like photovoltaic arrays and wind turbines can replace a portion of grid-supplied power, thus displacing environmentally damaging fossil fuel generation while providing energy cost savings and protection from price volatility.

If space constraints, unfavorable locations, or other limiting factors make renewable generation impractical, project teams can use green energy products like green power, renewable energy certificates (RECs), and carbon offsets. Purchasing RECs allows buildings that use nonrenewable power to create demand for renewable alternatives. Carbon offsets allow buildings or companies to fund activities that seek to decrease carbon emissions or remove carbon from the atmosphere.

STEP-BY-STEP GUIDANCE

STEP 1. INVESTIGATE AVAILABLE OPPORTUNITIES E

Review the renewable energy systems, green power, RECs, and carbon offsets available to the project. A combination of all four strategies can be used.

- Both existing and new renewable energy systems can contribute toward this credit. New systems must be in place before the performance period ends. If the system is not in place for the entire performance period, ensure that the building will be able to meet EA Prerequisite Minimum Energy Performance without the renewable energy contribution (see *Further Explanation, Designing New Renewable Energy Systems*).
- Green power and RECs must be Green-e Energy certified or the equivalent. Direct or local green power may be available through local utility providers; review their websites for green power cost premiums.
- Green power and RECs can be used only toward the electric energy use portion of the project's annual energy use (Scope 2, electricity). They cannot be applied toward nonelectric energy uses (see *Further Explanation, Scope 1 and Scope 2 Emissions*).
- Carbon offsets must be Green-e Climate certified or the equivalent. Unlike RECs and purchased green power, carbon offsets can be used toward both electric and nonelectric energy use.

STEP 2. ENSURE ELIGIBILITY OF NEW OR EXISTING RENEWABLE ENERGY SYSTEMS E

Determine whether the renewable energy meets the following requirements. (Not all alternative energy systems qualify for this credit; see *Further Explanation, Eligible Renewable Energy Systems*).

- All renewable energy systems must be submetered to track production and consumption.
- Any renewable energy sold back to the grid cannot contribute toward this credit unless the project purchases the equivalent amount of RECs for a minimum 10 years.
- Additional requirements apply if the renewable energy system is not owned by the project building owner (see *Further Explanation, Renewable Energy Systems and Third Parties*).

STEP 3. CONDUCT COST-BENEFIT ANALYSIS E

Undertake a cost-benefit analysis to understand the financial and environmental paybacks for the available options.

- Initial costs and payback periods of new renewable energy systems vary widely. Depending on the project's location and energy use, some systems may be more attractive than others. For example, a sunny site is a good candidate for solar thermal hot water, but this type of renewable resource is most cost-effective if the building has a constant demand for hot water.
- Local funding, financing, and incentives for renewable generation projects may be available for certain technologies and may be a significant factor.
- All carbon offsets are not the same. Some are associated with land-use development, others with energy efficiency projects. Teams are encouraged to purchase carbon offsets that align with their environmental interests and values.

STEP 4. ESTABLISH PROJECT GOAL E

Set a goal for the amount of energy or emissions to address. Establish any combination of renewable energy generation and purchase of green power, RECs, or offsets that offers the most value to the project and best fulfills the project goal.

- Projects that choose purchased green power, RECS, and/or carbon offsets can earn a maximum of 4 points.
- Projects that produce some renewable energy can achieve points with smaller purchases of green power, RECs, or carbon offsets. For example, if a project uses 1,000 MW of electricity and produces 30 MW in renewables, the team needs to purchase only 242.5 MW (rather than 250 MW) of RECs to earn an additional point.

STEP 5. CALCULATE POTENTIAL CONTRIBUTION FROM RENEWABLE ENERGY SOURCES P

Determine the annual energy use of the entire building and site. This must be consistent with EA Prerequisite Minimum Energy Performance and EA Credit Optimize Energy Performance. Prorate this value based on the length of the performance period.

- Determine the amount of renewable energy generated over the performance period based on metered renewable energy output data.
- Use Equation 1 (see *Further Explanation, Calculations*) to calculate the percentage of total energy consumption met with on-site renewable energy.
- A project receives the full 5 points for this credit if 7.5% of the energy consumed during the performance period is produced through qualified renewable energy systems.
- See *Further Explanation, Examples 1* and *3*.

STEP 6. CALCULATE GREEN POWER, RECS, AND/OR OFFSETS REQUIRED TO MEET PROJECT GOAL P

Determine the annual energy use of the entire building and site. This must be consistent with EA Prerequisite Minimum Energy Performance and EA Credit Optimize Energy Performance.

- If the project is also generating renewable energy, subtract the projected annual renewable energy amount from the building's total annual energy use.
- If the project team elects to use green power or RECs, convert annual grid-generated electricity use to MWh.
- If the project team elects to use carbon offsets, convert annual grid-generated electricity use to metric tons of CO_2e.
- Convert annual nonelectricity energy use to metric tons of CO_2e.

Use Equations 2 and 3 (see *Further Explanation, Calculations*) to calculate the total percentage of green power, RECs, and/or carbon offsets to be purchased and determine the number of points (4 maximum) (see *Further Explanation, Example 2*).

Ensure that the carbon offsets and GHG emissions in Equation 2 are represented in the same unit of CO_2e (see *Further Explanation, Calculating GHG Emissions*).

STEP 7. OBTAIN PROPOSALS FROM GREEN-E CERTIFIED PRODUCTS OR EQUIVALENT AND MAKE PURCHASE E

Once the percentage goal of energy use that will be covered by RECs, green power, and/or carbon offsets has been established, solicit proposals from providers of Green-e certified products. If Green-e certified products are not available, equivalency of other products must be demonstrated (see *Further Explanation, Establishing Green-e Equivalency*).

- For U.S. projects, the offsets must come from greenhouse gas (GHG) emissions reduction projects within the U.S.
- Projects outside the U.S. that cannot find local products that meet the Green-e standard or equivalent can still achieve this credit by purchasing Green-e certified products from the U.S.
- Evaluate the proposals from qualified providers, select the most appropriate, and retain all contract documentation.
- Contracts must cover a minimum of two years, with commitment to renew on an on-going basis to purchase qualified resources that will be delivered at least annually. Resources must have come online after January 1, 2005. Projects that apply for recertification must demonstrate that contracts have been renewed, without interruption.

STEP 8. COMPUTE TOTAL ELIGIBLE POINTS

Total the points from renewable energy production and green power, RECs, and carbon offsets.

FURTHER EXPLANATION

CALCULATIONS

EQUATION 1. Renewable energy systems contribution

$$\text{Points} = \left\{ \left(\frac{\text{Renewable energy generated}}{\text{(Total) building energy use}} \right) \% \right\} \div 1.5\%$$

Use Equations 2 and 3 to calculate the total percentage of green power, RECs, and carbon offsets purchased and determine number of points possible.

EQUATION 2. Percentage of energy purchased or offset by RECS, green power, and carbon offsets

$$\text{\% energy purchased or offset} = \left\{ \left(\frac{\text{Quantity of RECs in kWh}}{\text{Annual building energy use in kWhs}} \right) + \left(\frac{\text{Purchased green power in kWh}}{\text{Annual building energy use in kWh}} \right) + \left(\frac{\text{Purchased carbon offset}}{\text{GHG emissions associated with project's annual energy use}} \right) \right\}$$

Ensure that the carbon offsets and GHG emissions in the Equation 2 are represented in the same unit of CO_2e.

EQUATION 3. Contribution from RECS, green power, and carbon offsets

$$\text{Points} = \left\{ \text{Energy purchased or offset \%} \div 25\% \right\}$$

EQUATION 4. Determining CO_2e for nonelectric fuels

$$\text{Metric tons of } CO_2e\text{, Fuel A} = \left\{ \text{Annual use, Fuel A (kBtu)} \times \text{Direct GHG emissions factor, Fuel A (mt } CO_2e/\text{kBtu)} \right\}$$

EQUATION 5. Determining CO_2e for electricity

$$\text{Metric tons of } CO_2 \text{ equivalent, electricity factor} = \left\{ \text{Annual electricity, use (kWh)} \times 3.412 \text{ (kBtu / kWh)} \times \text{Indirect GHG emissions factor, mt } CO_2e \text{ / kBtu} \right\}$$

SCOPE 1 AND SCOPE 2 EMISSIONS

Scope 1 emissions are greenhouse gases emitted directly—that is, from sources owned or controlled by the entity (e.g., emissions from fossil fuels burned on site). Electricity produced on site through the burning of fossil fuels is measured by the Scope 1 emissions associated with that fossil fuel.

Scope 2 emissions are an entity's greenhouse gases associated with purchased electricity—and also with high temperature hot water, chilled water, or steam—that comes from a utility provider. Scope 2 emissions include transmission and distribution losses related to hot water, chilled water, and steam. Transmission and distribution losses associated with electricity are not included in Scope 2.

DESIGNING NEW ENERGY SYSTEMS

If a renewable energy system is not in place, evaluate options for installing one. Consider the building's energy needs as well as the availability of renewable resources like sun, wind, or biomass at the site. Daily and seasonal variability in energy demand and supply should also be reviewed. If a particular technology seems appropriate for the building, determine whether it is cost-effective and feasible to install the system and a submeter.

ELIGIBLE RENEWABLE ENERGY SYSTEMS

Allowable sources for renewable energy include the following:

- Photovoltaic
- Solar thermal
- Wind
- Biofuel (in some cases)
- Low-impact hydroelectricity
- Wave and tidal energy
- Geothermal energy (in some cases)

Some renewable energy systems do not meet the intent of the credit and are not eligible. Design options such as architectural features, passive solar heating, and daylighting strategies improve energy performance, but their contributions to a building's energy performance are rewarded through EA Prerequisite Minimum Energy Efficiency Performance and EA Credit Optimize Energy Performance and do not help achieve this credit.

Geothermal energy, such as electricity generated from subterranean steam or heat generated from subterranean steam or hot water, is eligible. However, geothermal energy used in conjunction with vapor compression cycles, as in a ground-source heat pump, is not.

If a biofuel is used in a cogeneration plant that produces both electricity and heat, both of these energy uses count as renewable energy. A biofuel used in a boiler to produce heat also qualifies. However, not all biofuels meet the intent of this credit. The following biofuels are ineligible:

- Combustion of municipal solid waste
- Forestry biomass waste other than mill residue
- Wood coated with paints, plastics, or laminate
- Wood treated for preservation with materials containing halogens, chlorine compounds, halide compounds, chromated copper arsenate, or arsenic; if more than 1% of the wood fuel has been treated with these compounds, the energy system is ineligible

RENEWABLE ENERGY SYSTEMS AND THIRD PARTIES

Some renewable energy systems that use fuels produced off-site (such as landfill gas) can still be eligible to receive points under this credit. In such a case, the project team must provide documentation showing the following:

- The project has a minimum 10-year contract with the fuel provider.
- The contract with the fuel provider includes both the fuel and all associated RECs.
- If the fuel provider does not also provide RECs, the project must purchase offsets for 100% of the renewable energy produced in the form of RECs every year for at least 10 years.

In some cases, renewable energy may be available from equipment, such as a PV array or wind turbine, owned by a third party, whether on- or off-site. Project teams wishing to receive credit for such an arrangement must submit documentation, including the agreement between the project owner and the power producer. The power purchase agreement must last for at least 10 years, and the project owner must retain all environmental benefits from the renewable energy.

For example, if a PV array owner sells electricity to the project building and then sells RECs to a different party, the project is not eligible for this credit unless RECs are purchased by the project in a sum equal to the electricity being purchased, for a period of 10 years.

ESTABLISHING GREEN-E EQUIVALENCY

Projects not using Green-e certified products must demonstrate the alternative's equivalency to the quality standards established for Green-e Energy and Green-e Climate products:

- Green-e Energy National Standard v2.3, Sections II, III (excluding G), IV (excluding A), and V
- Green-e Energy Code of Conduct and Customer Disclosure Requirements – Sections III-VII
- Green-e Climate Standard v2.1, Sections 4, 5, 6.1, 6.3, 6.4, and 7
- Green-e Climate Code of Conduct – Sections II-VII

The accounting process and standards must be equivalent to Green-e products and address the following:

- Verifiable chain of custody
- Verifiable age of renewable energy
- Tracking of GHG reductions from eligible projects
- Mechanism to prevent double-counting
- Third party–verified retail transaction

For carbon offsets, retirement of an eligible credit alone is not equivalent to Green-e Climate certification.

CALCULATING GREENHOUSE GAS EMISSIONS

EQUATION 6. Project greenhouse gas emissions

$$\text{GHG emissions } (CO_2e) = \text{Consumption} \times CO_2 \text{ emissions factor}$$

where

$$\text{emissions factor} = \text{mass } CO_2 \text{ per mass or volume unit of fuel}$$

TABLE 1. Direct GHG emissions factors

Fuel type	Mt CO_2e/kBtu	Mt CO_2e/kWh
Natural gas	5.32×10^{-5}	1.82×10^{-4}
Fuel oil (No. 2)	7.36×10^{-5}	2.51×10^{-4}
Wood	1.02×10^{-4}	3.47×10^{-4}
Propane	6.35×10^{-5}	2.17×10^{-4}
Liquid propane	6.36×10^{-5}	2.17×10^{-4}
Kerosene	7.27×10^{-5}	2.48×10^{-4}
Fuel oil (No. 1)	7.36×10^{-5}	2.51×10^{-4}
Fuel oil (No. 5 and 6)	7.92×10^{-5}	2.70×10^{-4}
Coal (anthracite)	1.04×10^{-4}	3.56×10^{-4}
Coal (bituminous)	9.42×10^{-5}	3.21×10^{-4}
Coke	1.14×10^{-4}	3.90×10^{-4}
Fuel oil (No. 4)	7.36×10^{-5}	2.51×10^{-4}
Diesel	7.36×10^{-5}	2.51×10^{-4}

TABLE 2. Indirect GHG emissions factors

Fuel type	Mt CO_2e/kBtu	Mt CO_2e/kWh
Purchased electricity (national average)	1.73×10^{-4}	5.90×10^{-4}
District steam	7.90×10^{-5}	2.69×10^{-4}
District hot water	7.90×10^{-5}	2.69×10^{-4}
District chilled water, electric-driven chiller (0.238095*purchased electricity national average)	4.11×10^{-5}	1.40×10^{-4}
District chilled water, absorption chiller using natural gas	6.65×10^{-5}	2.27×10^{-4}
District chilled water, engine-driven chiller using natural gas	4.43×10^{-5}	1.51×10^{-4}

EXAMPLES

Example 1. Renewable energy

A project building has an annual electricity use of 8,124,267 kWh and no other energy use. A submetered photovoltaic array installed on the roof generated 389,965 kWh in the same time period.

Using Equation 1, the team calculates the contribution of solar energy to its total energy use:

$$\left\{ \left(389{,}965 \text{ kWh} \div 8{,}124{,}267 \text{ kWh}\right) \% \right\} \div (1.5\%) = \left(4.8\% \div 1.5\%\right) = 3.2$$

The project is eligible for 3 points for renewable energy generation but could earn more by purchasing additional green power, RECs, or carbon offsets. The total electricity use for the project, minus renewables generated by the PV array, is 7,734,302 kWh. To earn the maximum number of points (5), the project would need to purchase green power equal to 3,480,436 kWh, or 45% of the project's net annual energy use. The calculation for the total points under this credit would be as follows:

Using Equation 2,

$$\text{\% Energy purchased or offset} = (3{,}480{,}436 \text{ kWh} \div 7{,}734{,}302 \text{ kWh}) = 45\%$$

$$\text{Points} = (4.8\text{ \% renewable generated} \div 1.5\%) + (45\% \text{ energy purchased/offset} \div 25\%) = 5$$

The project is eligible for 5 points through the combination of renewable energy and RECs.

Example 2. Green power, RECs, and offsets

A project building uses 5,077,667 kWh of electricity and 5,775,000 kBtu of natural gas per year. The project team wants to cover 100% of its energy use, for 4 points. The team can purchase RECs for the electricity consumption and carbon offsets for the natural gas consumption, as follows:

- RECs:
  5,077,667 kWh/yr
- Carbon offsets:
  5,775,000 kBtu/yr × (5.32×10^{-5} $mtCO_2e$/kBtu) = 307.2 $mtCO_2e$/yr

Alternatively, the team can purchase carbon offsets for all consumption (both Scope 1 and Scope 2 emissions):

- Carbon offsets to cover electricity use (Scope 2):
  5,077,667 kWh/yr × (5.90×10^{-4} $mtCO_2e$/kWh) = 2995.8 $mtCO_2e$/yr
- Carbon offsets to cover natural gas use (Scope 1):
  5,775,000 kBtu/yr × (5.32×10^{-5} $mtCO_2e$/kBtu) = 307.2 $mtCO_2e$/yr
- Total carbon offsets:
  3,303 $mtCO_2e$/yr

Either way, the project is eligible for 4 points because it is mitigating 100% of its annual energy use:

Points = (0% renewable generation ÷ 1.5%) + (100% energy purchased or offset ÷ 25%) = 4

Electricity accounts for 91% of this project's total annual energy use. If the team purchased only green power, the project could earn no more than 3 points: 91% / 25% = 3.64, for 3 points. Green power cannot offset more than the percentage of total energy use that comes from electricity.

Example 3. District energy system
A university classroom building is connected to a central hot and chilled water plant. The central plant has a dedicated photovoltaic array that can generate 15% of all electricity for the chilled water plant. Chilled water consumption represents 30% of the energy consumption of the classroom building. The project team does not intend to purchase any green power, RECs, or carbon offsets. Multiplying the percentage of renewables at the upstream DES plant by the percentage of building energy use represented by that energy stream gives the percentage of renewables used by the building for calculating the total points earned:

15% renewable × 30% of energy consumption = 4.5% renewable energy

Points = (4.5% renewable generation ÷ 1.5%)

The project is eligible for 3 points.

Buildings connected to the same DES may receive a different number of points under this credit, depending on their reliance on the renewable energy from the central plant. For another building on campus, chilled water is only 15% of annual energy consumption:

15% renewable × 15% of energy consumption = 2.25% renewable energy

Points = (2.25% renewable generation ÷ 1.5%)

Points = 1

This project is eligible for 1 point.

INTERNATIONAL TIPS

Projects must use Green-e qualified products or demonstrate Green-e equivalency but international projects are not required to purchase products from the country in which the building is located.

CAMPUS

Group Approach
All buildings in the group may be documented as one.

Campus Approach
Ineligible. Each LEED project may pursue the credit individually.

REQUIRED DOCUMENTATION

	Documentation	On-site renewable energy	Off-site renewable energy	RECs, green power, carbon offsets
P	Total annual energy use calculation	X	X	X
P	Renewable energy production	X	X	
P	Two-year contract or owner committment with Green-e provider for purchased green power, RECs, and/or carbon offsets, from sources that have come online since January 1, 2005			X
P	Credit point calculation showing the contribution of renewable energy, RECs, green power, and/or carbon offsets	X	X	X

RELATED CREDIT TIPS

EA Prerequisite Energy Efficiency Best Management Practices. ENERGY STAR tracking, as detailed in the related credit, can provide information about energy consumption that can be used to size renewable energy systems.

EA Prerequisite Minimum Energy Performance and EA Credit Optimize Energy Performance. On-site renewable energy systems will decrease the project's energy consumption from external sources, which will help the team achieve the related prerequisite and credit.

EA Credit Existing Building Commissioning. Renewable energy system equipment, such as submeters, must be included in building commissioning plans.

CHANGES FROM LEED 2009

- This credit was formerly titled On-Site and Off-Site Renewable Energy.
- Performance thresholds have been aligned with LEED Building Design & Construction rating systems.

REFERENCED STANDARDS

Center for Resource Solutions Green-e Energy and Green-e Climate Certification Program: green-e.org/

EXEMPLARY PERFORMANCE

Meet at least 10% of total energy use with on-site renewable energy.

DEFINITIONS

carbon offset a unit of carbon dioxide equivalent that is reduced, avoided, or sequestered to compensate for emissions occurring elsewhere (World Resources Institute)

district energy system (DES) a central energy conversion plant and transmission and distribution system that provides thermal energy to a group of buildings (e.g., a central cooling plant on a university campus). It does not include central energy systems that provide only electricity.

green power a subset of renewable energy composed of grid-based electricity produced from renewable energy sources

renewable energy energy sources that are not depleted by use. Examples include energy from the sun, wind, and small (low-impact) hydropower, plus geothermal energy and wave and tidal systems.

Scope 1 emissions direct greenhouse gas emissions from sources owned or controlled by the entity, such as emissions from fossil fuels burned on site

Scope 2 emissions indirect greenhouse gas emissions associated with the generation of purchased electricity, heating/cooling, or steam off site, through a utility provider for the entity's consumption

ENERGY AND ATMOSPHERE CREDIT

Enhanced Refrigerant Management

This credit applies to:

Existing Buildings (1 point)
Schools (1 point)
Retail (1 point)
Data Centers (1 point)
Hospitality (1 point)
Warehouses and Distribution Centers (1 point)

INTENT

To reduce ozone depletion and support early compliance with the Montreal Protocol while minimizing direct contributions to climate change.

REQUIREMENTS

EXISTING BUILDINGS, SCHOOLS, DATA CENTERS, HOSPITALITY, WAREHOUSES AND DISTRIBUTION CENTERS

ESTABLISHMENT E

OPTION 1. NO REFRIGERANTS OR LOW-IMPACT REFRIGERANTS (1 POINT)

Do not use refrigerants, or use only refrigerants (naturally occurring or synthetic) that have an ozone depletion potential (ODP) of zero and a global warming potential (GWP) of less than 50.

OR

OPTION 2. CALCULATION OF REFRIGERANT IMPACT (1 POINT)

Select refrigerants that are used in heating, ventilating, air-conditioning, and refrigeration (HVAC&R) equipment to minimize or eliminate the emission of compounds that contribute to ozone depletion and climate change. The combination of all new and existing base building and tenant HVAC&R equipment that serve the project must comply with the following formula:

IP UNITS: LCGWP + LCODP × 10^5 ≤ 100	SI UNITS: LCGWP + LCODP × 10^5 ≤ 13
Calculation definitions for LCGWP + LCODP x 10^5 ≤ 100 (IP units)	**Calculation definitions for LCGWP + LCODP x 10^5 ≤ 13 (SI units)**
LCODP = $\frac{[\text{ODPr} \times (\text{Lr} \times \text{Life} + \text{Mr}) \times \text{Rc}]}{\text{Life}}$	LCODP = $\frac{[\text{ODPr} \times (\text{Lr} \times \text{Life} + \text{Mr}) \times \text{Rc}]}{\text{Life}}$
LCGWP = $\frac{[\text{GWPr} \times (\text{Lr} \times \text{Life} + \text{Mr}) \times \text{Rc}]}{\text{Life}}$	LCGWP = $\frac{[\text{GWPr} \times (\text{Lr} \times \text{Life} + \text{Mr}) \times \text{Rc}]}{\text{Life}}$
LCODP: Lifecycle Ozone Depletion Potential (lb CFC 11/Ton-Year)	**LCODP:** Lifecycle Ozone Depletion Potential (kg CFC 11/(kW/year))
LCGWP: Lifecycle Direct Global Warming Potential (lb CO_2/Ton-Year)	**LCGWP:** Lifecycle Direct Global Warming Potential (kg CO_2/kW-year)
GWPr: Global Warming Potential of Refrigerant (0 to 12,000 lb CO_2/lbr)	**GWPr:** Global Warming Potential of Refrigerant (0 to 12,000 kg CO_2/kg r)
ODPr: Ozone Depletion Potential of Refrigerant (0 to 0.2 lb CFC 11/lbr)	**ODPr:** Ozone Depletion Potential of Refrigerant (0 to 0.2 kg CFC 11/kg r)
Lr: Refrigerant Leakage Rate (2.0%)	**Lr:** Refrigerant Leakage Rate (2.0%)
Mr: End-of-life Refrigerant Loss (10%)	**Mr:** End-of-life Refrigerant Loss (10%)
Rc: Refrigerant Charge (0.5 to 5.0 lbs of refrigerant per ton of gross AHRI rated cooling capacity)	**Rc:** Refrigerant Charge (0.065 to 0.65 kg of refrigerant per kW of AHRI rated or Eurovent Certified cooling capacity)
Life: Equipment Life (10 years; default based on equipment type, unless otherwise demonstrated)	**Life:** Equipment Life (10 years; default based on equipment type, unless otherwise demonstrated)

For multiple types of equipment, calculate a weighted average of all base building HVAC&R equipment, using the following formula:

IP UNITS

$$\frac{\sum\left(\text{LCGWP} + \text{LCODP} \times 10^5\right) \times \text{Qunit}}{\text{Qtotal}} \leq 100$$

SI UNITS

$$\frac{\sum\left(\text{LCGWP} + \text{LCODP} \times 10^5\right) \times \text{Qunit}}{\text{Qtotal}} \leq 13$$

CALCLULATION DEFINITIONS FOR (IP UNITS)

$$\frac{\sum\left(\text{LCGWP} + \text{LCODP} \times 10^5\right) \times \text{Qunit}}{\text{Qtotal}} \leq 100$$

Qunit = Gross AHRI rated cooling capacity of an individual HVAC or refrigeration unit (Tons)

Qtotal = Total gross AHRI rated cooling capacity of all HVAC or refrigeration

CALCLULATION DEFINITIONS FOR (SI UNITS)

$$\frac{\sum\left(\text{LCGWP} + \text{LCODP} \times 10^5\right) \times \text{Qunit}}{\text{Qtotal}} \leq 13$$

Qunit = Eurovent Certified cooling capacity of an individual HVAC or refrigeration unit (kW)

Qtotal = Total Eurovent Certified cooling capacity of all HVAC or refrigeration (kW)

RETAIL

Meet Option 1 or 2 for all HVAC systems.

Stores with commercial refrigeration systems must comply with the following.

- Use only non-ozone-depleting refrigerants.
- Achieve an average HFC refrigerant charge of no more than 1.75 pounds of refrigerant per 1,000 Btu/h (2.72 grams of refrigerant per kW) total evaporator cooling load.
- Achieve a store-wide annual refrigerant emissions rate of no more than 15%.

Alternatively, stores with commercial refrigeration systems may provide proof of attainment of EPA GreenChill's silver-level store certification for fully operational food retail stores.

PERFORMANCE P

None.

BEHIND THE INTENT

This credit addresses the two main threats to the environment posed by refrigerants: their ozone depletion potential (ODP) and global warming potential (GWP).

As is well known, chlorofluorocarbons (CFCs), hydrochlorofluorocarbons (HCFCs), and other ozone-depleting substances commonly used in refrigerants contribute to the depletion of the stratospheric ozone layer. Yet refrigerants released into the atmosphere also contribute to global climate change, having a disproportionately large effect compared with other greenhouse gases. For example, HCFC-22 contributes to warming at 1,780 times the potency of an equal amount of carbon dioxide.

However, trade-offs also exist between the above concerns and energy use. Alternatives to CFC and HCFC refrigerants, such as HFC-410A, have a lower GWP when directly released, but their use may require more energy—which also affects climate. In other cases, design choices, such as variable refrigerant flow (VRF) systems, may improve energy efficiency, but because they have a higher refrigerant charge, overall environmental effects can still increase.

Careful consideration of the refrigerant requirements of energy systems and appliances can improve performance and reduce operating cost. Refrigerants vary in operating pressure, material compatibility, flammability, and toxicity. Operating pressure and material compatibility are particularly critical factors to take into account when refrigerants in existing equipment are replaced.

The refrigerant impact calculation addresses the overall effect of each refrigerant's ODP and GWP combined by accounting for these interrelated factors.

STEP-BY-STEP GUIDANCE

STEP 1. GATHER INFORMATION ON SYSTEMS AND REFRIGERANTS IN PROJECT E

Identify all HVAC&R equipment that contains refrigerant and record the refrigerant charge and type for existing and new units. Projects that retain CFCs past initial occupancy, even if using a phase-out plan to meet the requirements of EA Prerequisite Fundamental Refrigerant Management, are ineligible for this credit.

- Small systems with less than 0.5 pound (225 grams) of refrigerants, such as individual water fountains or stand-alone refrigerators, do not need to be included in credit calculations.
- If a district energy system (DES) owned by the project is serving the building, data for the refrigerant-using equipment in the DES must be collected; DES equipment owned by a third party may be excluded.

STEP 2. SELECT ONE OPTION E

Choose the appropriate option for the project.

- Option 1 is for projects that have no refrigerants and projects with refrigerants that have an ODP of zero and a GWP of less than 50. These projects may achieve the credit; no additional steps are required.
- Option 2 is for projects that have refrigerants and projects whose refrigerants exceed the Option 1 limit.

Option 2. Refrigerant Impact Calculation

STEP 1. CALCULATE REFRIGERANT IMPACT OF ALL INSTALLED AND PROPOSED SYSTEM E

To determine the environmental effects of HVAC&R systems containing refrigerants, apply the following assumptions.

- Assume the ODP and GWP values listed in Table 1.

TABLE 1. Ozone depletion and global warming potentials of common refrigerants

Refrigerant	ODPr	GWPr	Common building application
Chlorofluorocarbons			
CFC-11	1.0	4,680	Centrifugal chiller
CFC-12	1.0	10,720	Refrigerators, chiller
CFC-114	0.94	9,800	Centrifugal chiller
CFC-500	0.605	7,900	Centrifugal chiller, humidifier
CFC-502	0.221	4,600	Low-temperature refrigeration
Hydrochlorofluorocarbons			
HCFC-22	0.04	1,780	Air-conditioning, chiller
HCFC-123	0.02	76	CFC-11 replacement
Hydrofluorocarbons			
HFC-23	~0	12,240	Ultra-low-temperature refrigeration
HFC-134a	~0	1,320	CFC-12 or HCFC-22 replacement
HFC-245fa	~0	1,020	Insulation agent, centrifugal chillers
HFC-404A	~0	3,900	Low-temperature refrigeration
HFC-407C	~0	1,700	HCFC-22 replacement
HFC-410A	~0	1,890	Air-conditioning
HFC-507A	~0	3,900	Low-temperature refrigeration
Natural refrigerants			
Carbon dioxide (CO_2)	0	1.0	
Ammonia (NH_3)	0	0	
Propane	0	3	

- Assume equipment life according to Table 2. For any HVAC&R equipment t not listed, assume an equipment life of 10 years. Different values for equipment life may be substituted, with manufacturers' documentation.
- For existing equipment, apply the default equipment life according to Table 2. The equation is based on refrigerant impact spread over the life of the equipment; estimated remaining equipment life should not be substituted because it would provide inaccurate results.

TABLE 2. Default equipment life

Equipment	Default equipment life
Window air-conditioner, heat pump	10 years
Unitary, split, packaged air-conditioner, package heat pump	15 years
Reciprocating and scroll compressor, reciprocating chiller	20 years
Absorption chiller	23 years
Water-cooled packaged air-conditioner	24 years
Centrifugal chiller	25 years

- Assume that refrigerant leakage rate (Lr) is 2% per year for all equipment types, both new and existing. Variations in the measurement approach and system capabilities make individual measurement of equipment leakage unreliable and may not be used. Assume that end-of-life refrigerant loss (Mr) is 10% for all equipment types. No alternative values may be substituted (see Further Explanation, Calculations and Examples).

Refrigerant charge (Rc) is the ratio of the total refrigerant used in a piece of equipment to the total cooling capacity of that equipment, expressed in pounds per ton or kilograms per kW. For example, if a packaged air-conditioning unit uses 7 pounds of refrigerant and its cooling capacity is 5 tons, the refrigerant charge is 1.4.

FURTHER EXPLANATION

CALCULATIONS

Weighted Average Refrigerant Impact for the Project Building:

The project team must develop a weighted average calculation based on both downstream and upstream equipment. The weighted average would be based on the entire downstream equipment capacity, but only the designed capacity of the equipment being served by the district cooling plan, not the entire capacity of the district cooling plant.

EQUATION 1. Weighted average refrigerant impact

$$\left\{ \frac{\left(\text{Project building design chilled water cooling load in tons} \times \text{Chilled water central plant refrigerant impact score}\right) + \left(\text{Project building refrigerant systems' total capacity in tons} \times \text{Project building refrigerant impact score}\right)}{\left(\text{Project building refrigerant systems' total capacity in tons} + \text{Project building design chilled water cooling load in tons}\right)} \right\}$$

For example, a building has 50 tons of packaged equipment with a refrigerant impact value of 150 per ton. The district energy plant has a refrigerant impact value of 70 per ton and a total capacity of 1,000 tons. The building also has a designed 500 tons of equipment served by the district cooling plant. The weighted average impact is calculated as follows:

$$\frac{(500 \text{ tons} \times 70) + (50 \text{ tons} \times 150)}{(500 \text{ tons} + 50 \text{ tons})} = 77.3 \text{ weighted average refrigerant impact}$$

ASSESS HVAC SYSTEMS TO MINIMIZE REFRIGERANT IMPACT

Replacing existing equipment that has a high refrigerant charge, such as multiple small packaged units or split systems, can make this credit easier to achieve. Larger systems generally have a lesser charge because it is based on the amount of refrigerant per rated cooling capacity. Other strategies to minimize refrigerant charge:

- Determine whether evaporative cooling strategies, including indirect and direct evaporative cooling, are viable.
- For renovations, evaluate the cost of retrofitting or replacing existing HVAC systems. Equipment with high run time and ready accessibility often has a reasonable return on investment for replacement or refrigerant swap.

EXAMPLES

Example 1. School building

The cooling equipment for a school consists of the following systems:

- Twelve 5-ton packaged HVAC units with HFC-410A for classrooms
- One 2-ton split system HVAC unit with HCFC-22 for a data room
- One 1-ton window HVAC unit with HCFC-22 for an office

TABLE 3. Example calculations for school

Inputs								
Units	**Qunit (tons)**	**Refrigerant**	**GWPr**	**ODPr**	**Rc (lb/ton)**	**Life (yrs.)**	**Lr (%)**	**Mr (%)**
12	5	R-410A	1,890	0	1.8	15	2	10
1	2	R-22	1,780	0.04	3.3	15	2	10
1	1	R-22	1,780	0.04	2.1	10	2	10
Qtotal	**63**							

Calculations				
Tr Total Leakage (Lr × Life +Mr)	**LCGWP (GWPr × Tr × Rc) / Life**	**LCODP × 10^5 100,000 × (ODPr × Tr × Rc) / Life**	**Refrigerant atmospheric impact = LCGWP + LCODP × 10^5**	**(LCGWP + LCODP × 10^5 × N × Qunit**
40%	90.72	0	90.7	5,443
40%	156.6	352	508.6	1,017
30%	112.1	252	364.1	364
			Subtotal	**6,825**

Average refrigerant atmospheric impact = ∑ (LCGWP + LCODP × 10^5) × Qunit / Qtotal 108.33

Lr = leakage rate Mr = refrigerant loss Qunit = cooling capacity of equipment Rc = refrigerant charge

Because the average refrigerant impact is greater than 100, the project does not earn the credit.

Example 2. Office building

The cooling equipment in an office building consists of the following systems:

- One 500-ton centrifugal chiller with HFC-134a
- One 50-ton reciprocating "pony" chiller with HCFC-22
- Five 10-ton computer room air-conditioning units with HCFC-22

TABLE 4. Example calculations for office building

Inputs								
Units	**Qunit (tons)**	**Refrigerant**	**GWPr**	**ODPr**	**Rc (lb/ton)**	**Life (yrs.)**	**Lr (%)**	**Mr (%)**
1	500	R-134a	1,320	0	2	25	2	10
1	50	R-22	1,780	0.04	2.1	20	2	10
5	10	R-22	1,780	0.04	2.4	15	2	10
Qtotal	**600**							

Calculations				
Tr Total Leakage (Lr × Life +Mr)	**LCGWP (GWPr × Tr × Rc) / Life**	**LCODP × 10^5 × 100,000 (ODPr × Tr × Rc) / Life**	**Refrigerant atmospheric impact = LCGWP + LCODP × 10^5**	**(LCGWP + LCODP × 10^5 × N × Qunit**
60%	63.36	0	63.36	31,680
50%	93.5	210	303	15,173
40%	113.9	256	369.9	18,496
			Subtotal	**65,349**

Average refrigerant atmospheric impact = ∑ (LCGWP + LCODP × 10^5) × Qunit / Qtotal 108.92

Lr = leakage rate Mr = refrigerant loss Qunit = cooling capacity of equipment Rc = refrigerant charge

Because the average refrigerant impact is greater than 100, the project does not earn the credit.

Example 3. Hotel (SI units)

A hotel's cooling system includes the following equipment:

- Three 1400 kW centrifugal chillers with HCFC-123
- One 140 kW commercial refrigeration compressor rack with HCFC-22
- Twelve 7 kW telephone and data room split-system cooling units with HCFC-22

TABLE 5. Example calculations for hotel

Inputs								
Units	**Qunit (kW)**	**Refrigerant**	**GWPr**	**ODPr**	**Rc (kg/kW)**	**Life (yrs.)**	**Lr (%)**	**Mr (%)**
3	1 400	R-123	76	0.02	0.21	25	2	10
1	140	R-22	1,780	0.04	0.27	20	2	10
12	7	R-22	1,780	0.04	0.4	15	2	10
Qtotal	**4 424**							

Calculations				
Tr Total Leakage (Lr × Life +Mr)	**LCGWP (GWPr × Tr × Rc) / Life**	**LCODP × 100,000**	**Refrigerant atmospheric impact = LCGWP + LCODP × 10⁵**	**(LCGWP + LCODP × 10⁵ x N x Qunit**
60%	.38	10.08	10.46	43 932
50%	12.02	27	39.02	5 462.8
40%	18.99	42.67	61.66	5 971.44
			Subtotal	**54 574.24**
Average refrigerant atmospheric impact = ∑ (LCGWP + LCODP × 10⁵) × Qunit / Qtotal 12.34				

Lr = leakage rate   Mr = refrigerant loss   Qunit = cooling capacity of equipment   Rc = refrigerant charge

Because the average refrigerant impact is less than 13, the project earns the credit.

Example 4. Residential building with variable refrigerant flow

An apartment building's cooling system consists of the following:

- Four 8-ton outdoor VRF units
- Each unit has a base refrigerant amount of 16.5 lbs
- Each unit has additional refrigerant amount of 2.7 lbs for distribution, which must be included
- Rc for each unit is (16.5 lbs + 2.7 lbs) / 8 tons = 2.4 lbs/ton

TABLE 6. Example calculations for apartment building

Inputs								
Units	**Qunit (tons)**	**Refrigerant**	**GWPr**	**ODPr**	**Rc (lb/ton)**	**Life (yrs.)**	**Lr (%)**	**Mr (%)**
4	8	R-410A	1,890	0	2.4	15	2	10
Qtotal	**32**							

Calculations				
Tr Total Leakage (Lr × Life + Mr)	**LCGWP (GWPr × Tr × Rc) / Life**	**LCODP × 10^5 × 100,000 (ODPr × Tr × Rc) / Life**	**Refrigerant atmospheric impact = LCGWP + LCODP × 10^5**	**(LCGWP + LCODP × 10^5 × N × Qunit**
40%	120.96	0	120.96	3,871
			Subtotal	**3,871**

Average refrigerant atmospheric impact = ∑ (LCGWP + LCODP × 10^5) × Qunit / Qtotal 120.96
Result: Average refrigerant impact has a value greater than 100, therefore this project does not earn this credit

Lr = leakage rate Mr = refrigerant loss Qunit = cooling capacity of equipment Rc = refrigerant charge

RATING SYSTEM VARIATIONS

Retail

For Retail HVAC systems, use the calculation methodology and assumptions listed for all projects.

Retail projects with commercial refrigeration systems may either follow the prescriptive criteria or pursue certification through U.S. EPA GreenChill's certification program for fully operational food retail stores. If pursuing EPA certification, follow the certification steps outlined on the program website.

Non-Retail projects that have commercial refrigeration systems may follow the prescriptive criteria available to retail projects for commercial refrigeration systems. Both these prescriptive criteria for the commercial refrigeration systems, and the credit requirements for the HVAC refrigerant-using systems must be met to achieve credit compliance in this case.

PROJECT TYPE VARIATIONS

District Energy Systems (DES)

If a project has only downstream refrigeration equipment, only that equipment must be included in the refrigerant impact calculation. If a project has only upstream refrigeration equipment, only that equipment must be included in the refrigerant impact calculation. If a project has both downstream and upstream refrigeration equipment, the following procedure must be used to show credit compliance.

Complete two separate refrigerant impact calculations: one to calculate the refrigerant impact using only the downstream equipment and another using only the upstream equipment. If both calculations meet the credit requirements, the project team has demonstrated credit compliance. If neither calculation meets the credit requirements, the project cannot achieve this credit. If one calculation fails but the other passes, the project team may demonstrate compliance using the weighted average refrigerant impact for the project building (see *Further Explanation, Calculations*).

CAMPUS

Group Approach

Submit separate documentation for each building.

Campus Approach

Option 1. Eligible.

Option 2. Ineligible. Each LEED project may pursue the credit individually.

REQUIRED DOCUMENTATION

	Documentation	Option 1	Option 2
E	Confirmation that only no or low-impact refrigerants are used	X	
E	Equipment type		X
E	Equipment cooling capacity		X
E	Equipment quantity		X
E	Refrigerant type		X
E	Refrigerant charge (plus supporting documentation, if applicable)		X
E	Equipment life (plus supporting documentation, if applicable)		X
E	Refrigerant charge calculations (for VRF systems only)		X
E	Provide refrigerant equipment schedule or GreenChill certification (commercial refrigeration systems only)		X
E	Provide leak test results (commercial refrigeration systems only)		X

CHANGES FROM LEED 2009

- Sector-specific requirements have been added for commercial refrigeration equipment.
- The default leakage rate, rather than a measured rate, must be used in the calculations.

REFERENCED STANDARDS

None.

RELATED CREDIT TIPS

EA Credit Optimize Energy Performance. Alternatives to CFCs and HCFCs, such as HFC-410A, have lower refrigerant impacts but may require higher levels of energy use. Variable refrigerant flow and some split systems rarely meet the requirements of this credit because of the long refrigerant piping runs and the high quantity of refrigerant needed.

EXEMPLARY PERFORMANCE

Not available.

DEFINITIONS

downstream equipment the heating and cooling systems, equipment, and controls located in the project building or on the project site and associated with transporting the thermal energy of the district energy system (DES) into heated and cooled spaces. Downstream equipment includes the thermal connection or interface with the DES, secondary distribution systems in the building, and terminal units.

natural refrigerant a compound that is not manmade and is used for cooling. Such substances generally have much lower potential for atmospheric damage than manufactured chemical refrigerants. Examples include water, carbon dioxide, and ammonia.

upstream equipment a heating or cooling system or control associated with the district energy system (DES) but not part of the thermal connection or interface with the DES. Upstream equipment includes the thermal energy conversion plant and all the transmission and distribution equipment associated with transporting the thermal energy to the project building or site.

Materials and Resources (MR)

OVERVIEW

The longest part of a building's life cycle is the use phase, commonly referred to as the operations phase. To target environmental impact reductions during building operations, the Materials and Resources (MR) credit category focuses on the constant flow of products being purchased and discarded to support building operations. The life cycle of these products and materials—from extraction, processing, and transportation to use and disposal—can cause a wide range of environmental and human health harms. To reduce these burdens and thus the overall impact of a building during its operations phase, project teams should take a close look at the purchasing and waste management operations in existing buildings.

PURCHASING FOR BUILDING MAINTENANCE AND RENOVATION

Although renovations to existing buildings generally cause less harm than new construction, the associated materials have already had a significant environmental impact by the time they arrive on site. The extraction or harvesting, manufacture, and transport of these materials contribute to water and air pollution, the degradation of habitats, and the depletion of natural resources. In addition, the introduction of volatile organic compounds (VOCs) and other contaminants to the site can degrade the building's indoor environmental quality before occupancy begins. Establishing an environmentally preferred purchasing policy for construction materials used for maintenance and renovations not only ensures a consistent approach to material selection but also helps reduce environmental harm by specifying low-VOC, sustainably harvested, or reused materials. Implementing such a policy creates the market demand needed to drive manufacturers to produce materials in a more environmentally preferable way.

PURCHASING FOR ONGOING OPERATIONS

In addition to the big expenses incurred during facility maintenance and renovations, buildings also require significant amounts of products, from floor wax to furniture to toilet paper, to ensure smooth operations. Though often overlooked, these ongoing purchases can have a large environmental impact. Like construction materials, the products are associated with environmental burden both before and after they are used in the building. Unlike construction materials, however, these ongoing purchases are often the responsibility of several individuals in different departments, locations, and sometimes companies. An environmental purchasing plan, with procedures, guidelines, and designated responsibilities, is therefore necessary. This MR section addresses both the purchasing and implementation challenges facing existing building projects.

WASTE FOR BUILDING OPERATIONS

A significant amount of waste is generated by daily building operations and maintenance activities. Landfill disposal has wide-ranging effects, including soil and groundwater contamination, release of methane and carbon dioxide, and land degradation. Today commercial and institutional buildings typically account for 35% to 45% of total municipal solid waste. The commercial building industry can greatly reduce waste going to landfills and incinerators by targeting two large categories: paper (office paper, paperboard, cardboard) and organics (yard trimmings, food scraps, and wood).

Another important ongoing maintenance waste stream to consider is hazardous waste. One of the most toxic and most common sources of indoor pollution is mercury, which is found in all fluorescent lamps. Standard fluorescent lamps offer high efficiency and long life and are therefore widely used; they light 96% of commercial floor space in the United States.[1] Once removed from a building, they often become part of the municipal solid waste stream and contribute to air, land, and water contamination. Properly storing both new and spent lamps on site and ensuring their safe disposal reduce the environmental damage.

Both building maintenance and renovation inevitably produce construction and demolition waste. The safe storage, installation, and disposal of base building elements, such as carpets, paint, casework, furniture, and lamps, contribute to a healthy environment inside and outside the building. Because renovation and maintenance activities can affect indoor air quality, it is important to comply with safe storage recommendations for materials and follow correct protocols when painting, installing carpets, and working with other base building elements. Reducing contamination during construction and before occupancy can help minimize potential problems, thereby enhancing occupants' comfort, lowering absenteeism, and improving productivity. Taking time during construction to clean and protect ventilation systems and building spaces can extend the lifetime of ventilation systems and improve their efficiency, reducing energy use.

CROSS-CUTTING ISSUES

REQUIRED PRODUCTS AND MATERIALS

Each prerequisite and credit outlines the exact scope of the requirements. The prerequisite and credit requirements are divided into two categories: products that are purchased on an ongoing basis, such as lamps, paper goods, or office equipment, and materials purchased for periodic maintenance or renovation work.

QUALIFYING PRODUCTS AND EXCLUSIONS

The MR section related to maintenance and renovation addresses "permanently installed building products," which as defined by LEED refers to products and materials that create the building or are attached to it. Examples include structure and enclosure elements, installed finishes, framing, interior walls, cabinets and casework, doors, and roof. Most of these materials fall into Construction Specifications Institute (CSI) 2012 MasterFormat Divisions 3-10, 31, and 32. Some products addressed by MR credits fall outside these divisions.

For the Operations and Maintenance rating system, furniture must be included in credit calculations and treated consistently across credits. Also included are items purchased to maintain furniture.

Excluded from MR credits are all mechanical, plumbing, and electrical equipment (MEP), specialty items (e.g., elevators, escalators, process equipment, fire suppression systems), and products purchased for temporary use on the project (e.g., formwork for concrete).

1. *U.S. Department of Energy. 2003 Commercial Buildings Energy Consumption Survey, 2006, http;//www.eia/gov/emeu/cbecs2003/detailed_tables_2003/detailed_tables_2003.html* (accessed May 2008)

DETERMINING PRODUCT COST

Calculations for purchasing credits are based on product and material cost, which excludes labor required for installation or replacement. Preferably, taxes, shipping, and delivery costs on purchases should be excluded but may be included, provided they are either included or excluded consistently throughout the calculations.

DETERMINING MATERIAL CONTRIBUTIONS OF AN ASSEMBLY

Many sustainable criteria in the MR category apply to the entire product, as is the case for product certifications and programs. However, some criteria apply to only a portion of the product. The portion of the product that contributes to the credit could be either a percentage of a homogeneous material or the percentage of qualifying components that are mechanically or permanently fastened together. In either case, the contributing value is based on weight. Examples of homogeneous materials include composite flooring, ceiling tiles, and rubber wall base. Examples of assemblies (parts mechanically or permanently fastened together) include office chairs, demountable partition walls, premade window assemblies, and doors.

Calculate the value that contributes toward credit compliance as the percentage, by weight, of the material or component that meets the criteria, multiplied by the total product cost (Figure 1, Table 1).

Product value ($) = Total product cost ($) x % meeting sustainble criteria

Figure 1. Sustainably produced components of $500 office chair

TABLE 1. Example calculation for $500 office chair

Chair component	Percentage of product, by weight	Value of component	Percentage of component meeting sustainability criteria	Value of sustainability criteria
Fastening hardware	2%	$10	25% preconsumer recycled content	$2.50
Cotton fabric	5%	$25	100% certified by Rainforest Alliance	$25.00
Plastic component	25%	$125	10% postconsumer recycled content	$12.50
Armrest	5%	$25	10% postconsumer recycled content	$2.50
Metal base	20%	$100	25% preconsumer recycled content	$25.00
Steel post	8%	$40	40% preconsumer recycled content	$16.00
Wheels	5%	$25	5% postconsumer recycled content	$1.25
Total value contributing to credit				$84.75

SELECTING AN APPROPRIATE PURCHASING TRACKING SYSTEM

Several credits in the MR section depend on tracking product purchasing decisions and materials types or streams. When deciding on a tracking system, make sure that the strategy works for the project team. A good tracking system is user-friendly, readily accessible, and easily coordinates multiple purchases from a variety of sources. Issues to consider include users' computer skills and accessibility, language barriers, and the need to merge information from multiple sources.

For example, if many individuals make purchases, an electronic tracking system may make it easier to share or combine purchase data. Standardized tracking tools ease the process of tracking the purchases of different parties and aggregating the data. Keep in mind that some vendors may not have ready access to computers for logging product deliveries.

Steps for using a tracking system proceed as follows:

1. Review current purchasing practices to evaluate which items already meet the requirements and what changes need to be made.
2. Log all purchases.
3. Identify which purchases meet the credit criteria.
4. Calculate the percentage, by cost, of portions of materials or assemblies that meet the criteria (in those cases where only a portion of a material meets the criteria).
5. Calculate the total percentage, by cost, of materials that meet the credit criteria.

It is recommended that teams pilot the chosen tracking system for one or two months before using it for LEED certification so that any problems can be addressed before the performance period.

MULTITENANT BUILDINGS

Because certification applies to whole buildings, it may be challenging for multitenant buildings to earn certain credits, especially in the MR category. All portions of a building under the site management's control are expected to comply with the credit requirements. If it is not possible to gather to necessary information on purchasing or waste management to document credit achievement, or if the LEED applicant does not have control over the entire building, the project team may exempt up to 10% of the building's gross floor area (see *Getting Started*).

Collecting waste information in multitenant buildings. Generally, waste collection falls under the responsibility of building management, through a service contract for the entire building. If waste collection or portions of waste collection (e.g., hazardous waste) are not under the site management's control, it is recommended that teams prioritize meeting local regulations for waste disposal, then focus on prerequisite achievement and, last, credit achievement.

Collecting purchasing information in multitenant buildings. The products, materials, and furniture (as applicable) purchased by tenants are included in the MR purchasing credits. It is recommended that project teams test the building-wide purchasing tracking systems before the start of the performance period. Establish a relationship with the primary purchaser in each tenant space to encourage participation, accurate reporting, and notification when relevant purchases will be made. Provide support (e.g., training in using the tracking tool) and clearly indicate what information is needed.

Excluding tenant purchases in credit documentation. If additional tenants beyond those in the excluded 10% gross floor area choose not to provide purchasing data, the purchases for those tenant spaces must be estimated and assumed to be noncompliant. To estimate these tenants' purchases, extrapolate the purchasing rate from elsewhere in the building on a per occupant or area basis, and assume that the purchases meet none of the criteria. Integrate the estimated data from the nonparticipating tenants into the whole-building purchasing data (for participating and nonparticipating tenants) to determine compliance for the whole building (Table 2).

TABLE 2. Example compliance calculation with nonparticipating tenants

Actual purchase rate for participating tenants			
Tenant	**Floor area (ft^2)**	**Total purchases**	**Compliant purchases**
Jones Hotelier	75,000	$2,000	$1,500
Big Red Offices	60,000	$1,000	$750
Total	135,000	$3,000	$2,250
Total purchases / ft^2 of participating tenants			$0.022
Estimated purchase rate for nonparticipating tenants			
Tenant	**Floor area (ft^2)**	**Estimated total purchases**	**Estimated compliant purchases**
Cranky's Depot	15,000	$0.022 x 15,000 ft^2 = $330	$0
Whole-building results			
Tenant	**Floor area (ft^2)**	**Total purchases**	**Compliant purchases**
Jones Hotelier	75,000	$2,000	$1,500
Big Red Offices	60,000	$1,000	$750
Cranky's Depot (estimated)	15,000	$330	$0
Total	150,000	$3,330	$2,250
Percentage compliant purchases			67.57%

MATERIALS AND RESOURCES PREREQUISITE

Ongoing Purchasing and Waste Policy

This prerequisite applies to:

Existing Buildings
Schools
Retail
Data Centers
Hospitality
Warehouses and Distribution Centers

INTENT

To reduce the environmental harm from materials purchased, used, and disposed of in the operations within buildings.

REQUIREMENTS

EXISTING BUILDINGS, SCHOOLS, RETAIL, DATA CENTERS, HOSPITALITY, WAREHOUSES AND DISTRIBUTION CENTERS

ESTABLISHMENT E

Environmentally Preferable Purchasing

Have in place an environmentally preferable purchasing (EPP) policy for products purchased during regular operations of the building. Include at a minimum:

- Ongoing Purchases
  - The five most purchased product categories based on total annual purchases.
  - Paper, toner cartridges, binders, batteries, and desk accessories.
  - Lamps (indoor and outdoor, hard-wired and portable fixtures)
  - Food (required for Schools and Hospitality only)
- Durable Goods Purchases
  - Office equipment, appliances, and audiovisual equipment
  - Electric powered equipment

The policy should address the criteria in the following credits:

- Materials and Resources Credit: Purchasing—Ongoing
- Materials and Resources Credit: Purchasing—Lamps

The policy must cover at least those product purchases within the building and site management's control.

Solid Waste Management

Establish storage locations for recyclable materials, including mixed paper, corrugated cardboard, glass, plastics, and metals. Establish safe storage areas for batteries and mercury-containing lamps.

Have in place an environmentally preferable solid waste management policy that addresses reuse, recycling, or composting of products purchased during regular operations of the building. Include at a minimum:

- Ongoing waste
  - The five most purchased product categories based on total annual purchases.
  - Food (required for Schools and Hospitality only)
- Durable goods waste
  - Office equipment, appliances, and audiovisual equipment
  - Electric powered equipment
- Hazardous waste
  - Safe disposal of batteries and lamps (indoor and outdoor, hard-wired and portable fixtures)

The policy must cover at least those product purchases within the building and site management's control.

RETAIL

In addition to the requirements above, retail projects should promote environmentally responsible sourcing of retail merchandise through one of the four following options.

OPTION 1. SUPPLY CHAIN SURVEY

Establish a supply chain survey.

The survey should collect information from each supplier regarding the following:

- social equity practices;
- energy and carbon reduction measures;
- material selection practices for products, packaging, and distribution;
- waste reduction and waste management measures; and
- human health protection measures.

OR

OPTION 2. SUPPLY CHAIN EDUCATION PROGRAM FOR RETAIL EMPLOYEES AND/OR RETAIL TENANT REPRESENTATIVES

Establish a program to inform employees and tenants engaged in merchandise purchasing, packaging, and distribution about environmentally preferable supply chain strategies.

Include the following in the education program:

- environmental best practices for supply chain decisions;
- resources for additional information; and
- internal contacts for more information.

OR

OPTION 3. SUPPLY CHAIN ENVIRONMENTAL CRITERIA LIST

Establish criteria for retail products encouraging an environmentally preferable supply chain strategy addressing the following areas:

- purchasing;
- materials handling and packaging;
- inventory;
- materials recovery during manufacturing;
- waste disposal; and
- product take-back.

OPTION 4. SUSTAINABLE PURCHASING EDUCATION FOR CUSTOMERS

Install an educational program display for customers displaying environmental initiatives that the store has implemented. The educational display should incorporate information that includes the supply chain environmental criteria listed in Option 3.

PERFORMANCE P

Maintain a high-performing solid waste management program by conducting a waste stream audit of ongoing consumables at least once every five years or by diverting 75% of ongoing waste and achieving Materials and Resources Credit Solid Waste Management—Ongoing.

BEHIND THE INTENT

Building owners and operators purchase high volumes of supplies whose environmental and human health consequences extend from extraction and manufacturing to use and disposal. Land-fill waste produces greenhouse gases such as methane and can contaminate soil and groundwater with hazardous substances. Paper is the largest single category of municipal solid waste in the U.S., representing 28.2% of the total 82 million tons produced in 2009[1]; waste paper is generated in particularly high quantities by office buildings.

Environmentally preferable purchasing policies reduce the harms by prioritizing products' green attributes and providing a framework for implementation. This prerequisite requires that the project institute a policy for typical purchases for ongoing operations; implementation is rewarded through the corresponding credit, MR Credit Purchasing—Ongoing.

A waste stream audit, in which the contents of the building's waste stream are sorted and analyzed, allows building managers to learn about the amounts and types of waste generated by the occupants and site. Waste stream audits help building managers identify opportunities for source reduction, reuse, recycling, and composting to decrease the quantity of waste disposed of through incineration or landfill, and reduces the associated operational and financial burdens associated with waste disposal.

STEP-BY-STEP GUIDANCE

ESTABLISHMENT E

ENVIRONMENTALLY PREFERABLE PURCHASING

STEP 1. IDENTIFY THE MOST PURCHASED ONGOING CONSUMABLE PRODUCTS BY CATEGORY E

Gather and analyze purchasing data from a representative year of purchasing.

- Categorize the data into product categories, chosen as appropriate to the project. Exclude materials purchased for facility renovations and maintenance, which are covered under MR Prerequisite Facility Maintenance and Renovation (see *Further Explanation, Purchasing Criteria and Goals*).
- If annual purchasing data are not available, estimate costs based on information for the most frequently purchased items.
- Consider confirming with building management personnel that the results reflect annual purchasing behavior. If the results seem atypical, adjust as necessary and submit an explanation for the change.
- It is recommended that project teams include purchases by building tenants. This prepares the project to achieve MR Credit Purchasing—Ongoing, which covers the entire building's ongoing consumables.
- Review purchasing records to determine which five product purchasing categories under the building management's control have the highest cumulative annual cost.
- The policy must address at least the five most-purchased product categories as well as those listed in the prerequisite. A project's top-five purchases may align with the categories in the prerequisite requirements; if not, add any project-specific top-five categories to those listed in the requirements.
- Office purchases not required in the policy that may constitute top purchases, based on annual cost, include notebooks, notepads, envelopes, and writing tools.

STEP 2. DEVELOP ENVIRONMENTALLY PREFERABLE PURCHASING POLICY E

Develop and implement an environmentally preferable purchasing policy that establishes product purchasing criteria and specific goals for purchasing ongoing consumables, electronic items, and appliances that meet the prerequisite requirements. Purchasing goals can be determined by the team; there is no performance threshold requirement for the prerequisite.

- The policy must cover at least the following:
  - Products in the top-five categories, by annual cost

1. *U.S. Environmental Protection Agency, "Municipal Solid Waste Generation, Recycling, and Disposal in the United States: Facts and Figures for 2009" EPA-530-F-010-012, December 2010, epa.gov/osw/nonhaz/municipal/pubs/msw2009-fs.pdf*

- All the required product categories for both ongoing and durable goods purchases, as specified in the prerequisite requirements
- Mercury-containing lamps (see MR Credit Purchasing—Lamps)

- The scope of the policy is regular operational purchasing for the facility. Exclude purchases covered under MR Prerequisite Facility Maintenance and Renovations Policy.
- Establish product purchasing criteria for each category. Refer to the requirements in MR Credit Purchasing—Ongoing and MR Credit Purchasing—Lamps to establish the criteria.
- See *Further Explanation, Purchasing Criteria and Goals,* and *Getting Started, Effective Policy Development.*

SOLID WASTE MANAGEMENT

STEP 1. IDENTIFY STORAGE AREAS FOR RECYCLABLE MATERIALS AND ESTABLISH DIVERSION PROCESS E

Ensure that storage areas have been designated at the building and/or site for recyclable materials. Recycling may be commingled, provided the collection area is sufficient for all the recyclable materials listed in the prerequisite requirements. Provide safe storage areas for hazardous materials.

Consider developing ways to ensure that diversion actually occurs. Strategies may include the following:

- Communicating about recyclables collection to building occupants and staff
- Sizing waste bins appropriately and placing them in convenient locations
- Training janitorial staff in collecting, transporting, and storing of recyclables
- Contracting with recycling vendors to haul the recyclables

Based on project location, individual vendors may be needed for different recyclables.

STEP 2. DEVELOP SOLID WASTE MANAGEMENT POLICY E

Develop and implement a solid waste management policy to divert the project's waste from landfills. Target high-volume materials for which recycling facilities exist.

- The policy should address at least the top-five products (by cost) identified in the environmentally preferable purchasing policy (Step 2, above) and the items listed in the prerequisite requirements.
- The scope of the policy is regular operational solid waste for the facility. Exclude waste covered under MR Prerequisite Facility Maintenance and Renovations Policy.
- Establish an achievable diversion goal for each identified waste stream that is under the building management's control. Conducting a waste stream audit during the performance period is a best practice to define baseline waste percentages, by volume or weight, of total waste generated and sent to landfills or diverted.
- Use or adapt the strategies in MR Credit Solid Waste Management—Ongoing requirements.
- Coordinate the solid waste management policy with the environmentally preferable purchasing policy in areas such as source reduction, contract agreements, and communications with building occupants (see *Getting Started, Effective Policy Development*).

PERFORMANCE P

STEP 1. MAINTAIN SOLID WASTE MANAGEMENT PROGRAM P

Demonstrate performance through either of the following:

- Reduce waste by achieving MR Credit Solid Waste Management—Ongoing and diverting 75% of ongoing waste.
- Alternatively, conduct a waste stream audit of the materials covered in this prerequisite once every five years. The scope of the audit is regular operational product disposal for the facility. Exclude construction waste.

It is recommended that project teams perform the audit as soon as possible and use the results to optimize waste reduction and diversion during the performance period. The results will inform the solid waste management and environmentally preferable purchasing policies.

- Waste audits require sorting and measuring the building's waste over a given time period. Diversion data from waste hauling vendors may assist in this audit.
- For the waste audit sample, select a period, such as a day or a week, that represents a typical period of waste generation for the building. Avoid time periods that are affected by holidays or other irregular occupancy patterns (see *Further Explanation, Waste Audit Procedures*).

RETAIL ONLY

STEP 1. FOLLOW STEPS ABOVE FOR ESTABLISHMENT AND PERFORMANCE SECTIONS

STEP 2. CHOOSE A COMPLIANCE PATH E

Select one of the four options in the credit requirements:

- Option 1. Supply chain survey
- Option 2. Education program for employees/tenant representatives
- Option 3. Supply chain environmental criteria
- Option 4: Education program for customers

When deciding on the option to pursue, consider ease and cost of implementation, the project's location, and the owner's priorities.

Option 1. Supply chain survey

STEP 1. CREATE SURVEY CRITERIA

Develop a survey that addresses the topics listed in the prerequisite requirements, as applicable to the project's suppliers.

- Many sustainability programs cover the supply chain. Consider researching third-party programs and certifications, such as Global Reporting Initiative (for social equity) or the Sustainable Packaging Coalition (for material selection in packaging, etc.).
- Consider including environmental metrics the supplier is meeting or aims to meet in the future, particularly for energy conservation and carbon reduction.
- Ask specific questions about suppliers' practices, and adapt the survey language as necessary.

STEP 2. DEVELOP SURVEY IMPLEMENTATION PROCEDURE

Determine the most effective way to conduct the survey; all suppliers must be included.

- Describe how information will be obtained. The narrative may describe the delivery method, procedures for follow-up, collection process, and addressing information gaps.
- State how often the survey will be conducted. There is no minimum or maximum requirement for survey cycle; determine the period that is appropriate to the project.

Option 2. Supply chain education program for retail employees and/or retail tenant representatives

STEP 1. IDENTIFY TARGET AUDIENCE

A comprehensive education program takes into account its intended audience, which will vary by project. The goal of the program is to ensure consistent implementation of sustainable supply chain practices.

- Target individuals who make purchasing and other supply chain decisions.
- Consider whether the target audience is the direct employee or a tenant.
- Tailor the content and delivery method to ensure the most effective result.

STEP 2. DEVELOP ENVIRONMENTAL BEST PRACTICES

Review the best practices and sustainable criteria described in this section of the reference guide. Determine the priority for sustainable criteria and educate employees and tenants on effective ways to implement them in their supply chain decisions.

STEP 3. DETERMINE PROGRAM DELIVERY METHOD

Based on the target audience and the content of the education program, determine the best approach. The program may include guidelines, a manual, a work practices report, or workshops.

- If training is part of orientation for new hires, the program may be delivered through a workshop; for retail tenants, a manual or guideline may be more effective.
- Consider including effectiveness checks or refresher materials on a periodic basis.

Option 3. Supply chain environmental criteria list

STEP 1. DEVELOP ENVIRONMENTAL CRITERIA FOR SUPPLY CHAIN

Using the sustainable criteria from MR credits for ongoing purchasing and ongoing waste, apply appropriate criteria to the required areas: purchasing, packaging, inventory, materials recovery, and waste. Determine the priority for sustainable criteria and educate employees and tenants on effective ways to implement them.

STEP 2. DEVELOP IMPLEMENTATION PLAN

Based on the individuals involved, develop an effective implementation strategy. Consider including effectiveness checks or refresher materials on a periodic basis.

Option 4. Sustainable purchasing education for customers

STEP 1. DEVELOP EDUCATION CONTENT

The goal of this option is to increase awareness of the environmental consequences of material sourcing and supply chains. Develop an education program for customers about business practices and retail products, covering the following topics.

- Purchasing: the attributes of the materials being purchased for retail products
- Materials handling and packaging: sustainability efforts to reduce the effect of retail product packaging
- Inventory: storage of retail products
- Materials recovery during manufacturing: pre-consumer recycling programs such as selling manufacturing byproducts to other industries
- Waste disposal: the disposal of waste products by retail products
- Product take-back: manufacturer's recovery of the retail product at the end of its useful life

STEP 2. IDENTIFY DELIVERY METHOD

The audience for this education program is customers, whose activities and interests vary by retail type. Target delivery methods appropriate. Consider displays, such as kiosks or boards, strategically placed for maximum exposure.

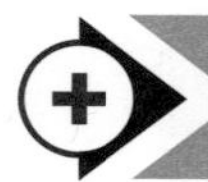

FURTHER EXPLANATION

EXAMPLES

The following is an excerpt from an example environmentally preferable purchasing policy, indicating the scope and sustainability goals and objectives. Project teams should expand on this basic information and make the policy specific to the project building.

ENVIRONMENTALLY PREFERABLE PURCHASING POLICY – PAPER COMPANY TOWER

Scope

The scope of this policy includes, at a minimum, purchases of the following that are within building management's control at the Paper Company Tower building and site:

- Five most purchased items, including:
  - copy paper
  - disposable kitchen goods for office breakrooms – cups, plates, and cutlery
  - envelopes
  - folders
  - toner cartridge
- Ongoing consumables
  - paper (printing or copy paper, notebooks, notepads, envelopes, etc.)
  - toner cartridges
  - binders
  - desk accessories
  - batteries
- Durable goods
  - electric-powered equipment
  - office equipment, appliances, and audiovisual equipment

Sustainability goals and objectives

The sustainability goals for this policy are as follows:

- Five most purchased product categories (copy paper, envelopes, folders, and toner cartridges)
  - Meet the criteria for ongoing consumables for at least 90%, by cost, of products purchased in these product categories.
- Disposable kitchen goods for office breakrooms (cups, plates, and cutlery)
  - Purchase at least 50%, by cost, of disposable kitchen goods that meet at least one of the following criteria:
- 100% compostable
- 100% recyclable
- Made from bio-based products (e.g. corn)
- FSC-certified products
- Durable goods
  - Purchase at least 40%, by cost, electric-powered equipment that meet at least one of the following criteria:
- Silver Electronic Product Environmental Assessment Tool (EPEAT) rating or better.
- ENERGY STAR rating. If the equipment does not yet fall under the EPEAT rating systems, it must be ENERGY STAR qualified.
- The equipment (either battery or corded) replaces conventional gas-powered equipment.
- Batteries
  - 100% of batteries purchased must be rechargeable.
- Lamps
  - The total overall maximum of 70 picograms of mercury per lumen hour for all mercury-containing lamps purchased for the building and associated grounds.

Figure 1. Example environmentally preferable purchasing policy

The following is an excerpt from an example solid waste management policy, summarizing results from the waste audit and identifying opportunities for improvement. Project teams should expand on this basic information and tailor waste diversion efforts to the project building.

PURCHASING CRITERIA AND GOALS

This prerequisite does not specify any thresholds for the percentage of environmental preferable products within a category; the goals are determined by the project team.

WASTE MANAGEMENT POLICY – PAPER COMPANY TOWER

Waste Audit Results

Waste Type	Weight (pounds)		Percentage of Waste Type Diverted	Percentage of Total Waste Associated with Waste Type
	Landfill Stream	Diversion Stream		
Glass, Metal, Plastics	5	250	98%	25.5%
Mixed Paper	20	400	95%	42%
Cardboard	25	100	80%	12.5%
Fluorescent Lamps	0	0		
Batteries	0	0		
Wet Waste	150	0	0%	15%
Restroom Waste	50	0	0%	5%
Miscellaneous	0	0		
Totals	**250**	**750**	**75%**	

The total amount of waste examined during the audit was 1000 lbs including the following subtotals for each waste type:

- 750 lbs of waste was successfully diverted for recycling
    - No batteries, lamps, or durable good items were misplaced in the ongoing recycling or landfill/incinerator waste streams.
- 250 lbs of waste was sent to the landfill

Opportunities for Improvement

- Increase the diversion rate
    - 150 lbs of wet waste were not diverted. A composting program in kitchen areas may significantly increase the building's overall diversion rate.
- Source reduction
    - A large portion of the glass, metal, and plastics recycling waste that was recycled was plastic water bottles. A program to decrease the use of disposable water bottles may significantly reduce the amount of recycled glass, metal, and plastics waste that is generated and recycled.
- Strategies may include providing filtered water to building occupants, durable water glasses, and a dishwasher for cleaning dirty water glasses.

Waste Diversion Process

- Communicate the waste diversion process to all tenants
- Ensure that janitorial staff are trained on the waste diversion process specific to the building
- Make sure there are clear location of storage areas for all waste streams in the building (recycling, batteries, lamps, durable goods, composting, etc) and procedures for moving waste to the storage areas
- Inform selected waste haulers on the building policy and process for collecting, diverting, and reporting on the all waste streams in the building (recycling, batteries, lamps, durable goods, composting, etc)
- Waste and recycling bins must be placed in all common areas and must be appropriately sized for the amount of waste generated by occupants of the space. Use blue bins for recycling and label clearly. Recycling bins must be similar in size to other waste bins in the same area.

Figure 2. Example solid waste management policy

The environmentally preferable purchasing policy addresses product purchases that are under the building management's control. However, the corresponding credit, MR Credit Purchasing—Ongoing, is based on whole-building purchases. To lay the foundation for achieving points under the credit, the project team should consider setting goals for purchases for the entire building.

Ongoing purchases. When developing the purchasing policy, set sustainability criteria and goals for each product category. Develop a process for maintenance staff to assess potential product purchases against the criteria. Develop a tracking system to measure progress against goals.

Electronic equipment purchases. Because the criterion for electronic equipment stipulates that the products be third party certified under EPEAT or ENERGY STAR, consider listing specific equipment brands and models in the policy to make adherence easier.

Replacement. An alternative approach to purchasing third party–certified electric equipment is to replace conventional gas-powered equipment with battery-powered or corded models.

When creating the purchasing policy, consider these common purchases. Refer to prerequisite requirements for the content of the policy. Durable goods include appliances and office equipment.

TABLE 1. Common office purchases

Ongoing purchases	Durable goods
Office paper	Computers, laptops
Notepads	Monitors
Notebooks	Printers
Envelopes	Copiers
Toner cartridges	Scanners
Binders	Fax machines
Batteries	Refrigerators
Writing tools (pencils, pens, etc.)	Dishwashers
	Water coolers
	External power adapters
	Televisions
	Projectors
	Maintenance equipment
	Cleaning equipment

WASTE AUDIT PROCEDURES

This prerequisite requires sorting and measuring the building's waste for a given time period. Diversion data from waste-hauling vendors may assist in this audit but is not sufficient for compliance. There are no requirements for the qualifications of those who conduct the audit.

1. **Decide on a strategy.** The two major waste streams to be audited are waste that goes to a landfill or incinerator, and waste that is recycled, reused, or composted. Choose a time period (typically 24 hours). Decide on a unit of measurement, either weight or volume, and use it consistently. Inform janitorial staff and waste-hauling vendors and enlist their cooperation, but do not notify building occupants; the results must reflect their typical disposal and recycling behaviors.
2. **Collect the waste to be audited.** Collect the contents of both waste streams. Keep the waste to be audited separate from that of previous or subsequent days, and separate the landfill and diverted waste. For more precise results, each bag or container of waste may be labeled with its origin (e.g., second-floor offices, fitness center, parking garage).

3. **Sort both waste streams.** Necessary equipment may include clothing (e.g., puncture-proof rubber gloves, safety glasses, protective suits), tarp or plastic sheet for waste sorting, containers or bags, a scale, and a camera for documentation. Wet waste (food and restroom waste) does not need to be sorted because of hygienic concerns, but the associated weight or volume and any diversion must be tracked.
4. **Measure landfill or incinerator waste.** Measure the total amount, and the amount of each recyclable material (mixed paper, corrugated cardboard, glass, plastics, and metals) that was inappropriately thrown away. Also measure the amount of inappropriately disposed e-waste, mercury-containing lamps, and (optional) compostable material. Some project teams (e.g., for hospitals) may wish to account for hazardous waste.
5. **Measure diverted waste.** Measure the total amount, and the amount of each recycled material (mixed paper, corrugated cardboard, glass, plastics, and metals). Note the amount and kinds of nonrecyclable waste that was placed in recycling bins, and any e-waste and mercury-containing lamps. If the project building has a reuse or composting program, measure the total amounts.
6. **Prepare the waste audit report.** The report must cover the following topics:
   - Procedures, including the time period, scope, and methods for sorting and measuring waste
   - Types of waste and the amounts of each type, by weight or volume
   - Opportunities to decrease waste generation (source reduction) and increase diversion rates
   - Brief analysis of how waste diversion and source reduction could reduce the project's waste-hauling costs (optional)

Project teams may include paper diverted by a document-shredding vendor if the vendor recycles the paper. If the vendor does not recycle, the shredded paper must be included in the calculations.

PROJECT TYPE VARIATIONS

Multitenant Buildings

This prerequisite covers all purchases and waste under the site management's control only, but project teams must describe how they will provide education and guidance to encourage tenants to adopt similar purchasing and waste management policies. (The corresponding credits, Purchasing—Ongoing and Solid Waste Management—Ongoing, require tenants' participation in source reduction and waste diversion efforts.)

INTERNATIONAL TIPS

Electronic equipment not covered by the EPEAT rating systems must be ENERGY STAR qualified to meet the requirements of this prerequisite. A project outside the U.S. may purchase products that are not labeled under the ENERGY STAR program if they meet the ENERGY STAR product specifications, available on the ENERGY STAR website. All products must meet the standards of the current version of ENERGY STAR as of the date of their purchase.

CAMPUS

Group Approach

Submit separate documentation for each building.

Campus Approach

Eligible.

REQUIRED DOCUMENTATION

	Documentation	All projects	Retail Option 1	Retail Option 2	Retail Option 3	Retail Option 4
E	Environmentally preferable purchasing policy	X	X	X	X	X
E	Floor and/or site plan identifying recycling storage areas	X	X	X	X	X
E P	Waste stream audit report	X	X	X	X	X
E	Solid waste management policy	X	X	X	X	X
E	Sample survey for suppliers		X			
E	Description of survey procedures		X			
E	Educational curriculum and description of delivery method			X		
E	Supply chain environmental criteria list, including all required criteria and implementation plan				X	
E	Documentation of educational display					X
E	Description of information presented, including all required supply chain environmental criteria					X

RELATED CREDIT TIPS

MR Prerequisite Facility Maintenance and Renovations. Coordinate the environmentally preferable purchasing policy and the solid waste management policies with the related credit to take advantage of synergies and reduce duplication.

MR Credit Purchasing—Ongoing. The related credit requires that ongoing consumables and durable goods be purchased according to the environmentally preferable purchasing policy developed in this prerequisite.

MR Credit Solid Waste Management—Ongoing. The related credit requires that ongoing consumables and durable goods be disposed of according to the solid waste management policy developed in this prerequisite.

CHANGES FROM LEED 2009

- MR Prerequisite Sustainable Purchasing Policy and MR Prerequisite Solid Waste Management Policy prerequisites have been combined into one prerequisite.
- The requirements of MR Credit Waste Stream Audit have been added to the prerequisite.
- Minimum recyclable storage requirements have been added to align with the prerequisite requirement in the Building Design and Construction rating systems.

REFERENCED STANDARDS

None.

EXEMPLARY PERFORMANCE

Not available.

DEFINITIONS

durable goods products with a useful life of approximately two or more years and that are replaced infrequently. Examples include furniture, office equipment, appliances, external power adapters, televisions, and audiovisual equipment.

durable goods waste stream the flow of long-lasting products from the project building after they are fully depreciated and have reached the end of their useful life for normal business operations. It includes leased durable goods returned to their owner but does not include durable goods that remain functional and are moved to another floor or building.

mixed paper white and colored paper, envelopes, forms, file folders, tablets, flyers, cereal boxes, wrapping paper, catalogs, magazines, phone books, and photos

ongoing consumable a product that has a low cost per unit and is regularly used and replaced in the course of business. Examples include paper, toner cartridges, binders, batteries, and desk accessories. Also known as ongoing purchases.

MATERIALS AND RESOURCES PREREQUISITE

Facility Maintenance and Renovation Policy

This prerequisite applies to:

Existing Buildings
Schools
Retail
Data Centers
Hospitality
Warehouses and Distribution Centers

INTENT

To reduce the environmental harms associated with the materials purchased, installed, and disposed of during maintenance and renovation of buildings.

REQUIREMENTS

EXISTING BUILDINGS, SCHOOLS, RETAIL, DATA CENTERS, HOSPITALITY, WAREHOUSES AND DISTRIBUTION CENTERS

ESTABLISHMENT E

Have in place a facility maintenance and renovation policy that includes guidelines for renovation and maintenance activities, using LEED rating system strategies, to be implemented at the discretion of building owners, operators, or tenants. Renovation activities include building improvements and tenant fit-outs. Maintenance activities include general repair and replacement.

The policy must cover at least those product purchases within the building and site management's control. The policy must address purchasing, waste management and indoor air quality.

Purchasing Policy for Maintenance and Renovations

Have in place a purchasing policy for product and materials purchased for facility maintenance and renovation activities. Include at a minimum:

- Base building elements permanently or semi- permanently attached to the building (mechanical, electrical and plumbing components and specialty items such as elevators are excluded). Exclude fixtures, and equipment, which are not considered base building elements;
- Furniture and furnishings as well as components and parts needed to maintain them

The policy should address the criteria in the following credits:

- MR Credit: Purchasing—Facility Maintenance and Renovation

Waste Management Policy for Maintenance and Renovations

Have in place a waste management policy addressing the following:

- **Facility maintenance waste.** The policy should address safe storage and recycling and diversion of waste associated with maintenance activities.
- **Renovation waste.** The policy should describe the procedure for creating an individual plan for each renovation project. Each renovation project should establish waste diversion goals, target five materials for diversion, approximate the volume of waste anticipated, and identify waste diversion strategies to be used.

Indoor Air Quality Policy for Maintenance and Renovations

Have in place an indoor air quality policy for facility maintenance and renovation activities addressing the criteria below. For maintenance activities implement the policy as applicable. For renovation activities create an individual plan for each renovation project as outlined in the policy.

- Follow the recommended control measures of the Sheet Metal and Air Conditioning National Contractors Association (SMACNA) IAQ Guidelines for Occupied Buildings under Construction, 2nd edition (2007), ANSI/SMACNA 008–2008, Chapter 3
  - Protect stored on-site and installed absorptive materials from moisture damage.
  - Do not operate permanently-installed air handling equipment during construction unless filtration media with a minimum efficiency reporting value (MERV) of 8, as determined by ASHRAE 52.2–2007, with errata (or equivalent filtration media class of F5 or higher, as defined by CEN Standard EN 779–2002, Particulate Air Filters for General Ventilation, Determination of the Filtration Performance), are installed at each return air grille and return or transfer duct inlet opening such that there is no bypass around the filtration media.
- Develop a procedure to, before occupancy, replace all filtration media with the final design filtration media.
- Develop a plan to determine whether a flush-out or air quality testing is needed after construction ends and all interior finishes are installed but before occupancy.

PERFORMANCE P

None.

BEHIND THE INTENT

Establishing an environmentally preferred purchasing policy for construction materials used for maintenance (e.g., painting, recarpeting) and renovations (e.g., tenant fit-outs, lobby upgrades) ensures a consistent approach to material selection, contributes to overall reduction in environmental harm, and drives market demand for green products.

Paint cans, worn carpeting, and other maintenance waste often require specialized storage and hauling for proper disposal. Renovations generate enormous quantities of solid waste from both demolition and construction. Planning for renovation waste management before the project begins promotes efficient use of materials, encourages recycling, reduces tipping fees, and can even generate revenue if high-valued scrap materials are sold.

Renovation inevitably introduces contaminants into building interiors that can degrade indoor air quality. Reducing contamination can help minimize potential problems with building equipment and occupants' comfort, in both the short and long terms.

This prerequisite covers products and waste associated with periodic maintenance and renovations. Together, the maintenance and renovations policies must address purchasing, waste, and indoor air quality management; the project team can determine how best to allocate items among the three policies.

STEP-BY-STEP GUIDANCE

STEP 1. DETERMINE THE SCOPE

The project team may determine the scope of this policy as it pertains to the facility. List maintenance tasks and identify the associated purchasing, waste, and air quality consequences of those activities.

- Include all items identified in the prerequisite requirements.
- Include all furniture purchases, not just those associated with fit-outs or renovations.
- Select specific, achievable sustainability goals.

Consider policy synergies and alignments (see *Related Credit Tips*). Examples include the following:

- Purchasing and waste activities (MR Prerequisite Ongoing Purchasing and Waste Policy)
- Cleaning activities (EQ Prerequisite Green Cleaning Policy)
- Upkeep and maintenance of HVAC ducts, entryway systems, filtration media, plumbing fixtures, and equipment (EQ Credit Indoor Air Quality Management Program and EQ Credit Enhanced Indoor Air Quality Strategies).

STEP 2. ESTABLISH IMPLEMENTATION CRITERIA

Clearly distinguish routine maintenance from renovations. Determine the typical scale and process for renovations and address smaller maintenance projects separately.

- At what point maintenance work becomes renovation is determined by the project team, but the policy must include, at a minimum, procedures for HVAC upgrades, building improvements, and tenant fit-outs—work that typically entails significant base building alterations.
- Mechanical, electrical, and plumbing (MEP) work that does not require significant alteration to the base building does not need to be included in the renovation policy, but base building waste produced as part of MEP maintenance must be covered in the policy.
- Renovation waste must be properly disposed of to minimize landfill waste, but the nature of each renovation determines whether large waste containers will be used on the site.
- Create a procedure for adding purchasing and waste management agenda items (e.g., progress updates on sustainability goals, status of implementation of renovation policy) in preconstruction and construction meetings.

STEP 3. DEFINE ENVIRONMENTALLY PREFERABLE PURCHASES FOR MAINTENANCE AND RENOVATIONS

Work with the responsible parties to identify strategies for purchasing items covered in this prerequisite. Use the criteria in MR Credit Purchasing—Facility Maintenance and Renovations for products, materials, and furniture; following the credit requirements when developing the policy will set up the project to earn points.

- Products and materials covered under the policy include base building elements, furniture and furnishings, and the components and parts needed to maintain them.
- Include general purchasing criteria as well as specific criteria for product and material types.
- The team may wish to suggest how the purchasing criteria and goals can be incorporated into the purchasing process and provide guidance on how to address substitution requests.
- Stress education so that purchasers, including subcontractors, learn how to identify preferable products.

STEP 4. DEFINE WASTE MANAGEMENT PRACTICES FOR MAINTENANCE AND RENOVATIONS

This prerequisite covers both waste produced by routine replacement and maintenance of base building elements and waste produced by renovation activity. Develop a section in the policy (or policies) to address each type of waste.

- Procedures may be customized to the individual project but should cover developing the diversion goals, selecting at least five materials for diversion, developing contracts with waste haulers, and properly sizing waste storage areas. Coordinate the waste management plan's diversion strategies and reporting procedures with MR Credit Solid Waste Management—Facility Maintenance and Renovations.
- For maintenance waste, consider dedicated storage for items that require special handling (e.g., hazardous waste like paint cans, recyclable waste like carpeting).
- Consider identifying waste haulers that can meet the project's sustainability goals. Work with local waste haulers to establish realistic procedures. Consider sorting waste on-site and setting up the associated infrastructure. If source separation is not possible, explain where commingled waste will be taken and how it will be sorted and processed off-site.
- Make sure that job-site workers understand and participate in construction waste recycling, and ask subcontractors to provide updates throughout construction.

STEP 5. DEFINE INDOOR AIR QUALITY PROCEDURES FOR MAINTENANCE AND RENOVATIONS

Create a renovation and maintenance policy that minimizes air quality disturbances for occupants and ensures high air quality. Each renovation project is required to implement construction indoor air quality (IAQ) measures that meet the prerequisite requirements.

- Develop procedures to meet all prerequisite requirements. Aligning the IAQ measures with the EQ Credit Indoor Air Quality Management Program will help the project earn points under the credit.
- Develop a procedure for determining whether and when flush-out or air quality testing is required for renovation projects. Both flush-outs and testing are conducted after construction ends, with all interior finishes installed, before occupancy begins (see *Further Explanation, Flush-Out Procedures* and *Air Quality Testing*).
- As a best practice for projects conducting IAQ testing, set up procedures for maintaining copies of testing reports and verifying that all required contaminants are accounted for and reported in the correct unit of measure.

STEP 6. REVIEW IMPLEMENTATION PROCEDURES

- Devise a process for tracking the new policy's effectiveness in minimizing the environmental and health harms of specific activities. Determine how building managers will implement the policies and track results.
- Identify the parties beyond building management responsible for policy implementation.
- See *Getting Started, Effective Policy Development.*

STEP 7. FINALIZE POLICY DOCUMENTS

Prepare the final policies according to the prerequisite requirements. Distribute the documents to tenants, custodial staff, and contractors, as appropriate.

- For projects with multiple tenants, include outreach to tenants and guidance in green purchasing, waste management, and indoor air quality measures.
- Educating all contractors, even those involved in only minor renovations or routine repairs, will help further implementation. Consider integrating policy language into contracts.

FURTHER EXPLANATION

MAINTENANCE AND RENOVATION POLICY GUIDANCE

Table 1 offers recommended guidelines for creating an effective and comprehensive policy for facility maintenance and renovations. More information on writing and establishing policies and procedures for existing buildings can be found in *Getting Started*.

TABLE 1. Suggested guidance for policy development

Policy	Product purchasing	Waste management	Indoor air quality
Sustainability criteria	• See MR Credit Purchasing—Facility Maintenance and Renovations. • Consider establishing policy that facilitates credit achievement.	• See MR Credit Solid Waste Management—Facility Maintenance and Renovations. • Consider establishing policy that facilitates credit achievement.	• See SMACNA IAQ Guidelines for Occupied Buildings Under Construction. • Consider establishing policy that facilitates credit achievement.
Physical and programmatic scope	• Include general purchasing criteria and specific criteria for product and material types (e.g., base building elements, furniture, and furnishings, maintenance parts).	• Include waste management strategies for regular maintenance activities.	• Develop procedure to determine whether flushout or air quality testing will be needed before occupancy.
Procedures and strategies for implantation	• Consider incorporating purchasing criteria and goals into purchasing process. • Consider process for approving substitutions. • Stress education of purchasers, including subcontractors. • Provide helpful contacts, websites. • Stress importance of following policy.	• Require customized waste management plan for each renovation project, with diversion goals and tactics for structural and nonstructural materials. • Anticipate volume of waste and ensure adequate storage. • Address diversion strategies and reporting procedures.	• Establish agenda items for preconstruction and construction meetings (e.g., updates on progress in meeting sustainability goals).
Metrics for performance evaluation	• Choose purchasing tracking tool that meets needs of users. • Consider tools that allow inputs from tenants. • Provide education support for tool used by staff and subcontractor	• Work with local waste haulers to establish realistic procedures and storage locations. • Explore on-site waste sorting opportunities and set up infrastructure for implementation. • Encourage job-site workers' participation in construction debris recycling. • Seek updates from contractors throughout construction.	• Set up procedures for maintaining copies of testing reports and verifying that all contaminants are accounted for and reported in correct unit of measure.

SMACNA CONTROL MEASURES

Refer to the SMACNA guidelines on minimizing air quality disturbances for occupants and ensuring long-term air quality. The guidelines are summarized here.

HVAC protection. Keep contaminants out of the HVAC system. Do not run permanently installed equipment if possible, or maintain proper filtration if it is used.

- If conditioning is required during construction, use supplementary HVAC units instead of permanently installed equipment if possible.
- If permanently installed HVAC system must be used during construction, install filtration to protect the return (negative pressure) side of the system. Replace these filters regularly during construction.
- Seal all ductwork, registers, diffusers, and returns with plastic when stored on-site or not in service. Seal unfinished runs of ductwork at the end of each day.

- Replace all filtration media before occupancy.
- Do not store materials in mechanical rooms, to reduce potential debris and contamination to mechanical systems.

Source control. Keep sources of contaminants out of the building and have a plan to eliminate any that are introduced.

- Use low-toxicity and low-VOC materials to the greatest extent possible.
- Develop protocols for the use of any high-toxicity materials. Isolate areas where high-toxicity materials are being installed and use temporary ventilation for that area.
- Prevent exhaust fumes (from idling vehicles, equipment, and fossil-fueled tools) from entering the building.
- Enforce the no-smoking job site policy.
- Protect stored materials from moisture because absorbent materials exposed to moisture during construction can mold and degenerate long after installation. Store materials in dry conditions indoors, under cover, and off the ground or floor.
- If materials are improperly exposed to moisture, replace the material and consider testing air quality before occupancy to make sure no mold contamination has occurred.

Pathway interruption. Prevent circulation of contaminated air when cutting concrete or wood, sanding drywall, installing VOC-emitting materials, or performing other activities that affect IAQ in other work spaces.

- Isolate areas of work to prevent contamination of other spaces, whether they are finished or not. Seal doorways, windows, or tent off areas as needed using temporary barriers such as plastic separations. Provide walk-off material at entryways to reduce introduced dirt and pollutants.
- Depressurize the work area to allow a differential between construction and clean areas. Exhaust to the outdoors using 100% outside air, if possible.
- Use dust guards and collectors on saws and other tools.

Housekeeping. Maintaining a clean job site results in fewer IAQ contaminants to manage in the first place.

- Maintain good job site housekeeping on a daily basis. Use vacuum cleaners with high-efficiency particulate filters, and use sweeping compounds or wetting agents for dust control when sweeping.
- Use walk-off material during construction, if possible.
- Keep materials organized to improve job site safety as well as indoor air quality.

Scheduling. Sequence construction activities to minimize impact on air quality in new construction projects. For major renovations, coordinate construction activities to minimize or eliminate disruption of operations in occupied areas.

- Keep trades that affect IAQ physically isolated on-site and separated from each other by the construction schedule. For example, schedule drywall finishing and carpet installation for different days or different sections of the building. Consider after-hours or weekend work if practical.
- Install absorptive-finish materials after wet-applied materials have fully cured whenever possible. For example, install carpet and ceiling tile after paints and stains are completely dry.
- If applicable, plan adequate time to conduct a flush-out and/or perform IAQ testing before occupancy, in compliance with EQ Credit Indoor Air Quality Assessment.
- Remove all temporary filtration media and replace them with new filters before occupancy.

FLUSH-OUT PROCEDURE

A flush-out may be needed. The following recommendations apply for those project teams that elect to conduct a flush-out:

The flush-out should not begin until all construction work, including punch-list items, is completed and all furniture and fixtures have been installed. Finalize all cleaning, complete the final testing and balancing of HVAC systems, and make sure the HVAC control is functional.

Before committing to a flush-out, check with the mechanical engineer to confirm that proposed mechanical systems are capable of providing outside air at the required rate. Systems that meet ASHRAE 62.1–2010 airflow rates and provide a fixed volume of outside air may not be able to provide sufficient outside air, or the flush-out could take a long time.

For systems that can provide a sufficient volume of outside air, confirm that heating and cooling equipment can handle the additional load from increased outside air during times of peak heating and cooling. The equipment must be able to maintain an internal temperature between 60°F (15°C) and 80°F (27°C), with a relative humidity no higher than 60%.

Buildings with air-side economizers may be able to provide the required outside air during the free cooling season, reducing the energy required to provide the increased outside air, assuming it can be provided at a constant volume.

If occupancy is desired before the flush-out is completed, as a best practice, ensure that the space has first received a minimum of 3,500 cubic feet of outdoor air per square foot (1 065 cubic meters of outdoor air per square meter) of gross floor area. Once the space is occupied, it should be ventilated at a minimum rate of 0.30 cubic foot per minute (cfm) per square foot of outdoor air (1.5 liters of outside air per second per square meter).

Use temporary supply and exhaust systems placed into windows or window openings. Make sure that the airflow is not short-circuited, which could leave remote corners with inadequate circulation or provide too much air in other parts of the building (e.g., a stack effect up elevator shafts).

If the central HVAC system is used, remove any temporary filters and duct coverings installed as part of the construction IAQ management plan.

Replace the used HVAC filtration media with new media; if the system is configured to filter only outside air, the filters do not need to be replaced. Depending on their condition following the flush-out, some or all filters might be ready for replacement, but this is not a condition for satisfying the credit requirements.

AIR QUALITY TESTING

The following recommendations apply to project teams that conduct air quality testing.

During construction, use the low-emitting materials specified in the purchasing policy to reduce the contaminant load and position the project for good test results. Use low-VOC cleaning supplies to prevent short-term high-VOC levels. Use vacuum cleaners with high-efficiency particulate air (HEPA) filtration to capture particulates. Replace all filtration media after the final cleaning and complete the testing and balancing of the HVAC system.

Test air quality when the HVAC system is operating under normal conditions with minimum outdoor airflow rates, so that the air tested will be as similar as possible to what the occupants will be breathing. The protocols for IAQ testing in the referenced publication, EPA's Compendium of Methods for the Determination of Air Pollutants in Indoor Air, are recommended, but others may be used, provided the team demonstrates their equivalency.

Select testing locations with the least ventilation but the greatest concentration of VOCs and other contaminants. Record the exact locations. If a test sample exceeds the maximum concentration level, flush-out the space by increasing the rate of outside air and retest in the same location.

CAMPUS

Group Approach

All buildings in the group may be documented as one. This prerequisite may be pursued by projects that have a campus-wide construction waste management policy, purchasing policy, and procedures for indoor air quality for renovations and maintenance activities. Each building must meet the IAQ requirements on its own. Flush-out and air quality testing must be done for each building.

Campus Approach

Eligible. This prerequisite may be pursued by projects that have a campus-wide construction waste management policy, purchasing policy, and procedures for indoor air quality for renovations and maintenance activities. Each building must meet the IAQ requirements on its own. Flush-out and air quality testing must be done for each building.

REQUIRED DOCUMENTATION

	Documentation	All projects
E	Facility maintenance and renovations policy (policies) addressing maintenance and renovation purchasing, waste management, and indoor air quality	X

RELATED CREDIT TIPS

MR Prerequisite Ongoing Purchasing and Waste Policy. Coordinate the facility maintenance and renovations solid waste management policy with the waste audit and ongoing solid waste management policy to take advantage of any synergies (e.g., using the same haulers). The maintenance and renovations purchasing policy must not overlap with the ongoing purchasing and waste policy. Ensure that each purchase is in the appropriate policy.

MR Credit Solid Waste Management—Facility Maintenance and Renovations. Waste management for the related credit must be conducted according to the strategy developed in this prerequisite.

MR Credit Purchasing—Facility Maintenance and Renovation. The purchases under the related credit must follow the policy developed in this prerequisite.

EQ Credit Indoor Air Quality Management Program. The plan developed in this prerequisite addresses many of the IAQ elements listed in EQ Credit Indoor Air Quality Management Program; their requirements can be coordinated.

CHANGES FROM LEED 2009

This is a new prerequisite.

REFERENCED STANDARDS

Sheet Metal and Air Conditioning National Contractors Association (SMACNA) IAQ Guidelines for Occupied Buildings under Construction, 2nd edition (2007), ANSI/SMACNA 008–2008, Chapter 3: smacna.org

European Standard EN 779: 2002, Particulate Air Filters for General Ventilation, Determination of the Filtration Performance: ashrae.org

EPA's Compendium of Methods for the Determination of Air Pollutants in Indoor Air: cen.eu

EXEMPLARY PERFORMANCE

Not available.

DEFINITIONS

base building materials and products that make up the building or are permanently and semi-permanently installed in the project (e.g., flooring, casework, wall coverings)

commingled waste building waste streams that are combined on the project site and hauled away for sorting into recyclable streams. Also known as single-stream recycling.

enclosure the exterior plus semi-exterior portions of the building. Exterior consists of the elements of a building that separate conditioned spaces from the outside (i.e., the wall assembly). Semiexterior consists of the elements of a building that separate conditioned space from unconditioned space or that encloses semi-heated space through which thermal energy may be transferred to or from the exterior or conditioned or unconditioned spaces (e.g., attic, crawl space, basement).

structure elements carrying either vertical or horizontal loads (e.g., walls, roofs, and floors) that are considered structurally sound and nonhazardous

waste diversion a management activity that disposes of waste through methods other than incineration or landfilling. Examples include reuse and recycling.

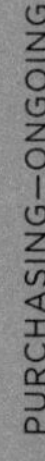

MATERIALS AND RESOURCES CREDIT

Purchasing—Ongoing

This credit applies to:

Existing Buildings (1 point)
Schools (1 point)
Retail (1 point)
Data Centers (1 point)
Hospitality (1 point)
Warehouses and Distribution Centers (1 point)

INTENT

To reduce environmental harm from materials used in the operations and maintenance of buildings.

REQUIREMENTS

EXISTING BUILDINGS, SCHOOLS, RETAIL, DATA CENTERS, HOSPITALITY, WAREHOUSES AND DISTRIBUTION CENTERS

ESTABLISHMENT E

None.

PERFORMANCE P

Ongoing Consumables

Purchase at least 60%, by cost, of total ongoing consumables that meet at least one of the following criteria. Include the product categories identified in the Materials and Resources prerequisite: Ongoing Purchasing and Waste Policy. Lamps are excluded from the calculation. Each purchase can receive credit for each criterion met.

- **Postconsumer recycled content.** The content of purchases must meet or exceed the levels listed in the U.S. Environmental Protection Agency Comprehensive Procurement Guidelines. Products not covered by the Guidelines can get credit for their recycled content with no minimum.
- **Extended use.** Batteries must be rechargeable. Toner cartridges for laser printers must be remanufactured.
- **Sustainable agriculture.** Food and beverages must be labeled USDA Organic, Food Alliance Certified, Rainforest Alliance Certified, Protected Harvest Certified, Fair Trade, or Marine Stewardship Council's Blue Eco-Label , or labeled with the European Community Organic Production logo in accordance with Regulations (EC) No. 834/2007 and (EC) No. 889/2008.

- **Local sourcing of food and beverages.** The food or beverage must contain raw materials harvested and produced within 100 miles (160 kilometers) of the site.
- **Bio-based materials.** Bio-based products must meet the Sustainable Agriculture Network's Sustainable Agriculture Standard. Bio-based raw materials must be tested using ASTM Test Method D6866 and be legally harvested, as defined by the exporting and receiving country. Exclude hide products, such as leather and other animal skin material.
- **Paper and wood products.** Paper and wood products must be certified by the Forest Stewardship Council or USGBC-approved equivalent.

Electric-Powered Equipment

Purchase at least 40%, by cost, electric-powered equipment that meets at least one of the following criteria. Include product categories specified in Materials and Resources prerequisite: Ongoing Purchasing and Waste Policy. In addition, create a phase-out plan to replace remaining products with compliant equipment at the end of their useful life.

- **EPEAT rating.** The equipment must have a silver Electronic Product Environmental Assessment Tool (EPEAT) rating or better.
- **ENERGY STAR rating.** If the equipment does not yet fall under the EPEAT rating systems, it must be ENERGY STAR® qualified or performance equivalent for projects outside the U.S.

SCHOOLS AND HOSPITALITY ONLY

Purchase at least 25%, by cost, of total combined food and beverage purchases must meet at least one of the following criteria. Exclude wine, beer, and liquor purchases from the credit calculations.

- **Sustainable agriculture.** The food or beverage must be labeled USDA Organic, Food Alliance Certified, Rainforest Alliance Certified, Protected Harvest Certified, Fair Trade, or Marine Stewardship Council's Blue Eco-Label, or labeled with the European Community Organic Production logo in accordance with Regulations (EC) No. 834/2007 and (EC) No. 889/2008.
- **Local sourcing.** The food or beverage must contain raw materials harvested and produced within 100 miles (160 kilometers) of the site.

BEHIND THE INTENT

Purchasing ongoing consumables that meet environmental criteria can significantly reduce the environmental footprint of building operations. For example, products made with recycled content reduce the demand for virgin materials, locally manufactured products support producers directly and benefit the local community, high-durability products lengthen the replacement cycle and reduce the use of the virgin materials, and products manufactured by companies with a corporate sustainability reporting program increase transparency to consumers. Purchasing ENERGY STAR–qualified electric-powered equipment also reduces a building's environmental footprint because these products uses less energy and, when not in use, automatically enter a low-power mode. Qualified office and imaging products use 30% to 75% less electricity than standard equipment, thereby reducing utility and operating costs.[1]

This credit builds on the environmentally preferable purchasing policy established in MR Prerequisite Ongoing Purchasing and Waste Policy by establishing thresholds for the purchase of ongoing consumables and electric-powered equipment that meet environmental criteria; for some project types, food and beverage purchases must be tracked separately. Each threshold must be met for purchases made during the performance period.

This credit also requires including purchases made by tenants in the calculations for compliance.

STEP-BY-STEP GUIDANCE

Project's must meet thresholds in two purchase categories—ongoing consumables and electric-powered equipment—over the performance period.

STEP 1. IDENTIFY ONGOING CONSUMABLES E

List ongoing consumables identified for MR Prerequisite Ongoing Purchasing and Waste Policy.

- Expand the survey of purchased products to the entire building, including tenants (see *Further Explanation, Multitenant Buildings,* and *MR Overview*).
- See MR Prerequisite Ongoing Purchasing and Waste Policy *Step-by-Step Guidance* for more detail on determining the top-five purchased items.

STEP 2. EVALUATE ONGOING CONSUMABLES PURCHASING PRACTICES E

To understand the extent of compliance with the credit requirements, evaluate the current purchasing patterns for the entire building before the performance period begins.

- If a product meets more than one of the criteria in the credit requirements, count its overall cost contribution by percentage of product weight for each criterion met (see *MR Overview, Determining Material Contributions*, and *Further Explanation, Example 1*).
- Include food and beverage purchases in calculations for ongoing consumables if purchased for the project.
- For purchases in buildings with multiple tenants, see *Further Explanation, Multitenant Buildings*, and *MR Overview, Multitenant Buildings*.

STEP 3. DEVELOP STRATEGY FOR ONGOING CONSUMABLES PURCHASES P

Determine the percentage of ongoing purchases that meet the criteria in the credit requirements for at least 60% of total purchases for the performance period, using Equation 1.

Strategies for reaching credit thresholds include the following:

- Develop a tracking system to gather data for all purchases for the building (see *MR Overview, Selecting an Appropriate Tracking System*).
- Focus first on high-cost or high-volume noncompliant items.
- Look for opportunities to swap noncompliant items for products that meet the criteria, are easy accessible, and are comparably priced (e.g., paper with recycled content)
- Help purchasing departments develop a list of approved products.

1. *U.S. Environmental Protection Agency and U.S. Department of Energy, Office Equipment, energystar.gov/index.cfm?c=ofc_equip.pr_office_equipment (accessed March 2013).*

MR

PURCHASING—ONGOING

EQUATION 1. Percentage of compliant ongoing consumable purchases

$$\text{\% compliant purchases} = \left(\frac{\text{Total cost of compliant ongoing purchases}}{\text{Total cost of all ongoing purchases}} \right) \times 100$$

- Pilot the use of compliant substitutes before fully committing to replacing current products.
- Consider revising the policy to capture the changes made to the product selection criteria and goals.

STEP 4. EVALUATE ELECTRIC-POWERED EQUIPMENT PURCHASING PATTERNS P

Evaluate current purchasing patterns to determine whether the project is on track to achieve the credit threshold, based on the percentage, by cost, of electric-powered equipment scheduled for purchase during the performance period that will meet at least one of the credit criteria. Use Equation 2.

- Determine whether old equipment can be serviced instead of replaced, to avoid unnecessary use of resources.
- If noncompliant equipment does not need to be replaced, create a phase-out plan for replacement at the end of its useful life.
- Electric-powered equipment and appliances not rated by ENERGY STAR or the Electronic Product Environmental Assessment Tool (EPEAT) are excluded from the credit requirements. Gas-powered equipment that does not have an electric alternative are also excluded.

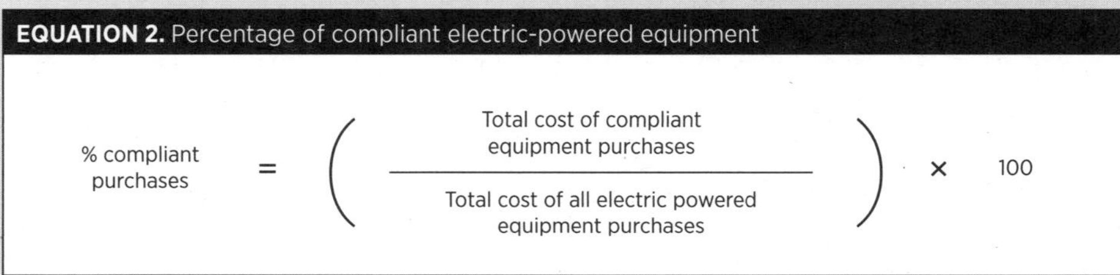

EQUATION 2. Percentage of compliant electric-powered equipment

$$\text{\% compliant purchases} = \left(\frac{\text{Total cost of compliant equipment purchases}}{\text{Total cost of all electric powered equipment purchases}} \right) \times 100$$

- ENERGY STAR–qualified equipment contributes toward compliance only if there is no EPEAT rating for the equipment type.
- For purchases in buildings with multiple tenants, see *Further Explanation, Multitenant Buildings* and *International Tips,* and *MR Overview*).

STEP 5. SET UP TRACKING SYSTEM P

Track the purchases of ongoing consumables and electric-powered equipment over the performance period.

- Determine the percentage of compliant purchases for ongoing consumables and electric-powered equipment.
- Collect documentation verifying that the products meet the criteria. Retain all documentation for all criteria. Documentation requirements differ for each criterion (see *Further Explanation, Product Documentation*).
- Submit all documentation for all of the following: new wood and paper products, bio-based materials, and sustainable agriculture purchases.
- Provide a representative sample of documentation for other products.

Schools and Hospitality

Projects must meet thresholds in three purchase categories—ongoing consumables, electric-powered equipment, and food and beverages—over the performance period.

STEP 1. MEET ONGOING CONSUMABLES AND ELECTRIC-POWERED EQUIPMENT REQUIREMENTS

Complete Steps 1–5, above.

STEP 2. EVALUATE FOOD AND BEVERAGE PURCHASING PATTERNS E

Examine food and beverage purchasing patterns to determine whether the project is on track to achieve the credit threshold based on percentage, by cost, of food and beverages purchases scheduled for purchase during the performance period that will meet at least one of the credit criteria. The threshold applies to 25% of total food and beverage purchases. Use Equation 3.

- Food and beverage purchases must be tracked, as a separate category.
- Wine, beer, and liquor purchases are excluded from the calculations.
- Food and beverages sold through vending machines may be included or excluded from the calculations.
- For more information on product cost, see *MR Overview, Determining Material Contributions.*
- For buildings with multiple tenants, see *Further Explanation, Multitenant Buildings*, and *MR Overview*.

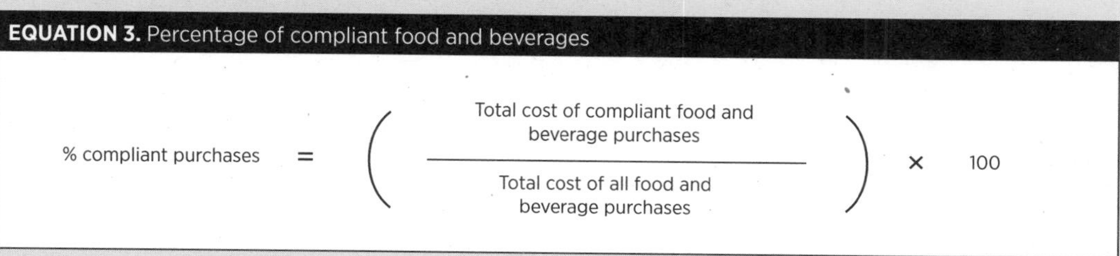

EQUATION 3. Percentage of compliant food and beverages

$$\text{\% compliant purchases} = \left(\frac{\text{Total cost of compliant food and beverage purchases}}{\text{Total cost of all food and beverage purchases}} \right) \times 100$$

STEP 3. DEVELOP STRATEGY FOR FOOD AND BEVERAGE PURCHASES P

- Identify alternative food and beverage products that meet at least one of the criteria.
- Consider working with current distributers to determine the availability of sustainable food products. Develop and maintain a list of those vendors and supplement with new vendors, as needed.
- To increase order size for distributers, explore the possibility of purchasing collectively within a company or with other buildings in the area.

STEP 4. SET UP TRACKING SYSTEM P

Track the purchases of compliant food and beverages over the performance period (see *MR Overview, Selecting a Tracking System*).

- Determine the percentage of purchases that meet the criteria in the credit requirements.
  - Collect documentation verifying that the products meet the criteria. Retain all documentation for all criteria. Documentation requirements differ for each criterion (see *Further Explanation, Product Documentation*).
  - Submit all documentation for sustainable agriculture purchases.
  - Provide a representative sample of documentation for other products.

FURTHER EXPLANATION

CALCULATIONS

See calculations in *Step-by-Step Guidance*.

EXAMPLES

Example 1. Multiple criteria met

One product can meet several credit criteria. Some criteria include a percentage of the assembly; others do not (see *MR Overview, Determining Material Contributions*). Table 1 shows the calculations for an order of plastic-covered binders costing a total of $400.

TABLE 1. Example product meeting multiple criteria

Attribute	Percentage of product compliance	Explanation	Amount contributing toward credit
Postconsumer recycled content	50%	Product meets U.S. EPA comprehensive procurement guideline minimum for plastic-covered binders	$200.00
Rechargeable batteries	0%	Criterion not applicable	$0.00
Sustainable agriculture	0%	Criterion not applicable	$0.00
Local sourcing of food	0%	Criterion not applicable	$0.00
Bio-based materials	0%	Criterion not applicable	$0.00
FSC-certified paper, wood	30%	Pressboard structure of binder is labeled FSC Mixed (30%)	$120.00
Total			**$320**

Example 2. Tracking purchases of electric-powered equipment

TABLE 2. Sample tracking tool for electric-powered equipment

Date purchased	Purchaser	Product name or manufacturer	EPEAT silver +	ENERGY STAR	Replaces gas-powered	Cost	Value toward compliance
5/6/2012	Tenant X	EP3X90 laptop (Computer Makers Inc.)	EPEAT gold	N/A	N/A	$500	$500
5/7/2012	Tenant Y	XLTv900 LCD screen (Screensters & Co.)	Rating available, product not rated	ENERGY STAR	N/A	$300	$0
5/8/2012	Building management	All-in-one printer (Print Master)	None	None	None	$200	$0
Total						**$1000**	**$500**
Percentage of compliant purchases							**50%**

MULTITENANT BUILDINGS

This credit applies to all ongoing consumables, electric-powered equipment, and food and beverages purchased in the project building, including those purchased by individual tenants and the property manager or building owner. Project teams may exclude up to 10% of the project building's total floor area from the credit calculations if those spaces are under separate management (see *MR Overview, Multitenant Buildings*).

PRODUCT DOCUMENTATION

For criteria related to products categorized as ongoing consumables only, documentation of purchases meeting at least one credit criteria may be made via contractual language with vendor highlighting sustainable criteria agreement per criteria as well as total contractual amount. See Table 3 for an example.

TABLE 3. Example types of product documentation for each criterion

Criterion met	Example product documentation
Recycled content	Manufacturer or supplier documentation, webpage screenshot, or invoice confirming postconsumer recycled content values
Local sourcing	Scaled map showing locations of project and product manufacture and purchase, indicating 100-mile (160-kilometer) radius from project building. Online purchases meet this criterion, provided manufacturer and distributor are within 100-mile (160-kilometer) radius.
Extended use	Manufacturer or supplier documentation or webpage screenshot confirming that purchased batteries are rechargeable and toner cartridges for laser printers are remanufactured
Sustainable agriculture	Manufacturer or supplier documentation or webpage screenshot confirming that purchased food and beverages are labeled USDA Organic, Food Alliance Certified, Rainforest Alliance Certified, Protected Harvest Certified, Fair Trade, or Marine Stewardship Council's Blue Eco-Label, or labeled with European Community Organic Production logo in accordance with Regulations (EC) No. 834/2007 and (EC) No. 889/2008.
Bio-based materials	Certification from program demonstrating product's compliance. For FSC, include invoice with manufacturer's chain-of-custody number. For SAN, show certification in good standing from Rainforest Alliance. For more information on documenting these claims see MR Credit Purchasing - Facility Maintenance and Renovations, Further Explanation, Documentation for Biobased Materials.
EPEAT rating	Manufacturer's or supplier's documentation or webpage screenshot confirming that purchased electric-powered equipment has a silver EPEAT rating or better
ENERGY STAR rating	Manufacturer's or supplier's documentation or webpage screenshot confirming that purchased electric-powered equipment is ENERGY STAR qualified (or equivalent). ENERGY STAR-qualified equipment counts toward compliance only if no EPEAT rating is available for equipment type (see epeat.net for equipment types).
Replacement of gas-powered with electric-powered	Invoice from purchase and manufacturer's or supplier's documentation confirming that equipment is electric-powered

Project teams may circle or highlight the product documentation section that indicates compliance with the criteria.

INTERNATIONAL TIPS

A project outside the U.S. may purchase products that are not labeled under the ENERGY STAR program if they meet the ENERGY STAR product specifications, available on the ENERGY STAR website. All products must meet the standards of the current version of ENERGY STAR as of the date of their purchase.

CAMPUS

Group Approach

All buildings in the group may be documented as one.

Campus Approach

Ineligible. Each LEED project may pursue the credit individually.

REQUIRED DOCUMENTATION

	Documentation	All projects	Hospitality and Schools
P	List of compliant ongoing consumable purchases made during performance period, including product name, manufacturer, cost, data of purchase, and quantity	X	X
P	List of compliant electric-powered equipment purchases made during -performance period, including name of product, manufacturer, cost, data of purchase, and quantity	X	X
P	List of compliant food and beverage purchases made during the performance period, including name, manufacturer, cost, date of purchase, and quantity		X
P	Documentation verifying products meet credit criteria (e.g., manufacturer's documentation, third-party certifications)	X	X
P	Total cost of ongoing consumables and electric powered equipment	X	X
P	Total cost of food and beverage purchases		X

RELATED CREDIT TIPS

MR Prerequisite Ongoing Purchasing and Waste Policy. Ongoing consumables and electric-powered equipment must follow the purchasing policy established in the related prerequisite.

CHANGES FROM LEED 2009

- MR Credit Sustainable Purchasing—Ongoing Consumables and the MR Credit Sustainable Purchasing—Durable Goods requirements for electric-powered equipment have been combined into one credit.
- The purchasing criteria have been revised to align with the Building Design and Construction MR credits.
- Requirements for food and beverages have been added for Schools and Hospitality projects.

REFERENCED STANDARDS

U.S. Environmental Protection Agency Comprehensive Procurement Guidelines: epa.gov/epawaste/conserve/tools/cpg/index.htm

ASTM Test Method D6866: astm.org/Standards/D6866.htm

Forest Stewardship Council: fsc.org/

Sustainable Agriculture Network's Sustainable Agriculture Standard: sanstandards.org/sitio/

Clean Production Action's Green Screen v1.2 Benchmark 1: cleanproduction.org/Greenscreen.php

REACH: ec.europa.eu/environment/chemicals/reach/reach_intro.htm

EPEAT: epeat.net/

ENERGY STAR: energystar.gov/

USDA Organic: ams.usda.gov/AMSv1.0/nop

Food Alliance Certified: foodalliance.org/

Rainforest Alliance Certified: rainforest-alliance.org/certification-verification

Protected Harvest Certified: protectedharvest.org/?page_id=42

Fair Trade: fairtradeusa.org/

Marine Stewardship Council's Blue Eco Label: msc.org/

European Community Organize Production logo in accordance with Regulations (EC) No. 834/2007 and (EC) No. 889/2008: imo.ch/imo_regulation_organic_eu_standard_en,1528,998.html

EXEMPLARY PERFORMANCE

Purchase at least 95% of total ongoing consumables and at least 80% of electric-powered equipment meeting at least one of the sustainable criteria listed.

For Schools and Hospitality projects, purchase at least 50% food and beverage purchases meeting one or more criteria.

DEFINITIONS

bio-based material commercial or industrial products (other than food or feed) that are composed in whole, or in significant part, of biological products, renewable agricultural materials (including plant, animal, and marine materials), or forestry materials. For the purposes of LEED, this excludes leather and other animal hides.

durable goods products with a useful life of approximately two or more years and that are replaced infrequently. Examples include furniture, office equipment, appliances, external power adapters, televisions, and audiovisual equipment.

ongoing consumable a product that has a low cost per unit and is regularly used and replaced in the course of business. Examples include paper, toner cartridges, binders, batteries, and desk accessories. Also known as ongoing purchases.

postconsumer recycled content waste generated by households or commercial, industrial and institutional facilities in their role as end users of a product that can no longer be used for its intended purpose

preconsumer recycled content matter diverted from the waste stream during the manufacturing process, determined as the percentage of material, by weight. Examples include planer shavings, sawdust, bagasse, walnut shells, culls, trimmed materials, overissue publications, and obsolete inventories. The designation excludes rework, regrind, or scrap materials capable of being reclaimed within the same process that generated them (ISO 14021). Formerly known as postindustrial content.

recycled content defined in accordance with the International Organization of Standards document ISO 14021, Environmental labels and declarations, Self-declared environmental claims (Type II environmental labeling)

remanufactured product an item that has been repaired or adjusted and returned to service. A remanufactured product can be expected to perform as if it were new.

USDA Organic the U.S. Department of Agriculture's certification for products that contain at least 95% ingredients (excluding water and salt) produced without synthetic chemicals, antibiotics, or hormones. Any remaining ingredients must consist of USDA-approved nonagricultural substances or agricultural products that are not commercially available in organic form.

wood plant-based materials that are eligible for certification under the Forest Stewardship Council. Examples include bamboo and palm (monocots) as well as hardwoods (angiosperms) and softwoods (gymnosperms)

MATERIALS AND RESOURCES CREDIT

Purchasing—Lamps

This credit applies to:

Existing Buildings (1 point)
Schools (1 point)
Retail (1 point)
Data Centers (1 point)
Hospitality (1 point)
Warehouses and Distribution Centers (1 point)

INTENT

To establish and maintain a toxic material source reduction program to reduce the amount of mercury brought onto the building site through purchases of lamps.

REQUIREMENTS

EXISTING BUILDINGS, SCHOOLS, RETAIL, DATA CENTERS, HOSPITALITY, WAREHOUSES AND DISTRIBUTION CENTERS

ESTABLISHMENT E

None.

PERFORMANCE P

Implement the lighting purchasing plan that specifies an overall building average of 70 picograms of mercury per lumen-hour or less for all mercury-containing lamps purchased for the building and associated grounds within the project boundary. Include lamps for both indoor and outdoor fixtures, as well as both hard-wired and portable fixtures. Lamps containing no mercury may be counted only if their energy efficiency at least equals that of their mercury-containing counterparts.

BEHIND THE INTENT

Mercury is a persistent bioaccumulative toxic (PBT) chemical element and a neurotoxin. PBTs, which break down extremely slowly in the environment, accumulate within animal tissues in increasing concentrations up the food chain. Once present in an organism, mercury can affect the central nervous system, ultimately damaging the brain, spinal cord, kidneys, and liver. Released into the environment, it is difficult to contain.

The breakage of lamps containing mercury releases a powder that requires extensive cleanup to limit harm to human health. Mercury-containing lamps that are disposed of improperly become part of the solid waste stream and contribute to air, land, and water contamination.

Manufacturers have increased the efficiency of bulbs while reducing mercury content and maintaining illuminance. This credit therefore requires project teams to develop and implement a purchasing plan for lighting with low mercury content.

STEP-BY-STEP GUIDANCE

STEP 1. INVENTORY INSTALLED LAMPS P

Gather information about all lamps installed in the building.

- The inventory must include lamps in tenant spaces, even if tenants are responsible for their own lamp procurement (see *Getting Started, Tenant Space Exclusion Allowance*).
- Include lamps in outdoor fixtures and portable task lighting, in addition to directly wired lamps.
- Design documents and relamping records may assist the effort. Also consider combining the inventory with an energy audit, which often involves counting lamps and associated power requirements.

Record the following information for each type of lamp:

- NAED code, if available (a unique five- or six-digit number used to identify specific lamps)
- Manufacturer
- Quantity installed

STEP 2. GATHER MANUFACTURERS' DOCUMENTATION P

Obtain product cutsheets to find information for each bulb installed in the building (see *Further Explanation, Reading Lamp Cutsheets*). Use the manufacturers' websites and NAED codes to find the following data:

- Mean lumen output (design or actual)
- Rated average life at three-hour instant start
- Mercury content

STEP 3. CALCULATE MERCURY CONTENT OF INSTALLED LAMPS P

To calculate the picograms per lumen hour for each purchased lamp, enter the information into the MR purchasing calculator provided by USGBC or an equivalent custom tool.

- If a manufacturer provides mercury content in milligrams, convert it to picograms per lumen hour (see *Further Explanation, Equation 1*).
- The lighting inventory can serve as the purchasing plan if the average picograms per lumen hour for all lamps is below the limit in the credit requirements.
- If the building's mercury content is under the limit, the project team earns the credit and is encouraged to identify strategies for further improvement.

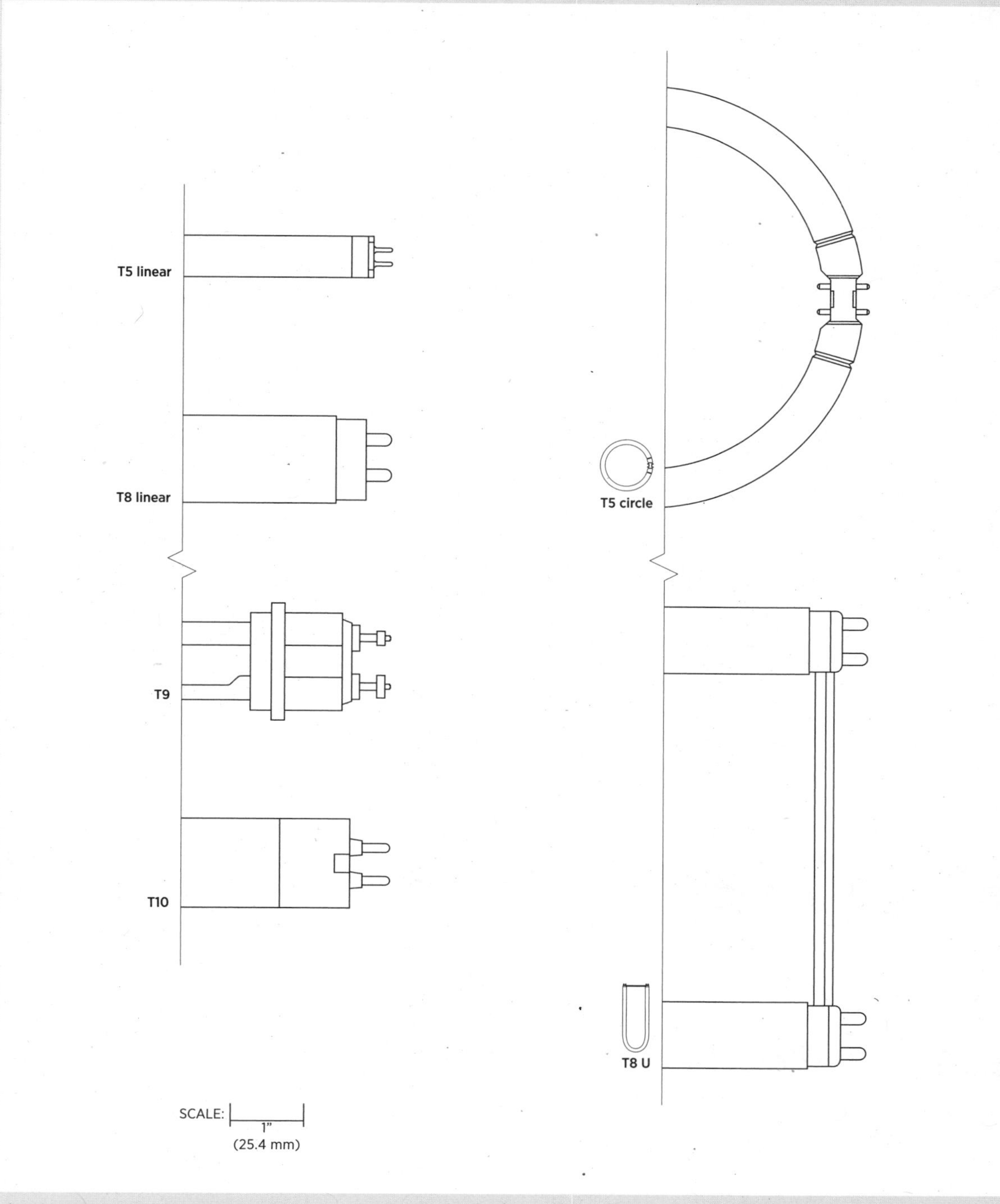

Figure 1. Mercury-containing lamp types

STEP 4. IDENTIFY ALTERNATIVE LAMPS, IF NECESSARY P

If additional reductions in mercury content are required to achieve the credit, review the building's lamp inventory and identify lamps with high mercury content. Research low-mercury alternatives, to be purchased when the existing lamps require replacement (see *Further Explanation, Reducing Mercury Content in Lighting*). Gather manufacturers' documentation and list the mercury levels of both existing and proposed lamps.

- Teams are not expected to replace any lamps that have not yet reached the end of their useful life. For lamps that remain, write a purchasing plan for their eventual replacement. This purchasing plan may be included in the ongoing purchasing policy.
- Consider pilot-testing the alternative lamps before committing to them in the purchasing plan, taking into consideration cost, lighting quality, and energy efficiency.
- Communicate the purchasing plan to all entities that procure lamps in the building. This may require coordinating with individual tenants.
- In some cases, such as buildings with many T-12 lamps, fixture upgrades may be needed to meet the credit requirements; upgrades would also deliver energy efficiency benefits.

STEP 5. PURCHASE LOW-MERCURY LAMPS DURING PERFORMANCE PERIOD P

During the performance period, follow the lamp purchasing plan to reduce the building's overall mercury levels below the credit limit.

- Lamps must be purchased during the performance period for project teams to earn this credit. Not every lamp must comply with the credit requirements; it is the combined mercury content for all lamps listed in the purchasing plan that must meet the requirements. Lamps purchased during the performance period must follow the purchasing plan.
- List all lamps in the MR purchasing calculator provided by USGBC and confirm that the lamps were purchased during the performance period.
- Collect manufacturers' documentation for new lamps. The documentation must list the product's mercury content, design mean lumen output, and rated lamp life at three-hour instant start.

FURTHER EXPLANATION

CALCULATIONS

Use Equation 1 to convert mercury content in milligrams to picograms per lumen hour.

EQUATION 1. Mercury conversion

$$\text{Picograms per lumen hour} = \frac{\text{milligrams}}{\text{lumens} \times \text{lamp life}} \times 10^{9}$$

where

milligrams = mercury content in milligrams (mg)
lumens = design mean lumen output
lamp life = rated lamp life at 3-hour instant start.

Use Equation 2 to calculate the overall picograms per lumen hour for the project building.

EQUATION 2. Building pictograms per lumen hour

$$\text{Overall picograms per lumen hour} = \frac{\text{Total picograms per lumen hour}}{\text{Total \# of lamps purchased}}$$

READING LAMP CUTSHEETS

Manufacturers' cutsheets can help project teams specify low-mercury lamps. They also provide the documentation showing achievement of this credit. Look for the following information:

Mean lumen output (design mean lumen output). This value is measured with an instant-start ballast, with a ballast factor of 1.0 at 40% of lamp life (except for T-5 lamps that use a program-start ballast). Use mean lumens, not initial lumens. If the manufacturer does not list mean lumens, subtract 20% from the initial lumen value. The documentation for a given lamp may show several values for lumen output, based on different testing protocols. Mean lumen values are not listed for compact fluorescents (CFLs).

Rated average life. This value is based on three hours on for every 20 minutes off for fluorescents, and 11 hours on for high-density discharge lamps. Use the value for the three-hour instant start for fluorescent lamps.

Mercury content. Manufacturers list this information as either picograms per lumen hour or milligrams per bulb. If mercury content is provided as a range, use the highest value. Manufacturers may also provide TCLP concentrations or indicate that a lamp is TCLP compliant. The TCLP test does not measure total mercury content and therefore is not acceptable documentation. Mercury-free lamps, such as LEDs, can be included in the pictogram per lumen-hour calculations only if their energy efficiency levels are equal to or greater than those of comparable mercury-containing lamps.

Luminous intensity. Manufacturers often express the output of an LED as "luminous intensity." This measurement can be based on a variety of testing parameters. If possible, use the value for average LED intensity (ALI).

If the required information is not included in product literature, contact the vendor or the lamp manufacturer directly. Manufacturers' verification of lamp technical data is acceptable documentation.

REDUCING MERCURY CONTENT IN LIGHTING

When selecting alternatives to lamps with high mercury content, look for products with high lumen output, long life, and/or low mercury content. Long-life lamps can increase operational savings by requiring a less frequent relamping cycle.

Other strategies for reducing mercury in the building include the following:

- Retrofit existing T-12 lamps through lighting upgrades targeting energy efficiency.
- Target lamp replacements for high-volume items that have higher-than-average picograms per lumen hour values.
- Check for low-mercury product lines offered by the current vendor or a familiar manufacturer and compare rated hours, color, and quality.
- Pilot new lamp models before committing to replacement.

EXAMPLES

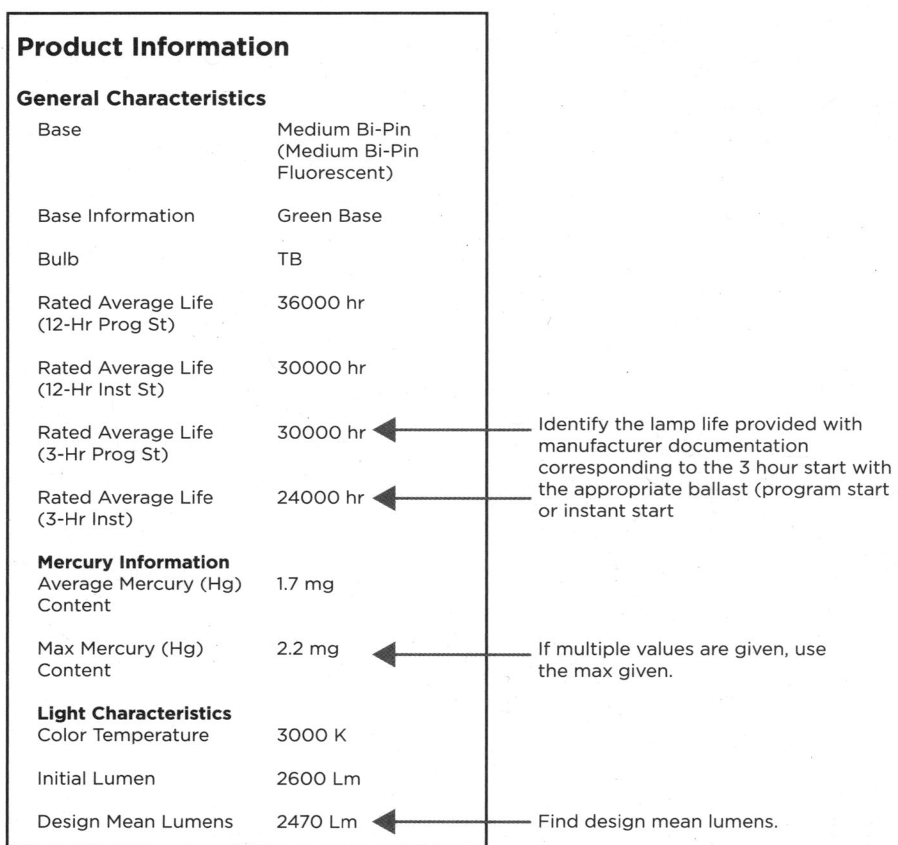

Product Information

General Characteristics

Base	Medium Bi-Pin (Medium Bi-Pin Fluorescent)
Base Information	Green Base
Bulb	TB
Rated Average Life (12-Hr Prog St)	36000 hr
Rated Average Life (12-Hr Inst St)	30000 hr
Rated Average Life (3-Hr Prog St)	30000 hr
Rated Average Life (3-Hr Inst)	24000 hr
Mercury Information	
Average Mercury (Hg) Content	1.7 mg
Max Mercury (Hg) Content	2.2 mg
Light Characteristics	
Color Temperature	3000 K
Initial Lumen	2600 Lm
Design Mean Lumens	2470 Lm

Figure 2. Example manufacturer's information

PROJECT TYPE VARIATIONS

Multitenant Projects

Multitenant projects may find it challenging to track lamps purchased by tenants. Developing tracking tools and working with tenants and their vendors can help teams aggregate purchasing data for the entire building (see *Getting Started, Tenant Space Exclusion Allowance*).

CAMPUS

Group Approach

All buildings in the group may be documented as one.

Campus Approach

Ineligible. Each LEED project may pursue the credit individually.

REQUIRED DOCUMENTATION

	Documentation	All projects
P	MR purchasing calculator or equivalent tracking tool listing lamps included in the plan with calculated pictograms per lumen hour	X
P	Verification of mercury-free lamps and energy efficiency of mercury-containing counterparts	X
P	List of purchased lamps, verifying compliance with plan	X
P	Lamp purchasing plan	X

RELATED CREDIT TIPS

MR Prerequisite Ongoing Purchasing and Waste Management Policy. The policy developed for the related prerequisite establishes a foundation for pursuing this credit.

MR Credit Solid Waste Management—Ongoing. All mercury-containing lamps must be diverted from landfills or incinerators at the end of their useful life. When specifying lamps, include products from vendors with take-back programs to support achievement of the related credit.

CHANGES FROM LEED 2009

- The mercury limit has been reduced from 90 picograms per lumen hour to 70.
- The NEMA exemption for compact fluorescent lamps has been removed.

REFERENCED STANDARDS

None.

EXEMPLARY PERFORMANCE

Reduce the mercury content of lamps to an average 35 picograms per lumen hour or less.

DEFINITIONS

average LED intensity (**ALI**) the illumination output for light-emitting diode lamps, as specified in the International Commission on Illumination Standard 127–2007

elemental mercury mercury in its purest form (rather than a mercury-containing compound), the vapor of which is commonly used in fluorescent and other bulb types

lamp a device emitting light in a fixture, excluding lamp housing and ballasts. Light-emitting diodes packaged as traditional lamps also meet this definition.

lamp life the useful span of operation of a source of artificial light, such as bulbs. Lamp life for fluorescent lights is determined by testing three hours on for every 20 minutes off. For high-density discharge lamps, the test is based on 11 hours on for every 20 minutes off. Lamp life depends on whether the start ballast is program or instant. This information is published in manufacturers' information. Also known as rated average life.

mean lumen output a measurement of a source's emitted light derived from industry standards, taken with an instant-start ballast that has a ballast factor of 1.0 as measured at 40% of lamp life (except for T-5 lamps, which use a program-start ballast)

NAED code a unique five- or six-digit number used to identify specific lamps, used by the National Association of Electrical Distributors

persistent bioaccumulative toxic chemical a substance that poses a long-term risk to both humans and the environment because it remains in the environment for long periods, increases in concentration as it moves up the food chain, and can travel far from the source of contamination. Often these substances can become more potent and harmful to ecosystems the longer they persist. See U.S. EPA's website on persistent bioaccumulative toxic chemicals, www.epa.gov/pbt/.

MATERIALS AND RESOURCES CREDIT

Purchasing—Facility Maintenance and Renovation

This credit applies to:

Existing Buildings (1–2 points)
Schools (1–2 points)
Retail (1–2 points)
Data Centers (1–2 points)
Hospitality (1–2 points)
Warehouses and Distribution Centers (1–2 points)

INTENT

To reduce the environmental harm from materials used in building renovations.

REQUIREMENTS

EXISTING BUILDINGS, SCHOOLS, RETAIL, DATA CENTERS, HOSPITALITY, WAREHOUSES AND DISTRIBUTION CENTERS

ESTABLISHMENT E

None.

PERFORMANCE P

OPTION 1. PRODUCTS AND MATERIALS (1 POINT)

Purchase at least 50%, by cost, of the total maintenance and renovation materials that meet at least one of the following criteria. Include products specified in Materials and Resources prerequisite: Facility Maintenance and Renovation Policy. There is no minimum scope of renovation or new construction work required for eligibility of this credit. Each purchase can receive credit for each criterion met.

- **Recycled content.** Recycled content is the sum of postconsumer recycled content plus one-half the preconsumer recycled content.

- **Wood products.** Wood products must be certified by the Forest Stewardship Council or USGBC-approved equivalent.
- **Bio-based materials.** Bio-based products must meet the Sustainable Agriculture Network's Sustainable Agriculture Standard. Bio-based raw materials must be tested using ASTM Test Method D6866 and be legally harvested, as defined by the exporting and receiving country. Exclude hide products, such as leather and other animal skin material.
- **Materials reuse.** Reuse includes salvaged, refurbished, or reused products.
- **Extended producer responsibility.** Products purchased from a manufacturer (producer) that participates in an extended producer responsibility program or is directly responsible for extended producer responsibility. Products valued at 50% of their cost.
- **GreenScreen v1.2 Benchmark.** Products that have fully inventoried chemical ingredients to 100 ppm that have no Benchmark 1 hazards.
  - If any ingredients are assessed with the GreenScreen List Translator, value these products at 100% of cost.
  - If all ingredients are have undergone a full GreenScreen Assessment, value these products at 150% of cost.
- **Cradle to Cradle Certified.** End use products are certified Cradle to Cradle. Products will be valued as follows:
  - Cradle to Cradle v2 Gold: 100% of cost
  - Cradle to Cradle v2 Platinum: 150% of cost
  - Cradle to Cradle v3 Silver: 100% of cost
  - Cradle to Cradle v3 Gold or Platinum: 150% of cost
- **International Alternative Compliance Path** – REACH Optimization. End use products and materials that do not contain substances that meet REACH criteria for substances of very high concern. If the product contains no ingredients listed on the REACH Authorization or Candidate list, value at 100% of cost.
- **Product Manufacturer Supply Chain Optimization.** Use building products that:
  - Are sourced from product manufacturers who engage in validated and robust safety, health, hazard, and risk programs which at a minimum document at least 99% (by weight) of the ingredients used to make the building product or building material, and
  - Are sourced from product manufacturers with independent third party verification of their supply chain that at a minimum verifies:
    - Processes are in place to communicate and transparently prioritize chemical ingredients along the supply chain according to available hazard, exposure and use information to identify those that require more detailed evaluation
    - Processes are in place to identify, document, and communicate information on health, safety and environmental characteristics of chemical ingredients
    - Processes are in place to implement measures to manage the health, safety and environmental hazard and risk of chemical ingredients
    - Processes are in place to optimize health, safety and environmental impacts when designing and improving chemical ingredients
    - Processes are in place to communicate, receive and evaluate chemical ingredient safety and stewardship information along the supply chain
    - Safety and stewardship information about the chemical ingredients is publicly available from all points along the supply chain
- **Low emissions of volatile organic compounds.** The following products must either be inherently nonemitting or be tested and determined compliant in accordance with California Department of Public Health Standard Method V1.1–2010, using the applicable exposure scenario. The default scenario is the private office scenario; classroom furniture may use the school classroom scenario. Both first-party and third-party statements of product compliance must follow the guidelines in CDPH SM V1.1–2010, Section 8. Organizations that certify manufacturers' claims must be accredited under ISO Guide 65. Laboratories that conduct the tests must be accredited under ISO/IEC 17025 for the test methods they use. Projects outside the U.S. may use (1) the CDPH standard method or (2) the German AgBB Testing and Evaluation Scheme (2010). Test products either with (1) ISO 16000-3: 2010, ISO 16000-6: 2011, ISO 16000-9: 2006, ISO 16000-11:2006, or (2) the DIBt testing method (2010). U.S. projects must follow the CDPH standard method.

  - thermal and acoustic insulation
  - flooring materials and finishes
  - ceiling materials and finishes
  - wall materials and finishes
- **VOC content requirements for wet-applied products.** In addition to meeting the general requirements for VOC emissions (above), on-site wet-applied products must not contain excessive levels of VOCs, for the health of the installers and other tradesworkers who are exposed to these products. To demonstrate compliance, a product or layer must meet the following requirements, as applicable. Disclosure of VOC content must be made by the manufacturer. Any testing must follow the test method specified in the applicable regulation.
  - All paints and coatings wet-applied on site must meet the applicable VOC limits of the California Air Resources Board (CARB) 2007, Suggested Control Measure (SCM) for Architectural Coatings, or the South Coast Air Quality Management District (SCAQMD) Rule 1113, effective June 3, 2011.
  - All adhesives and sealants wet-applied on site must meet the applicable chemical content requirements of SCAQMD Rule 1168, July 1, 2005, Adhesive and Sealant Applications, as analyzed by the methods specified in Rule 1168. The provisions of SCAQMD Rule 1168 do not apply to adhesives and sealants subject to state or federal consumer product VOC regulations.
  - For projects outside North America, all paints, coatings, adhesives, and sealants wet-applied on site must either meet the technical requirements of the above regulations, or comply with applicable national VOC control regulations, such as the European Decopaint Directive (2004/42/EC), the Canadian VOC Concentration Limits for Architectural Coatings, or the Hong Kong Air Pollution Control (VOC) Regulation.
  - If the applicable regulation requires subtraction of exempt compounds, any content of intentionally added exempt compounds larger than 1% weight by mass (total exempt compounds) must be disclosed.
  - If a product cannot reasonably be tested as specified above, testing of VOC content must comply with ASTM D2369-10; ISO 11890, part 1; ASTM D6886-03; or ISO 11890-2.
  - For projects in North America, methylene chloride and perchloroethylene may not be intentionally added in paints, coatings, adhesives, or sealants.
- **Low emissions of formaldehyde.** Built-in cabinetry and architectural millwork containing composite woods must be constructed from materials documented to have low formaldehyde emissions that meet the California Air Resources Board requirements for ultra-low-emitting formaldehyde (ULEF) resins or no-added formaldehyde based resins. Salvaged and reused architectural millwork more than one year old at the time of occupancy is considered compliant, provided it meets the requirements for any site-applied paints, coatings, adhesives, and sealants.
- **USGBC approved program.** Other USGBC approved programs meeting leadership extraction criteria.

For credit achievement calculation, products sourced (extracted, manufactured, purchased) within 100 miles (160 km) of the project site are valued at 200% of their base contributing cost.

AND/OR

OPTION 2. FURNITURE (1 POINT)

Purchase at least 75%, by cost, of total furniture and furnishings that meet one or more of the following criteria. Each purchase can receive credit for each criterion met.

- **Recycled content.** Recycled content is the sum of postconsumer recycled content plus one-half the preconsumer recycled content, based on cost.
- **Wood products.** Wood products must be certified by the Forest Stewardship Council or USGBC-approved equivalent.
- **Bio-based materials.** Bio-based products must meet the Sustainable Agriculture Network's Sustainable Agriculture Standard. Bio-based raw materials must be tested using ASTM Test Method D6866 and be legally harvested, as defined by the exporting and receiving country. Exclude hide products, such as leather and other animal skin material.
- **Materials reuse.** Reuse includes salvaged, refurbished, or reused products.

- **Extended producer responsibility.** Products purchased from a manufacturer (producer) that participates in an extended producer responsibility program or is directly responsible for extended producer responsibility. Products valued at 50% of their cost.
- **GreenScreen v1.2 Benchmark.** Products that have fully inventoried chemical ingredients to 100 ppm that have no Benchmark 1 hazards.
  - If any ingredients are assessed with the GreenScreen List Translator, value these products at 100% of cost.
  - If all ingredients are have undergone a full GreenScreen Assessment, value these products at 150% of cost.
- **Cradle to Cradle Certified.** End use products are certified Cradle to Cradle. Products will be valued as follows:
  - Cradle to Cradle v2 Gold: 100% of cost
  - Cradle to Cradle v2 Platinum: 150% of cost
  - Cradle to Cradle v3 Silver: 100% of cost
  - Cradle to Cradle v3 Gold or Platinum: 150% of cost
- **International Alternative Compliance Path – REACH Optimization.** End use products and materials that do not contain substances that meet REACH criteria for substances of very high concern. If the product contains no ingredients listed on the REACH Authorization or Candidate list, value at 100% of cost.
- **Product Manufacturer Supply Chain Optimization.** Use building products that:
  - Are sourced from product manufacturers who engage in validated and robust safety, health, hazard, and risk programs which at a minimum document at least 99% (by weight) of the ingredients used to make the building product or building material, and
  - Are sourced from product manufacturers with independent third party verification of their supply chain that at a minimum verifies:
    - Processes are in place to communicate and transparently prioritize chemical ingredients along the supply chain according to available hazard, exposure and use information to identify those that require more detailed evaluation
    - Processes are in place to identify, document, and communicate information on health, safety and environmental characteristics of chemical ingredients
    - Processes are in place to implement measures to manage the health, safety and environmental hazard and risk of chemical ingredients
    - Processes are in place to optimize health, safety and environmental impacts when designing and improving chemical ingredients
    - Processes are in place to communicate, receive and evaluate chemical ingredient safety and stewardship information along the supply chain
    - Safety and stewardship information about the chemical ingredients is publicly available from all points along the supply chain
- **Low emissions of volatile organic compounds.** Products must have been tested, following ANSI/BIFMA Standard Method M7.1–2011, and must comply with ANSI/BIFMA e3-2011 Furniture Sustainability Standard, Sections 7.6.1 (valued at 50% cost) or 7.6.2 (valued at 100% cost), using either the concentration modeling approach or the emissions factor approach. For classroom furniture, use the standard school classroom model in CDPH Standard Method v1.1. Salvaged and reused furniture more than one year old at the time of use is considered compliant, provided it meets the requirements for any site-applied paints, coatings, adhesives, and sealants.
- **USGBC approved program.** Other USGBC approved programs meeting leadership extraction criteria.

For credit achievement calculation, products sourced (extracted, manufactured, purchased) within 100 miles (160 km) of the project site are valued at 200% of their base contributing cost.

OPTION 3. NO ALTERATIONS OR FURNITURE PURCHASING (1 POINT)

Make no alterations to the project space and do not purchase any furniture.

BEHIND THE INTENT

Purchases of durable and long-lasting items, whether for routine maintenance or major renovations, lengthen the replacement cycle, thereby reducing the amount of waste sent to landfills and incinerators and saving money. Products and materials with sustainable attributes can also increase the healthfulness and longevity of the building. Building owners may avoid additional materials-based resource use altogether by forgoing renovation projects and by reusing existing furniture.

This credit builds on the environmentally preferable purchasing policy established for MR Prerequisite Facility Maintenance and Renovations Policy by specifying thresholds for products, materials, and furniture that meet environmental criteria.

STEP-BY-STEP GUIDANCE

STEP 1. DETERMINE LIKELIHOOD OF MAINTENANCE, RENOVATIONS, OR FURNITURE PURCHASES DURING PERFORMANCE PERIOD P

Review schedules for space planning or tenant fit-outs to determine whether maintenance, renovations, or furniture purchases will occur during the performance period. In multitenant buildings, consider both base building projects and tenant space projects. This credit has no minimum scope of renovation or new construction work.

STEP 2. SELECT ONE OR TWO OPTIONS P

Determine which options are suitable for the project and timeline. Teams may select Option 1 and 2 simultaneously, or Option 3.

- Option 1 is appropriate if a planned renovation project will include replacement or purchase of elements permanently or semipermanently attached to the base building or site but not include furniture or interior furnishings.
- Option 2 is appropriate if a planned renovation project will include replacement or purchase of any furniture and interior furnishings.
- Option 3 is for projects that will not undergo any alterations or purchase any furniture, products, or materials for maintenance and renovations during the performance period, which for this option is one year.

Option 1. Products and Materials & Option 2. Furniture

STEP 1. EVALUATE PURCHASING PATTERNS P

Review current purchasing patterns to determine whether the project is on track to achieve the credit threshold for facility maintenance and renovation (FMR) activities.

- Estimate the total FMR material and product costs anticipated for the base building and site (for Option 1) and/or for furniture and furnishings (for Option 2) during the performance period (see *Further Explanation, Calculations*).
- Include taxes, shipping, and delivery in the cost of products; exclude labor costs for installation.
- For multitenant buildings, include any tenant-controlled FMR material and products purchasing data (see *Further Explanation, Project Type Variations*).
- Exclude mechanical and electrical equipment, plumbing components, and specialty equipment, such as escalators and elevators.

STEP 2. DETERMINE CURRENT PERCENTAGE COMPLIANCE P

Use Equation 1 to determine the percentage of materials and products by cost that will meet at least one of the credit criteria.

- Review the material purchase directives in the environmentally preferable purchasing policy developed for MR Prerequisite Facility Maintenance and Renovations Policy.

- For more information on standards for low-emitting products and materials, see *Further Explanation, Testing Standards.*
- For a product that meets more than one criterion, calculate the contribution as the percentage (by weight) of the qualifying component times the cost of the product. Use the same approach for material assemblies (see *Further Explanation, Examples 1* and *2*).
- For material assemblies, determine recycled content by allocating the percentage of product cost according to weight of the component. Large manufacturers can likely provide this information (see *MR Overview, Determining Material Contributions*).

EQUATION 1. Percentage of compliant FMR purchases

$$\text{Compliant FMR purchases} = \frac{\text{Total cost of compliant FMR purchases}}{\text{Total cost of all FMR purchases}} \times 100$$

STEP 3. IDENTIFY PRODUCTS TO MEET 50% THRESHOLD P

To meet or exceed the 50% threshold, specify products that meet one or more criteria.

- Focus first on high-cost or high-volume noncompliant items.
- Look for opportunities to swap noncompliant items for products that meet the criteria, are easy accessible, and are comparably priced (e.g., locally sourced alternatives).
- Pilot the use of compliant substitutes before fully committing to replacing current materials and products.
- Consider revising the policy to capture the changes made to the product selection criteria and goals.
- Help purchasing departments develop a list of approved products and communicate the requirements for environmentally preferable purchases (see *Further Explanation, Engaging Responsible Parties*).

STEP 4. SET UP TRACKING SYSTEM P

Develop a tracking system to gather data for all FMR purchases for the building (see *MR Overview, Selecting a Tracking System*). Use the MR purchasing calculator provided by USGBC or an equivalent tracking tool.

- For multitenant buildings, it is recommended that project teams test the building-wide purchasing tracking system before the performance period begins (see *MR Overview, Multitenant Buildings*).
- This credit applies to all facility alterations, renovations, furniture, and routine maintenance products and materials, including materials purchased by individual tenants and the property manager or building owner. All purchasing data must be tracked and aggregated to demonstrate compliance.

STEP 5. TRACK PURCHASES MADE DURING PERFORMANCE PERIOD P

Track purchases of products and materials for the base building and site (for Option 1) and/or purchases of furniture and furnishings (for Option 2) over the performance period (see *Further Explanation, Ensuring Credit Compliance*).

- Determine the percentage of compliant purchases, by cost.
- Collect documentation verifying that the products and materials meet the criteria. Retain all documentation for all criteria. Documentation requirements differ for each criterion.
- Submit all documentation for the following: wood products, bio-based materials, GreenScreen v1.2 Benchmark, Cradle to Cradle certification, and REACH Optimization (see *Further Explanation, Documentation for Wood and Biobased Materials* and *Documentation for Material Ingredients*).
- Submission of documentation for other FMR purchases is not required.

Option 3. No Alterations or Furniture Purchasing

STEP 1. VERIFY LACK OF FMR ACTIVITIES DURING PERFORMANCE PERIOD P

During the performance period, verify that no FMR activities will be undertaken. Review the capital improvements plan for the performance period (in this case, one year) and ensure that no FMR activities will take place. For multitenant buildings, the credit requirements also apply to any tenant-controlled FMR activities.

FURTHER EXPLANATION

CALCULATIONS

See Equation 1 in *Step-by-Step Guidance.*

Calculating materials cost

Calculate the total percentage, by cost, of purchases of FMR products and materials that meet one or more of the environmental criteria listed in the credit requirements. Each product that meets several criteria receives credit for each criterion met. For instance, a product that contains both bio-based materials and recycled content can receive credit for both criteria.

For material assemblies, the percentage of the product that is compliant, by weight, determines the perçentage of the product cost that contributes toward the credit. For instance, if a product contains 10% postconsumer recycled material by weight, 10% of the product cost contributes to credit achievement.

Divide the total cost of products or materials purchases by the percentage cost that meets the environmental criteria (see *Further Explanation, Examples 1* and 2, and *MR Overview, Determining Material Contributions*).

Exclude furniture from Option 1 calculations; these items are counted separately in Option 2.

The standard default percentage for the recycled content of steel is 25% preconsumer.

The cost of reused or reclaimed materials is the actual cost paid or the replacement value, whichever is higher.

Replacement value

The replacement value can be determined by pricing a comparable material in the local market; exclude labor. If a project team receives a discount from a vendor, the replacement value should be the discounted price, not the list value.

If the actual cost of the reused or salvaged material is below the cost of an equivalent new item, use the higher value (actual cost) of the new item. If the cost to reclaim an item found on site is less than the cost of an equivalent new item, use the cost of the new item (or replacement cost).

Generally, opportunities to reuse building materials may be limited. Core materials that may be eligible include salvaged brick, structural timber, railroad ties, stone, and pavers. When considering the reuse of salvaged materials, confirm that they do not contain toxic substances, such as lead or asbestos.

MATERIAL REUSE CONSIDERATIONS

Reused materials found on-site

Components that are retained either in their original function or in a new role are eligible for this credit. For reused materials found on site, the source location distance is zero.

Reused materials found off-site

Materials obtained off site qualify as reused if they were previously used in a building or other application. These materials may be purchased as salvaged, like any other project material, or moved from another facility, including facilities used or owned by the LEED project owner.

For salvaged furniture taken from the owner's previous facility or location, demonstrate that these materials were purchased at least two years before the date of project registration. For example, if the owner is moving to a new building, furniture and furnishings relocated to the new site can contribute to this credit because their reuse will eliminate the need for purchasing new furniture and furnishings. Alternatively, furniture that is leased must have been in service for at least two years before being installed in the current project. Document this claim.

DOCUMENTATION FOR WOOD AND BIOBASED MATERIALS

Documentation for Wood

To contribute toward credit achievement, wood products that are not reused, salvaged, or recycled must be certified to the standards of the Forest Stewardship Council. Bamboo, nonwood forest products, and other materials that are not actually wood but are certified by FSC can count toward this credit. Collect vendor invoices for wood products purchased for the project (see *Further Explanation, FSC Chain of Custody*).

Documentation for Biobased materials

Biobased products are defined by ASTM D6866, but testing (by the manufacturer or a contracted party) is not required in all cases. Manufacturers use this test to determine the amount of biobased material in a product. If the percentage of biobased materials, by weight, in the product are known, testing to this standard may not be necessary.

Nonwood products must be grown on farms that meet the Sustainable Agriculture Standard of the Sustainable Agricultural Network (SAN). Products originating on farms that meet the Sustainable Agriculture Standard must adhere to the guidelines and policies of the Rainforest Alliance—including traceability, chain of custody and use of seal—and receive pre-approval from the Rainforest Alliance in order to bear the Rainforest Alliance Certified™ seal. The Rainforest Alliance is a member of SAN and hosts its international secretariat, providing traceability, market linkages, and technical assistance. Several certification bodies in different countries are accredited to conduct Rainforest Alliance certification. A full listing of certified farms and operations can be found on the SAN website, sanstandards.org. A list of Rainforest Certified products can be found at rainforest-alliance.org. To date, nearly all Rainforest Alliance Certified agricultural products are foods, coffee, tea, and cut flowers.

Because the number of Rainforest Alliance–certified crops in building materials is limited, project teams may include products with manufacturer-declared conformance to the Sustainable Agriculture Standard (except bamboo and nonwood forest products that could be FSC certified) under the following three conditions:

- The product's manufacturer provides a signed letter on company letterhead from the raw material supplier attesting that its practices meet the standard.
- The letter includes a link to a publicly available document that specifies how the raw material supplier's practices conform to each paragraph in all 10 sections of the standard and attesting that each "critical criterion" is met.
- Both the letter and the detailed documentation are dated within one year before the date of project registration.

FSC CHAIN OF CUSTODY

Chain-of-Custody (CoC) certification requirements are established by Forest Stewardship Council Chain of Custody Standard 40-004 v2-1. To view this and all FSC standards, see the FSC website, ic.fsc.org, for listings.

Every entity that processes or trades FSC-certified material before it is shipped to the project site must have FSC CoC certification. On-site installers of FSC-certified products must have CoC certification only if they modify the products off the project site.

CALCULATING FSC CREDIT CONTRIBUTIONS

FSC-certified products must be itemized on the vendor's invoice. Their value toward credit contribution is calculated as one of the following, as determined by the FSC claim on the invoice provided by the supplier(terminology in parenthesis is being phased out but may still be in use):

- Products identified as FSC 100% (FSC Pure) contribute 100% FSC content.
- Products identified as FSC Mix Credit (FSC Mixed Credit) contribute 100% FSC content.
- Products identified as FSC Mix [NN]% (FSC Mixed [NN]%) contribute the FSC content percentage indicated. For example, a product identified as "FSC Mix 75%" is valued at 75% of the product's cost (Equation 3).

EQUATION 3. Credit contribution of FSC Mix

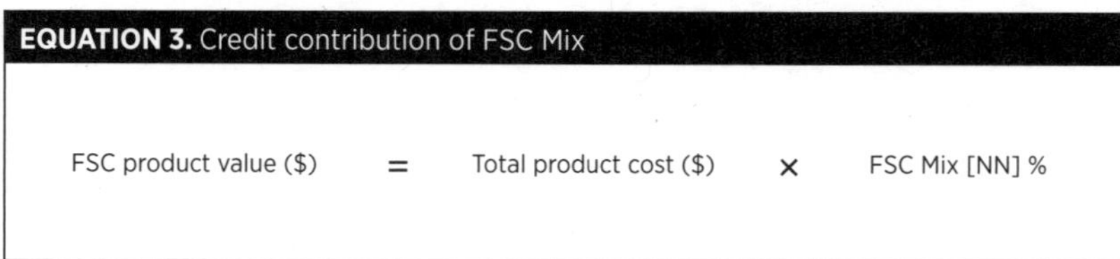

$$\text{FSC product value (\$)} = \text{Total product cost (\$)} \times \text{FSC Mix [NN] \%}$$

- Products identified as FSC Recycled Credit contribute 100% postconsumer recycled content.
- Products identified as FSC Recycled [NN] % contribute the percentage postconsumer recycled content percentage indicated [NN].

Multiple Sustainable Claims and FSC
FSC and recycled content. Some products identified as FSC Mix Credit or FSC Mix [NN] % also have pre- or postconsumer recycled content, the latter of which is commonly reported separately by the product manufacturer. In these instances the project team must choose whether to classify the product (or some fraction of the assembly) as FSC certified or as recycled content; the material cannot contribute to both claims simultaneously.
FSC and SAN certified products. Products certified by both FSC and to the Sustainable Agriculture Standard they may receive credit for each criteria.

DOCUMENTING FSC CLAIMS

Project teams must document FSC certification for all wood products that contribute to credit achievement. FSC-certified products qualify for credit only when purchased from a vendor with an FSC chain-of-custody certificate that is current at the time of sale. The status of a CoC certification can be verified at info.fsc.org.

Each product shipped to the project site and contributing toward credit must be documented by an invoice from the CoC certificate holder as follows:

- The invoice must have the vendor's CoC certificate code (e.g., RA-COC-001025, SCS-COC-000345, or SGS-COC-002563). The invoice must itemize FSC-certified products and specific FSC claims.
- The invoice may aggregate the value of products, provided the cost of FSC products is isolated from other wood products and the vendor's CoC certificate code is on the invoice.
- The invoice must show the entity being invoiced and indicate the delivery is intended for the LEED project.

An alternative documentation process is available for architectural woodworkers (manufacturers of millwork, casework, and furniture) who supply custom wood products to the project. The purpose of this alternative process is to allow FSC-certified materials used in a custom millwork, casework, or furniture package to contribute toward the credit even if the entire package is not eligible to be invoiced with a FSC claim. Documentation for this alternative process must meet all of the following requirements:

- The woodworker (whether an individual or a company) must be FSC CoC certified, and the CoC certificate number must appear on the project invoice.
- The woodworker must install the custom millwork, casework, or furniture.
- The woodworker's invoice must isolate product costs from installation costs.
- The woodworker must provide a document, separate from the project invoice, detailing FSC-certified wood materials used and total cost of wood materials used. (The woodworker does not need to provide itemized material cost calculations but must maintain calculation records for auditing purposes by the FSC certifying body.)
- The contract cost may include assembly labor but must exclude on-site labor (see MR Overview, Determining Product Cost).

The project team should complete a spreadsheet itemizing wood components by cost and identifying FSC-certified and noncertified components to determine overall contributions to the credit, to be entered into the MR calculator. Calculate the FSC-certified contribution value toward the credit by multiplying the percentage of FSC-certified wood by the overall value of the contract. Calculate the percentage of FSC-certified wood by dividing the cost of FSC-certified wood by the total cost of the wood.

Submit the FSC-certified contribution value as well as the total contract amount. Include the woodworker's CoC certificate number, invoice, and itemized costs.

DOCUMENTATION FOR MATERIAL INGREDIENTS

GreenScreen Benchmark 1

GreenScreen version 1.2 is based on a toxicological assessment that starts with a collection of authoritative lists of "chemicals of concern" published by governmental and nongovernmental organizations (GreenScreen List Translator). These substances are known to be associated with certain health problems. The assessment then proceeds to reviews of the scientific literature, use of structure activity relationship models and chemical analog data to fill data gaps (Full GreenScreen). Chemicals are assigned to one of four main categories: those of highest concern, as indicated in the authoritative lists, are assigned Benchmark 1. Chemicals that are not on the major authoritative lists and pass a toxicological review based on Clean Production Action's protocols can be assigned benchmarks that indicate lower levels of concern; Benchmark 4 is the lowest level of concern. A full GreenScreen assessment overrides the results of screening using the GreenScreen List Translator only.

The GreenScreen List Translator has been automated by two software providers. It can be accessed through the Chemical and Material Library found in Healthy Building Network's Pharos Tool and in the GS List Translator module in the GreenWERCS software tool by The Wercs. The Interstate Chemicals Clearinghouse has created a website where GreenScreen assessments can be posted by various participating State governments and shared with no costs or restrictions.

This credit requires the Full GreenScreen toxicological assessment to ensure that none of the ingredients are Benchmark 1. Project teams should look for documentation from manufacturers that shows each ingredient in the product has been subject to a full GreenScreen assessment by a licensed GreenScreen Profiler and that the product contains only Benchmark 2 and higher ingredients.

For Manufacturers and Suppliers

GreenScreen's List Translator assigns hazard classifications based on the various governmental and authoritative hazard lists including lists of chemicals classified using the Globally Harmonized System of Classification and Labeling. The GreenScreen List Translator can be used to identify chemicals that achieve or may achieve the Benchmark 1 level of concern. Under Option 1, manufacturers that keep certain ingredients proprietary must characterize any health hazards from those ingredients, as indicated by the List Translator or a full GreenScreen assessment.

Under this credit, the manufacturer must warrant that no ingredients in the product at levels of 0.01% or more (100 ppm) are designated as Benchmark 1 chemicals based on the referenced lists defined by the List Translator. These products achieve compliance at the first level of the option.

The second level of compliance requires that all ingredients be Benchmark 2 or higher. There is no definitive List Translator for Benchmark 2, so manufacturers must engage an independent third party to screen all their ingredients, using the screening protocol defined by GreenScreen, and certify that none of them are Benchmark 1.

Cradle to Cradle Certified, version 2.1.1 and version 3.0

Project teams may also select Cradle to Cradle Certified (C2C) products. C2C requires that ingredients be disclosed to an independent, accredited C2C assessor. The percent of the product defined and assessed impacts the level of certification. Products certified under v2.1.1, have had at least 95% by weight of their materials assessed at any level and 100% of their materials assessed at the Gold and Platinum levels. Products certified under v3.0, have had at least 75% or 95% by weight of their materials assessed at the Bronze and Silver levels respectively, and 100% of their materials at the Gold and Platinum levels. Eligible products will have their scorecard available in the C2C product registry. The product scorecard shows the level of achievement for all five standard attributes, the overall certification level for the product (Basic, Bronze, Silver, Gold, or Platinum), the certificate expiration date, and the version of the standard that the product is certified against. For each certified product the registry includes an image of the product, the product description and certification level, and the expiration date of the current certification. Product certification claims from manufacturers' websites should always be verified against this registry because they may be out-of-date (see *Further Explanation, Example, Cradle to Cradle (C2C) certification*). During the material health assessment, assessors review the scientific literature available for all chemical ingredients contained in a material above 100 ppm, use structure activity relationship models and chemical analog data to fill data gaps, and compare the collected information against the C2C hazard criteria. Through this process, the environmental and human health hazards of the chemical ingredients are classified using a green–yellow–red rating system. In a second step, assessors evaluate whether exposure to any of the identified or suspected hazardous chemicals are plausible in the context of the materials containing these chemicals and the product use and end of life scenarios. If avenues for exposure to these chemicals in a material exist, the material will receive an overall risk assessment rating of 'x'. Gold and Platinum certified products do not contain any x-assessed materials. Products certified at the Silver level under v3.0 do not contain materials that have been x-assessed due to the presence of a carcinogen, mutagen, or reproductive toxicant (CMR). Products certified at any level under v3.0 do not contain banned list chemicals. Chemicals on the v3.0 banned lists include PVC and related compounds, certain flame retardants, PFOS and PFOA, certain phthalates, halogenated hydrocarbons and toxic heavy metals. C2C certification addresses a total of five product attributes and ingredient screening is just one part of the program.

Other USGBC-approved programs

As the industry evolves, additional programs and protocols for reporting on material ingredients are likely to emerge. USGBC will determine whether any new programs are acceptable and issue rating system addenda to include them as additional approaches to earning the credit.

EMISSIONS AND VOC CONTENT

Inherently Nonemiting Materials

Naturally occurring materials and products that are made from inorganic materials (e.g., granite) emit either very low or no VOCs. USGBC recognizes that such products do not need to undergo testing to prove they do not emit VOCs. For the purposes of this credit, untreated and unfinished solid wood (not engineered wood) flooring can also be considered nonemitting even though such flooring will likely emit some amount of formaldehyde naturally. This applies only to flooring materials, not to wood paneling or cabinetry.

Testing Standards

CDPH Standard Method v1.1

This credit uses the California Department of Public Health (CDPH) Standard Method for the Testing and Evaluation of Volatile Organic Chemical Emissions from Indoor Sources Using Environmental Chambers, v. 1.1–2010, for the emissions testing and requirements of all products and materials except furniture. The method, widely recognized as a leadership standard for its stringent scientific criteria and detailed specificity, was developed through an open, consensus process. It uses the chronic reference exposure levels established by the California Office of Environmental Health Hazard Assessment, which include some of the most stringent criteria in use. It also adopted and incorporated the first edition of the ANSI/BIFMA M7.1 standard test method for furniture.

There is no total volatile organic compound (TVOC) pass-fail requirement in the CDPH standard, which focuses on measuring and limiting individual VOCs. However, this credit requires manufacturers using the CDPH standard to also disclose the range of TVOC for each product, a requirement intended to provide greater transparency for project teams, especially when they are comparing similar materials. Though TVOC alone is a crude measurement not suitable for health-based determinations of acceptability, it is useful as a general indicator in combination with individual VOC measurements, since higher TVOC may suggest the need for additional investigation.

CARB ATCM composite wood formaldehyde regulation

This credit uses the California Air Resources Board (CARB) 93120 Airborne Toxic Control Measure (ATCM) for formaldehyde emissions from composite wood products. It provides a way to determine the compliance of composite wood materials used in products not covered by full VOC testing in other categories. CARB 93120 ATCM is required in California but widely used internationally.

This credit uses not the minimum requirements of the CARB 93120 ATCM but the more stringent requirements for ultra-low-emitting formaldehyde (ULEF) resins or no added formaldehyde based resins, as defined in the CARB ATCM. These criteria are some of the strongest available for formaldehyde emissions from composite wood.

Although composite wood compliance with the CARB formaldehyde criteria is beneficial, chamber testing for a broader range of individual VOCs emitted from assembled products that include composite wood in combination with other components can provide a better determination of a product's potential effect on indoor air quality. Therefore, the composite wood criteria of this credit do not apply to composite wood covered by the full VOC testing of other categories.

ANSI/BIFMA standards

This credit requires that all furniture VOC emissions testing be conducted in accordance with the ANSI/BIFMA M7.1–2011 Standard Test Method for Determining VOC Emissions from Office Furniture Systems, Components and Seating. The second edition of this standard incorporates important advances that include defining an emissions factor approach for compliance, refining the mathematical estimation procedures for nonmeasured time points, and adding specific, highly detailed surface area calculation requirements to ensure consistency.

This credit also requires furniture to comply with the low-emitting requirements in the ANSI/BIFMA e3–2011 Furniture Sustainability Standard. This standard includes both the historical VOC emissions requirements for furniture from earlier versions of LEED and the health-based requirements from the 2010 version of the CDPH standard, both as concentration limits and as maximum emissions factors. These emissions factor limits effectively increase the stringency of the standard and make it easier for furniture component suppliers to modify their products for compliance.

For Existing Schools and other project with classrooms, classroom furniture is to comply with CDPH testing scenarios for classroom furniture, not the ANSI/BIFMA test method.

International standards

Recognizing the need for additional compliance options for projects outside the U.S., this credit also references select international standards, which can be used only under specific conditions because of the complicated nature of air quality standards.

The German AgBB Testing and Evaluation Scheme (2010) is a leading industry standard that can be used for this credit, with some limitations. The AgBB standard does not represent a European consensus but does share common attributes with several European counterparts. It addresses six times more individual VOC requirements than the CDPH standard, and it specifies TVOC and total semivolatile organic compound (TSVOC) limits for all nonregulated substances. However, the standard has limitations, including the following:

- The formaldehyde limit value of 10 $\mu g/m^3$ at 28 days must also be met when using the AgBB alternative, as specified for class A+ in French compulsory VOC emissions class labeling.
- The AgBB requirements use different exposure scenario conditions than CDPH. Because VOC emissions from building materials generally decrease over time, the point in time for determining compliance is critical. The more time there is for off-gassing to occur, the easier it may be to meet the standard, even though in many cases the difference is minor (most emissions decay within the first week). CDPH requires compliance at 14 days; the full AgBB requirements apply at three or 28 days, which this credit does not take into account.

Similarly, this credit allows the use of the ISO 16000 series standards when combined with the AgBB standard, the cited French legislation (Decree no 2011-321 and arrêté of 19 April 2011), or the DIBT method (German Institute for Building Technology, *Principles of Health Assessment of Construction Products in Indoor Environments*, 2010 dibt.de/de/data/Aktuelles_Ref_II_4_6.pdf). The ISO 16000 series standards do not contain enough detail to be cited alone for testing in this credit. The same requirements for formaldehyde also apply in each of these cases.

Referenced mass VOC regulatory standards

The U.S. regulatory system for adhesives and sealants captures a limited range of listed product categories and excludes small packages intended for consumer use. The leading CARB and SCAQMD regulations are well ahead of other state and national regulations. Historically, CARB has developed the suggested control measure (SCM) coatings regulatory framework later adopted by some U.S. states and Canada. SCAQMD created a widely cited regulatory system for sealants and adhesives packaged and designed for commercial applications.

All products are to adhere to the general requirements for VOC emissions, as listed in the credit requirements. Wet applied products (paint, sealants, and adhesives) must in addition comply with VOC content and emissions requirements.

This credit includes requirements for all product categories found in the referenced standards. Product categories that are not listed do not need to be tracked. The credit incorporates various district, state, and national regulations limiting the overall VOC content in coatings, sealants, and adhesives. These regulatory limits serve as a minimum requirement, in addition to emissions testing standards listed in the general emissions requirements.

Because of divergent regulatory development processes, the coatings categories, category definitions, and VOC limits vary between CARB SCM and SCAQMD Rule 1113. Suppliers should provide information on the proper categorization of their materials consistent with definitions in the referenced regulations.

For projects outside the U.S., existing national VOC regulations may serve as the credit requirement. The Canadian VOC Concentration Limits for Architectural Coatings and the Hong Kong Air Pollution Control (VOC) Regulation are examples of local regulations deemed equivalent to the CARB SCM and SCAQMD Rule 1113. Project teams should contact USGBC to determine additional equivalent regulations. Establishing parity or a direct comparison with cited U.S. regulations is difficult, given varying definitions of product categories, the VOC status of specific solvents, and varying applications of the less-water and exempt-solvent approaches.

Information on any VOC compounds exempt from regulation is required for credit compliance. Cited regulatory limits do not include the VOC content of colorants added to coatings at the point of sale. Pretinted flat, nonflat, industrial maintenance coatings and stains include the VOC content of all ingredients, including colorants.

LOCATION VALUATION FACTOR

To incentivize the purchase of products that support the local economy, products and materials that are extracted, manufactured, and purchased within 100 miles (160 kilometers) of the project are valued at 200% of their cost (i.e., the valuation factor is 2).

For a product to qualify for the location valuation factor, it must meet two conditions: all extraction, manufacture, and purchase (including distribution) of the product and it's materials must occur within that radius (Figure 1) and the product (or portion of an assembled product) must meet at least one of the sustainability criteria (e.g., FSC certification, recycled content) specified in the credit. Products and materials that do not meet the location radius but do meet at least one of the sustainability criteria are valued 100% of their cost (i.e., the valuation factor is 1).

The distance is measured as the crow flies, not by actual travel distance. The point of purchase is considered the location of the purchase transaction. For online or other transactions that do not occur in person, the point of purchase is considered the location of product distribution.

For reused materials, the source location of extraction or harvest is the location of the materials before their removal to the project site.

For material taken directly from another building, the source location is the building. For items purchased from a building materials salvage store or recycling facility, the source location is the store or facility. In this case, it is not necessary to track material to the original building.

For this project in western Pennsylvania the process of extracting and manufacturing concrete does not meet the location valuation factor requirements because the silica, Portland cement, and lime extraction are outside the 100 mile radius.

Figure 1. Example material radius

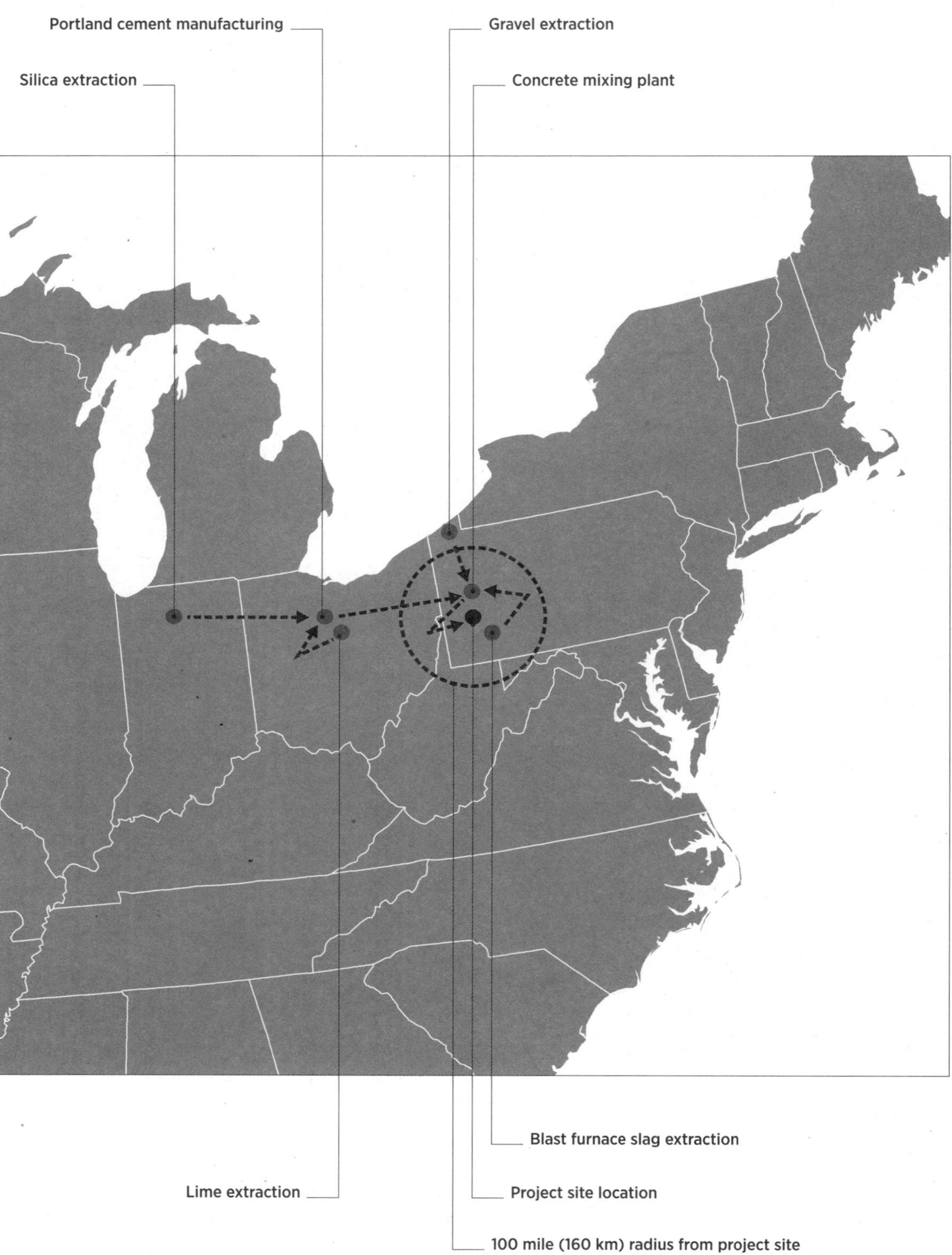

EXAMPLES

Example 1. Calculating compliance for products that meet multiple criteria

A project team installs $2,000 worth of carpet that qualifies for recycled content (60% recycled by weight), extended producer responsibility, and material ingredient optimization. The team values each element separately, according to its percentage of the total cost, and then sums the values (Table 1).

TABLE 1. Example calculation for multiple criteria

Product	Criterion	Percentage compliant	Contributing value
Carpet, $2,000 (excluding installation labor)	Recycled content (60%)	60%	0.6 X $2,000 = $1,200
	Extended producer responsibility	100%	$2,000
	Cradle-to-Cradle v2 certified	100%	$2,000
	Total		**$5,200**

The $2,000 carpet contributes $5,200 toward credit compliance.

Example 2. Calculating compliance for material assemblies

Most furniture consists of several components. A project team purchases a $100 table with steel legs and a homogeneous top. Each component each meets one sustainable criterion but makes up only a percentage of the entire product. The team calculates the contribution of each component, using weight to determine the percentage of the total cost.

TABLE 2. Example calculation for material assemblies

Product	Component	Percentage by weight	Criterion	Percentage compliant	Contributing value
Table, $100 (100 lbs.)	Plastic top (30 lbs.)	30%	Recycled content (100%)	0.3 X 100% = 30.0%	$30.00
	Steel legs (70 lbs.)	70%	Recycled content (25%, default value)	0.7 X 25% = 17.5%	$17.50
Total				**47.5%**	**$47.50**

Example 3. Cradle to Cradle (C2C) certification

Figure 2. Cradle to Cradle (C2C) certification

MANUFACTURERS' DATA

For many products, the material safety data sheet (MSDS) or product literature includes the third-party standards met; look online or ask the vendor or manufacturer for the information. Some certifiers have online databases that teams can use to verify certification. Some furniture company representatives may also be able to supply the required information.

ENGAGING RESPONSIBLE PARTIES

To meet performance thresholds, project teams must work with the various responsible parties and purchasing entities involved in facility alterations, additions, and furniture and fittings purchases. Responsible parties may include representatives of building owners and tenants, vendors, contractors, specification writers, architects, and the facilities manager. It is recommended that one person be responsible for reviewing potential purchases against the criteria, even when multiple individuals are involved in ordering.

To help purchasing entities find compliant products and materials and develop their own protocols for evaluating future purchases, develop a list of items that meet the credit requirements. Consider including high-priority requirements in the specifications for renovation projects.

Tips for engaging vendors and contractors include the following:

- Familiarize vendors and building staff with the facility maintenance and renovations policy.
- Elicit feedback from vendors and contractors on product and material effectiveness, particularly when sourcing new purchases.
- Train purchasing managers in using the tracking tools.
- Check in regularly to measure performance and program effectiveness.

Engagement with tenants and occupants might be slightly different. Recommendations include the following:

- Explain the human and environmental benefits of sustainable building products via email, letter, flyer, or other means.
- Encourage tenants to designate a representative who will serve as a point of contact.
- Reach out to tenant representatives and familiarize them with the facility alterations and additions policy, including the product purchasing requirements.
- Provide support in helping tenants transition to compliant products, and offer training in using the tracking tools.

ENSURING CREDIT COMPLIANCE

Verify the validity of certifications and labels for each product or material. The U.S. Environmental Protection Agency's Environmentally Preferable Purchasing Program guidelines can be helpful for confirming claims of recycled content.

To meet the credit criteria, it may be necessary to swap noncompliant products and materials for compliant items. Work with subcontractors and suppliers to find materials and products that meet the criteria, are easy accessible, and are comparably priced.

Pilot-test new products or construct mockups of proposed construction to help prevent dissatisfaction with the new policy.

RATING SYSTEM VARIATIONS

Schools

For classroom furniture, use the standard school classroom model in CDPH Standard Method v1.1.

PROJECT TYPE VARIATIONS

Multitenant Projects

Project teams may exclude up to 10% of the project building's total floor area from the credit calculations if those spaces are under separate management (see *MR Overview, Multitenant Buildings*).

INTERNATIONAL TIPS

Alternative Compliance Path for International Projects: Registration, Evaluation, Authorisation and Restriction of Chemicals (REACH).

The European Union's REACH legislation requires all chemicals sold in quantity in the EU to be registered in a central database and prioritized for evaluation and possible avoidance based on their hazard profile. The program maintains several lists of "Substances of Very High Concern."

Products can contribute to Option 2 under this credit if they come with clear documentation from the supplier that they do not contain any substances on the "Authorization List" (chemicals that can only be used with special authorization) nor on the "Candidate List" (chemicals being considered for the Authorization List). Because these lists can change over time, the supplier documentation must be dated; if a substance in the product was added to one of these lists after that documentation was produced and after the project's registration date, the product is still considered compliant. Projects in the U.S. may also use this alternative compliance path.

- Authorization List: echa.europa.eu/web/guest/addressing-chemicals-of-concern/authorisation/recommendation-for-inclusion-in-the-authorisation-list/authorisation-list
- Candidate List: echa.europa.eu/web/guest/candidate-list-table

REACH also provides for a "Restriction List" of chemicals that are to be banned from production and use, but as of August 2013 no substances had made it onto that list. Any substances that are moved from the Authorization List and Candidate List to the Restriction List continue to be treated as substances to be avoided in Option 2-compliant products.

CAMPUS

Group Approach
All buildings in the group may be documented as one.

Campus Approach
Ineligible. Each LEED project may pursue the credit individually.

REQUIRED DOCUMENTATION

	Documentation	Option 1	Option 2	Option 3
P	Total cost of materials and products for base building and site FMR activities	X		
P	Total cost of materials and products for furniture and furnishings		X	
P	List of compliant material and product purchases for base building and site FMR activities, including product name, environmental criterion, manufacturer, cost, date of purchase, and quantity, with any weighted average calculations	X		
P	Documentation verifying purchases meet credit criteria (e.g., manufacturer's documentation, third-party certifications)	X	X	
P	Documentation demonstrating that no maintenance or renovation activities occurred during performance period			X

RELATED CREDIT TIPS

MR Prerequisite Facility Maintenance and Renovations Policy. The environmentally preferable purchasing policy developed in the related prerequisite serves as the basis for purchasing in this credit.

MR Credit Solid Waste Management—Facility Maintenance and Renovations. Purchasing environmentally preferable materials, such as those with recycled content or that can be reused or recycled, can reduce the amount of waste generated in a project.

CHANGES FROM LEED 2009

- Single attributes were aligned with the Building Design and Construction rating systems.
- Furniture was moved from the former MR Credit Purchasing—Durable Goods to this credit.
- A third option has been added to give credit to projects that perform no facility maintenance and renovations.
- Previously, even if only a portion of a material met the credit requirements, the entire material would receive credit; now, only the percentage of the material meeting the requirements can contribute toward credit achievement, unless otherwise noted.

REFERENCED STANDARDS

ASTM Test Method D6866: astm.org/Standards/D6866.htm

Forest Stewardship Council: fsc.org/

Sustainable Agriculture Network's Sustainable Agriculture Standard: sanstandards.org/sitio/

California Department of Public Health Standard Method V1.1–2010: standards.nsf.org/apps/group_public/download.php/17161/2010%20Test%20Procedure%2001350%20CDPH-IAQ_StandardMethod_V1_1_2010.pdf

ISO Guide 65, ISO/IEC 17025, ISO 16000-3: 2010, ISO 16000-6: 2011, ISO 16000-9: 2006, ISO 16000-11:2006: iso.org/

German AgBB Testing and Evaluation Scheme (2010): umweltbundesamt.de/produkte-e/bauprodukte/agbb.htm

DIBt testing method (2010): dibt.de/de/data/Aktuelles_Ref_II_4_6.pdf

California Air Resources Board (CARB) 2007, Suggested Control Measures (SCM) for Architectural Coatings and requirements for ultra-low-emitting formaldehyde (ULEF): arb.ca.gov/homepage.htm

South Coast Air Quality Management District (SCAQMD) Rule 1113, effective June 3, 2011, SCAQMD Rule 1168, effective July 1, 2005, Adhesive and Sealant Applications: aqmd.gov/default.htm

European Decopaint Directive: ec.europa.eu/environment/air/pollutants/stationary/paints/paints_legis.htm

Canadian VOC Concentration Limits for Architectural Coatings: ec.gc.ca/lcpe-cepa/eng/regulations/detailReg.cfm?intReg=117

Hong Kong Air Pollution Control Regulation: epd.gov.hk/epd/english/environmentinhk/air/air_maincontent.html

Clean Production Action's Green Screen v1.2 Benchmark 1, Avoid Chemicals of High Concern: cleanproduction.org/Greenscreen.php

European Commission EC No. 1907/2006 Registration, Evaluation, Authorization, and Restriction of Chemicals (REACH) including Annexes I, II, IV, V, XI, XIII, XIV, and XVII: ec.europa.eu/environment/chemicals/reach/reach_intro.htm

ANSI/BIFMA Standard Method M7.1–2011: bifma.org/standards/standards.html

BIFMA e3–2010 Furniture Sustainability Standard, Sections 7.6.1 and 7.6.2: bifma.org/public/e3interps.html

EXEMPLARY PERFORMANCE

Option 1. Purchase at least 95% of materials for facility alterations and additions that meet the credit requirements.

Option 2. Not available.

Option 3. Not available.

DEFINITIONS

assembly a product formulated from multiple materials (e.g., concrete) or a product made up of subcomponents (e.g., a workstation)

base building materials and products that make up the building or are permanently and semi-permanently installed in the project (e.g., flooring, casework, wall coverings)

bio-based material commercial or industrial products (other than food or feed) that are composed in whole, or in significant part, of biological products, renewable agricultural materials (including plant, animal, and marine materials), or forestry materials. For the purposes of LEED, this excludes leather and other animal hides.

building exterior a structure's primary and secondary weatherproofing system, including waterproofing membranes and air- and water-resistant barrier materials, and all building elements outside that system

building interior everything inside a structure's weatherproofing membrane

extended producer responsibility measures undertaken by the maker of a product to accept its own and sometimes other manufacturers' products as postconsumer waste at the end of the products' useful life. Producers recover and recycle the materials for use in new products of the same type. To count toward credit compliance, a program must be widely available. For carpet, extended producer responsibility must be consistent with NSF/ANSI 140–2007. Also known as closed-loop program or product take-back.

furniture and furnishings the stand-alone furniture items purchased for the project, including individual and group seating; open-plan and private-office workstations; desks and tables; storage units, credenzas, bookshelves, filing cabinets, and other case goods; wall-mounted visual-display products (e.g., marker boards and tack boards, excluding electronic displays); and miscellaneous items, such as easels, mobile carts, freestanding screens, installed fabrics, and movable partitions. Hospitality furniture is included as applicable to the project. Office accessories, such as desktop blotters, trays, tape dispensers, waste baskets, and all electrical items, such as lighting and small appliances, are excluded.

homogeneous material an item that consists of only one material throughout or a combination of multiple materials that cannot be mechanically disjointed, excluding surface coatings

postconsumer recycled content waste generated by households or commercial, industrial and institutional facilities in their role as end users of a product that can no longer be used for its intended purpose

preconsumer recycled content matter diverted from the waste stream during the manufacturing process, determined as the percentage of material, by weight. Examples include planer shavings, sawdust, bagasse, walnut shells, culls, trimmed materials, overissue publications, and obsolete inventories. The designation excludes rework, regrind, or scrap materials capable of being reclaimed within the same process that generated them (ISO 14021). Formerly known as postindustrial content.

recycled content defined in accordance with the International Organization of Standards document ISO 14021, Environmental labels and declarations, Self-declared environmental claims (Type II environmental labeling)

salvaged material a construction component recovered from existing buildings or construction sites and reused. Common salvaged materials include structural beams and posts, flooring, doors, cabinetry, brick, and decorative items.

wood plant-based materials that are eligible for certification under the Forest Stewardship Council. Examples include bamboo and palm (monocots) as well as hardwoods (angiosperms) and softwoods (gymnosperms)

MATERIALS AND RESOURCES CREDIT

Solid Waste Management—Ongoing

This credit applies to:

Existing Buildings (2 points)
Schools (2 points)
Retail (2 points)
Data Centers (2 points)
Hospitality (2 points)
Warehouses and Distribution Centers (2 points)

INTENT

To reduce the waste that is generated by building occupants and hauled to and disposed of in landfills and incinerators.

REQUIREMENTS

EXISTING BUILDINGS, SCHOOLS, RETAIL, DATA CENTERS, HOSPITALITY, WAREHOUSES AND DISTRIBUTION CENTERS

ESTABLISHMENT E

None.

PERFORMANCE P

Maintain a waste reduction and recycling program that reuses, recycles, or composts the following:

- at least 50% of the ongoing waste as specified in Materials and Resources Prerequisite: Ongoing Purchasing and Waste Policy (by weight or volume); and
- at least 75% of the durable goods waste as specified in Materials and Resources Prerequisite: Ongoing Purchasing and Waste Policy (by weight, volume or replacement value).

In addition, safely dispose of the following:

- all discarded batteries; and
- all mercury-containing lamps.

SCHOOLS ONLY

K–12 schools may exclude food waste from the final performance calculations of the total building waste stream by meeting both of the following requirements.

- Provide documentation that food waste composting services are not available in the region or are not economically feasible, based on the school or district's operational budget for solid waste management.
- During the performance period, implement an awareness program that encourages occupants to reduce food waste. Compliant programs should include at least two of the following:
  1. signage in food service and cafeteria areas;
  2. food service employee training on reducing waste in food preparation and selecting menu options to reduce the potential for food waste; and
  3. extracurricular activities or student organizations that promote awareness of the environmental benefits associated with composting food waste.

BEHIND THE INTENT

A significant amount of solid waste is generated through daily operations of buildings. Environmentally preferred management strategies include source reduction, recycling, composting, and reuse, all of which reduce the volume of waste transported to landfills and incinerators. The reprocessing of used materials into new goods avoids the harms associated with raw material extraction and manufacturing and supports regional recycling and reuse facilities. Effective solid waste management may also reduce waste disposal fees and expenditures on new materials.

Waste management programs are often highly visible, and effective materials management can give occupants and tenants an important signal of the building owner's overall commitment to sustainability.

STEP-BY-STEP GUIDANCE

STEP 1. IMPLEMENT WASTE MANAGEMENT POLICY FOR ONGOING CONSUMABLES P

For ongoing consumables, implement the solid waste management programs and strategies developed for MR Prerequisite Ongoing Purchasing and Waste Policy.

- Divert ongoing consumables waste from landfills and incinerators through reuse, recycling, and composting. Measure this waste by either weight or volume, as determined for the related prerequisite, and use this unit of measurement consistently throughout credit calculations.
- Provide safe collection, safe and secure storage, and proper disposal through qualified channels for batteries and mercury-containing lamps (see *Further Explanation, Waste Diversion Best Practices*).
- K–12 schools projects may exclude food waste from the calculations if they meet the additional requirements listed in the credit requirements (see *Further Explanation, Rating System Variations*).

STEP 2. IMPLEMENT WASTE MANAGEMENT POLICY FOR DURABLE GOODS P

For durable goods, implement the solid waste management programs and strategies developed for MR Prerequisite Ongoing Purchasing and Waste Policy.

- Divert durable goods waste from landfills and incinerators through reuse and recycling. Measure this waste by weight, volume, or replacement value and use this unit of measurement consistently throughout credit calculations.
- Durable goods must be defined consistently throughout the MR credits.
- Exclude furniture and furnishings, which are covered under MR Credit Solid Waste Management—Facility Maintenance and Renovations.
- If no durable goods are purchased during the performance period, provide an explanation.

STEP 3. DEVELOP TRACKING SYSTEM P

Continuous tracking during the performance period is highly recommended for managing ongoing consumables and durable goods waste.

- Track material quantities in the same unit (weight, volume, or for durable goods only, replacement value) consistently over the performance period. If different units are used for different products or materials, use an appropriate conversion factor to convert all ongoing consumables to a common metric and all durable goods to a common metric.
- Find out whether any tenants contract with waste haulers that recycle material separately from the building's recycling program. Data from specialty vendors may improve the project's overall diversion performance (see *Further Explanation, Specialty Waste Haulers*).
- Work with waste haulers to ensure that they provide the right information to demonstrate compliance with the credit requirements. If haulers may not be willing or able to provide the necessary information, develop alternative tracking procedures and tools (see *Further Explanation, Strategies for Tracking Waste* and *Example Waste Management Tracking Form*).

STEP 4. VERIFY ADEQUATE WASTE DIVERSION DURING PERFORMANCE PERIOD P

Collect data on the total amounts of waste disposed of and diverted over the performance period, for both ongoing consumables and durable goods.

- Data must represent the entire performance period. Teams may not extrapolate data from portions of the performance period.
- Collect data for how waste leaves the site, consistent with the building's collection categories. For example, if glass, plastic, and metal are commingled and sorted off-site, report the commingled quantity; amounts for each material need not be isolated.
- Do not include furniture, furnishings, or construction waste from facility maintenance and renovation activities; these materials are tracked under MR Credit Solid Waste Management—Facility Maintenance and Renovations.
- Consider requesting haul reports on a regular basis (e.g., monthly) rather than gathering all documentation when the performance period ends. This strategy can help teams identify areas to improve diversion, gauge the effect of new waste management programs, and quickly remedy any deficiencies.

STEP 5. DETERMINE PERCENTAGE OF ONGOING CONSUMABLES WASTE DIVERSION P

Use Equation 1 to determine whether the project is diverting the required percentage of consumables waste from incinerators or landfills.

EQUATION 1. Ongoing consumables performance

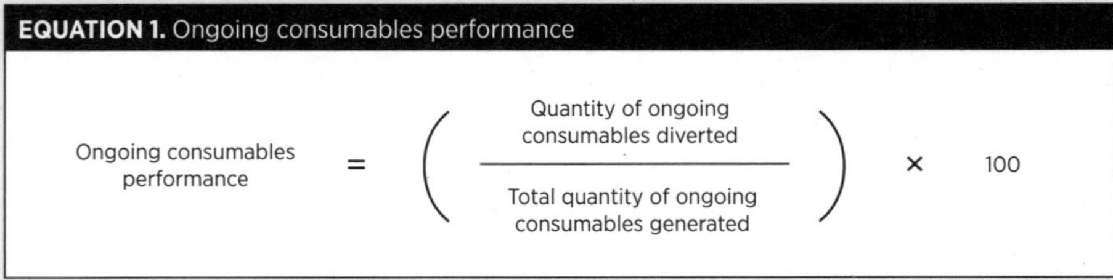

STEP 6. DETERMINE PERCENTAGE OF DURABLE GOODS WASTE DIVERSION P

Use Equation 2 to determine whether the project is diverting the required percentage of durable goods waste from incinerators or landfills.

EQUATION 2. Durable goods performance

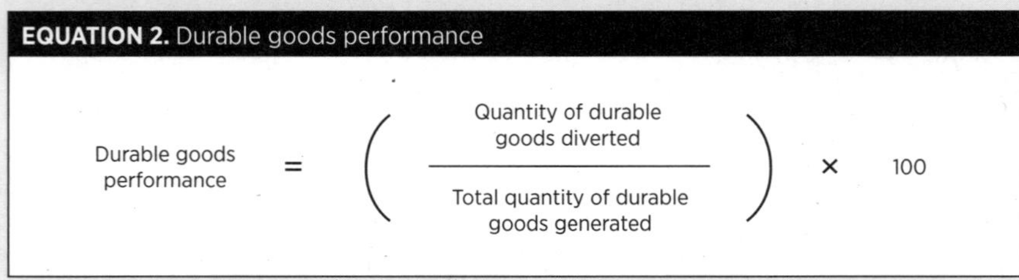

FURTHER EXPLANATION

CALCULATIONS

See calculations in *Step-by-Step Guidance*.

WASTE DIVERSION BEST PRACTICES

Consider implementing the following best practices for safe disposal of hazardous items and effective recycling and reuse of other products and materials.

Ongoing Consumables

- Periodically check recycling bins for convenience and capacity.
- Communicate with building occupants about preferred waste disposal practices. Using clear, concise, and consistent messaging can improve diversion. Consider including recycling procedures in orientation materials for new hires.
- Educate cleaning staff on proper waste collection practices and provide the tools required for collection. Coordinate training with waste haulers and cleaning vendors so that everyone involved understands the waste management policy.
- Consider source reduction opportunities, such as providing reusable items like coffee mugs and working with vendors to reduce packaging waste. This is particularly important for materials that are not easily recycled, reused, or composted.

Durable Goods

- Develop procedures for separating durable goods from ongoing consumables waste. Communicate the policy to tenants.
- Set aside adequate space for storing used durable goods before they are collected for recycling or reuse.
- Establish programs that facilitate reuse of items in the building and encourage tenants to participate.
- Research local diversion opportunities (e.g., local organizations or charities that accept used durable goods, recyclers that specialize in durable goods) and share the list with tenants.

Batteries

- Review state and local laws that govern disposal and recycling of batteries in the project's location. Ensure compliance with the laws, and include the legal requirements in communications with tenants.
- Provide clearly labeled battery collection bins in high-visibility areas, such as near mailboxes or in the lobby. In multitenant buildings, encourage each tenant to provide its own collection bin to make battery recycling convenient.
- Regularly remind tenants of the building's battery recycling policy and provide clear instruction on how to properly recycle this waste. Communication strategies might include email reminders, signage in the lobby, or notices on lobby television screens.
- Identify a qualified, licensed recycler that will recycle batteries in accordance with state and federal requirements.

Mercury-Containing Lamps

- Warn tenants about handling used lamps. Generally, only people who have been trained in managing universal waste should handle and dispose of mercury-containing lamps.
- Establish procedures for handling broken lamps and managing the clean-up. Provide all employees charged with handling lamps with adequate training.
- Designate a dry and secure space for storing used lamps before they are collected for recycling. Prevent cracking or breaking. Do not use tape or rubber bands to hold bulbs together. Label and seal boxes containing used lamps.
- Identify a qualified, licensed recycler that will recycle lamps in accordance with state and federal requirements. Mercury-containing lamps are considered hazardous waste, and the project is liable for improper disposal by third parties. Some lighting vendors offer a recycling service at little or no additional cost. Recycle used lamps within one year of collection.
- Refer to the U.S. Environmental Protection Agency's guidelines for establishing recycling programs for mercury-containing light bulbs, at epa.gov/.

SPECIALTY WASTE HAULERS

Tenants that do not participate in the project building's solid waste management program are expected to report data for inclusion in the credit calculations. If this waste cannot be tracked because of confidentiality, hazard, processing, or other issues, provide an explanation.

Many tenants contract for shredding of sensitive documents, and typically the shredded material is recycled. Work with tenants to gather tracking information, or exclude recycled shredded paper from the credit calculations.

Despite the extra time and effort required, including tenants' data in the calculations can increase the project's overall diversion rate. The extent of the increase depends on the quantity of material recycled by tenants' haulers compared with the building's regular recycling program.

STRATEGIES FOR TRACKING WASTE

If waste haulers cannot provide the data required to document this credit, the team may count waste containers just before collection and record quantities in units of volume. Though acceptable, this approach can produce highly inaccurate measurements, especially for containers less than full.

If the team must use this approach, consider strategies for improving consistency and accuracy. For example, drawing lines inside bins at 25%, 50%, and 75% full makes it easier to determine the volume. Give staff good instructions for assessing and recording waste quantities.

When writing new hauling contracts, consider specifying reporting requirements (by time intervals and units of weight or volume).

EXAMPLES

A spreadsheet can be used to regularly track waste data provided by waste haulers or collected by the building (Table 1).

TABLE 1. Example waste management tracking form

Waste Management Tracking Form	
Building Name	ABC Building
Performance period	June 1, 2013–August 31, 2013

Instructions
Use this form to track waste disposal quantities over the performance period. Revise each column heading to include the material type and appropriate units for each material. All quantities must be converted to the same unit to produce an accurate diversion rate. Create additional columns as necessary to include all material types generated during the performance.

Performance Period Waste																	
			Landfill Trash		Cardboard		Paper		Commissioned Recyclables		Batteries		Durable Goods		Light Bulbs	
Month	Diversion Method	Hauler/ Destination	Quantity	Units	Quantity	Units	Quantity	Units	Quantity	Units	Quantity	Units	Quantity	Units	Quantity	Units
Example - June 2013	Commingled Recycling	StarHauler			5.30	Tons	7.80	Tons	2.20	Tons	0.04	Tons				
Example - June 2013	Landfill	StarHauler	15.02	Tons												
Example - June 2013	Recycling	LitesOut													2.85	Tons

Total Waste Material Disposed	**33.21**
Material Diverted	**18.19**
Diversion Rate	**54.77%**

RATING SYSTEM VARIATIONS

Schools

Schools may exclude food waste from the final performance period calculations if composting services are not available or economically feasible. For the project to claim this exemption, an awareness program must be in place during the performance period that encourages building occupants to reduce food waste. The awareness program must include at least two of the three following components:

- Signage in food service and cafeteria areas
- Food service employee training on menu selection strategies and food preparation techniques that reduce food waste.
- Extracurricular activities that promote awareness of the environmental benefits of composting and reducing food waste.

INTERNATIONAL TIPS

If the project's area has little or no recycling infrastructure and tracking is difficult, consider achieving the credit through material reuse or donation strategies.

CAMPUS

Group Approach

All buildings in the group may be documented as one.

Campus Approach

Ineligible. Each LEED project may pursue the credit individually.

REQUIRED DOCUMENTATION

	Documentation	All projects	Schools
P	Quantity of ongoing consumables waste both produced and diverted	X	X
P	Quantity of durable goods waste both produced and diverted	X	X
P	Narratives describing safe storage and disposal of batteries and mercury-containing lamps	X	X
P	Documentation that composting of food waste is not available or economically feasible		X

RELATED CREDIT TIPS

MR Prerequisite Ongoing Purchasing and Waste Policy. Project teams may demonstrate compliance with the Performance requirements of the related prerequisite by achieving this credit.

MR Credit Purchasing—Ongoing. Reducing purchases of landfill-bound ongoing consumables will contribute to the waste reduction levels required for this credit. support achievement of the related credit.

CHANGES FROM LEED 2009

- This credit combines two LEED 2009 credits: MR Credit Solid Waste Management—Ongoing Consumables and MR Credit Solid Waste Management—Durable Goods.
- Furniture and furnishings are excluded from this credit and now covered under MR Credit Solid Waste Management—Facility Maintenance and Renovations.
- The threshold for battery recycling has been raised from 80% to 100%.
- A requirement for 100% recycling of mercury-containing lamps has been added.

REFERENCED STANDARDS

None.

EXEMPLARY PERFORMANCE

Divert 75% of ongoing consumables and 100% of durable goods from landfills and incinerators.

DEFINITIONS

durable goods products with a useful life of approximately two or more years and that are replaced infrequently. Examples include furniture, office equipment, appliances, external power adapters, televisions, and audiovisual equipment.

durable goods waste stream the flow of long-lasting products from the project building after they are fully depreciated and have reached the end of their useful life for normal business operations. It includes leased durable goods returned to their owner but does not include durable goods that remain functional and are moved to another floor or building.

ongoing consumable a product that has a low cost per unit and is regularly used and replaced in the course of business. Examples include paper, toner cartridges, binders, batteries, and desk accessories. Also known as ongoing purchases.

MATERIALS AND RESOURCES CREDIT

Solid Waste Management—Facility Maintenance and Renovation

This credit applies to:

Existing Buildings (2 points)
Schools (2 points)
Retail (2 points)
Data Centers (2 points)
Hospitality (2 points)
Warehouses and Distribution Centers (2 points)

INTENT

To divert construction, renovation, and demolition debris from disposal in landfills and incinerators and recover and recycle reusable materials.

REQUIREMENTS

EXISTING BUILDINGS, SCHOOLS, RETAIL, DATA CENTERS, HOSPITALITY, WAREHOUSES AND DISTRIBUTION CENTERS

ESTABLISHMENT E

None.

PERFORMANCE P

Divert at least 70% of the waste (by weight or volume) generated by facility maintenance and renovation activities from disposal in landfills and incinerators. Include base building elements as specified in the Materials and Resources prerequisite: Facility Maintenance and Renovation Policy.

Exclude furniture and furnishings that pose human health concerns (e.g., mold) as well as components not considered base building elements; mechanical, electrical, and plumbing components; and specialty items, such as elevators.

BEHIND THE INTENT

Commercial construction generates an average of 3.9 pounds of waste per square foot (19 kilograms of waste per square meter) of building area, most of which can be recycled.[1] The U.S. Environmental Protection Agency estimates that in 2003, construction and demolition debris amounted to 170 million tons (154.2 million tonnes). The European Commission estimates that the European Union member nations generate 510 million metric tonnes of construction waste annually.[2]

Recycling of construction and demolition waste reduces demand for virgin resources and the environmental and health burdens associated with resource extraction, processing, and transportation. Recycling this waste also encourages the development of regional recycling industries by making recycled content available for building products. Effective solid waste management practices can extend the lifetime of existing landfills and reduce the demand for new or larger landfills, which in turn reduces groundwater contamination, encroachment on green space, and air pollution.

This credit builds on the requirements established in MR Prerequisite Facility Maintenance and Renovations Policy.

STEP-BY-STEP GUIDANCE

STEP 1. IMPLEMENT FACILITY MAINTENANCE AND RENOVATIONS SOLID WASTE MANAGEMENT POLICY P

Implement the facility maintenance and renovations (FMR) solid waste management policy developed in the corresponding prerequisite. As maintenance and renovation projects are scheduled, sharing the policy with prospective contractors and other personnel involved in the work is recommended to ensure that all parties understand the criteria and optimize waste diversion.

STEP 2. FOR RENOVATION ACTIVITIES, ADJUST POLICY AS NEEDED P

The policy developed in the prerequisite covers maintenance activities as well as a general plan for renovations; however, because renovations may involve different materials, scopes of work, and project teams, use the plan as a guideline and adapt it to fit the requirements of each activity scheduled to occur during the performance period.

- Distinguish between ongoing or frequent projects that are typically completed by in-house staff and larger projects that involve outside contractors.
- Waste management policies for frequent projects should be documented and followed on an ongoing basis.
- For larger projects, develop tailored strategies and procedures to ensure that practices align with the type of work and the capabilities of those performing it.
- Project teams may use both on-site and commingled waste diversion, depending on which is more appropriate for each material (see *Further Explanation, Identifying a Waste Hauler*).
- Train workers, including subcontractors, in recycling protocols. A brief orientation with each trade as its phase of work begins can be an effective approach.
- Consider a quality control program to document that FMR waste is sorted properly and not leaving the project without being monitored.

STEP 3. SET UP TRACKING SYSTEM P

Develop a tracking system to gather data on all FMR waste during the performance period.

- Track material by either weight or volume and use this unit of measurement consistently throughout credit calculations.
- If different units are used for different products or materials, use an appropriate conversion factor to convert all waste to a common metric. Determine whether any tenants have scheduled maintenance and renovations during the performance period. Waste generated and diverted from tenant FMR must also be tracked.

1. *Monroe, Linda. "Diverting Construction Waste". Buildings Magazine. March 01 2008. Online. Accessed October 2013. buildings.com/tabid/3334/ArticleID/5758/Default.aspx*
2. *European Commission. "The Story Behind the Strategy: EU Waste Policy" ec.europa.eu/environment/waste/pdf/story_book.pdf*

- Work with waste haulers to ensure that they provide the right information to demonstrate compliance with the credit requirements.

STEP 4. VERIFY ADEQUATE WASTE DIVERSION DURING PERFORMANCE PERIOD P

Collect data on the total amounts of waste disposed of and diverted over the performance period, using Equation 1.

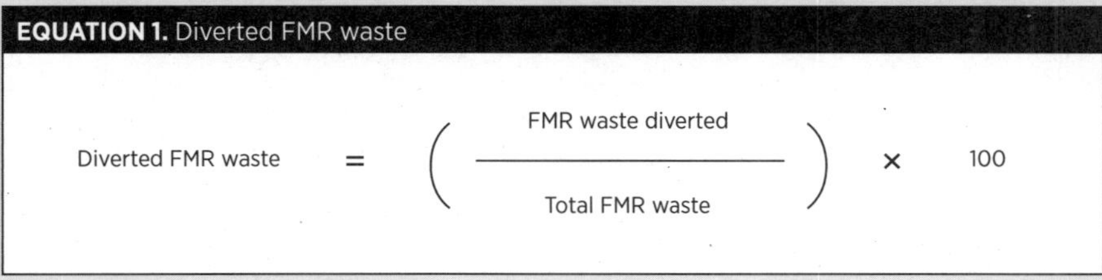

EQUATION 1. Diverted FMR waste

$$\text{Diverted FMR waste} = \left(\frac{\text{FMR waste diverted}}{\text{Total FMR waste}} \right) \times 100$$

- Data must represent the entire performance period. Do not extrapolate from portions of the performance period.
- Collect data for how waste leaves the site, consistent with the building's collection categories. For example, if glass, plastic, and metal are commingled and sorted off-site, report the commingled quantity; amounts for each material need not be isolated (see *Further Explanation, Example 1*).
- Do not include waste from ongoing consumption activities; these products and materials are tracked under MR Credit Solid Waste Management—Ongoing.
- Exclude furniture and furnishings that pose human health concerns (e.g., mold); mechanical, electrical, and plumbing components; and specialty items (e.g., elevators).
- Consider requesting haul reports on a regular basis (e.g., monthly) rather than gathering data when the performance period ends. This may help identify areas to improve diversion, gauge the effect of new waste management programs, and quickly remedy any deficiencies.

FURTHER EXPLANATION

CALCULATIONS

See calculations in *Step-by-Step Guidance*.

IDENTIFYING A WASTE HAULER

Work with the waste hauler and contractor to determine whether separating materials on-site or sending commingled waste to a recycling facility is more appropriate for the project or particular materials. The choice may be project-specific and depends on such variables as types and amounts of waste generated, local and regional markets for recyclables, on-site space, and the capability of recycling haulers and handlers.

If materials are sorted on-site, plan the locations of separate waste containers, label all containers to prevent cross-contamination, and determine where haulers will take the waste.

If materials are commingled, ask the waste hauler about their subsequent sorting, recycling, and reuse.

Identify waste haulers who are experienced with diversion. Questions to ask might include the following:

- What is the typical diversion rate for the hauler's other buildings?
- How does the hauler track waste and recycling—by weight or by volume?
- What recommendations can the hauler offer for improving diversion rates during facility maintenance and renovations?
- Can the hauler provide training for construction contractors?

EXAMPLE

Example 1. FMR solid waste calculation

The renovation project team separated steel waste on-site. Gypsum board, carpet, and wood were commingled and sorted off-site, and the hauler then reported the amounts to the project team. Table 1 is the project's documentation for tracking waste. The team must achieve a diversion rate of 70% or better. At 93.5%, the project earns the credit but does not demonstrate exemplary performance (95% or better).

TABLE 1. Example FMR solid waste tracking

Material	Diverted?	Hauler	Amount (lbs.)	Diverted (lbs.)
Gypsum wallboard	Reuse	ABC	1,000	1,000
Carpet	No	Standard	200	0
Steel	Recycle	ABC	1,000	1,000
Wood	Reuse	ABC	900	900
Total FAA waste		**3,100**	**2,900**	
Percentage diverted		**93.5%**		
Exemplary performance		**No**		

CAMPUS

Group Approach

All buildings in the group may be documented as one.

Campus Approach

Ineligible. Each LEED project may pursue the credit individually.

REQUIRED DOCUMENTATION

	Documentation	All projects
P	Solid waste management plan for each renovation during performance period	X
P	Total waste generated and waste diverted for FMR activities during performance period	X
P	Description of hazardous materials excluded from credit calculations	X

RELATED CREDIT TIPS

MR Prerequisite Facility Maintenance and Renovations Policy. Waste management for facility maintenance and renovations should be completed according to the policy outlined in the related prerequisite. A well-designed FMR policy will help with credit achievement.

MR Credit Purchasing—Facility Maintenance and Renovations. Purchasing products and materials that can be reused or recycled reduces the amount of materials sent to landfills and incinerators and makes it easier to achieve this credit. Source reduction can also reduce end waste and therefore help achieve this credit.

CHANGES FROM LEED 2009

- Minimum number of trades defining the scope of credit has been removed.
- Furniture is now included in the credit.

REFERENCED STANDARDS

None.

EXEMPLARY PERFORMANCE

Divert at least 95% of FMR waste from landfills and incinerators.

DEFINITIONS

base building materials and products that make up the building or are permanently and semi-permanently installed in the project (e.g., flooring, casework, wall coverings)

commingled waste building waste streams that are combined on the project site and hauled away for sorting into recyclable streams. Also known as single-stream recycling.

enclosure the exterior plus semi-exterior portions of the building. Exterior consists of the elements of a building that separate conditioned spaces from the outside (i.e., the wall assembly). Semiexterior consists of the elements of a building that separate conditioned space from unconditioned space or that encloses semi-heated space through which thermal energy may be transferred to or from the exterior or conditioned or unconditioned spaces (e.g., attic, crawl space, basement).

furniture and furnishings the stand-alone furniture items purchased for the project, including individual and group seating; open-plan and private-office workstations; desks and tables; storage units, credenzas, bookshelves, filing cabinets, and other case goods; wall-mounted visual-display products (e.g., marker boards and tack boards, excluding electronic displays); and miscellaneous items, such as easels, mobile carts, freestanding screens, installed fabrics, and movable partitions. Hospitality furniture is included as applicable to the project. Office accessories, such as desktop blotters, trays, tape dispensers, waste baskets, and all electrical items, such as lighting and small appliances, are excluded.

structure elements carrying either vertical or horizontal loads (e.g., walls, roofs, and floors) that are considered structurally sound and nonhazardous

waste diversion a management activity that disposes of waste through methods other than incineration or landfilling. Examples include reuse and recycling.

Indoor Environmental Quality (EQ)

OVERVIEW

The Indoor Environmental Quality (EQ) category rewards decisions made by project teams about indoor air quality, thermal and visual comfort, and occupants' satisfaction. Green buildings with good indoor environmental quality protect the health and comfort of building occupants. High-quality indoor environments also enhance productivity, decrease absenteeism, improve the building's value, and reduce liability for building designers and owners.[1]

The relationship between the indoor environment and the health and comfort of building occupants is complex and still not fully understood. Local customs and expectations, occupants' activities, and the building's site, design, and construction are just a few of the variables that make it difficult to quantify and measure the direct effect of a building on its occupants.[2] The EQ section encourages project teams to develop policies and programs based on proven methods that prioritize the health and comfort of the building occupants and to measure performance with well-established indicators.

Ventilation has a large effect on the health and well-being of a building's occupants. Existing buildings' HVAC systems may have fallen out of calibration or were never designed to provide adequate amounts of outside air for diluting contaminants. The EQ section focuses on optimizing existing HVAC systems and minimizing sources of contaminants, such as cleaning products and laser printers. (Emissions from products used in renovations, maintenance work, and furniture are addressed in the Materials and Resources credit category.) The EQ category also encourages building owners to determine priorities for improving the indoor environment by surveying occupants.

1. *U.S. Environmental Protection Agency, Health Buildings Healthy People: A Vision for the 21st Century, epa.gov/iaq/pubs/hbhp.html (October 2001) (accessed July 25, 2013).*
2. *Mitchell, Clifford S., Junfeng Zhang, Torben Sigsgaard, Matti Jantunen, Palu J. Lioy, Robert Samson, and Meryl H. Karol, Current State of the Science: Health Effects and Indoor Environmental Quality, Environmental Health Perspectives 115(6) (June 2007).*

CROSS-CUTTING ISSUES

FLOOR AREA CALCULATIONS AND FLOOR PLANS

For many of the credits in the EQ category, compliance is based on the percentage of floor area that meets the credit requirements. In general, floor areas and space categorization should be consistent across EQ credits. Any excluded spaces or discrepancies in floor area values should be explained and highlighted in the documentation. See *Space Categorization*, below, for additional information on which floor area should be included in which credits.

SPACE CATEGORIZATION

The EQ category focuses on the interaction between the occupants of the building and the indoor spaces in which they spend their time. For this reason, it is important to identify which spaces are used by the occupants, including any visitors (transients), and what activities they perform in each space. Depending on the space categorization, the credit requirements may or may not apply (Table 1).

Occupied versus unoccupied space

All spaces in a building must be categorized as either occupied or unoccupied. Occupied spaces are enclosed areas intended for human activities. Unoccupied spaces are places intended primarily for other purposes; they are occupied only occasionally and for short periods of time—in other words, they are inactive areas.

Examples of spaces that are typically unoccupied include the following:

- Mechanical and electrical rooms
- Egress stairway or dedicated emergency exit corridor
- Closets in a residence (but a walk-in closet is occupied)
- Data center floor area, including a raised floor area
- Inactive storage area in a warehouse or distribution center

For areas with equipment retrieval, the space is unoccupied only if the retrieval is occasional.

Regularly versus nonregularly occupied spaces

Occupied spaces are further classified as regularly occupied or nonregularly occupied, based on the duration of the occupancy. Regularly occupied spaces are enclosed areas where people normally spend time, defined as more than one hour of continuous occupancy per person per day, on average; the occupants may be seated or standing as they work, study, or perform other activities. For spaces that are not used daily, the classification should be based on the time a typical occupant spends in the space when it is in use. For example, a computer workstation may be largely vacant throughout the month, but when it is occupied, a worker spends one to five hours there. It would then be considered regularly occupied because that length of time is sufficient to affect the person's well-being, and he or she would have an expectation of thermal comfort and control over the environment.

Occupied spaces that do not meet the definition of regularly occupied are nonregularly occupied; these are areas that people pass through or areas used an average of less than one hour per person per day.

Examples of regularly occupied spaces include the following:

- Airplane hangar
- Auditorium
- Auto service bay
- Bank teller station
- Conference room
- Correctional facility cell or day room
- Data center network operations center
- Data center security operations center
- Dorm room
- Exhibition hall
- Facilities staff office
- Facilities staff workstation
- Food service facility dining area
- Food service facility kitchen area
- Gymnasium
- Hospital autopsy and morgue
- Hospital critical-care area
- Hospital dialysis and infusion area
- Hospital exam room
- Hospital operating room
- Hospital patient room
- Hospital recovery area
- Hospital staff room
- Hospital surgical suite
- Hospital waiting room
- Hospital diagnostic and treatment area
- Hospital laboratory
- Hospital nursing station
- Hospital solarium
- Hospital waiting room
- Hotel front desk
- Hotel guest room
- Hotel housekeeping area
- Hotel lobby
- Information desk
- Meeting room
- Natatorium
- Open-office workstation
- Private office
- Reception desk
- Residential bedroom
- Residential dining room
- Residential kitchen
- Residential living room
- Residential office, den, workroom
- Retail merchandise area and associated circulation
- Retail sales transaction area
- School classroom
- School media center
- School student activity room
- School study hall
- Shipping and receiving office
- Study carrel
- Warehouse materials-handling area

Examples of nonregularly occupied spaces include the following:

- Break room
- Circulation space
- Copy room
- Corridor
- Fire station apparatus bay
- Hospital linen area
- Hospital medical record area
- Hospital patient room bathroom
- Hospital short-term charting space
- Hospital prep and cleanup area in surgical suite
- Interrogation room
- Lobby (except hotel lobby)*
- Locker room
- Residential bathroom
- Residential laundry area
- Residential walk-in closet
- Restroom
- Retail fitting area
- Retail stock room
- Shooting range
- Stairway

** Hotel lobbies are considered regularly occupied because people often congregate, work on laptops, and spend more time there than they do in an office building lobby.*

Occupied space subcategories

Occupied spaces, or portions of an occupied space, are further categorized as individual or shared multioccupant, based on the number of occupants and their activities. An individual occupant space is an area where someone performs distinct tasks. A shared multioccupant space is a place of congregation or a place where people pursue overlapping or collaborative tasks. Occupied spaces that are not regularly occupied or not used for distinct or collaborative tasks are neither individual occupant nor shared multioccupant spaces.

Examples of individual occupant spaces include the following:

- Bank teller station
- Correctional facility cell or day room
- Data center staff workstation
- Hospital nursing station
- Hospital patient room
- Hotel guest room
- Medical office
- Military barracks with personal workspaces
- Open-office workstation
- Private office
- Reception desk
- Residential bedroom
- Study carrel

Examples of shared multioccupant spaces include the following:

- Active warehouse and storage
- Airplane hangar
- Auditorium
- Auto service bay
- Conference room
- Correctional facility cell or day room
- Data center network operations center
- Data center security operations center
- Exhibition hall
- Facilities staff office
- Food service facility dining area
- Food service facility kitchen area
- Gymnasium
- Hospital autopsy and morgue
- Hospital critical-care area
- Hospital dialysis and infusion area
- Hospital exam room
- Hospital operating room
- Hospital surgical suite
- Hospital waiting room
- Hospital diagnostic and treatment area
- Hospital laboratory
- Hospital solarium
- Hotel front desk
- Hotel housekeeping area
- Hotel lobby
- Meeting room
- Natatorium
- Retail merchandise area and associated circulation
- Retail sales transaction area
- School classroom
- School media center
- School student activity room
- School study hall
- Shipping and receiving office
- Warehouse materials-handling area

Occupied spaces can also be classified as densely or nondensely occupied, based on the concentration of occupants in the space. A densely occupied space has a design occupant density of 25 people or more per 1,000 square feet (93 square meters), or 40 square feet (3.7 square meters) or less per person. Occupied spaces with a lower density are nondensely occupied.

Table 1 outlines the relationship between the EQ credits and the space categorization terms. If the credit is listed, the space must meet the requirements of the credit.

TABLE 1. Space types in EQ credits

Space category	Prerequisite or credit
Occupied space	• Minimum Indoor Air Quality Performance, ventilation rate procedure and natural ventilation procedure • Enhanced Indoor Air Quality Strategies, Option 2, Filtration (Existing Buildings, Schools, Retail, Hospitality, Warehouses & Distribution Centers) • Thermal Comfort, design requirements (Existing Buildings, Schools, Retail, Hospitality, Warehouses & Distribution Centers)
Regularly occupied space	• Enhanced Indoor Air Quality Strategies, Option 2, Filtration (Data Centers) • Thermal Comfort, design requirements (Data Centers) • Interior Lighting, Option 2, strategy A • Interior Lighting, Option 2, strategy D • Interior Lighting, Option 2, strategy E • Interior Lighting, Option 2, strategy G • Interior Lighting, Option 2, strategy H • Daylight and Quality Views
Individual occupant space	• Interior Lighting, Option 1
Shared multioccupant space	• Interior Lighting, Option 1
Densely occupied space	• Enhanced Indoor Air Quality Strategies, Option 2 Carbon Dioxide Monitors

Table 2 outlines the relationship between the EQ credits and the space categorization terms specific to each rating system (see *Definitions*). Unless otherwise stated, if the credit is listed, the space must meet the requirements of the credit.

TABLE 2. Rating system–specific space classifications		
Rating system	**Space type**	**Prerequisite or credit**
Hospitality	Guest rooms	• Thermal Comfort, control requirements* • Interior Lighting*
Warehouses and Distribution Centers	Office areas	• Daylight and Quality Views, Option 2
Warehouses and Distribution Centers	Areas of bulk storage, sorting, and distribution	• Daylight and Quality Views, Option 2

*Hotel guest rooms are excluded from the credit requirements.

The following credits are not affected by space classifications:

- Environmental Tobacco Smoke Control
- Green Cleaning Policy
- Indoor Air Quality Management Program
- Enhanced Indoor Air Quality Strategies, Option 1
- Enhanced Indoor Air Quality Strategies, Option 2, Outdoor Air Monitoring for Mechanically Ventilated Spaces
- Enhanced Indoor Air Quality Strategies, Option 2 Outdoor Air Monitoring for Naturally Ventilated Spaces
- Enhanced Indoor Air Quality Strategies, Option 2, Alarmed Openings for Naturally Ventilated Spaces
- Interior Lighting, Option 2, Lighting Quality, strategy B
- Interior Lighting, Option 2, Lighting Quality, strategy C
- Interior Lighting, Option 2, Lighting Quality, strategy F
- Green Cleaning—Custodial Effectiveness Assessment
- Green Cleaning—Products and Materials
- Green Cleaning—Equipment
- Integrated Pest Management
- Occupant Comfort Survey

TRICKY SPACES

Pay extra attention to how the following types of spaces are classified in specific credits.

Residential

- Minimum Indoor Air Quality Performance and Environmental Tobacco Smoke have specific requirements and considerations for residential projects.
- See the *Project Type Variations* sections in Interior Lighting for guidance on providing appropriate controllability in residential buildings.

Auditoriums

- Exceptions to Daylight and Quality Views are permitted. See the *Project Type Variations* sections in Daylight and Quality Views.

Gymnasiums

- See the *Project Type Variations* section in Thermal Comfort for guidance on dealing with high levels of physical activity.
- An exception to the views requirements in Daylight and Quality Views is permitted. See the *Project Type Variations* section in Daylight and Quality Views.

Transportation Terminals

- For Interior Lighting, Option 1, Lighting Control, most of the areas in a transportation terminal can be considered shared multioccupant. Most areas in transportation terminals are also regularly occupied.

Dormitories and Military Barracks

- These spaces fall in-between a work space and residence.
- Dorm rooms or military barracks with personal workspaces are considered individual occupant spaces. Military barracks without personal workspaces are considered shared multioccupant.

Industrial Facilities

- For Interior Lighting, Option 1, Lighting Control, most of the active warehouse and storage areas are considered multioccupant.
- Most areas in industrial facilities are also regularly occupied.

INDOOR ENVIRONMENTAL QUALITY PREREQUISITE

Minimum Indoor Air Quality Performance

This prerequisite applies to:

Existing Buildings
Schools
Retail
Data Centers
Hospitality
Warehouses and Distribution Centers

INTENT

To contribute to the comfort and well-being of building occupants by establishing minimum standards for indoor air quality (IAQ).

REQUIREMENTS

ESTABLISHMENT E

Each air-handling unit in the building must comply with either Case 1 or Case 2. If some air-handling units can provide the outdoor airflow required by Case 1 and others cannot, those that can must do so.

Mechanically Ventilated Spaces

For mechanically ventilated spaces (and for mixed-mode systems when the mechanical ventilation is activated), chose one of the following:

Case 1. Systems Able to Meet Required Outdoor Airflow Rates

OPTION 1. ASHRAE STANDARD 62.1-2010

Modify or maintain each outdoor air intake, supply air fan, and ventilation distribution system to meet the outdoor air intake flow rates, using the ASHRAE ventilation rate procedure or a local equivalent, whichever is more stringent and meet the minimum requirements of ASHRAE Standard 62.1–2010, Sections 4–7, Ventilation for Acceptable Indoor Air Quality (with errata), or a local equivalent, whichever is more stringent.

OPTION 2. CEN STANDARDS EN 15251–2007 AND EN 13779–2007

Projects outside the U.S. may instead meet the minimum outdoor air requirements of Annex B of Comité Européen de Normalisation (CEN) Standard EN 15251–2007, Indoor environmental input parameters for design and assessment of energy performance of buildings addressing indoor air quality, thermal environment, lighting and acoustics; and meet the requirements of CEN Standard EN 13779–2007, Ventilation for nonresidential buildings, Performance requirements for ventilation and room conditioning systems, excluding Section 7.3, Thermal environment; 7.6, Acoustic environment; A.16; and A.17.

Case 2. Systems Unable to Meet Required Outdoor Airflow Rates

If meeting the outdoor airflow rates in Case 1 is not feasible because of the physical constraints of the existing ventilation system, complete an engineering assessment of the system's maximum outdoor air delivery rate. Supply the maximum possible to reach the minimum setpoint in Case 1 and not less than 10 cubic feet per minute (5 liters per second) of outdoor air per person.

Naturally Ventilated Spaces

For naturally ventilated spaces (and for mixed-mode systems when the mechanical ventilation is inactivated), determine the minimum outdoor air opening and space configuration requirements using the natural ventilation procedure from ASHRAE Standard 62.1–2010 or a local equivalent, whichever is more stringent. Confirm that natural ventilation is an effective strategy for the project by following the flow diagram in the Chartered Institution of Building Services Engineers (CIBSE) Applications Manual AM10, March 2005, Natural Ventilation in Nondomestic Buildings, Figure 2.8 and meet the requirements of ASHRAE Standard 62.1–2010, Section 4, or a local equivalent, whichever is more stringent.

All Spaces

The indoor air quality procedure defined in ASHRAE Standard 62.1–2010 may not be used to comply with this prerequisite.

PERFORMANCE P

Show compliance through measurements taken at the system level within five years of the end of the performance period.

Implement and maintain an HVAC system maintenance program, based on ASHRAE 62.1–2010, Section 8, or a local equivalent, whichever is more stringent, to ensure the proper operations and maintenance of HVAC components as they relate to outdoor air introduction and exhaust.

BEHIND THE INTENT

By diluting pollutants created by a building's occupants and other contaminant sources, ventilation with outdoor air contributes to the occupants' comfort and well-being. The exact connections between ventilation rates and occupants' health are still being researched, but a multidisciplinary scientific review of the current state of knowledge shows some strong associations[1]. Maintaining good indoor air quality (IAQ) depends on controlling pollutant sources, removing contaminants from outdoor air, and supplying at least some fresh air, among other factors.

The standards referenced in this prerequisite outline up-to-date, well-tested methods for determining the amount of outdoor air each type of space requires. These standards were chosen because they strike a balance between providing fresh air and maintaining energy efficiency.

STEP-BY-STEP GUIDANCE

STEP 1. EVALUATE OUTDOOR AIR QUALITY E

Investigate local outdoor air quality at the project location. If pursuing Option 1 for mechanically ventilated spaces, or using naturally ventilated spaces, follow ASHRAE 62.1–2010, Section 4, or a local equivalent, whichever is more stringent. If pursuing Option 2 for mechanically ventilated spaces see Comité Européen de Normalisation (CEN) Standard EN 13779–2007, Section 6.2.3, Outdoor Air.

STEP 2. IDENTIFY PROJECT'S VENTILATION STRATEGY E

Determine whether the building includes mechanical, natural, and/or mixed-mode ventilation systems.

- **Mechanical ventilation.** The project's HVAC systems provide the outdoor air.
- **Natural ventilation.** Outdoor air is provided through operable windows or other openings in the building envelope.
- **Mixed-mode ventilation.** The building has both natural ventilation and mechanical ventilation, or the ventilation strategy changes seasonally.

STEP 3. CATEGORIZE SPACES E

Create a table that appropriately summarizes the occupied rooms, spaces, or zones in the project (see *Further Explanation, Occupied versus Occupiable*).

Enter the following information:

- Net occupiable space, as defined in ASHRAE Standard 62.1–2010, page 4, or room floor area if using CEN Standard 15251.
- Occupancy category, as listed in ASHRAE Standard 62.1–2010, Table 6.1 or CEN Standard 15251, Table B.2.
- If applicable, identify whether the building is very low polluting, low polluting, or non low polluting (see CEN Standard 15251, Annex C).
- Track the occupancy rate before the performance period. Include visitors in the occupancy count. See *Getting Started, Occupancy* and *Variable Occupancy*. It may be appropriate to group rooms or spaces into ventilation zones (see *Further Explanation, Types of Mechanical Ventilation Systems*).

STEP 4. IDENTIFY APPROPRIATE PREREQUISITE REQUIREMENTS E

Follow the steps below for mechanical ventilation or natural ventilation, depending on the ventilation strategy used in each space.

For mixed-mode systems, projects must comply with mechanical ventilation requirements when the mechanical system is active, and natural ventilation requirements when the mechanical ventilation system is inactive.

1. *Sundell, Jan, Hal Levin, and Davor Novosel, Ventilation Rates and Health: Report of an Interdisciplinary Review of the Scientific Literature (National Center for Energy Management and Building Technologies Task 06-01, September 2006), ncembt.org/downloads/Sundell%20J_VentilationRatesAndHealthReportOfAnInterdisciplinaryReviewOfTheScientificLiterature_NCEMBT-070914.pdf (accessed June 10, 2013).*

Mechanically Ventilated Spaces (and Mixed-Mode Spaces When Mechanical Ventilation Is Active)

STEP 1. IDENTIFY RESPONSIBLE PARTY E

Determine whether outside professional assistance is needed to perform calculations, take airflow measurements, and document the process used. The calculations and measurements require considerable engineering knowledge, judgment, and estimations. For buildings with building automation systems (BAS) that monitor outdoor airflow, the facility's operating engineer may have the appropriate expertise, but if not, outside assistance will be needed. Most project teams need to contract with testing and balancing technicians for this prerequisite.

STEP 2. DETERMINE HVAC SYSTEM CONFIGURATION(S) E

Use as-built drawings, BAS data, and/or field investigations to understand the HVAC system.

- Locate all air-handling units (AHUs), rooftop units (RTUs), and ventilation fans that supply ventilation to occupied spaces. Determine the total supply air for each piece of equipment handling outdoor air and whether the outdoor air supply is fixed or adjustable. If the equipment has variable airflow, also identify the minimum supply flow.
- Determine whether the equipment operates in cooling-only mode or both heating and cooling modes.
- Determine the system type: single-zone, 100% outdoor air, or multiple-zone (see *Further Explanation, Types of Mechanical Ventilation Systems*). If the project has multiple systems, determine which spaces or ventilation zones are served by each system.
- Determine how air is distributed to individual zones—that is, whether the system has variable air volume (VAV) or constant volume (CV). Identify the locations of supply diffusers and return grilles in each space: underfloor, overhead, or sidewall.
- For multiple-zone systems, if as-built mechanical drawings and schedules or BAS data are unavailable, determine the supply air flow to each potentially critical zone (for a detailed discussion of identifying critical zones, see ASHRAE Standard 62.1–2010, Appendix A–A3.1, Selecting Zones for Calculation, and ASHRAE 62.1–2010 User's Manual, Example 6-L). Evaluate the system for all variables required for the ventilation rate procedure calculation (see *Further Explanation, Calculations for Multiple-Zone Recirculating Systems*).

STEP 3. MEET MINIMUM REQUIREMENTS E

Ensure that the project meets the minimum requirements of the selected referenced standard.

Option 1. ASHRAE Standard 62.1–2010

- Confirm compliance with Sections 4 through 7.
- Indicate whether the project is in a nonattainment area for fine particulate matter (PM2.5), and if so, confirm that filters with minimum efficiency reporting values (MERV) of 11 or higher have been installed.
- Indicate whether the project is in an area where ozone exceeds the most recent three-year average, annual fourth-highest daily maximum eight-hour average ozone concentration of 0.107 ppm, and if so, confirm that the project has air-cleaning devices for ozone.
- If using a local code instead of ASHRAE 62.1–2010, see *Further Explanation, Local Equivalent to ASHRAE 62.1–2010.*

Option 2. CEN Standard EN 13779–2007

- Confirm compliance with all sections except Section 7.3 (Thermal Environment), 7.6 (Acoustic Environment), A.16, and A.17.

STEP 4. CALCULATE REQUIRED OUTDOOR AIRFLOW UNDER OPTION 1 E

Complete the ventilation rate procedure in ASHRAE Standard 62.1–2010, Section 6.2, for each ventilation system identified in Step 2 to determine the minimum amount of outdoor air that must be supplied. Account for all occupied spaces in the ventilation rate procedure calculation(s).

- Perform ventilation rate procedure calculations for worst-case conditions, which typically occur in the heating mode when supply airflows are lowest or supply air temperature is highest. From Table 6-2 of the standard, select the zone air distribution effectiveness (E_z) value that corresponds to the air distribution configuration of the worst-case conditions. E_z is typically less than 1.0 when the system is in heating mode. If E_z is greater than 1.0, see EA Prerequisite Minimum Energy Performance, *Further Explanation, Common Issues with Energy Modeling, Ventilation (zone air distribution effectiveness).*

- As applicable, evaluate and document assumptions for all variables required for the ventilation rate procedure calculation. These variables include the percentage of total design airflow rate at condition analyzed (Ds), the primary air fraction of supply air at condition analyzed (Ep), the system ventilation efficiency (Ev), and the fraction of local recirculated air that is representative of system return air (Er).
- For special conditions that apply to systems designed to respond to varying operating conditions, such as with demand-controlled ventilation, see *Further Explanation, Considerations for Variable Operating Conditions.*

Ensure that the appropriate method is selected for each system in the project. The ventilation rate procedure calculation differs for single-zone, 100% outdoor air, and multiple-zone systems. Suggested methods are as follows:

- For single-zone systems or 100% outdoor air systems, use the calculator provided by USGBC or a user-generated spreadsheet. The 62MZCalc spreadsheet is not applicable to these systems and should not be used to perform the ventilation calculations.
- For multiple-zone systems, use the 62MZCalc spreadsheet. This includes VAV and CV systems in which one or more air handlers supply a mixture of outdoor air and recirculated air to more than one ventilation zone (see *Further Explanation, Calculations for Multiple-Zone Recirculating Systems*).

Energy modeling software may also be used to perform ventilation rate procedure calculations for all three system types. Direct outputs from the programs are acceptable, provided they include sufficient information about the values used for all variables in the calculation.

If the local code is more stringent than ASHRAE 62.1–2010, see *Further Explanation, Local Equivalent to ASHRAE 62.1–2010.*

ALTERNATIVE STEP 4. CALCULATE REQUIRED OUTDOOR AIRFLOW UNDER OPTION 2 E

Complete the calculations outlined in CEN Standard 15251–2007, Annex B, for each ventilation system identified in Step 2 to determine the minimum amount of outdoor air that must be supplied. Account for all occupied spaces in the calculation(s).

STEP 5. MEASURE OUTDOOR AIRFLOW RATES P

During the performance period, measure outdoor airflow rate for each ventilation system (see *Further Explanation, Outdoor Air Measurement Procedures*).

As a best practice, consider taking measurements in accordance with ASHRAE Standard 111–2008, Measurement, Testing, Adjusting, and Balancing of Building HVAC Systems.

Project teams may be able to exclude ventilation systems or perform a sampling of tests to reduce the number of measurements required (see *Further Explanation, Testing Exceptions*).

STEP 6. EVALUATE COMPLIANCE AND MAKE ADJUSTMENTS IF NECESSARY E P

For each ventilation system, compare measured outdoor airflow rates with the required outdoor airflow rates previously calculated.

If a system does not provide sufficient outdoor air, adjust the unit control or minimum damper settings, improve the functionality of components by cleaning ducts, grilles or other components, or make repairs and address other maintenance items as necessary. Then repeat the outdoor airflow measurement to confirm that the minimum outdoor airflow requirements are met.

If the system is physically incapable of meeting the minimum outdoor airflow requirement even after adjustments have been made, Case 2 of the rating system applies.

- Complete an engineering assessment that clearly identifies the maximum amount of outdoor air the system can deliver and the constraints that prevent any increase.
- Provide the maximum amount of outdoor air possible while maintaining indoor conditions as specified in the building operating plan. At least 10 cubic feet per minute (5 liters per second) of outdoor air per person must be supplied.

Prepare a summary report of measured ventilation rates provided by each system.

STEP 7. IMPLEMENT MAINTENANCE PROGRAM P

Develop a maintenance plan that complies with ASHRAE 62.1–2010, Section 8, or a local equivalent. Section 8 lists required maintenance activities and minimum frequency of maintenance for ventilation components, such as filters, outdoor air dampers and actuators, drain pans, outdoor air louvers, and sensors.

The maintenance plan for ventilation systems is typically satisfied through the preventive maintenance plan required under EA Prerequisite Energy Efficiency Best Management Practices.

The maintenance plan must include the following information:

- Maintenance requirements and frequencies for each ventilation system component
- Ventilation system testing

Naturally Ventilated Spaces (and Mixed-Mode Systems When Mechanical Ventilation Is Inactivated)

STEP 1. CONFIRM NATURAL VENTILATION EFFECTIVENESS E

Use Chartered Institution of Building Services Engineers (CIBSE) Applications Manual AM10, Natural Ventilation in Non-Domestic Buildings, Figure 2.8 (flow chart), to demonstrate that natural ventilation strategies in the building are appropriate. Retain a copy of the flow chart path for the project.

STEP 2. IDENTIFY CEILING HEIGHTS AND NATURAL VENTILATION OPENINGS E

Collect the following information for each naturally ventilated space and add to the table of rooms and spaces:

- Minimum ceiling height in the space
- Location of natural ventilation openings (on one side, two opposite sides, or two adjacent sides)
- Size of the natural ventilation openings (openable area)

STEP 3. PERFORM NATURAL VENTILATION PROCEDURE E

Complete the natural ventilation procedure in ASHRAE 62.1–2010, Section 6.4, for each space to determine the size of openings required and the maximum distance from the openings that can be considered naturally ventilated.

STEP 4. EVALUATE COMPLIANCE AND MAKE ADJUSTMENTS IF NECESSARY E P

For each space, compare the calculation results with the information collected in Step 2.

ASHRAE 62.1–2010, Section 6.5. Conduct this assessment early in the project timeline, since capital- or time-intensive improvements may be needed to bring the building into compliance with the natural ventilation requirements. If the upgrades required to comply with the natural ventilation requirements are not feasible, project teams may be able to achieve the prerequisite through mechanical ventilation (see Step 4 under Mechanically Ventilated Spaces).

If the project includes an engineered natural ventilation system approved by the authority having jurisdiction, the requirements of Section 6.4 do not apply (see *Further Explanation, Authority Having Jurisdiction Exception*).

STEP 5. CONFIRM MECHANICAL SYSTEM EXCEPTION OR COMPLIANCE E P

Ensure that the ventilation system complies with the requirements for mechanical ventilation.

ASHRAE Standard 62.1–2010 requires mechanical ventilation systems in addition to natural ventilation unless specific exceptions are met (see *Further Explanation, Natural Ventilation Exceptions*). If the project qualifies for exception to the mechanical ventilation requirement in ASHRAE 62.1–2010, Section 6.4, prepare a narrative to explain the qualifications.

If the project does not qualify for exception, follow the step-by-step instructions for mechanical ventilation systems to demonstrate compliance with ASHRAE 62.1–2010 when mechanical ventilation is operational.

STEP 6. IMPLEMENT MAINTENANCE PROGRAM P

Develop a maintenance plan that complies with ASHRAE 62.1–2010, Section 8, or a local equivalent (see *Step 7* under Mechanically Ventilated Spaces).

FURTHER EXPLANATION

CALCULATIONS

For mechanical ventilation, Option 1, see ASHRAE 62.1–2010, Section 6.2, and ASHRAE 62.1–2010 User's Manual, Chapter 6.2. Refer to ASHRAE Journal articles[2] for additional information on the calculations.

For mechanical ventilation, Option 2, see CEN Standards EN 15251–2007 and EN 13779–2007.

For natural ventilation, see ASHRAE 62.1–2010, Section 6.4, and ASHRAE 62.1–2010 User's Manual, Chapter 6.4.

NATURAL VENTILATION EXCEPTIONS

ASHRAE Standard 62.1–2010, Section 6.4, requires naturally ventilated spaces to include a mechanical ventilation system unless one of the following exceptions applies:

- Ventilation openings comply with Section 6.4 and are permanently open.
- Ventilation openings comply with Section 6.4 and have controls that prevent them from being closed during times of expected occupancy.
- The naturally ventilated zone is not served by heating or cooling equipment.
- The system is an engineered natural ventilation system approved by the authority having jurisdiction (see *Further Explanation, Authority Having Jurisdiction Exception*).

TYPES OF MECHANICAL VENTILATION SYSTEMS

ASHRAE 62.1–2010 defines a ventilation zone as any area with similar occupancy categories, occupant density, zone air distribution effectiveness, and zone primary airflow per unit area. This differs from the definition of a thermal zone.

There are three main types of mechanical ventilation systems.

Single-zone system

This system delivers a mixture of outdoor air and recirculated air to only one ventilation zone. For example, a single rooftop unit that provides ventilation and conditioned air to three separate offices may be considered a single-zone system, provided the offices are similar, as defined above.

Alternatively, a single rooftop unit that provides ventilation and conditioned air to an office and a conference room would not be considered a single-zone system, since these two spaces differ in occupancy category and occupant density, even though the unit itself is often considered "single-zone" because it only has one thermal zone. In this case, the unit must be analyzed using the method for multiple-zone recirculating systems.

A separate ventilation rate procedure calculation must be made for each single-zone system serving the building.

100% outdoor air system

This type of system delivers only outdoor air directly to one or more ventilation zones. The ventilation air cannot contain any recirculated air. For example, an energy recovery unit that provides 100% outdoor ventilation air to each space via a separate distribution system and mixes this air with air from only the same zone would be considered a 100% outdoor air system.

Alternatively, an energy recovery unit that provides 100% outdoor ventilation air to zone-level fan coil units that mix outdoor air with return air from other ventilation zones before delivering it to the space would not be considered a 100% outdoor air system. In this case, each fan coil unit must be analyzed as either a single-zone or a multiple-zone recirculating system.

A separate ventilation rate procedure calculation must be made for each 100% outdoor air system serving the building.

2. *Stanke, Dennis, "Single-Zone and Dedicated-OA Systems," ASHRAE Journal (October 2004); "Single-Path Multiple-Zone System Design," ASHRAE Journal (January 2005); "Designing Dual-Path Multiple-Zone Systems," ASHRAE Journal (May 2005).*

Multiple-zone recirculating system
This type of system delivers a mixture of outdoor air and recirculated air to more than one ventilation zone. Typical examples include a constant volume rooftop unit that serves more than one ventilation zone or a VAV system that serves an entire building.

A separate ventilation rate procedure calculation must be made for each multiple-zone recirculating system serving the building (see *Further Explanation, Calculations for Multiple-Zone Recirculating Systems*).

CALCULATIONS FOR MULTIPLE-ZONE RECIRCULATING SYSTEMS

Because of the complexity of the calculations for multiple-zone recirculating systems, project teams must use the 62MZCalc spreadsheet or energy modeling software to perform the ventilation rate procedure calculations and determine the amount of outdoor air required at the system level.

System ventilation efficiency
Multiple-zone system calculations need to account for the inefficiency that occurs when the zones have different ratios of outdoor ventilation air to supply the air required for thermal conditioning. The calculations account for this through system ventilation efficiency (E_v) and by determining the critical zone.

The critical zone is the zone with the highest proportion of required outdoor air to provided supply air. Critical zones are often densely occupied spaces, such as conference rooms. When all zones are entered into the 62MZCalc spreadsheet, the critical zone for the system is determined automatically.

For large projects, it may not be feasible to enter each individual zone into the 62MZCalc spreadsheet. In these cases, the mechanical engineer can determine the outdoor air required for the system simply by identifying the potentially critical zone(s). For a detailed discussion of identifying critical zones, see ASHRAE Standard 62.1–2010, Appendix A–A3.1, Selecting Zones for Calculation, and ASHRAE 62.1–2010 User's Manual, Example 6-L.

Diversity factor
Alternatively, the multiple-zone system calculations may include a diversity factor to account for the movement of occupants between spaces, per ASHRAE Standard 62.1–2010, Section 6.2.5.3.1. For example, in a school, it is reasonable to assume that not all rooms are occupied simultaneously, because students and staff would not be in a classroom if they are eating lunch in the cafeteria. In this case, diversity can be applied, provided the classroom and cafeteria are served by the same ventilation system.

Diversity may not be applied to either single-zone or 100% outdoor air systems. If applying diversity, all calculations and assumptions must be included with the documentation.

If preliminary calculations indicate that a multiple-zone system does not comply with ASHRAE 62.1–2010 outdoor air requirements, consider the following before increasing outdoor air at the air-handling unit(s):

- Increase the amount of supply air (e.g., zone primary airflow, Vpz) to the critical zone. This has the effect of decreasing the primary outdoor air fraction, Zpz, which will increase system efficiency and reduce the total amount of outdoor air required.
- For systems with VAV terminal units, increase the minimum terminal unit flow rate setting for the critical zone. This has the same effect described above.

CONSIDERATIONS FOR VARIABLE OPERATING CONDITIONS

ASHRAE 62.1–2010 permits ventilation systems to reflect or respond to changes in zone occupancy in two ways, time-average population and dynamic reset. These two strategies cannot be applied simultaneously, however.

Time-average population. In spaces where peak occupancy occurs over only a short period, a time-average design population may be used, per ASHRAE 62.1–2010, Section 6.2.6.2 (see ASHRAE 62.1–2010 User's Manual, Examples 6-W, 6-X, 6-Y, 6-Z, and 6-AA). Project teams must include all calculations and assumptions used when submitting the ventilation rate procedure calculations for time-average population.

Dynamic reset. The system varies the flow of outdoor air as operating conditions change, thereby reducing the amount of energy needed to condition outdoor air. Demand-controlled ventilation is one of the most common reset strategies. Refer to ASHRAE 62.1–2010, Section 6.2.7, for dynamic reset requirements, some of which include the following:

- A minimum level of outdoor, based on the area outdoor air rate, must be provided to each ventilation zone at all times when dynamic reset is implemented. Refer to the ASHRAE standard's Section 6.2.7.1.2.
- The ventilation system must be controlled to provide the required amount of outdoor air in each zone, based on current occupancy. For a multiple-zone recirculating system, a single CO_2 sensor mounted in the return duct does not meet the requirements of ASHRAE 62.1–2010, since it does not guarantee that the appropriate amount of outdoor air will be provided to the critical zones. Refer to ASHRAE 62.1–2010 User's Manual, Appendix A, and the *ASHRAE Journal*[3] for demand-controlled ventilation approaches for multiple-zone systems and for CO_2 setpoint calculations.

LOCAL EQUIVALENT TO ASHRAE STANDARD 62.1–2010

If local code is more stringent than ASHRAE 62.1–2010, use the local code.

For mechanically ventilated spaces, prepare the following documentation:

- A detailed summary comparing the two standards' requirements
- A comparison demonstrating that outdoor air requirements established by the local code for occupants and for floor area are at least as stringent as the ASHRAE standard
- Evidence that the local code incorporates the zone- and system-level efficiency of the ventilation systems in an equivalent or more stringent way than the ASHRAE ventilation rate procedure

For naturally ventilated spaces, prepare the following documentation:

- A detailed summary comparing the two standards' requirements for fenestration opening area, distance from window, and ceiling height
- A description of the engineered ventilation modeling approach, and documentation of approval by the local code authority

AUTHORITY HAVING JURISDICTION EXCEPTION

In some situations, compliance with this prerequisite is acceptable through an authority having jurisdiction exception. With this exception, the local code authority (the authority having jurisdiction) approves the plans and specifications used for the building's engineered natural ventilation approach. There are three possible situations for this exception: (1) the local code is ASHRAE Standard 62.1–2010, (2) the ventilation code governing the project is any code other than ASHRAE Standard 62.1–2010, and (3) USGBC is serving as the authority having jurisdiction for the purposes of LEED certification.

If USGBC is the authority having jurisdiction, a ventilation strategy that meets the intent of ASHRAE 62.1–2010 but does not meet the requirements of the ventilation rate procedure may be approved. It is highly recommended that project teams contact USGBC for approval of the engineered natural ventilation approach as early as possible, rather than waiting until the system has been fully designed.

If the local code is ASHRAE Standard 62.1–2010, provide the following documentation:

- Evidence that ASHRAE Standard 62.1–2010 (or a later version) is required for local building code compliance
- A description of the engineered ventilation modeling approach
- Documentation of plan approval by the local code authority

If the ventilation code governing the project is other than ASHRAE Standard 62.1–2010, provide the following:

- Evidence that the alternate code is at least as stringent as ASHRAE 62.1–2010 in its entirety (see *Further Explanation, Local Equivalent to ASHRAE Standard 62.1–2010*).
- A description of the engineered ventilation modeling approach
- Documentation of plan approval by the local code authority

3. *Stanke, Dennis, "Dynamic Reset for Multiple-Zone Systems," ASHRAE Journal* (March 2010).

If USGBC is serving as the authority having jurisdiction for the purposes of LEED certification, provide the following:

- A description of the engineered ventilation modeling approach
- Drawings and calculations or airflow analyses
- Evidence that the project's engineered natural ventilation system meets the intent of ASHRAE 62.1–2010. This documentation must clearly identify how the project does not meet the standard's natural ventilation requirements, and how the ventilation design has been engineered to meet the intent of the standard.

OCCUPIED VERSUS OCCUPIABLE

ASHRAE Standard 62.1–2010 requires occupiable spaces to be ventilated. For consistency with other LEED credits, this prerequisite uses the term occupied. Spaces classified as occupiable per Standard 62 are considered occupied for the purposes of LEED certification (see *Definitions*).

OUTDOOR AIR MEASUREMENT PROCEDURES

Measurements must be taken under worst-case operating conditions. Building systems may need to be adjusted to mimic these conditions if measurements are not performed during the worst-case operating condition.

For systems with an accessible ducted outdoor air connection, measure outdoor airflow directly, with a pilot tube or other device in the duct.

For systems without an accessible ducted connection, an alternative is to measure the temperature of outdoor air that enters the mixing plenum, the temperature of return air to the plenum, and the temperature of mixed outdoor and return air (before the air has reached any heating or cooling coils). Use the three temperatures to calculate the percentage of outdoor air being introduced to the building. This technique is appropriate only under certain conditions. Refer to ASHRAE Standard 111–2008, Measurement, Testing, Adjusting, and Balancing of Building HVAC Systems, to identify the most appropriate testing technique for the building ventilation system.

For projects in which a dedicated outdoor air supply fan supplies outdoor air to multiple air-handling units, the outdoor air should be measured at the individual air-handling units rather than at the dedicated outdoor supply fan.

TESTING EXCEPTIONS

Project teams may be able to exclude some ventilation systems from testing under any of the following three conditions.

- Systems replaced or tested and found compliant with ASHRAE 62.1–2010 within two years before the establishment period begins do not need to be retested during the performance period. Submit a letter from the building management confirming that the occupancy and function of the space served by each system have not changed since the test. Provide BAS data confirming that the minimum outdoor air setpoints are no less than the setpoints established when the systems were last tested or installed.
- Systems that have undergone outdoor air testing as part of a test and balance completed within two years before the establishment period begins do not need to be retested during the performance period, provided the measured outdoor air quantity was taken at worst-case conditions and meets ASHRAE 62.1–2010 minimum requirements. Submit test and balance results showing minimum outdoor air quantities at worst-case conditions. Sampling these systems (see below) is permitted.
- ASHRAE 62.1–2010 calculations and outdoor air testing are not required for systems slated for replacement. Submit documentation showing that the systems have already been procured, will be installed within one year after the performance period begins, will comply with ASHRAE 62.1–2010, and will be tested to verify the outdoor air rates. Confirm that the existing system is configured to supply the maximum possible amount of outdoor air and no less than 10 cfm per person of outdoor air.

Sampling of outdoor airflow measurements is permissible under the following conditions.

- All ventilation systems in a sample group must have similar parameters. Submit documentation identifying the following for each system:
  - Constant volume or variable air volume

- Single-zone or multizone
- Occupancy per unit floor area for area served by the system
- Primary space function served by the system
- BAS data for minimum outdoor air setpoints

- At least three ventilation systems from the sample group must be sampled.
- At least 10% of the ventilation systems in the sample group must be sampled.

If any sampled system fails to meet the minimum requirements based on ASHRAE 62.1–2010 calculations and outdoor air testing, proceed as follows, adjust the system and retest to determine compliance. Then perform the calculations and conduct testing for three additional systems from the representative group.

If any of the additional three tested systems fail to meet the requirements, complete ASHRAE 62.1–2010 calculations and outdoor air testing for all systems in the representative group.

EXAMPLES

For mechanical ventilation, see ASHRAE 62.1–2010 User's Manual, Examples 6-F through 6-V.

For natural ventilation, see ASHRAE 62.1–2010 User's Manual, Examples 6-AC through 6-AF.

CAMPUS

Group Approach
Submit separate documentation for each building.

Campus Approach
Ineligible. Each LEED project must pursue the prerequisite individually.

REQUIRED DOCUMENTATION

	Documentation	Case 1, Options 1, 2	Case 2	Naturally ventilated	Mixed -mode
E	Confirmation that project meets minimum requirements of ASHRAE 62.1-2010, Sections 4–7 or CEN Standard 13779–2007	X	X		X
E	Confirmation that project has MERV 11 or higher filters (if project is in nonattainment area for PM2.5)	X	X		X
E	Confirmation that the project is in a non-attainment area for ozone (if applicable)	X	X		X
E	Ventilation rate procedure or CEN calculations and documentation of assumptions for calculation variables	X	X		X
P	Measured outdoor airflow rates and description of method or protocol used to take measurements	X	X		X
P	Engineering assessment of system's maximum outdoor air delivery rate, as applicable		X		X (if using Case 2)
E	Confirmation that project meets minimum requirements of ASHRAE Standard 62.1–2010, Section 7, and exhaust ventilation requirements of Section 6.5			X	X
E	Documentation of CIBSE flow diagram process for project			X	X
E	Natural ventilation procedure calculations and ventilation opening information			X	X
E	Any natural ventilation exception from mechanical ventilation system (ASHRAE 62.1–2010, Section 6.4)			X	
E	Any exception from authority having jurisdiction			X	X
P	Ventilation maintenance program	X	X	X	X

RELATED CREDIT TIPS

EA Prerequisite Minimum Energy Performance. Outdoor air can increase heating and cooling loads. Dynamic reset, such as demand-controlled ventilation, can offset the additional energy required.

EQ Credit Indoor Air Quality Management Program. The management and maintenance program developed for the related credit will help achieve an effective ventilation system that delivers clean, fresh air to occupied spaces.

CHANGES FROM LEED 2009

- ASHRAE Standard 62.1 has been updated to version 2010 from version 2007.
- The prerequisite now requires compliance with the minimum requirements of ASHRAE Standard 62.1–2010, Sections 4–7 (for mechanically ventilated spaces, Option 1); the requirements of CEN Standard EN 13779–2007, Ventilation for nonresidential buildings, Performance requirements for ventilation and room conditioning systems, excluding Sections 7.3 (Thermal environment), 7.6 (Acoustic environment), A.16, and A.17 (for mechanically ventilated spaces, Option 2); or the minimum requirements of ASHRAE Standard 62.1–2010, Section 4 (for naturally ventilated spaces).
- ASHRAE 62.1–2010 natural ventilation calculations now consider window configuration and ceiling height.
- ASHRAE 62.1–2010 now requires supplementary mechanical ventilation systems for naturally ventilated spaces in some cases.

- Project teams are required to confirm the appropriate application of natural ventilation through CIBSE AM10, Figure 2.8 (flow chart).
- Projects outside the U.S. are now allowed to demonstrate achievement via CEN requirements (rather than ASHRAE 62.1–2010).
- The maintenance program must comply with the requirements of ASHRAE 62.1–2010, Section 8.

REFERENCED STANDARDS

ASHRAE 62.1–2010: ashrae.org

CEN Standard EN 15251–2007: cen.eu

CEN Standard EN 13779–2007: cen.eu

CIBSE Applications Manual AM10, March 2005: cibse.org

EXEMPLARY PERFORMANCE

Not available.

DEFINITIONS

occupiable space an enclosed space intended for human activities, excluding those spaces that are intended primarily for other purposes, such as storage rooms and equipment rooms, and that are occupied only occasionally and for short periods of time (ASHRAE 62.1–2010)

occupied space an enclosed space intended for human activities, excluding those spaces that are intended primarily for other purposes, such as storage rooms and equipment rooms, and that are only occupied occasionally and for short periods of time. Occupied spaces are further classified as regularly occupied or nonregularly occupied spaces based on the duration of the occupancy, individual or multioccupant based on the quantity of occupants, and densely or nondensely occupied spaces based on the concentration of occupants in the space.

unoccupied space an area designed for equipment, machinery, or storage rather than for human activities. An equipment area is considered unoccupied only if retrieval of equipment is occasional.

INDOOR ENVIRONMENTAL QUALITY PREREQUISITE

Environmental Tobacco Smoke Control

This prerequisite applies to:

Existing Buildings
Schools
Retail
Data Centers
Hospitality
Warehouses and Distribution Centers

INTENT

To prevent or minimize exposure of building occupants, indoor surfaces, and ventilation air distribution systems to environmental tobacco smoke.

REQUIREMENTS

EXISTING BUILDINGS, RETAIL, DATA CENTERS, HOSPITALITY, WAREHOUSES AND DISTRIBUTION CENTERS

ESTABLISHMENT E

Prohibit smoking in the building.

Prohibit smoking outside the building except in designated smoking areas located at least 25 feet (7.5 meters) from all entries, outdoor air intakes, and operable windows. Also prohibit smoking outside the property line in spaces used for business purposes.

If the requirement to prohibit smoking within 25 feet (7.5 meters) cannot be implemented because of code, provide documentation of these regulations.

Signage must be posted within 10 feet (3 meters) of all building entrances indicating the no-smoking policy.

RESIDENTIAL ONLY

OPTION 1. NO SMOKING

Meet the requirements above.

OR

OPTION 2. COMPARTMENTALIZATION OF SMOKING AREAS

Prohibit smoking in all common areas of the building. The prohibition must be communicated in building rental or lease agreements or condo or coop association covenants and restrictions. Make provisions for enforcement.

Prohibit smoking outside the building except in designated smoking areas located at least 25 feet (7.5 meters) from all entries, outdoor air intakes, and operable windows. The no-smoking policy also applies to spaces outside the property line used for business purposes.

If the requirement to prohibit smoking within 25 feet (7.5 meters) cannot be implemented because of code, provide documentation of these regulations.

Signage must be posted within 10 feet (3 meters) of all building entrances indicating the no-smoking policy.

Each unit must be compartmentalized to prevent excessive leakage between units:

- Weather-strip all exterior doors and operable windows in the residential units to minimize leakage from outdoors.
- Weather-strip all doors leading from residential units into common hallways.
- Minimize uncontrolled pathways for the transfer of smoke and other indoor air pollutants between residential units by sealing penetrations in the walls, ceilings, and floors and by sealing vertical chases (including utility chases, garbage chutes, mail drops, and elevator shafts) adjacent to the units.
- Demonstrate a maximum leakage of 0.50 cubic feet per minute per square foot (2.54 liters per second per square meter) at 50 Pa of enclosure (i.e., all surfaces enclosing the apartment, including exterior and party walls, floors, and ceilings) or establish a baseline for a future 30% improvement.

SCHOOLS

Prohibit smoking on site.

Signage must be posted at the property line indicating the no-smoking policy.

PERFORMANCE P

None.

RESIDENTIAL ONLY

Demonstrate on a regular basis (at least once every five years) a maximum leakage of 0.50 cubic feet per minute per square foot (2.54 liters per second per square meter) at 50 Pa of enclosure (i.e., all surfaces enclosing the apartment, including exterior and party walls, floors, and ceilings).

Projects that do not meet the leakage requirement may demonstrate a 30% improvement over the most recent baseline. The current measurement establishes the new baseline.

BEHIND THE INTENT

Tobacco use kills more than five million people worldwide every year.[1] Smoking also puts nonsmokers at risk by exposing them to environmental tobacco smoke (ETS), often called secondhand smoke. In 2006, nearly half of all nonsmoking Americans were regularly exposed to secondhand smoke.[2] ETS exposure at home or in the workplace increases nonsmokers' risk of developing lung cancer, heart disease, and other serious health problems.[3]

Prohibiting indoor smoking is the only way to fully eliminate the health risks associated with ETS.[4] For this reason, designated indoor smoking rooms are not allowed in LEED-certified buildings. Only residential projects are excepted, because of legal ownership issues. The prerequisite also prohibits smoking in outdoor areas used for business purposes. A business that uses a public sidewalk or courtyard for seating or kiosks still maintains control over those areas, even though they are typically outside the property boundary line. They are included under this prerequisite because the business owner still has control over the smoking policy in these areas.

Restricting the introduction of ETS into the building interior not only benefits human health, it also improves the longevity of building surfaces, air distribution systems, furniture, and furnishings when compared with those in buildings that allow smoking.[5]

STEP-BY-STEP GUIDANCE

STEP 1. DETERMINE SMOKE-FREE LOCATIONS E

Obtain confirmation from the owner that smoking is prohibited inside the building. Residential projects may allow smoking in specific units, with specific requirements for ensuring that those units are adequately isolated (see *Further Explanation, Project Type Variations*).

- Identify the location of building openings, including entries, outdoor air intakes, and operable windows. Identify the property line and the location of outdoor areas used for business purposes, both inside and outside the property line. Indicate these elements on a site plan, map, or sketch.
- Emergency exits do not qualify as building openings if the doors are alarmed, because alarmed doors will not be opened. Emergency exits without alarms qualify as building openings.

STEP 2. DESIGNATE LOCATIONS OF EXTERIOR SMOKING AREAS E

Determine whether the project has or will have designated outdoor smoking areas. Locate any area designated for smoking at least 25 feet (7.5 meters) from smoke-free areas, based on the information gathered in Step 1. The 25-foot (7.5-meter) distance is a straight-line calculation.

- Consider design strategies that may encourage people to use the designated smoking area, such as covered seating.
- Educate occupants on the smoking policy and encourage them to self-police. This is particularly important in retail situations.
- Ashtrays signal that smoking is allowed in a particular area. Be sure these are placed outside the 25-foot (7.5-meter) perimeter.

STEP 3. CONFIRM THAT SMOKING IS PROHIBITED IN NONDESIGNATED AREAS E

Provide confirmation from the owner that smoking outside designated areas is prohibited in any space used by the building for business purposes, even if the space falls outside the property line. Examples of spaces used for business purposes include sidewalk seating, kiosks, and courtyards.

1. *World Health Organization, WHO Report on the Global Tobacco Smoke Epidemic. (Geneva, Switzerland, 2009), who.int/tobacco/mpower/2009/gtcr_download/en/index.html (accessed June 10, 2013).*
2. *U.S. Department of Health and Human Services, The Health Consequences of Involuntary Exposure to Tobacco Smoke: A Report of the Surgeon General (Atlanta, Georgia, 2006), surgeongeneral.gov/library/reports/secondhandsmoke/report-index.html (accessed June 10, 2013).*
3. *Ibid.*
4. *Ibid.*
5. *Mudarri, D.H., The Costs and Benefits of Smoking Restrictions: An Assessment of the Smoke-Free Environment Act of 1993 (H.R.3434) (Washington, DC: Environmental Protection Agency, Office of Radiation and Indoor Air, Indoor Air Division, 1994), tobaccodocuments.org/landman/89268337-8360.html (accessed June 10, 2013).*

- Smoking must be prohibited in areas within 25 feet (7.5 meters) from building openings.
- If smoking cannot be prohibited for the full 25-foot (7.5-meter) distance because of code restrictions, provide documentation of the regulation (see *Further Explanation, Code Limitations and Restrictions*).
- Smoking in the prohibited area is not allowed, even when the 25-foot (7.5-meter) distance extends beyond the property line. The boundary of the space for business purposes, other than a building opening, indicates the end of a nonsmoking area (see *Further Explanation, Property Line Less Than 25 Feet from the Building*).

STEP 4. DETERMINE LOCATIONS OF "NO SMOKING" SIGNAGE E

Post signage within 10 feet (3 meters) of all building entrances indicating that smoking is not allowed.

- School projects must post signage at the property line adjacent to all pedestrian and vehicular entrances indicating the no-smoking policy for the school site.
- Language on the signage is up to the project team. Two examples of successful language include "No smoking allowed within 25 feet" and "Smoking is allowed in designated smoking areas only."
- It may be helpful to stripe sidewalks to show the no-smoking boundary.

Figure 1. Example of no smoking signage

FURTHER EXPLANATION

PROPERTY LINE LESS THAN 25 FEET (7.5 METERS) FROM THE BUILDING

Projects with a property line less than 25 feet (7.5 meters) from the building must consider space usage when determining the outdoor smoking policy. The no-smoking requirement still applies to spaces outside the property line used for business purposes. Public sidewalks are not considered used for business purposes, but smoking must still be prohibited on sidewalks within 25 feet (7.5 meters) of openings. Building staff should be educated about this policy so that they can direct smokers to designated smoking areas and away from entrances or windows.

Examples of common business activities that would require the smoking prohibition include outdoor seating, outdoor stadium areas, courtyards, and banking kiosks.

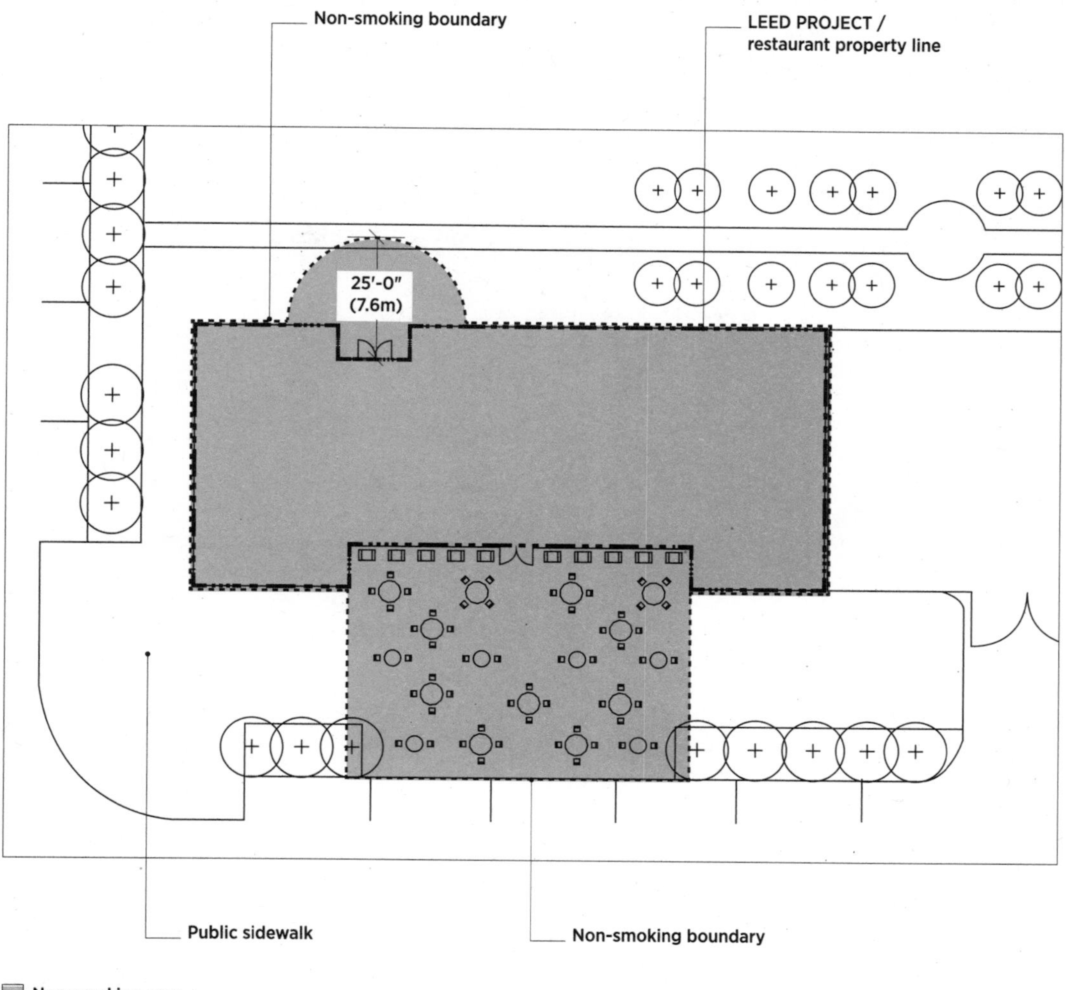

Figure 2. Example site plan with no smoking areas

CODE LIMITATIONS AND RESTRICTIONS

Many local governments ban smoking in the workplace and in public spaces. These regulations do not always meet the 25-foot (7.5-meter) distance for exterior smoking required by this prerequisite. In most cases, LEED projects can extend the smoking ban to the required 25 feet (7.5 meters), regardless of existing code. However, if existing code explicitly prohibits this, building owners may still achieve the prerequisite by providing documentation of the code.

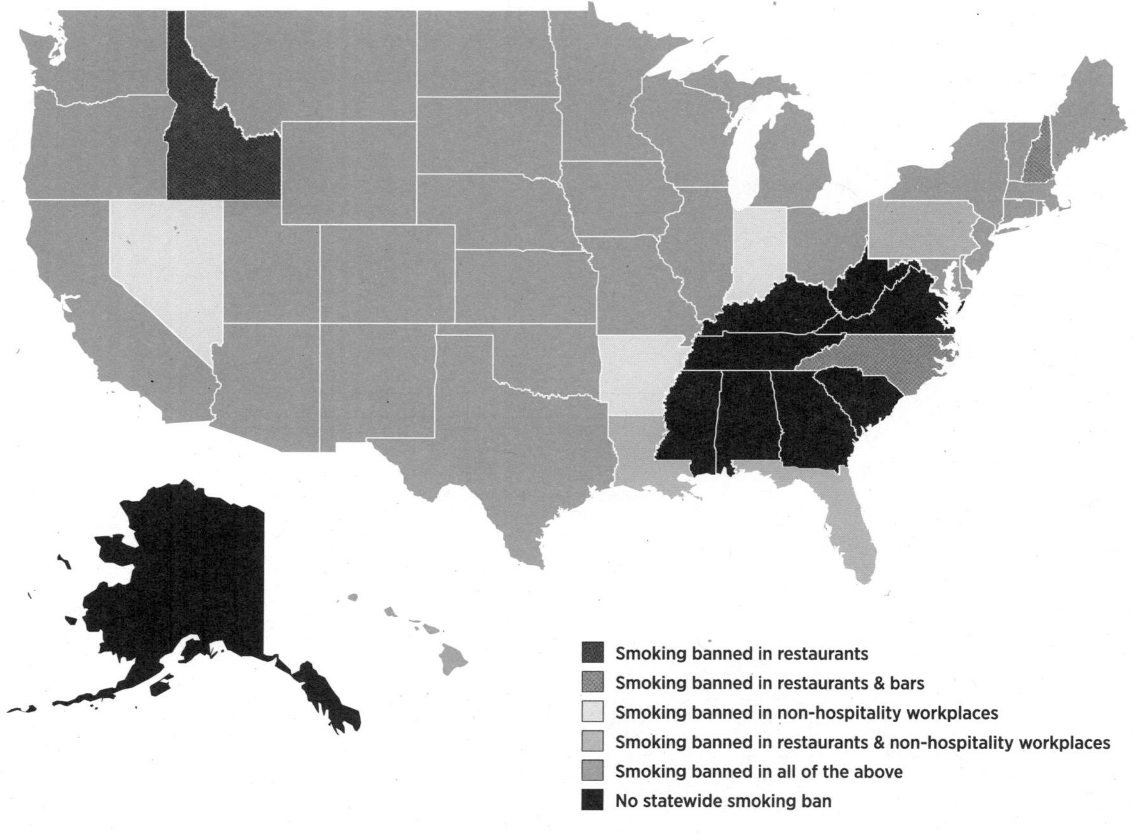

Figure 3. Smoking bans by state

PROJECT TYPE VARIATIONS

Multitenant

Owners and property management teams for multitenant buildings may find it useful to communicate the interior and exterior smoking policy in tenant guidelines, handbooks, or similar documents.

Residential healthcare

Residential health care projects, such as long-term care facilities, may allow smoking inside residential units if there is a clinical need to permit residents to smoke. Examples of clinical needs include medical treatments for substance abuse and psychiatric programs.

Residential

If teams cannot meet the stated threshold, they can establish a project baseline. For example, if the maximum leakage rate for a building is 1.0 cfm per square foot per unit, 1.0 becomes the new baseline. To achieve the prerequisite, the project team must show at least a 30% improvement from 1.0, or a maximum leakage rate of 0.7 cfm per square foot in every unit.

Residential projects are the only project type that may choose to allow smoking indoors in specific units. If smoking is permitted in residential projects, leakage from smoking units to other areas of the building must be prevented. Confirm the following requirements:

- All applicable doors and windows are weather-stripped.
- All residential units are sealed in applicable places.
- Testing results demonstrate compliance with the identified leakage rate requirements (see *Referenced Standards*).

Smoking must be prohibited in all building common areas. This prohibition must be communicated through rental or lease agreements, or condo or co-op association covenants and restrictions.

Prohibiting smoking on private residential balconies is a best practice for protecting nearby nonsmoking units and balconies from ETS infiltration. Consider prohibiting smoking on balconies in lease agreements.

All units must be compartmentalized because of potential tenant turnover. The following strategies are recommended to achieve proper air sealing:

- Use caulk for cracks and smaller gaps.
- Use expanding foam sealant for larger openings.
- Use mastic to seal all ducts.
- Use high-quality, durable, exterior-grade weatherstrip on all exterior doors, operable windows, and doors leading from residential units into common hallways.
- Confirm that all recessed can lights in insulated ceilings are airtight and IC-rated.
- Block stud cavities at changes in ceiling height and joist cavities under attic kneewall.
- Use sealed exterior sheathing and/or netting for dense insulation at attic kneewall.

Seal the following areas:

- Bottom plate to subfloor
- Penetrations in the top plate
- Drywall to framing
- Window and door rough openings with expanding foam
- Gaps in exterior wall sheathing
- Exterior walls of fireplace chase
- Shower and tub drains
- Cantilevered floor above supporting wall
- Seams in band joist between conditioned floors
- Electrical and communication boxes

Properly seal all penetrations in unit walls, ceilings, and floors, including the following:

- Perimeter doors, windows, and baseboards
- Plumbing and electrical penetrations, including outlets and switches, through insulated floors, ceilings, and walls
- Recessed lights and fans in insulated ceilings
- Dropped ceilings and cantilevered floors
- Exhaust vent penetrations
- Sheathing, including exterior light fixtures
- Band joist, including exhaust ducts
- Through drywall in attached garage
- Insulated subfloor, including HVAC boots

Properly seal airpath connections to all vertical chases adjacent to smoking units:

- Utility chases
- Garbage chutes
- Mail drops
- Elevator shafts
- All other adjacent vertical chases

Compartmentalization is achieved when individual residential units are adequately isolated from adjacent units and spaces. This must be demonstrated for all units. The most common way to meet this requirement is to conduct a blower door test that follows either the RESNET standards, Energy Star Multifamily Testing Protocol, ASTM E779-03, or ASTM E1827-11 (see *Referenced Standards*).

Consider having a building performance technician visit the job site to explain proper air-sealing techniques before insulation and drywall are installed. Perform blower door testing after drywall is installed and before painting. Testing a single representative unit first can help identify any leakages and pinpoint areas where additional sealing is likely to be required in other units. Use the test results to improve the construction process so that the remaining units pass the test.

A sampling rate of at least one in seven smoking units can be used, per the Residential Manual for Compliance with California's 2001 Energy Efficiency Standards, Chapter 4.

The results must demonstrate a maximum leakage of 0.23 cubic feet per minute per square foot (1.17 liters per second per square meter) at 50 Pa of enclosure.

Teams may use another air leakage test, such as tracer gas testing, provided that the same performance results as a blower door test can be documented. Testing must follow CEN Standard EN 1779 or CEN Standard EN 13185 with EN 13192.

CAMPUS

Group Approach
All buildings in the group may be documented as one.

Campus Approach
Eligible.

REQUIRED DOCUMENTATION

	Documentation	All projects where smoking is prohibited	Residential projects where smoking is permitted
E	Description of project's no-smoking policy, including information on how policy is communicated to building occupants and enforced	X	X
E	Copy of no-smoking policy, signed letter from owner describing project's no-smoking policy and enforcement, or copy of any legally binding covenants or restrictions to verify status of residential units as nonsmoking	X	
E	Door schedule demonstrating weather-stripping at exterior unit doors and doors leading from units to common hallways		X
P	Differential air pressure test report for units in project building		X
E	Scaled site plan or map showing location of designated outdoor smoking and no-smoking areas, location of property line, and site boundary and indicating 25-foot (7.5-meter) distance from building openings	X	X
E	Drawings, photos, or other evidence of signage communicating no-smoking policy	X	X
E	Any code or landlord restrictions that prevent establishment of nonsmoking requirements	X	X

CHANGES FROM LEED 2009

- Designated interior smoking rooms are no longer permitted, with the exception of residential spaces. This change recognizes the overwhelming evidence and broad consensus that exposure to ETS harms human health, and it supports higher indoor air quality in LEED projects.
- The no-smoking policy has been expanded to apply to spaces outside the property line if the space is used for business purposes and is within 25 feet (7.5 meters) of building openings or outdoor air intakes.
- A specific requirement for the location of exterior posted signs has been added.

- The acceptable procedure for demonstrating compliance with air leakage requirements in residential projects has been expanded. This change allows teams to use testing procedures other than blower door testing.
- Residential EBOM projects not able to meet the leakage requirements may demonstrate compliance through the 30% improvement option.

REFERENCED STANDARDS

Standard Test Method for Determining Air Leakage Rate by Fan Pressurization, ASTM E779-03: astm.org

Standard Test Methods for Determining Airtightness of Buildings Using an Orifice Blower Door, ASTM E1827-11: astm.org

Nondestructive testing, Leak testing—Criteria for method and technique selection, CEN Standard EN 1779—1999: cen.eu

Nondestructive testing, Leak testing, Tracer gas method, CEN Standard EN 13185—2001: cen.eu

Nondestructive testing, Leak testing, Calibration of reference leaks for gases, CEN Standard EN 13192—2001: cen.eu

RESNET Standards: resnet.us/standards

ENERGY STAR Multifamily Testing Protocol: energystar.gov/ia/partners/bldrs_lenders_raters

EXEMPLARY PERFORMANCE

Not available.

DEFINITIONS

None.

INDOOR ENVIRONMENTAL QUALITY PREREQUISITE

Green Cleaning Policy

This prerequisite applies to:

Existing Buildings
Schools
Retail
Data Centers
Hospitality
Warehouses and Distribution Centers

INTENT

To reduce levels of chemical, biological, and particulate contaminants that can compromise air quality, human health, building finishes, building systems, and the environment.

REQUIREMENTS

OPTION 1. IN-HOUSE GREEN CLEANING POLICY

ESTABLISHMENT E

Have in place a green cleaning policy for the building and site addressing the green cleaning credits, goals and strategies, and personnel listed below. At a minimum, the policy must cover green cleaning procedures, materials, and services that are within the building and site management's control, and include the organization responsible for cleaning the building and building site.

Address the requirements of the following credits:

- EQ Credit: Green Cleaning—Purchase of Cleaning Products and Materials
- EQ Credit: Green Cleaning—Cleaning Equipment

Goals and Strategies

- Establish standard operating procedures addressing how an effective cleaning and hard floor and carpet maintenance system will be consistently used, managed, and audited.
- Address protection of vulnerable building occupants during cleaning.
- Address selection and appropriate use of disinfectants and sanitizers.
- Develop guidelines addressing the safe handling and storage of cleaning chemicals used in the building, including a plan for managing hazardous spills and mishandling incidents.
- Develop goals and strategies for reducing the toxicity of the chemicals used for laundry, ware washing, and other cleaning activities.

- Develop goals and strategies for promoting the conservation of energy, water, and chemicals used for cleaning.
- Develop strategies for promoting and improving hand hygiene.

Personnel

- Develop requirements for maintenance personnel. Specifically address contingency planning to manage staffing shortages under a variety of conditions to ensure that basic cleaning services are met and critical cleaning needs are addressed. Include a process to obtain occupant and custodial staff input and feedback after contingency plans are implemented.
- Determine the timing and frequency of training for maintenance personnel in the hazards of use, disposal, and recycling of cleaning chemicals, dispensing equipment, and packaging.

PERFORMANCE P

Implement a high-performance cleaning program based on the above policy and track performance goals associated with this policy.

OPTION 2. CERTIFIED CLEANING SERVICE

ESTABLISHMENT E

None.

PERFORMANCE P

Clean the building with a cleaning service provider, either in-house custodial staff or a contracted service contractor, certified under one of the following:

- Green Seal's Environmental Standard for Commercial Cleaning Services (GS-42); or
- International Sanitary Supply Association (ISSA) Cleaning Industry Management Standard for Green Buildings (CIMS-GB); or
- Local equivalent for projects outside the U.S.

Confirm that the building was audited by the third party within 12 months of the end of the performance period.

In addition, the cleaning contractor must develop goals and strategies for promoting the conservation of energy, water, and chemicals used for cleaning the building.

BEHIND THE INTENT

To establish of a viable green cleaning program, project teams need to create a policy that establishes goals and strategies. A good policy also clearly identifies responsible parties and outlines how to measure progress toward the goals. The green cleaning policy defines the actions necessary to reduce the level of chemical use, protect the life of the building, increase indoor air quality, and reduce the environmental harms caused by traditional cleaning programs.

The requirements of the green cleaning prerequisite align with already-established third-party certifications. These certification programs outline the practices, procedures, products, and equipment of a viable green cleaning program.

STEP-BY-STEP GUIDANCE

STEP 1. DETERMINE PROJECT SCOPE E

Identify the areas of the building and site that are applicable to this credit.

- For single-tenant buildings, include all areas of the building and site that are inside the LEED project boundary.
- For multitenant projects, include all areas of the building and site that are under the building management's control. The entire building, including tenant spaces, must be included to earn related credits, but only the portion under building management's control is required in this prerequisite.
- As a best practice, teams should consider sharing the green cleaning program information with tenants and gauging their interest in helping develop and implement the green cleaning policy. Also consider evaluating tenants' cleaning practices and working with them to improve their programs.

STEP 2. SELECT COMPLIANCE OPTION E

Choose the appropriate option for the project.

- Option 1 is appropriate for projects that have a highly engaged cleaning staff or contract with a service that can demonstrate compliance. Third-party certification is not required. Project teams using a cleaning vendor that is not third-party-certified but is willing to go through the certification process may want to select Option 2.
- Option 2 is for projects that use a certified cleaning company or hire staff who are certified by the approved third parties identified in the prerequisite requirements. Projects may need to modify their cleaning contracts. Option 2 provides building owners with a quality assurance program implemented by an approved third party.
- Options 1 and 2 may be combined, provided all the green cleaning procedures, materials, and services that are under the building and site management's control are addressed by one or both options. Track which elements of the building are addressed by which option.

Option 1. In-House Green Cleaning Policy

STEP 1. DEVELOP GREEN CLEANING POLICY E

Create a green cleaning policy that addresses all the prerequisite requirements for goals, strategies, staffing, and training (see *Getting Started, Effective Policy Development*).

- Standard operating procedures
  - Hard floor and carpet cleaning and maintenance
  - Protection of vulnerable building occupants during cleaning
  - Disinfectant and sanitizer selection and use
  - Safe storage and handlings of cleaning chemicals, including spill management

EQ

GREEN CLEANING POLICY

- Performance metrics and strategy development
  - Reductions in water use, energy use, and chemical toxicity
  - Green cleaning products purchasing
  - Green cleaning equipment purchasing
- Staffing and training plans
  - Staffing requirements and contingency for staffing shortages
  - Timing and frequency of staff training

STEP 2. CREATE TRACKING PLAN E

Create and implement a tracking plan for each component in the green cleaning policy that must be tracked, starting at the beginning of the performance period. The tracking program should address each element of the policy that has a performance metric.

- **Water, energy, and toxic chemicals.** For items not covered under cleaning products purchasing, identify how cleaning affects water and energy use and introduces toxic chemicals into the building. Track measures to reduce these effects. For example, use cold water instead of hot or make sure all lights are turned off after nighttime cleaning is complete. The exact amount of energy or water saved or toxic chemicals avoided may be difficult to track, but devise a way of tracking the strategies selected.
- **Staffing and staff training.** Create a log to track staff training for new hires and continuing staff, according to the timing and frequency specified in the green cleaning policy.
- **Cleaning products purchasing.** List compliant cleaning materials and products (including hand sanitizers) for the project. These items must meet the requirements for EQ Credit Green Cleaning—Products and Materials. Any substitutions must be approved by the responsible party overseeing the green cleaning policy.
- **Cleaning equipment purchasing.** Inventory the equipment that meets the sustainability criteria in EQ Credit Green Cleaning—Equipment.

STEP 3. IMPLEMENT GREEN CLEANING POLICY P

Take action to implement the green cleaning policy at the beginning of the performance period (see *Further Explanation, Implementing a Green Cleaning Policy*).

- Give the responsible individuals the tracking tools they need and make sure they are aware of any performance metrics.
- Regularly (monthly if possible) report progress to all janitorial, management, and project staff to communicate success and establish new best practices that build on current approaches.
- Establish a process for team members to report issues or problems. This will allow them to voice concerns about how the policy is affecting daily operations.

Option 2. Certified Cleaning Service

STEP 1. DEFINE GREEN CLEANING STRATEGY P

Determine whether the current vendor is certified by one of the approved third parties. If not, decide whether the project team will work with this vendor to achieve third-party certification or hire a new, already-certified cleaning service provider. A combination of certified cleaning staff and a certified cleaning service or vendor may also be pursued.

STEP 2. INITIATE CERTIFICATION OF VENDOR P

If the current cleaning vendor will seek certification, provide the information needed to complete the process (see *Further Explanation, Third-Party Certification*).

STEP 3. VERIFY VENDOR'S CERTIFICATION P

If the project is using a third-party-certified cleaning vendor, verify that the certification is current.

- The required certification must be current and the required audit must be completed within 12 months of the end of the performance period. GS-42 audits may or may not include the building pursuing certification. CIMS-GB audits must include the building pursuing certification.

- If certification is not current, require the cleaning vendor to renew its certification and schedule an audit for the performance period.

STEP 4. REVIEW VENDOR'S PROGRAM FOR MEETING CONSERVATION GOALS P

Require that the certified cleaning vendor develop a plan with goals and implementation strategies to reduce the use of water, energy, and toxic chemicals at the project.

Determine cleaning activities' contributions to water and energy use and toxic chemicals in the building. Identify and track measures to reduce these effects. For example, use cold water instead of hot, and make sure all lights are turned off after nighttime cleaning is complete. Tracking the results of each strategy is required, but quantifying the amount of energy or water saved or toxic chemicals avoided is not.

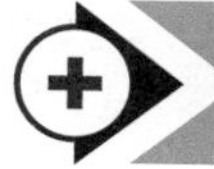

FURTHER EXPLANATION

IMPLEMENTING A GREEN CLEANING POLICY

Conduct a kick-off meeting a few weeks before the start of the performance period so that all parties understand their responsibilities and tasks. The meeting should include the following people:

- Representative from the purchasing department
- Building manager
- Custodial staff and/or janitorial contractors

Familiarize all parties on the green cleaning policy's intent and requirements and the tools being used to track performance. Highlight changes from previous cleaning practices.

Go over the responsibilities and reporting process for performance tracking. Create a plan for regular check-ins with custodial staff to ensure that they are following the policy. Building management supervisors should conduct regular spot-checks to verify that the plan is being implemented.

Post copies of the policy goals at convenient locations (e.g., janitor's closet and staff break room) for easy reference. Consider posting instructions in multiple languages as necessary.

Include all policy activities and goals, approved product lists, audit procedures, and tracking tools in custodial staff training materials, such as binders, online resource pages, and best management practice documents. Maintain a list of staff who have attended trainings or read the green cleaning policy.

THIRD-PARTY CERTIFICATION

Obtaining third-party certification can be time consuming, so the process needs to be started well in advance of the performance period. Anticipate delays, like a second round of auditing.

The approved third-party certifications are as follows:

- **GS-42.** Green Seal evaluates cleaning services in the areas of planning, products, supplies, equipment, procedures, training, communications, and labeling.
- **CIMS-GB.** The International Sanitary Supply Association (ISSA) certification applies to cleaning management, operations, performance systems, processes, and delivery of environmentally preferable cleaning service.

PROJECT TYPE VARIATIONS

Multifamily

In multifamily residential projects, the entire area under the building management's control must follow either Option 1 or Option 2. Although not required, a best practice is to give residents educational materials about sustainable purchasing options and guidance in making personal purchasing decisions about cleaning products and equipment.

Multitenant Buildings
Although not required, a best practice is to give tenants educational materials about sustainable purchasing options for cleaning products and cleaning equipment.

INTERNATIONAL TIPS

Project teams outside the U.S. may demonstrate compliance with Option 2 using equivalent certification programs. Submit documentation that demonstrates equivalency. Performance must be verified on a regular basis by a third party.

CAMPUS

Group Approach
The same green cleaning policy may be used for all the buildings within the LEED project boundary.

Campus Approach
The policy may be implemented on a campus-wide basis and must address any unique features of the buildings included.

REQUIRED DOCUMENTATION

	Documentation	Option 1	Option 2
E	Green cleaning policy addressing procedures, materials, and services under building and site management's control, with name of organization responsible for cleaning	X	
P	Copy of contract with certified cleaning vendor		X
P	Documentation demonstrating that vendor is certified under GS-42 or CIMS-GB		X
P	Description of goals and strategies to conserve energy and water and reduce chemicals used for cleaning	X	X
P	Date of audit for certification		X

RELATED CREDIT TIPS

EQ Credit Green Cleaning—Custodial Effectiveness Assessment. Implementing the cleaning strategies outlined in the green cleaning policy should enable the project to achieve the related credit.

EQ Credit Green Cleaning—Products and Materials. The purchase of green cleaning products and materials contributes toward the achievement of the related credit. All products and equipment used in the building must be included.

EQ Credit Green Cleaning—Equipment. Good maintenance of the green cleaning equipment listed in the inventory can contribute toward the achievement of the related credit. All products and equipment used in the building must be included.

CHANGES FROM LEED 2009

- The former Green Cleaning Policy prerequisite and High Performance Green Cleaning Program credit have been incorporated into this prerequisite.
- A second option is now available, for projects using a certified green cleaning vendor.

REFERENCED STANDARDS

Green Seal's Environmental Standard for Commercial Cleaning Services (GS-42):
greenseal.org/GreenBusiness/Standards.aspx

International Sanitary Supply Association (ISSA) **Cleaning Industry Management Standard for Green Buildings** (CIMS-GB): issa.com/

EXEMPLARY PERFORMANCE

Not available.

DEFINITIONS

None.

INDOOR ENVIRONMENTAL QUALITY CREDIT

Indoor Air Quality Management Program

This credit applies to:

Existing Buildings (2 points)
Schools (2 points)
Retail (2 points)
Data Centers (2 points)
Hospitality (2 points)
Warehouses and Distribution Centers (2 points)

INTENT

To maintain the well-being of occupants by preventing and correcting indoor air quality problems.

REQUIREMENTS

ESTABLISHMENT E

Develop and implement an indoor air quality (IAQ) management program based on the EPA Indoor Air Quality Building Education and Assessment Model (I-BEAM). Include the IAQ management program in the project's current facilities requirements and operations and maintenance Plan.

PERFORMANCE P

Conduct an I-BEAM audit on a regular basis (at least once every five years) and revise the IAQ management program as appropriate.

BEHIND THE INTENT

Maintaining indoor air quality (IAQ) is critical for the comfort and health of building occupants. Buildings with poor indoor air quality can make their occupants sick, potentially costing owners, property managers, operators, and employers economic losses in sick time, legal issues, and lost productivity.[1] To maintain good indoor air quality, building and mechanical systems need to be operating at peak performance, and common building maintenance problems like dust and mold must be controlled. A comprehensive IAQ management plan can prevent problems and improve conditions.

To help building operators identify and act on air quality issues in their facilities, the U.S. Environmental Protection Agency (EPA) created the Indoor Air Quality Building Education and Assessment Model (I-BEAM), a tool that can form the basis for an IAQ management program and help teams focus on critical management issues. This credit requires the use of I-BEAM to develop and implement an IAQ management program.

STEP-BY-STEP GUIDANCE

STEP 1. IDENTIFY IAQ MANAGER E

Designate someone who will serve as the IAQ manager and perform the I-BEAM audit. This is typically the building engineer or facility manager. The IAQ manager should review the I-BEAM educational modules (see *Further Explanation, Using the I-BEAM Website*).

STEP 2. ESTABLISH IAQ MANAGEMENT PROGRAM BASED ON I-BEAM E

The IAQ management program can be a stand-alone document, or teams can incorporate their IAQ management program into the project's current facilities requirements and operations and maintenance (O&M) plan, developed for EA Prerequisite Energy Efficiency Best Management Practices—Planning, Documentation, and Opportunity Assessment. Having all these procedures in one place may make it easier for building management teams to stay organized and facilitate best practices for operations and maintenance, but project teams are encouraged to organize their plans in the way most appropriate for their facilities

At a minimum, the IAQ management program must include the following components:

- Outline of the team responsible for maintenance
- Procedures to perform a full I-BEAM audit at least once every five years
- Preventive maintenance for each piece of equipment
- Periodic inspection for unusual conditions
- Periodic inspections for leaks, rust, dirt, and mechanical problems
- Regular lubrication
- Mechanical and electrical adjustments
- HVAC testing and balancing
- Operational checks
- Parts replacement
- Coil cleaning and filter replacement
- Procedures for repair work orders for when equipment fails or preventive maintenance reveals a problem
- IAQ pollutant control protocols

STEP 3. PREPARE FOR BASELINE I-BEAM AUDIT E P

Before conducting the audit, review the I-BEAM audit forms and tailor the forms to the project building. At a minimum, base the audit on the baseline IAQ audit forms (Section A).

1. *EPA's website on IAQ: epa.gov/iaq/ia-intro.html*

- It is recommended that teams consider incorporating additional audit forms into the investigation process, such as the IAQ operations and maintenance forms (Section B) or the IAQ management forms (Section C).
- To provide clear tracking of issues and resolution, consider recording issues on hard copies of the I-BEAM forms.

STEP 4. CONDUCT BASELINE I-BEAM AUDIT P

Conduct an I-BEAM audit of occupied spaces, mechanical systems, and the building exterior at least once during the performance period.

- Designate someone on staff who has time to complete the audit and also understands building systems and is familiar with building operations and mechanical systems. An I-BEAM audit does not typically require an external contractor, and this credit does not require any testing, balancing, or technically difficult preventive maintenance; those aspects are covered by related LEED prerequisites.
- For guidance on IAQ vendors, see *Further Explanation, Incorporating I-BEAM into Existing IAQ Service Programs.*

STEP 5. DEVELOP PLAN FOR RESOLVING ANY ISSUES P

Once the audit is complete, list the identified issues and develop a strategy and timeline for their resolution.

- For no- or low-cost remedies, consider staff training, staff time, or management buy-in, and then prioritize.
- For issues whose resolution requires expenditures, consider whether budget is the only issue or whether other resources are needed. Quotes from vendors and payback information may be helpful for setting priorities.

STEP 6. COMPLETE AUDIT REPORT P

Develop a summary report of the audit. Although completed audit forms are not required, the report must include the following:

- List of the spaces and systems audited and a description of the checklist used for each
- List or brief description of all issues identified during the audit
- Description of actions taken to remedy no-cost issues and date of completion
- Description of the strategy and timeline to remedy issues that require expenditure

STEP 7. IMPLEMENT IAQ MANAGEMENT PROGRAM CONTINUOUSLY P

- Conduct a complete I-BEAM audit at least once every five years.
- Ensure that any issues that require expenditure to remedy are addressed and recorded according to the timelines established in the resolution plan.

FURTHER EXPLANATION

USING THE I-BEAM WEBSITE

The I-BEAM website has two components that can help teams complete the indoor air quality audit.

Educational tools. Also called education modules, these instructional units inform the IAQ manager—someone from the operations staff—about common IAQ issues, such as sick building syndrome. The modules come in either text format (epa.gov/iaq/largebldgs/i-beam/text/index.html) or in a more graphical format (epa.gov/iaq/largebldgs/i-beam/visual_reference/index.html).

I-BEAM forms. Use these forms to support the IAQ audit (epa.gov/iaq/largebldgs/i-beam/forms.html).

INCORPORATING I-BEAM INTO EXISTING IAQ SERVICE PROGRAMS

Some building managers contract with vendors to perform periodic air quality testing or IAQ audits of the facility. These activities often exceed the minimum I-BEAM requirements. Additionally, many of these vendors are familiar with the technical aspects of the I-BEAM IAQ audit, even though they may not necessarily perform the nontechnical aspects of the audit required to earn this credit.

If using an outside vendor to conduct the audit, ensure that this contractor understands the documentation requirements, is familiar with the I-BEAM forms, and will adjust standard practices accordingly.

EXAMPLES

TABLE 1. Log of no-cost problems and remediation

Date	IAQ problem	Remedy	Date remedied
August 18, 2011	Condensing equipment dirty	Clean retail and commercial cooling towers	October 2012
August 18, 2011	Baffles dirty	Clean baffles	October 2012
August 18, 2011	Weatherstripping on lobby doors damaged	Replace weatherstripping	November 2012

TABLE 2. Log of capital issues and scheduled remediation

Issue	Notes	Cost	Schedule
Damaged ceiling tiles	Ceiling tiles on 12th floor need to be replaced after leaks are repaired	Low	Completed November 2012
Cooling coils not easily accessible	Inlet side of coils difficult to access	Medium	Completed September 2012
Pollution source near outdoor air intake	Drain vent is 6 feet from main air intake; relocate	Low	January 2013
Visible fungal growth	Insulation inside AHUs 12, 8 and 6 has fungal growth accumulation	Medium	January 2013
Rust	Base of AHU coils are rusted on most AHUs	High	June 2013
Corrosion	Fan chambers have corrosion and need to be painted	Medium	September 2013
Fans not easily accessible to be cleaned	Fan blades are not easily accessible bec. of vortex damper on chamber	Medium	September 2013

CAMPUS

Group Approach

All buildings in the group may be documented as one. A single O&M plan may be created that addresses each building. The same IAQ program may be followed for each building. Note in the O&M plan whether any building in the application has special or unique circumstances or systems that affect IAQ.

Campus Approach

Ineligible. Each LEED project may pursue the credit individually.

REQUIRED DOCUMENTATION

	Documentation	All projects
E	O&M plan with IAQ management program, addressing all components	X
P	Summary of audit with issues summary or list	X

RELATED CREDIT TIPS

EA Prerequisite Energy Efficiency Best Management Practices. The preventive maintenance plan for building equipment that is developed for the related credit and the HVAC system maintenance program should be included in the building's O&M plan.

MR Prerequisite Facility Alterations and Additional Policy. The requirements in the related prerequisite are more stringent than those in the I-BEAM documents. The IAQ management program should be drafted accordingly.

EQ Prerequisite Minimum Indoor Air Quality Performance. The HVAC system maintenance program developed for the related prerequisite should be included in the building's O&M plan.

EQ Credit Integrated Pest Management. The IAQ management program for this credit must have at least two IAQ pollutant control protocols, which could overlap with the policies and plans established for pest management.

EQ Prerequisite Green Cleaning Policy. The two IAQ pollutant control protocols could overlap with the policies and plans established for the related prerequisite.

CHANGES FROM LEED 2009

- All preventive maintenance and periodic inspection procedures are included in one document, the O&M plan.
- Only an audit was previously required; the credit now requires developing an IAQ management program as well.

REFERENCED STANDARDS

EPA I-BEAM guidance and audit forms: epa.gov

EXEMPLARY PERFORMANCE

Not available.

DEFINITIONS

None.

INDOOR ENVIRONMENTAL QUALITY CREDIT

Enhanced Indoor Air Quality Strategies

This credit applies to:

Existing Buildings (1–2 points)
Schools (1–2 points)
Retail (1–2 points)
Data Centers (1–2 points)
Hospitality (1–2 points)
Warehouses and Distribution Centers (1–2 points)

INTENT

To promote occupants' comfort, well-being, and productivity by improving indoor air quality.

REQUIREMENTS

OPTION 1. ENTRYWAY SYSTEMS (1 POINT)

ESTABLISHMENT E

Have in place permanent entryway systems at least 10 feet (3 meters) long in the primary direction of travel to capture dirt and particulates entering the building at regularly used exterior entrances. Acceptable entryway systems include permanently installed grates, grilles, slotted systems that allow for cleaning underneath, rollout mats, and any other materials manufactured as entryway systems with equal to or better performance. Maintain all on a weekly basis.

WAREHOUSES AND DISTRIBUTION CENTERS ONLY

Buildings are not required to provide entryway systems at doors leading from the exterior to the loading dock/garage, but must provide them between these spaces and adjacent office areas.

PERFORMANCE P

Confirm that entryway systems have been maintained on a weekly basis.

OPTION 2. ADDITIONAL ENHANCED IAQ STRATEGIES (1 POINT)

Comply with the requirements of at least one of the following.

Filtration for Mechanically Ventilated Spaces

ESTABLISHMENT E

Each ventilation system that supplies outdoor air to occupied spaces must have particle filters or air cleaning devices. These filters or devices must meet one of the following filtration media requirements:

- minimum efficiency reporting value (MERV) of 13 or higher, in accordance with ASHRAE Standard 52.2–2007;
- Class F7 or higher as defined by CEN Standard EN 779–2002, Particulate Air Filters for General Ventilation, Determination of the Filtration Performance.

Establish a regular schedule for maintenance and replacement of filtration media according to the manufacturer's recommended interval.

DATA CENTERS ONLY

The above filtration media requirements are required only for ventilation systems serving regularly occupied spaces.

PERFORMANCE P

Follow the schedule for maintenance and replacement of filtration media.

Carbon Dioxide Monitors

ESTABLISHMENT E

Have in place CO_2 monitors in all densely occupied spaces. Rooms smaller than 150 square feet (14 square meters) are exempt. CO_2 monitors must be between 3 and 6 feet (900 and 1 800 millimeters) above the floor.

Configure the system to generate a visual alarm to the system operator if the differential CO_2 concentration in any zone rises more than 15% above that corresponding to the minimum outdoor air rate required in the ventilation section of EQ Prerequisite Minimum Indoor Air Quality Performance.

Test and calibrate CO_2 sensors to have an accuracy of no less than 75 parts per million or 5% of the reading, whichever is greater.

PERFORMANCE P

Sensors must be tested and calibrated at least once every five years or per the manufacturer's recommendation, whichever is shorter.

Monitor CO_2 sensors with a system configured to trend CO_2 concentrations in intervals no greater than 30 minutes.

Outdoor Air Monitoring for Mechanically Ventilated Spaces

ESTABLISHMENT E

For variable air volume systems, provide a direct outdoor airflow measurement device capable of measuring the minimum outdoor air intake flow for at least 80% of the outdoor air flow. This device must measure the minimum outdoor air intake flow with an accuracy of +/–10% of the design minimum outdoor airflow rate required in the ventilation section of EQ Prerequisite Minimum Indoor Air Quality Performance. An alarm must indicate when the outdoor airflow value varies by 15% or more from the outdoor airflow setpoint.

For constant-volume systems, balance outdoor airflow to the design minimum outdoor airflow rate required in the ventilation section of EQ Prerequisite Minimum Indoor Air Quality Performance, or higher. Install a current transducer on the supply fan, an airflow switch, or similar monitoring device.

PERFORMANCE P

Calibrate all measurement devices within the manufacturer's recommended interval.

Outdoor Air Monitoring for Naturally Ventilated Spaces

ESTABLISHMENT E

Provide a direct exhaust airflow measurement device capable of measuring the exhaust airflow. This device must measure the exhaust airflow with an accuracy of +/–10% of the design minimum exhaust airflow rate. An alarm must indicate when airflow values vary by 15% or more from the exhaust airflow setpoint.

PERFORMANCE P

Calibrate all measurement devices within the manufacturer's recommended interval.

Alarmed Openings for Naturally Ventilated Spaces

ESTABLISHMENT E

Provide automatic indication devices on all openings intended to meet the minimum opening requirements. An alarm must indicate when any one of the openings is closed during occupied hours.

PERFORMANCE P

None.

BEHIND THE INTENT

Indoor pollutants and particulates are brought indoors by occupants, through ventilation system intakes or building openings, and from activities conducted within the building. By establishing effective indoor air quality (IAQ) best management practices, building managers can promote a comfortable indoor environment for building occupants and prevent the human health problems associated with poor indoor air quality.

This credit identifies IAQ strategies that extend beyond the outdoor air requirements of EQ Prerequisite Minimum Indoor Air Quality Performance. Best management practices include the installation of entryway systems to prevent contaminants from being brought inside by occupants, use of enhanced filtration media, and monitoring strategies for ventilation systems. Each strategy alone is beneficial, but a combination of multiple strategies is encouraged.

STEP-BY-STEP GUIDANCE

STEP 1. IDENTIFY EXISTING IAQ STRATEGIES E

Determine whether any enhanced IAQ strategies are already in place at the project building. If so, determine whether adjustments are necessary to meet the requirements.

If compliant IAQ strategies are not already in place, review the credit options early in the project timeline. Phasing for the implementation of new strategies will be critical, since the budget and schedule need to allow for their purchase and installation. Additionally, staff training and testing may be required for new systems or new IAQ practices.

STEP 2. SELECT ONE OR BOTH OPTIONS E

Determine which option(s) to pursue, based on any existing IAQ strategies and the information in Table 1.

- Option 1 is available to all projects, regardless of the ventilation system in place.
- Option 2 allows teams to select from multiple strategies; however, some strategies are acceptable only for certain system types. If the project has multiple ventilation system types (i.e., mixed-mode), only one strategy needs to be attempted. For example, if a space is both naturally and mechanically ventilated, the project team could select the Outdoor Air Monitoring for Naturally Ventilated Spaces strategy and install a measuring device for use whenever the space was operating in natural ventilation mode. The same strategy could also be applied to the naturally ventilated spaces in a project that has both naturally and mechanically ventilated spaces.

TABLE 1. Option 2 strategies, by type of ventilation

	Filtration	CO_2 monitoring	Outdoor air monitoring	Alarmed openings
Mechanically ventilated space	Select 1			N/A
Naturally ventilated space	N/A	Select 1		
Mixed-mode system	Select 1			

Option 1. Entryway Systems

STEP 1. IDENTIFY APPLICABLE ENTRIES E

Identify all regularly used exterior entrances (see *Definitions* and *Further Explanation, Rating System Variations* and *Project Type Variations*).

STEP 2. VERIFY ENTRYWAY SYSTEMS E

Determine which type of permanent entryway systems are present or will be installed (see *Further Explanation, Permanent Entryway Systems*).

Indicate the compliant entryways on project plans.

STEP 3. IMPLEMENT MAINTENANCE STRATEGY E P

Maintain the permanent entryway systems on a weekly basis. Consider developing a manual that describes for cleaning personnel (either staff or vendors) the process and frequency for cleaning and maintaining the entryways, with guidelines and a schedule. Track all maintenance activities in a log. Ensure that entryway maintenance procedures are consistent with the requirements of other credits related to cleaning and maintenance.

Option 2. Additional Enhanced IAQ Strategies

FILTRATION FOR MECHANICALLY VENTILATED SPACES

STEP 1. INVENTORY FILTERS FOR HVAC SYSTEMS E

Refer to the information on the HVAC system (collected for EQ Prerequisite Minimum Indoor Air Quality Performance) and determine the type of air filtration media installed for each piece of HVAC equipment.

- Identify filters by MERV rating (or filter class, as defined by CEN).
- List equipment type, filter type, filter replacement schedule, and regular servicing and maintenance.

STEP 2. VERIFY THAT FILTRATION MEETS CREDIT REQUIREMENTS E

Verify that all equipment has filtration media that meets the credit requirements. All outdoor air supplied to occupied spaces must be filtered.

- For any equipment with filtration that does not comply, determine whether the system can accommodate MERV 13 (F7) filters. This is often a difficult modification for older equipment that is not appropriately sized for MERV 13 (F7) filters (see *Further Explanation, Filtration Media*).
- Recirculated return air can also be filtered with MERV 13 (F7) or higher, but this is not required.
- If the project design includes a dedicated outdoor air system with local distribution systems, the filtration requirement applies only to the dedicated outdoor air system.
- For Data Center projects, see *Further Explanation, Rating System Variations.*

STEP 3. IMPLEMENT FILTRATION MEDIA MAINTENANCE PROGRAM E P

Develop and follow a filtration media maintenance and replacement program that meets the credit requirements.

CARBON DIOXIDE (CO_2) MONITORS

STEP 1. IDENTIFY DENSELY OCCUPIED SPACES E

Identify all spaces with an occupant density greater than 25 people per 1,000 square feet (93 square meters). Spaces less than 150 square feet (14 square meters) are exempt.

STEP 2. DESIGN AND INSTALL CO_2 MONITORING SYSTEM E

Install a CO_2 sensor in each densely occupied space.

- CO_2 sensors must be located in the breathing zone, as defined in the credit language. CO_2 sensors installed in return air ducts cannot be used to meet the requirements (see *Further Explanations, CO_2 Monitors*).
- Determine CO_2 concentration setpoint(s) using the methods in ASHRAE 62.1–2010, Appendix C. See ASHRAE 62.1–2010 User's Manual, Appendix A, for calculations and examples.
- Configure the CO_2 monitoring system to generate a visual alarm to the system operator if the differential CO_2 concentration exceeds the setpoint by more than 15%. Ensure that the system is capable of trending CO_2 concentration data at 30-minute intervals or less.

STEP 3. TEST AND CALIBRATE CO_2 MONITORING DEVICES E P

Test and calibrate installed sensors, per the credit requirements. Develop and follow a preventive maintenance program to recalibrate sensors within the time interval specified in the credit requirements.

OUTDOOR AIR MONITORING FOR MECHANICALLY VENTILATED SPACES

STEP 1. IDENTIFY TYPES OF AIR DISTRIBUTION SYSTEMS IN PROJECT E

Determine whether the project uses variable air volume (VAV) or constant volume (CV) systems.

STEP 2. VERIFY AIRFLOW MEASUREMENT DEVICES E

Confirm or incorporate airflow monitoring equipment into the HVAC system. See the credit requirements for VAV and CV systems (see *Further Explanation, Airflow Measurement Devices* and *Examples*).

- Ensure that each system supplying outdoor air to occupied spaces has the appropriate measurement device. For example, if the building has a dedicated outdoor air system with distributed variable air volume AHUs, each distributed AHU must have a direct outdoor airflow measurement device.
- For CV systems with distributed heat pumps, the outdoor airflow may be measured at the dedicated outdoor air system.
- Retain equipment cutsheets showing the accuracy of the monitoring devices, copies of control sequences and diagrams, and test and balance reports that show airflow setpoints for each AHU.

STEP 3. CALIBRATE AIRFLOW MEASUREMENT DEVICES E P

Develop and follow a preventive maintenance program to recalibrate within the time interval specified in the credit requirements.

OUTDOOR AIR MONITORING FOR NATURALLY VENTILATED SPACES

STEP 1. IDENTIFY NATURALLY VENTILATED SPACES AND THEIR EXHAUST SYSTEMS E

STEP 2. VERIFY AIRFLOW MEASUREMENT DEVICES E

Incorporate exhaust airflow monitoring equipment, per the credit requirements (see *Further Explanation, Airflow Measurement Devices*).

- Because naturally ventilated systems induce passive air movement from openings to the point of exhaust, airflow measurement devices must be placed at the exhaust location.
- Retain cutsheets for the monitoring devices, plans indicating sensor locations, and copies of control sequences and diagrams for documentation.

STEP 3. CALIBRATE AIRFLOW MEASUREMENT DEVICES E P

Develop and follow a preventive maintenance program to recalibrate within the time interval specified in the credit requirements.

ALARMED OPENINGS FOR NATURALLY VENTILATED SPACES

STEP 1. IDENTIFY NATURAL VENTILATION OPENINGS E

Identify all windows, louvers, and trickle vents used for natural ventilation. Each opening counted as a natural ventilation intake for EQ Prerequisite Minimum IAQ Performance must have an alarm. For example, an office with two windows required for acceptable natural ventilation must have alarms installed on both windows. However, if only one window is required for acceptable natural ventilation, only one window needs to have an alarm.

STEP 2. VERIFY ALARM DEVICES E

For each natural ventilation opening, provide automatic indication devices and configure the alarms, per the credit requirements.

FURTHER EXPLANATION

PERMANENT ENTRYWAY SYSTEMS

Permanent entryway systems must catch and hold dirt particles and prevent contamination of the building interior. Acceptable permanent entryway systems include the following:

- Permanently installed grates
- Grilles
- Slotted systems that allow for cleaning underneath
- Rollout mats
- Carpet tile specifically designed for entryway system or similar use
- Other materials manufactured for use as an entryway system or similar that performs at least as well as the above systems

Typical building carpeting is not an acceptable permanent entryway system.

Consider permanent entryway systems that have solid backings. A nonporous backing captures dirt and moisture and helps prevent contaminants from collecting underneath. Consider permanent entryway systems made with mold- and mildew- resistant materials.

The permanent entryway system should be at least 10 feet (3 meters) long. Exceptions to the 10-foot (3-meter) distance are allowed if the team submits documentation verifying that the proposed entryway system performs at least as well as a full-length system. The product should be appropriate for the project's climate. Areas with high precipitation, for example, may need more absorbent mats to prevent occupants from slipping.

Evaluate the best way to maintain the permanent entryway system. All permanent entryway systems must be maintained on a weekly basis.

FILTRATION MEDIA

Project teams whose ventilation systems do not already have high-efficiency filtration media may want to consider adaptations to allow MERV 13 (or Class 7) filters. The building engineer or a consulting engineer should determine whether the fans are correctly sized and operate with enough static pressure to accommodate the effects of using denser filters.

Most systems not designed to accommodate the required filters will require customization, which may include resizing ductwork, increasing fan capacity to maintain air delivery despite the added resistance, or making other modifications to system design. Implementing high-efficiency filtration can increase operational costs for energy use and filter replacement.

CO_2 MONITORS

Installing permanent CO_2 sensors that provide continuous monitoring and generate alarms is easiest in buildings with a building automation system or existing outdoor airflow monitoring. For buildings without a BAS, a CO_2 monitoring system can be difficult and expensive to install. CO_2 sensors must be located in the breathing zone, as defined in the credit requirements. CO_2 sensors installed in return air ducts do not meet the requirements (see Figure 1).

Demand-controlled ventilation adjusts the amount of outdoor air in response to occupancy. Most commonly, buildings rely on CO_2 measurements to determine whether additional outdoor air is required. Frequently, CO_2 measurements are taken in return air ducts. In such a case, the demand-controlled ventilation system does not qualify as a form of CO_2 monitoring for this credit. Although it may not be rewarded under this credit, such a system can significantly reduce energy use by decreasing the volume of outdoor air that must be conditioned by the building's HVAC systems, helping projects earn energy-related points.

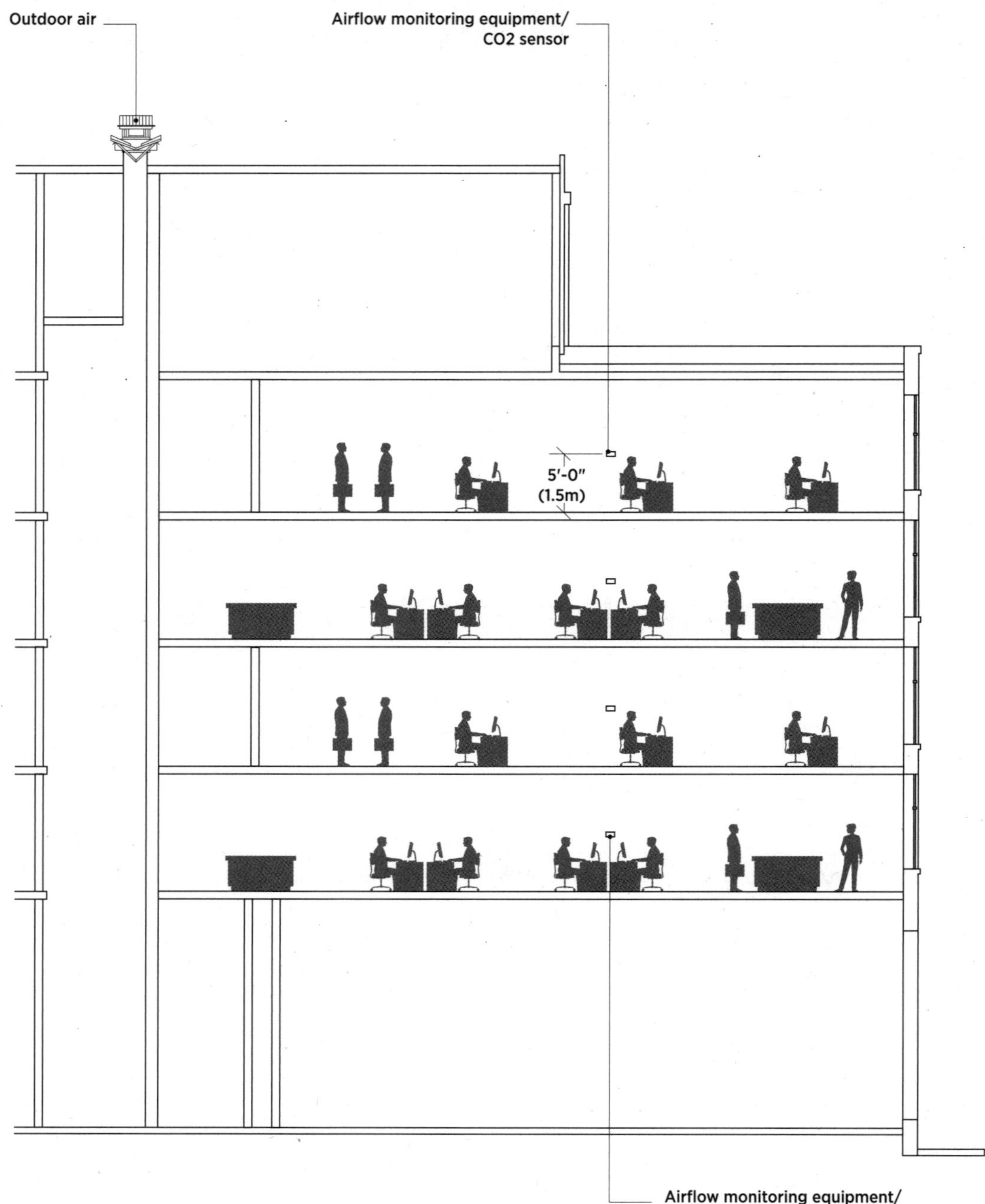

Figure 1. Example CO_2 sensor locations

AIRFLOW MEASUREMENT DEVICES

For naturally ventilated systems, airflow devices must be a part of the exhaust system. Naturally ventilated systems induce passive air movement from openings to the point of exhaust, requiring that airflow measurement devices be at the exhaust location. A current flow meter is the most appropriate device for this application.

For mechanically ventilated systems, airflow measurement devices must be a part of the air duct system. Two common types of these devices are those that measure intake volume directly by measuring air velocity and those that measure differential pressure across a fixed opening.

The technique for monitoring outdoor air depends on the HVAC system. For VAV and CV systems, refer to the credit requirements.

For VAV systems—for example, a 100% outdoor air energy recovery unit with demand-controlled ventilation, or any system that provides a variable amount of supply or outdoor air—a direct outdoor airflow measurement device must measure the intake flow rate (Figure 2).

- Indirect measurements, such temperature or current transducers, cannot directly measure the airflow rate and thus are not allowed for VAV systems.
- If a 100% outdoor air system provides ventilation air to the return of downstream terminal devices (e.g., fan coil units, heat pumps), the measurement device must measure the outdoor airflow rate at the 100% outdoor air unit only, not at each terminal device.

For device requirements, see the specific language in the credit requirements.

- For constant volume systems, current transducers on the supply fan, airflow switches, pressure transducers, or similar monitoring device are acceptable.
- If a 100% outdoor air system provides ventilation air to the return of downstream terminal devices (e.g., fan coil units, heat pumps), the measurement device needs to be in the 100% outdoor air system only, not at each terminal device.

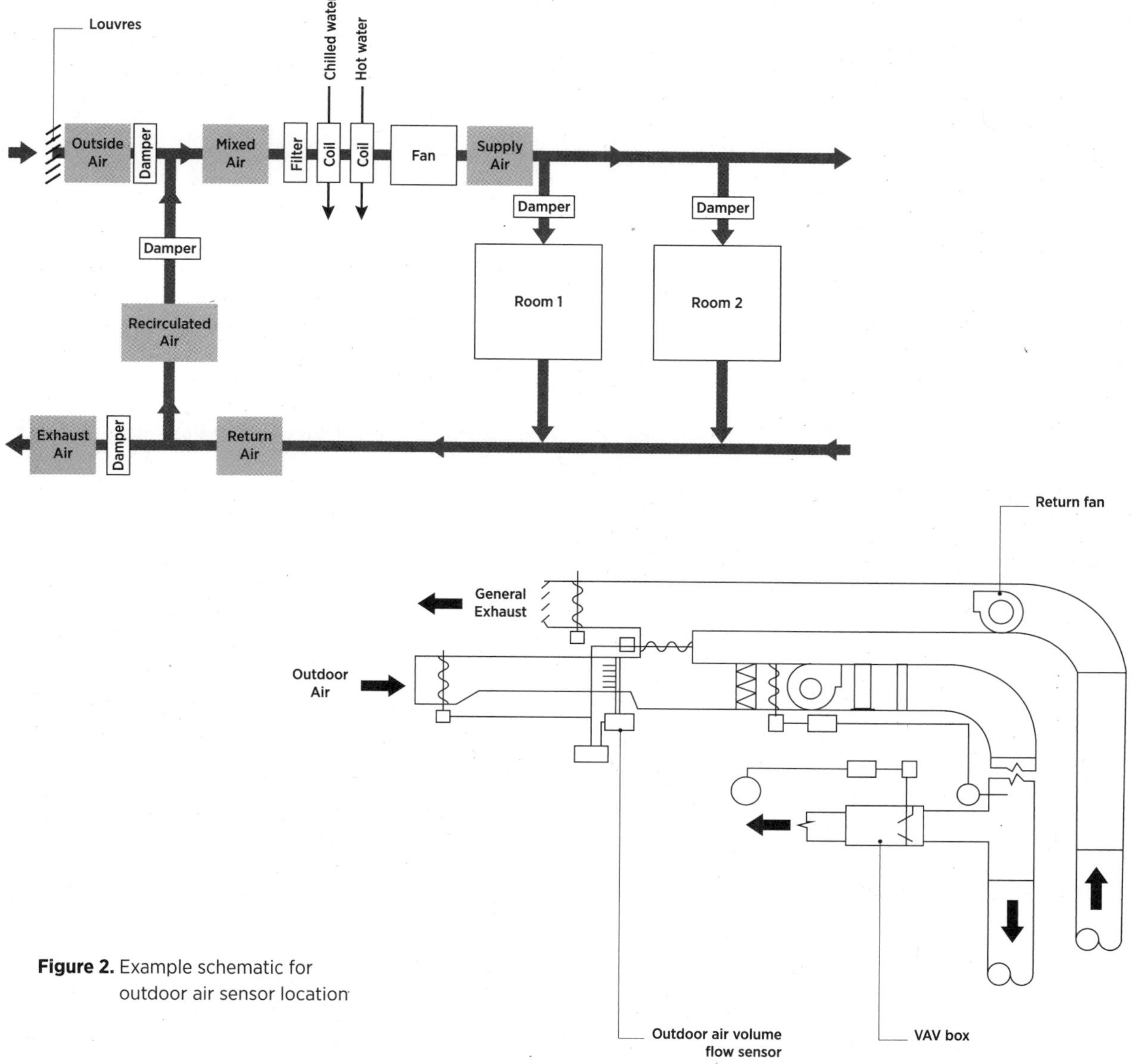

Figure 2. Example schematic for outdoor air sensor location

EXAMPLES

Example 1. Outdoor air monitoring for mechanically ventilated spaces
A small commercial building has the following constant-volume air handlers:

TABLE 2. Air handlers

Unit	Supply cfm (lps)	Outdoor air cfm (lps)
AHU-1	16,000 (7 551)	4,000 (1 888)
AHU-2	8,000 (3 776)	1,000 (472)
AHU-3	6,000 (2 832)	3,000 (1 416)

Although AHU-1 and AHU-2 provide 80% of the supply air to the building, they provide only 62.5% of the outdoor air. If monitoring all AHUs is not feasible, the project could comply with this credit by monitoring AHU-1 and AHU-3. Together, those AHUs provide 87.5% of the outdoor air to the building.

Example 2. Building with heat pumps
A large office building has more than 100 heat pumps, each of which is provided with outdoor air at a constant volume via ducts from a dedicated outdoor air system (DOAS). Because the outdoor air connection is fully ducted, and provided at a constant volume, it is acceptable to monitor the flow at the DOAS.

If outdoor air were provided by the DOAS to mechanical rooms, mixing plenums, or another indirect point, outdoor air monitoring would be required at the individual heat pumps.

RATING SYSTEM VARIATIONS

Warehouses and Distribution Centers
For Option 1, exterior entrances to loading docks and garages are not required to have entryway systems. Regularly used entrances from these areas into adjacent spaces in the building (typically office areas of the building) must have entryway systems.

Data Centers
For Option 2, filtration requirements apply only to ventilation systems serving regularly occupied spaces. Data centers often have dedicated HVAC and exhaust systems because of their varying schedules and cooling needs.

PROJECT TYPE VARIATIONS

Residential Projects
For Option 1, entryway systems are required for each residential entrance from the outdoors, not just for regularly used entrances. Entryway systems are required only at the ground level.

CAMPUS

Group Approach
Submit separate documentation for each building.

Campus Approach
Ineligible. Each LEED project may pursue the credit individually.

REQUIRED DOCUMENTATION

	Documentation	Option 1	Option 2
E	Entryway systems: photos, drawings, or scaled floor plans highlighting locations and measurements	X	
P	Entryway systems: confirmation that entryway systems were maintained weekly	X	
E	Filtration: list of filtration media highlighting MERV (or class) rating for all units, and summary of maintenance plan		X
P	Filtration: documentation, such as activity logs or detailed narrative, showing that filters were maintained per maintenance plan and highlighting any filters replaced		X
E	CO_2 monitors: description of maintenance plan		X
E	CO_2 monitors: controls drawing sample, photos, or list of each densely occupied space and associated carbon dioxide monitors		X
P	CO_2 monitors: documentation, such as activity logs or detailed narrative, showing that sensors were maintained per maintenance plan and highlighting any sensors tested and calibrated		X
P	CO_2 monitors: carbon dioxide trending data for 24-hour period		X
P	Outdoor air monitoring for mechanically ventilated spaces: description of maintenance plan		X
P	Outdoor air monitoring for mechanically ventilated spaces: controls drawing sample or list of monitoring devices		X
E	Outdoor air monitoring for mechanically ventilated spaces: documentation, such as activity logs or detailed narrative, showing that sensors were maintained per maintenance plan and highlighting any sensors tested and calibrated		X
E	Outdoor air monitoring for naturally ventilated spaces: description of maintenance plan		X
E	Outdoor air monitoring for naturally ventilated spaces: controls drawing sample or list of exhaust airflow measurement devices		X
P	Outdoor air monitoring for naturally ventilated spaces: documentation, such as activity logs or detailed narrative, showing that sensors were maintained per maintenance plan and highlighting any sensors tested and calibrated		X
E	Alarmed openings for naturally ventilated spaces: description of maintenance plan		X
E	Alarmed openings for naturally ventilated spaces: controls drawing sample or list of automatic indication devices.		X

RELATED CREDIT TIPS

EA Prerequisite Minimum Energy Performance and EA Credit Optimize Energy Performance. Increased filtration and increased ventilation increase energy consumption. Consider incorporating dedicated outdoor air systems, economizers, and demand-controlled ventilation to offset the energy penalties of the strategies required for this credit.

EQ Prerequisite Minimum Indoor Air Quality. The ventilation system referenced in the related prerequisite must be consistent with that under this credit.

EQ Prerequisite Green Cleaning Policy, EQ Credit Green Cleaning—Custodial Effectiveness Assessment, EQ Credit Green Cleaning—Cleaning Equipment, and EQ Credit Green Cleaning—Cleaning Products and Equipment. Using green cleaning practices reduces internal generation of contaminants.

EQ Prerequisite Indoor Air Quality Management Program. Instituting an IAQ management program can establish standards for monitoring outdoor air delivery under this credit.

CHANGES FROM LEED 2009

- Portions of IEQ Credit 1.2 Indoor Air Quality Best Management Practices—Outdoor Air Delivery Monitoring, IEQ Credit 1.4 Indoor Air Quality Best Management Practices—Reduce Particulates in Air Distribution, and IEQ Credit 3.5 Green Cleaning—Indoor Chemical and Pollutant Source Control have been combined into a single credit.
- Additional options for naturally ventilated spaces have been included.
- Additional guidance has been incorporated regarding warehouses, distribution centers, data centers, and residential projects.
- An additional option for filtration media requirements, CEN Standard EN 779-2002, Particulate Air Filters for General Ventilation, Determination of the Filtration Performance, has been added.

REFERENCED STANDARDS

ASHRAE Standard 52.2–2007: ashrae.org

CEN Standard EN 779–2002: cenorm.be

ASHRAE Standard 62.1–2010: ashrae.org

Charted Institution of Building Services Engineers (CIBSE) Applications Manual AM10, March 2005: cibse.org

Charted Institution of Building Services Engineers (CIBSE) Applications Manual 13–2000: cibse.org

National Ambient Air Quality Standards (NAAQS): epa.gov/air

EXEMPLARY PERFORMANCE

Achieve both Option 1 and Option 2 and incorporate an additional Option 2 strategy.

DEFINITIONS

densely occupied space an area with a design occupant density of 25 people or more per 1,000 square feet (93 square meters)

occupied space an enclosed space intended for human activities, excluding those spaces that are intended primarily for other purposes, such as storage rooms and equipment rooms, and that are only occupied occasionally and for short periods of time. Occupied spaces are further classified as regularly occupied or nonregularly occupied spaces based on the duration of the occupancy, individual or multioccupant based on the quantity of occupants, and densely or nondensely occupied spaces based on the concentration of occupants in the space.

regularly occupied space an area where one or more individuals normally spend time (more than one hour per person per day on average) seated or standing as they work, study, or perform other focused activities inside a building. The one-hour timeframe is continuous and should be based on the time a typical occupant uses the space. For spaces that are not used daily, the one-hour timeframe should be based on the time a typical occupant spends in the space when it is in use.

regularly used exterior entrance a frequently used means of gaining access to a building. Examples include the main building entrance as well as any building entryways attached to parking structures, underground parking garages, underground pathways, or outside spaces. Atypical entrances, emergency exits, atriums, connections between concourses, and interior spaces are not included.

INDOOR ENVIRONMENTAL QUALITY CREDIT

Thermal Comfort

This credit applies to:

Existing Buildings (1 point)
Schools (1 point)
Retail (1 point)
Data Centers (1 point)
Hospitality (1 point)
Warehouses and Distribution Centers (1 point)

INTENT

To promote occupants' productivity, comfort, and well-being by providing quality thermal comfort.

REQUIREMENTS

Meet the requirements for both thermal comfort design and thermal comfort control.

Thermal Comfort Design

ESTABLISHMENT E

Have in place a system for continuous tracking and optimization of systems that regulate indoor comfort and conditions (air temperature, radiant temperature, humidity, and air speed) in occupied spaces.

OPTION 1. ASHRAE 55–2010

Have a permanent monitoring system to ensure ongoing building performance to the desired comfort criteria, as specified by ASHRAE Standard 55–2010, Thermal Comfort Conditions for Human Occupancy, Section 5.2 or 5.3, with errata, or a local equivalent.

OR

OPTION 2. ISO AND CEN STANDARDS

Have a permanent monitoring system to ensure ongoing building performance of the desired comfort criteria, as specified by the applicable standard:

- ISO 7730:2005 Ergonomics of the Thermal Environment, analytical determination and interpretation of thermal comfort using calculation of the PMV and PPD indices and local thermal comfort criteria; and
- CEN Standard EN 15251:2007, Indoor Environmental Input Parameters for Design and Assessment of Energy Performance of Buildings, addressing indoor air quality, thermal environment, lighting, and acoustics, Section A2.

DATA CENTERS ONLY

Meet the above requirements for occupants in regularly occupied spaces.

HOSPITALITY ONLY

Guest rooms are assumed to provide adequate thermal comfort and are therefore not included in the credit calculations.

PERFORMANCE P

The monitoring system must meet the following requirements.

- **Continuous monitoring.** Monitor at least air temperature and humidity in occupied spaces, at sampling intervals of 15 minutes or less.
- **Periodic testing.** Monitor air speed and radiant temperature in occupied spaces. Using handheld meters is permitted.
- **Alarms.** An alarm must indicate conditions that require system adjustment or repair.
- **Prompt repair.** Specify procedures for adjustments or repairs to be made in response to problems identified.
- **Calibration.** All monitoring devices must be calibrated within the manufacturer's recommended interval.

BEHIND THE INTENT

A large body of laboratory and field research has demonstrated how thermal conditions inside buildings directly affect people's satisfaction and performance.[1] This credit encourages the operation of buildings with comfortable indoor conditions that support occupants' productivity and well-being. Although often associated only with air temperature, thermal comfort is a complex amalgam of six primary factors (Figure 1), all of which are influenced by building design and operation. An effective thermal comfort strategy considers all six concurrently, meaning that close collaboration among the owner, occupants, and building operators is critical to achieving this credit.

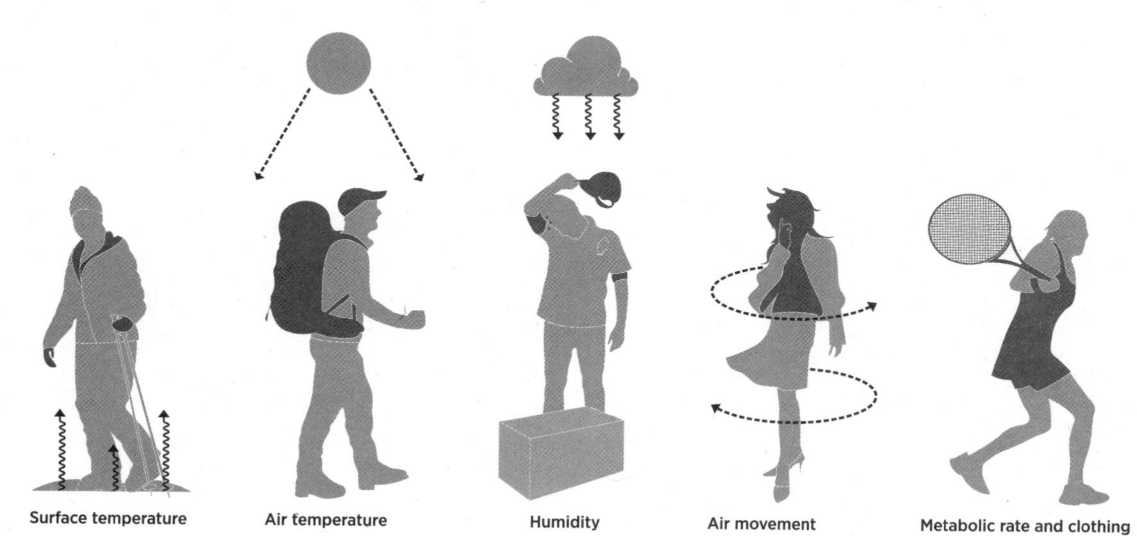

Figure 1. Primary factors that affect thermal comfort

Modifying one or more of the six comfort factors can greatly improve occupants' perception of the thermal environment while still supporting energy reduction goals. Working closely with the owner, the project team can maximize comfort by coordinating systems with operational policies. For example, a flexible dress code that permits seasonally appropriate clothing can allow thermostat setpoints to be adjusted upward during the cooling season and downward during the heating season without affecting occupants' perception of comfort. An effective thermal comfort policy clearly articulates these expectations and relationships so that the building operator can implement a control strategy that optimizes both thermal comfort and energy use.

Many facilities operators spend much time and effort adjusting thermostat setpoints and other operational parameters to address occupants' complaints. Systems that continuously track temperature, relative humidity, and air speed will help system operators optimize thermal comfort and minimize complaints.

1. *Fisk, W., "Estimates of Potential Nationwide Productivity and Health Benefits from Better Indoor Environments: An Update," in Spengler, J., J. Samet, and J. McCarthy (eds.), Indoor Air Quality Handbook (New York: McGraw Hill, 2001), 4.1–4.31.*

STEP-BY-STEP GUIDANCE

STEP 1. ESTABLISH A PERMANENT MONITORING SYSTEM E

Ensure that the building has a permanent air temperature and humidity monitoring system with measurement frequency and sensor locations consistent with the following:

- **Air temperature.** At least one air temperature sensor must be installed for each thermal zone with occupied spaces. The sensors may be placed close to where the occupants are known to spend time. Sensors in the return air duct to the air-handling unit are not acceptable. Additional sensors are required if a single measurement point is not representative of the entire thermal zone because of its use or configuration, if a space includes both perimeter and core area, if a space can be subdivided (e.g., with a movable wall), or if other drivers of large air temperature variance are present.
- **Humidity.** At least one humidity sensor must be installed for each humidity zone in the building. The sensor may be located in a typical space in the zone, the return air duct to the air-handling unit, or another location representative of typical conditions. Additional sensors are required if a single measurement point is not representative of the entire humidity zone.
- **Data logging.** The monitoring system must record measurements at intervals of 15 minutes or less.
- **Alarm conditions.** A system alarm must be triggered when measured temperature or humidity is outside a defined range. (Acceptable temperature and humidity ranges will be established in a later step.)

If new monitoring equipment must be installed, plan to complete upgrades before the performance period begins. A building automation system is not required to meet the credit requirements, but it may be a useful tool for permanent monitoring.

Review the submittal documentation required for the performance period to that ensure temperature, relative humidity, and/or alarm data are logged and stored for a sufficient time.

STEP 2. ESTABLISH PROCEDURES FOR PERIODIC MEASUREMENTS E

Determine how periodic measurements of air speed and radiant temperature will be taken and develop a testing schedule.

- Decide on instrumentation. Handheld meters or other monitoring equipment may be used. Recommendations for anemometer and temperature-sensor characteristics are provided in ASHRAE Standard 113–2009, Method of Testing for Room Air Diffusion, Section 5.1.
- Determine when the measurements will be taken. At a minimum, seasonal measurement is required. Measurements should be taken during a period of typical occupancy for each space. This may require multiple measurements for multiuse spaces.
- Determine where the measurements will be taken. At least one set of air speed and radiant temperature measurements must be taken for each thermal zone with occupied spaces. As recommended in ASHRAE 55–2010, the measurements must be taken in locations where the most extreme values of the thermal parameters are estimated or observed.
- Measurements should be taken close to where the occupants are known to spend time. Consider the recommendations in ASHRAE 55–2010, Section 7.2, or ASHRAE 113–2009, Sections 7.1 and 7.4.
- Determine how the data will be collected and compared with the thermal comfort criteria.
- The thermal comfort criteria for air speed are specified in ASHRAE 55–2010, Section 5.2.4.2, and ISO 7730–2005, Section 6.2. For ASHRAE 55–2010 and ISO 7730–2005, Category B, the percentage of occupants dissatisfied because of drafts must be less than 20%. Additional guidance on air speeds is provided in ASHRAE 113–2009, Section B.2, and ISO 7730, Figure A.2. Example calculations are provided in ASHRAE 113–2009, Section C.2.
- The thermal comfort criteria for radiant temperature asymmetry are specified in ASHRAE 55–2010, Section 5.2.4.1, and ISO 7730–2005, Section 6.5. For ASHRAE 55–2010 and ISO 7730–2005 Category B, the percentage of occupants dissatisfied because of radiant asymmetry must be less than 5%.
- Prepare a narrative that summarizes the procedure for measuring air speed and radiant temperature. Address instrumentation, timing, location, and recording and analysis of the data.

STEP 3. ESTABLISH PROCEDURES FOR RESPONDING TO THERMAL COMFORT ISSUES E

Develop a process for reviewing thermal conditions, with procedures for adjustments or repairs.

- Include regular review of trending data from continuous monitoring and periodic measurement reports.

- Include prompt investigation and remediation for permanent monitoring system alarms, which indicate out-of-range temperature and humidity values.

STEP 4. COLLECT BASELINE INFORMATION E

Work with the owner to understand occupants' comfort factors, such as seasonal clothing and activities.

- Walk through the building and talk with occupants about their thermal comfort expectations. Observe their clothing and activities.
- Take an initial set of air temperature, radiant temperature, humidity, and air speed measurements using handheld meters or permanent monitoring equipment (if present).
- Document all the baseline data to inform the thermal comfort zone calculation that will be used to establish alarm setpoints (Table 1).

TABLE 1. Example baseline thermal comfort data

	Space type	Metabolic rate (met)	Clothing insulation (clo)				Operative temperature F (C)				Relative humidity (%)				Design air speed (fpm)			
			Spring	Summer	Fall	Winter	Spring	Summer	Fall	Winter	Spring	Summer	Fall	Winter	Spring	Summer	Fall	Winter
Cooling	Office	1.1	0.7	0.5	0.7	0.9	76 (24)	76 (24)	76 (24)	76 (24)	50	50	50	50	25	25	25	25
Cooling	File Room	1.4	0.7	0.5	0.7	0.9	72 (22)	72 (22)	72 (22)	72 (22)	50	50	50	50	30	30	30	30
Heating	Office	1.1	0.7	0.5	0.7	0.9	70 (21)	70 (21)	70 (21)	70 (21)	50	50	50	50	20	20	20	20
Heating	File room	1.4	0.7	0.5	0.7	0.9	68 (20)	68 (20)	68 (20)	68 (20)	50	50	50	50	30	30	30	30

STEP 5. SELECT THERMAL COMFORT STANDARD E

Determine which standard or set of standards is suited to the project. Either option is appropriate for common space types, such as offices, educational buildings, hospitals, hotels and restaurants, and retail buildings. For other building types, see *Further Explanation, Project Type Variations.*

- Option 1 is suitable for most U.S. project teams, who are likely to be familiar with ASHRAE 55–2010. This option allows projects to use the same standard for both mechanically and naturally conditioned spaces.
- Option 2 relies on two international standards, ISO 7730–2005 and EN 15251–2007, to document mechanically and naturally conditioned spaces, respectively.

Both options are based on the same comfort models.

STEP 6. DETERMINE ALARM CONDITIONS AND ACCEPTABLE VALUES FOR PERIODIC MEASUREMENTS E

Establish the boundaries of the thermal comfort zone for the project based on the baseline thermal comfort data and the selected option.

- Identify temperature and relative humidity values that trigger an alarm.
- Identify the air speed and radiant temperature values that are acceptable.
- For Option 1 calculation examples, see *Further Explanation, Using ASHRAE 55–2010.*
- For Option 2 calculation examples, see *Further Explanation, Using ISO 7730–2005 and EN 15251–2007 Standards.*

STEP 7. MAKE SYSTEM ADJUSTMENTS E

Before the performance period begins, make operational adjustments, equipment repairs, and upgrades as necessary to ensure that the building conditioning systems are capable of maintaining the thermal comfort conditions.

Adjustments may include changing current setpoints and establishing alarm setpoints. Repairs may include sensor replacement and calibration. Upgrades may include adding sensors or monitoring equipment that meets the credit requirements for measurement interval and data logging.

STEP 8. IMPLEMENT ONGOING MEASUREMENT P

During the performance period, undertake the following required activities:

- Perform and record at least one set of air speed and radiant temperature measurements for each thermal zone with occupied spaces. Indicate whether the measurements meet the required comfort criteria.
- Maintain temperature, humidity, and alarm trend logs from the permanent monitoring system. Prepare one of the following trend graphs or reports:
  - Trend graphs for at least 20% of the air temperature sensors and 20% of the relative humidity sensors, covering at least one week of operation
  - Trend graphs of air temperature and relative humidity readings in at least 20% of the occupied building floor area, covering at least one week of operation
  - A summary system report of all alarms that occurred during the entire performance period when temperature and humidity fell outside acceptable ranges
- Make system adjustments or repairs after all alarms during the performance period. Retain all information about the cause of the alarm and the corrective action taken.
- Calibrate measurement equipment at the manufacturer's recommended interval and maintain records of calibration. If no manufacturer-recommended calibration is scheduled to occur during the performance period, maintain cutsheets, installation records, or records of previous calibration.

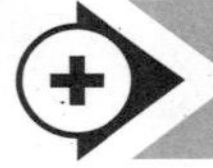

FURTHER EXPLANATION

CALCULATIONS

All calculations are found in the referenced standards.

USING ASHRAE 55–2010

To determine thermal comfort criteria that meet ASHRAE 55–2010, identify the sections appropriate for the building.

- **Mechanically conditioned spaces.** Follow Section 5.2 (Methods for Determining Acceptable Conditions in Occupied Spaces), including Section 5.2.4 for potential sources of local discomfort.
- **Naturally conditioned spaces.** Follow Section 5.3 (Optional Method for Determining Acceptable Thermal Conditions in Naturally Conditioned Spaces). This method is available only for spaces that meet the criteria for occupant-controlled naturally conditioned spaces (see *Further Explanation, Criteria for Occupant-Controlled Naturally Conditioned Spaces*). Spaces that do not meet the criteria must follow the mechanically conditioned spaces methods.
- **Mixed-mode spaces.** Each seasonal conditioning strategy must be documented separately. For example, demonstrate heating season compliance using Section 5.2 and cooling season compliance using Section 5.3.

Use the baseline information collected in Step-by-Step Guidance, Step 4 for the following analyses (see *Further Explanation, Examples*).

- Mechanically conditioned spaces. Calculate the acceptable range of comfort conditions. Select a method from ASHRAE 55–2010, Section 5.2, to calculate the acceptable range of comfort conditions. Review the requirements for the local discomfort effects of draft and radiant temperature.

- Naturally conditioned spaces. Calculate the acceptable range of comfort conditions. Use Figure 5.3 or the equations in Section 5.3 to establish the upper and lower operative temperature limits of the comfort zone. Document the acceptable range of comfort conditions. Review *Required Documentation* for information that should be prepared.

USING ISO 7730–2005 AND EN 15251–2007 STANDARDS

To determine thermal comfort criteria that meets ISO 7730–2005 or EN 15251–2007, identify the standard and sections appropriate for the building.

- Mechanically conditioned spaces. Use ISO 7730–2005.
- Follow EN 15251–2007, Annex A.2, Acceptable Indoor Temperatures for Design of Buildings without Mechanical Cooling Systems. EN method is available only for projects that meet certain criteria (see *Further Explanation, Criteria for Occupant-Controlled Naturally Conditioned Spaces*). Otherwise, use ISO 7730–2005.
- Mixed-mode spaces. Each seasonal conditioning strategy must be documented separately. For example, demonstrate heating season compliance using ISO 7730–2005 and cooling season compliance using EN 15251–2007.

Use the baseline information in *Step-by-Step Guidance*, Step 4, to identify the applicable space category and comfort threshold for the project based on the appropriate standard classifications. ISO 7730–2005, Annex A, and EN 15251–2007 each set different ranges of comfort acceptability for specific building types and occupant populations (Table 2). Category C for ISO 7730–2005 and Category III for EN 15251–2007 are appropriate for most existing buildings.

TABLE 2. Comparison of comfort acceptability ranges, ISO 7730-2005 and EN 15251-2007

Category		Description	Allowable predicted mean vote	Allowable predicted percentage dissatisfied
ISO 7730-2005	EN 15251-2007			
A	I	Recommended for spaces occupied by very sensitive and fragile persons with special requirements (very young children, elderly, ill)	-0.2 < PMV < 0.2	<6%
B	II	Suitable for most new buildings and renovations	-0.5 < PMV < 0.5	<10%
C	III	Suitable for existing buildings	-0.7 < PMV < 0.7	<15%
	IV	Values outside of the above; only acceptable for part of the year	PMV < -0.7 or PMV > 0.7	>15%

PMV = predicted mean vote (index of thermal comfort)   PPD = predicted percentage (of people) dissatisfied

Source: This excerpt is adapted and modified from ISO 7730:2005 and EN 15251:2007 with the permission of ANSI on behalf of ISO.

Taking the baseline information collected in *Step-by-Step Guidance*, Step 4, calculate the acceptable range of comfort conditions.

- **Mechanically conditioned spaces.** Use the simplified look-up method in ISO 7730–2005, Annex E, to determine acceptable operative temperatures and air speeds for the allowable PMV. For spaces that do not meet Annex E criteria, calculate PMV as described in Section 4.1 or Annex D and local thermal discomfort according to Section 6.
- **Naturally conditioned spaces.** Use EN 15251–2007 Figure A1 or the equations in Section A.2 to establish the upper and lower operative temperature limits of the comfort zone. Document the acceptable range of comfort conditions. Review *Required Documentation* for information that should be prepared.

See *Further Explanation, Examples.*

CRITERIA FOR OCCUPANT-CONTROLLED NATURALLY CONDITIONED SPACES

The referenced standards, ASHRAE 55–2010, Section 5.3, and EN 15251–2007, Section A.2, set the following requirements for when the occupant-controlled naturally conditioned spaces (or adaptive) method may be used:

- Occupants' metabolic rate is between 1.0 and 1.3 metabolic equivalent of task (MET).
- Occupants are free to adapt their clothing to the indoor and/or outdoor thermal conditions.
- User-controlled operable windows are present.
- No mechanical cooling is installed.
- Running mean outdoor temperatures are within the ranges specified in the standards at times of year when natural conditioning is used.

The natural conditioning comfort model cannot be applied to times of the year when the heating system is operating.

EXAMPLES

Example 1. Option 1, mechanically conditioned, graphic method

An office space is cooled with an underfloor air system and heated by perimeter fin tube radiators. The metabolic rate for the space is 1.1, per ASHRAE Appendix A. The clothing insulation (clo) is calculated as 0.9 when the outdoor environment is cool and 0.6 when the outdoor environment is warm.

The project team has decided to determine the permanent monitoring alarm setpoints using the graphic method, described in ASHRAE 55–2010, Section 5.2.1.1. The air speeds (less than 40 feet per minute), clothing insulation levels (0.5–1.0 clo), and occupant metabolic rate (1.0–1.3 MET) are all within the specified ranges for this method.

The comfort zone boundaries are calculated using the ASHRAE equations for T_{max}, I_{cl}, T_{min}, I_{cl}, and I_{cl}.

- For the heating season, operative temperatures must be between 68.5°F and 79.8°F (20.3°C and 26.6°C). The alarms are configured to sound if operative temperatures and the associated relative humidity are outside this range.
- For the cooling season, operative temperatures must be between 73.0°F and 83.1°F (22.8°C and 28.4°C). The alarms are configured to sound if operative temperatures and the associated relative humidity are outside this range.

The comfort zone boundaries were plotted on a psychometric chart, indicating the comfort zone in heating and cooling modes and alarm setpoints (Figure 2). The team has determined that any local thermal discomfort effects are unlikely. Because the space's temperature and humidity levels fall within the comfort zone in heating and cooling modes, the project achieves the credit.

Figure 2. Supporting documentation for Example 1

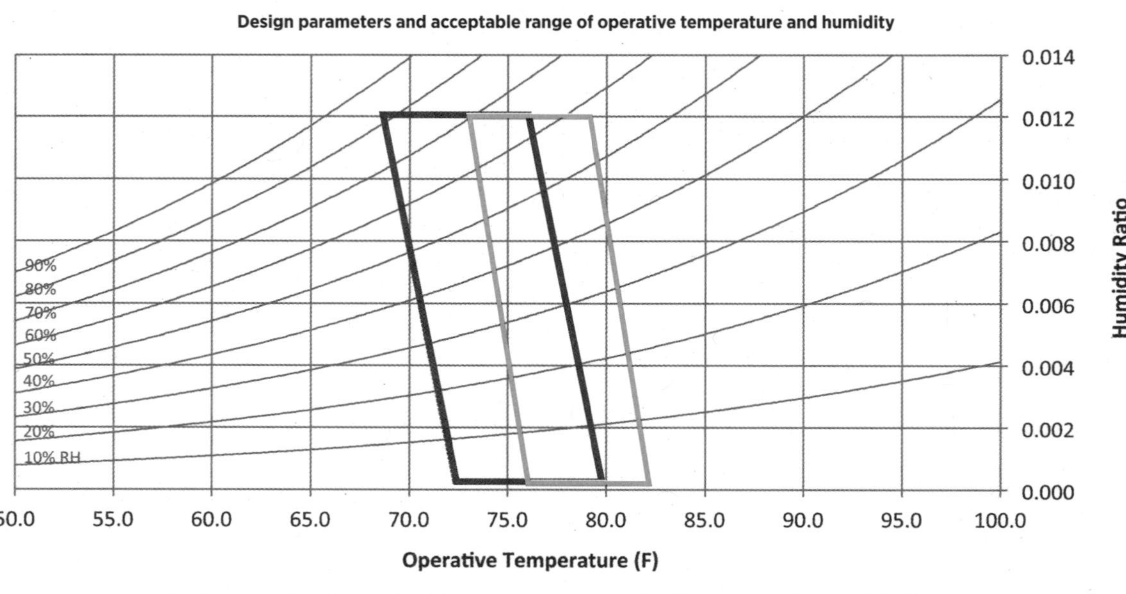

Example 2. Option 1, naturally conditioned, adaptive method

An open office space is naturally cooled with occupant-controlled operable windows and does not have any mechanical cooling system installed. Heating is provided by fin tube radiators.

The project team has decided to determine the permanent monitoring alarm setpoints for the cooling period (April through October) using the adaptive method, described in ASHRAE 55–2010, Section 5.3 (Optional Method for Determining Acceptable Thermal Conditions in Naturally Conditioned Spaces).

For the adaptive method, the comfort zone boundaries are determined from ASHRAE 55–2010, Figure 5.3 (Figure 3). The alarms are configured to sound if operative temperatures are outside this range.

The project team must also determine the permanent monitoring setpoints for the mechanically conditioned heating period (November through March) and use a method similar to that in Example 1.

Figure 3. Supporting documentation for Example 2.

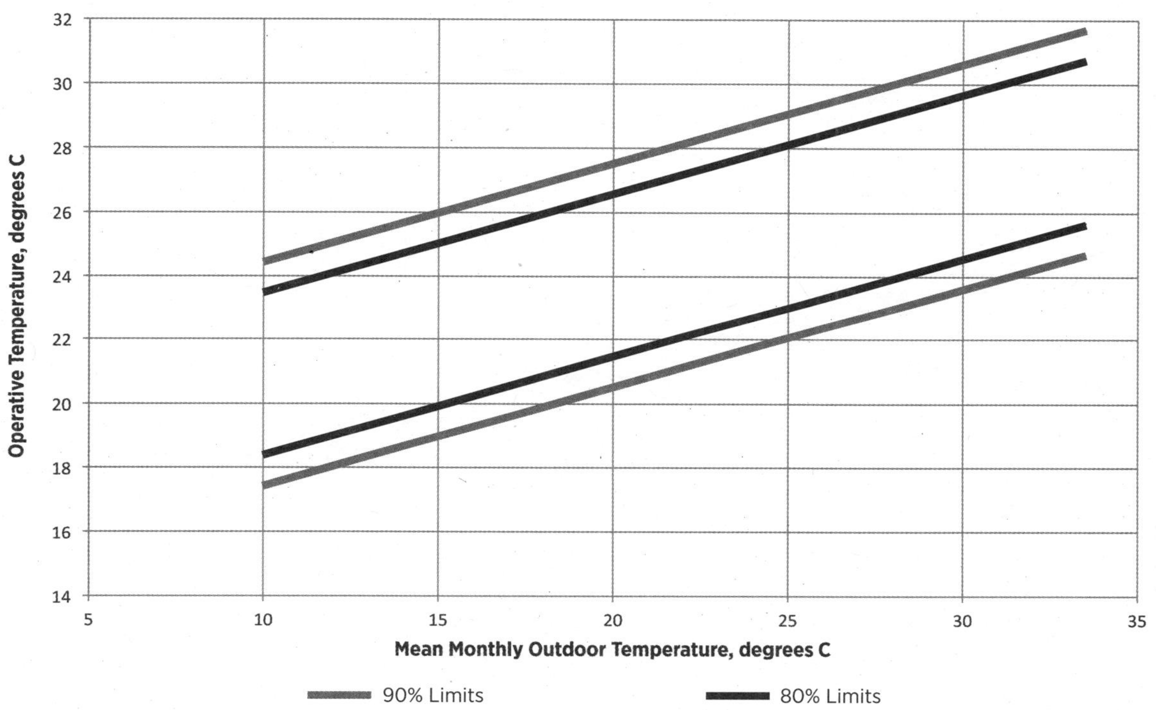

Example 3. Option 2

A classroom is naturally cooled via operable windows that are manually operated by teachers and students. The heating system consists of a hydronic radiant panel supplied with hot water from a central boiler system and controlled by a local thermostat in each classroom.

The project team has decided to determine the permanent monitoring alarm setpoints for the cooling period and heating period using the adaptive method, described in EN 15251–2007, Annex A, Section A.2, and ISO 7730–2005, Table E.3, respectively.

The project team creates a summary table for the calculation parameters and alarm setpoints (Table 3).

TABLE 3. Summary table for Example 3

	Space type	Activity level (MET)	Operative temperature (°C)	Mean monthly outdoor temperature (°C)	Relative humidity (%)	Air speed (m/s)
Cooling	Classroom	1.2	25.5	20	N/A	1
Heating	Classroom	1.2	22.2	N/A	50	0.15

For the adaptive method, the comfort zone boundaries are determined from EN 15251–2007, Annex A, Figure A1 (Figure 4). The alarms are configured to sound if operable temperatures are outside of this range.

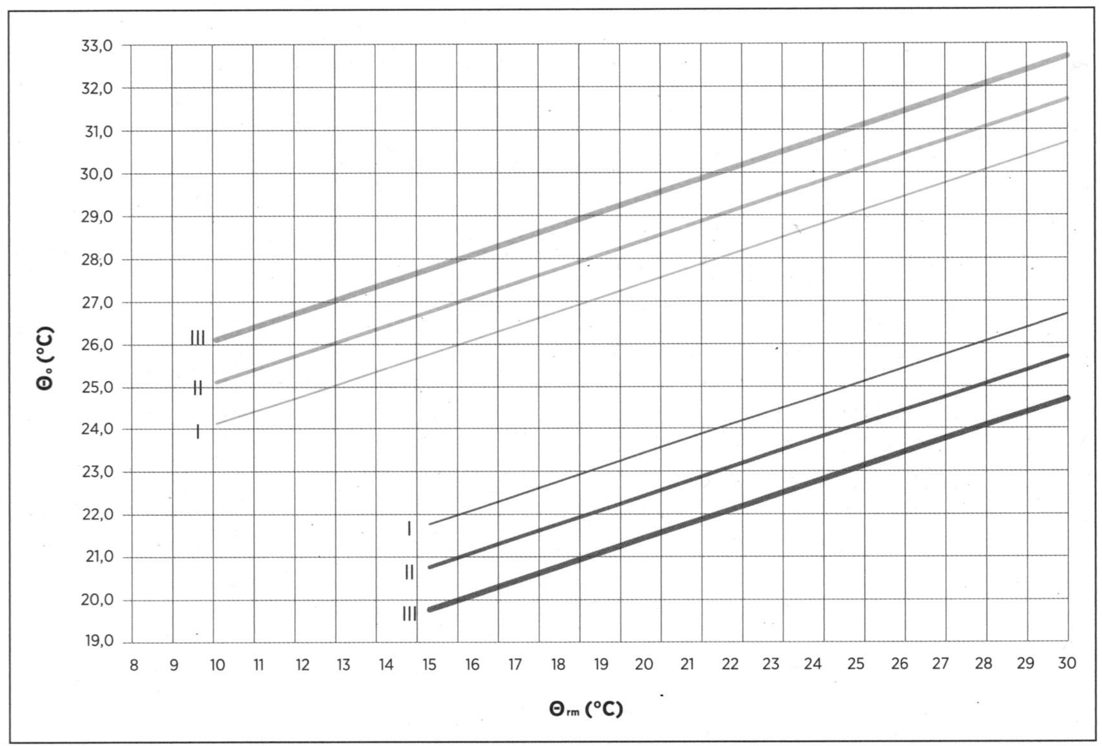

Figure 4. Supporting documentation for naturally conditioned period for Example 3. This excerpt is adapted and modified from ISO 7730:2005 and EN 15251:2007 with the permission of ANSI on behalf of ISO.

For the ISO 7730–2005, Table E.3, method, the parameters are compared with ISO 7730–2005, Annex E, Table E.3 (Figure 5), and the acceptable comfort conditions for a Category C building are based on a PMV of –0.7<PMV<+0.7. The alarms are configured to sound if operative temperatures and the associated relative humidity are outside this range (Figure 5).

Table E.3 — Activity level: 69,6 W/m² (1,2 met)

Clothing		Operative temperature	Relative air velocity							
			m/s							
clo	m² · K/W	°C	< 0,10	0,10	0,15	0,20	0,30	0,40	0,50	1,00
0	0	25	−1,33	−1,33	−1,59	−1,92				
		26	−0,83	−0,83	−1,11	−1,40				
		27	−0,33	−0,33	−0,63	−0,88				
		28	0,15	0,12	−0,14	−0,36				
		29	0,63	0,56	0,35	0,17				
		30	1,10	1,01	0,84	0,69				
		31	1,57	1,47	1,34	1,24				
		32	2,03	1,93	1,85	1,78				
0.25	0,039	23	−1.18	−1.18	−1,39	−1,61	−1.97	−2,25		
		24	−0,79	−0,79	−1,02	−1,22	−1,54	−1,80	−2,01	
		25	−0,42	−0,42	−0,64	−0,83	−1,11	−1,34	−1,54	−2,21
		26	−0,04	−0,07	−0,27	−0,43	−0,68	−0,89	−1,06	−1,65
		27	0,33	0,29	0.11	−0,03	−0,25	−0,43	−0,58	−1,09
		28	0,71	0,64	0,49	0,37	0.18	0,03	−0,10	−0,54
		29	1,07	0,99	0,87	0,77	0,61	0,49	0,39	0,03
		30	1,43	1,35	1,25	1,17	1,05	0,95	0,87	0,58
0,50	0,078	18	−2,01	−2,01	−2,17	−2,38	−2,70			
		20	−1,41	−1,41	−1,58	−1,76	−2,04	−2,25	−2,42	
		22	−0,79	−0,79	−0,97	−1,13	−1,36	−1,54	−1,69	−2,17
		24	−0,17	−0,20	−0,36	−0,48	−0,68	−0,83	−0,95	−1,35
		26	0,44	0,39	0,26	0,16	−0,01	−0,11	−0,21	−0,52
		28	1,05	0,96	0,88	0,81	0,70	0,61	0,54	−0,31
		30	1,64	1,57	1,51	1,46	1,39	1,33	1,29	1,14
		32	2,25	2,20	2.17	2.15	2.11	2.09	2.07	1,99
0,75	0,116	16	−1,77	−1,77	−1,91	−2,07	−2,31	−2,49		
		18	−1,27	−1,27	−1,42	−1,56	−1,77	−1,93	−2,05	−2,45
		20	−0,77	−0,77	−0,92	−1,04	−1,23	−1,36	−1,47	−1,82
		22	−0,25	−0,27	−0,40	−0,51	−0,66	−0,78	−0,87	−1,17
		24	0,27	0,23	0,12	0,03	−0,10	−0,19	−0,27	−0,51
		26	0,78	0,73	0,64	0,57	0,47	0,40	0,34	0,14
		28	1,29	1,23	1.17	1.12	1,04	0,99	0,94	0,80
		30	1,80	1,74	1,70	1,67	1,62	1,58	1,55	1,46
1.00	0.155	16	−1.18	−1.18	−1,31	−1,43	−1,59	−1,72	−1,82	−2,12

Figure 5. Supporting documentation for mechanically conditioned period for Example 3. This excerpt is adapted and modified from ISO 7730:2005 and EN 15251:2007 with the permission of ANSI on behalf of ISO.

RATING SYSTEM VARIATIONS

Hospitality

The requirements are the same as those in *Step-by-Step Guidance* with the exception of guest rooms, which are assumed to have individual thermal comfort controls and are therefore excluded from the requirements of this credit.

Data Centers

The requirements are the same as those in *z* but only apply to regularly occupied spaces, such as network operation centers, security offices, and administrative spaces. Spaces that are not regularly occupied, such as areas that house data center equipment and mechanical equipment, may be excluded.

PROJECT TYPE VARIATIONS

Gymnasiums, Fitness Areas, and Other Spaces with High Metabolic Rates

ASHRAE 55–2010, Normative Appendix A, permits use of a time-weighted average metabolic rate over a period of an hour or less. Any space with a rate of 2.0 MET or less must be addressed using standard compliance methods. Although the ASHRAE standard does not apply where the time-averaged metabolic rate is above 2.0 MET, thermal comfort in these spaces must still be addressed. For spaces with a rate above 2.0 MET, address how the project meets the intent of the credit.

ISO 7730–2005 addresses metabolic rates up to 4.0 MET.

Kitchens

Many kitchens are not conditioned, not cooled, or are only indirectly cooled and may have difficulties achieving the requirements of ASHRAE 55–2010 or ISO 7730–2005. For kitchens that cannot meet the requirements of these standards, address how the project meets the intent of the credit.

Apparatus Bays in Fire Stations

Typically, these spaces are not used for human occupancy and thus would not be required to meet the credit requirements. However, if these spaces are used for human occupancy, the project must meet the thermal comfort criteria.

Vehicle Repair Facility

The thermal comfort criteria must be met. This space type, which is not typically cooled, also includes military buildings where trucks, tanks, aircraft, and other vehicles are being serviced.

CAMPUS

Group Approach

Submit separate documentation for each building.

Campus Approach

Ineligible. Each LEED project may pursue the credit individually.

REQUIRED DOCUMENTATION

	Documentation	All projects
E	Description of thermal comfort criteria established for occupied spaces	X
E	Description of continuous monitoring of air temperature and humidity, including sensor locations, frequency, instrumentation, and data logging and analysis	X
E	Description of periodic monitoring of air speed and radiant temperature, including measurement location, instrumentation, and data analysis	X
P	Confirmation that periodic testing was performed and continuous monitoring and alarms were in place during performance period	X
P	Description of how monitoring, testing, and alarms inform adjustments or repairs	X

RELATED CREDIT TIPS

EQ Prerequisite Minimum Indoor Air Quality Performance. Requirements for natural ventilation (ASHRAE 62.1–2010) are different from those for natural conditioning (ASHRAE 55–2010). Project teams with naturally ventilated and/or conditioned buildings should review the requirements of both standards.

EQ Credit Enhanced Indoor Air Quality Strategies. Consider the monitoring requirements of both credits when specifying or upgrading building monitoring systems.

EQ Credit Occupant Comfort Survey. Surveys of building occupants may reveal thermal comfort issues not evident in monitoring data and may also help prioritize adjustments or modifications.

CHANGES FROM LEED 2009

- The ASHRAE referenced standard has been updated to 2010. Refer to ASHRAE Journal (June 2011) for an explanation of changes from the 2004 version of the standard: ashrae.org/resources--publications/periodicals/ashrae-journal/.
- International standards have been included to provide more relevant compliance options for non-U.S. projects.
- Humidity monitoring is required at the humidity zone level (e.g., for each air-handling system) rather than in each occupied space.
- A new compliance path has been established for data centers, which are required to meet the credit requirements in regularly occupied spaces only.

REFERENCED STANDARDS

ASHRAE Standard 55–2010, Thermal Environmental Conditions for Human Occupancy: ashrae.org

ISO 7730–2005 Ergonomics of the thermal environment, Analytical determination and interpretation of thermal comfort using calculation of the PMV and PPD indices and local thermal comfort criteria: iso.org

CEN Standard EN 15251–2007, Indoor environmental input parameters for design and assessment of energy performance of buildings addressing indoor air quality, thermal environment, lighting and acoustics: cen.eu

EXEMPLARY PERFORMANCE

Not available.

DEFINITIONS

nonregularly occupied space an area that people pass through or an area used for focused activities an average of less than one hour per person per day. The one-hour timeframe is continuous and should be based on the time a typical occupant uses the space. For spaces that are not used daily, the one-hour timeframe should be based on the time a typical occupant spends in the space when it is in use.

unoccupied space an area designed for equipment, machinery, or storage rather than for human activities. An equipment area is considered unoccupied only if retrieval of equipment is occasional.

occupied space an enclosed space intended for human activities, excluding those spaces that are intended primarily for other purposes, such as storage rooms and equipment rooms, and that are only occupied occasionally and for short periods of time. Occupied spaces are further classified as regularly occupied or nonregularly occupied spaces based on the duration of the occupancy, individual or multioccupant based on the quantity of occupants, and densely or nondensely occupied spaces based on the concentration of occupants in the space.

regularly occupied space an area where one or more individuals normally spend time (more than one hour per person per day on average) seated or standing as they work, study, or perform other focused activities inside a building. The one-hour timeframe is continuous and should be based on the time a typical occupant uses the space. For spaces that are not used daily, the one-hour timeframe should be based on the time a typical occupant spends in the space when it is in use.

INDOOR ENVIRONMENTAL QUALITY CREDIT

Interior Lighting

This credit applies to:

Existing Buildings (1–2 points)
Schools (1–2 points)
Retail (1–2 points)
Data Centers (1–2 points)
Hospitality (1–2 points)
Warehouses and Distribution Centers (1–2 points)

INTENT

To promote occupants' productivity, comfort, and well-being by providing high-quality lighting.

REQUIREMENTS

EXISTING BUILDINGS, SCHOOLS, RETAIL, DATA CENTERS, HOSPITALITY, WAREHOUSES AND DISTRIBUTION CENTERS

ESTABLISHMENT E

OPTION 1. LIGHTING CONTROL (1 POINT)

For at least 50% of individual occupant spaces, have in place individual lighting controls that enable occupants to adjust the lighting to suit their individual tasks and preferences, with at least three lighting levels or scenes (on, off, midlevel). Midlevel is 30% to 70% of the maximum illumination level (not including daylight contributions).

For all shared multi-occupant spaces, meet all of the following requirements.

- Have in place multizone control systems that enable occupants to adjust the lighting to meet group needs and preferences, with at least three lighting levels or scenes (on, off, midlevel).
- Lighting for any presentation or projection wall must be separately controlled.
- Switches or manual controls must be located in the same space as the controlled luminaires. A person operating the controls must have a direct line of sight to the controlled luminaires.

HOSPITALITY ONLY

Guest rooms are assumed to have adequate lighting controls and are therefore not included in the credit calculations.

AND/OR

OPTION 2. LIGHTING QUALITY (1 POINT)

Choose four of the following strategies.

A. For all regularly occupied spaces, have in place light fixtures with a luminance of less than 2,500cd/m² between 45 and 90 degrees from nadir.
Exceptions include wallwash fixtures properly aimed at walls, as specified by manufacturer's data, indirect uplighting fixtures, provided there is no view down into these uplights from a regularly occupied space above, and any other specific applications (i.e. adjustable fixtures).

B. For the entire project, have in place light sources with a CRI of 80 or higher. Exceptions include lamps or fixtures specifically designed to provide colored lighting for effect, site lighting, or other special use.

C. For at least 75% of the total connected lighting load, have in place light sources that have a rated life (or L70 for LED sources) of at least 24,000 hours (at 3-hour per start, if applicable).

D. Have in place direct-only overhead lighting for 25% or less of the total connected lighting load for all regularly occupied spaces.

E. For at least 90% of the regularly occupied floor area, meet or exceed the following thresholds for area-weighted average surface reflectance: 85% for ceilings, 60% for walls, and 25% for floors.

F. Meet or exceed the following thresholds for area-weighted average surface reflectance: 45% for work surfaces and 50% for movable partitions.

G. For at least 75% of the regularly occupied floor area, meet a ratio of average wall surface illuminance (excluding fenestration) to average work surface illuminance that does not exceed 1:10. Must also meet strategy E, strategy F, or demonstrate area-weighted surface reflectance of at least 60% for walls.

H. For at least 75% of the regularly occupied floor area, meet a ratio of average ceiling illuminance (excluding fenestration) to work surface illuminance that does not exceed 1:10. Must also meet strategy E, strategy F, or demonstrate area-weighted surface reflectance of at least 85% for ceilings.

PERFORMANCE P

None.

BEHIND THE INTENT

Studies of lighting in buildings have shown that workers are more comfortable and productive in an environment that is carefully illuminated and where lighting controls are provided for individual and group needs.[1]

Also, high-quality lighting helps eliminate distractions, creates visual interest and a sense of place, supports interaction and communication, contributes to occupants' well-being, and reduces health problems.[2] This credit rewards lighting quality that dramatically improves occupants' comfort and productivity.[3]

The credit encourages lighting quality in multiple ways.

- Minimizing light fixture luminance (strategy A) helps reduce disability and discomfort glare; the limit, 2,500 candela per square meter, was selected because research by the Light Right Consortium found that above that level, glare became objectionable.
- Having light sources with a color rendering index above 80 (strategy B) helps approximate natural light.
- Installing lamps with a long life (strategy C) can lengthen the period over which the integrity of the lighting design is maintained; it also reduces maintenance costs and lowers material and resource inputs. A lamp life of 24,000 hours promotes the use of longer-life fluorescents.
- Using less direct-only overhead lighting (strategy D) helps minimize glare, reduces the perceived brightness of the direct luminaires, and reduces contrast between ceiling and luminaire.
- Having surfaces with high reflectance (strategies E and F) help make the space brighter through reflection, minimizing the difficulty of viewing light documents on dark surfaces; the specific surface reflectance values for ceilings, walls, and floors are above the standard industry assumptions of 80, 50, and 20, respectively, as recommended in the latest edition of the Illuminating Engineering Society (IES) Lighting Handbook.[4]
- Maintaining an illuminance ratio less than 1:10 (strategies G and H) minimizes the amount of contrast that occupants experience between their work surface and the ceiling and wall surfaces around them; the 1:10 illuminance ratio represents one log scale difference in lighting levels (human eyes are logarithmic, but illuminance is linear).

Research on lighting and visual performance is cited in *Further Explanation, Additional Lighting Resources*.

STEP-BY-STEP GUIDANCE

STEP 1. DETERMINE EXISTING INTERIOR LIGHTING CONDITIONS E

Inventory and evaluate the interior lighting in the building to understand the existing lighting conditions.

- Categorize controls for all lighting, including task lighting, by location type (either individual occupant space or multioccupant space).
- Identify luminaire characteristics, including lamp specifications. Identify sources of light distribution patterns from manufacturers' literature. Measurements may be required for discontinued luminaires.
- Estimate reflectances and illuminance ratios.

STEP 2. SELECT OPTION(S) E

Work with the owner to understand the occupants' lighting needs, review the results of the interior lighting inventory, and determine which interior lighting credit option(s) the project should pursue.

1. *Lighting Quality and Office Work: A Field Simulation Study, lrc.rpi.edu/researchAreas/pdf/LRAlbanyStudyReport.pdf.*
2. *Federal Lighting Guide, eere.energy.gov/femp/pdfs/light_controls.pdf (accessed June 11, 2013).*
3. *Veitch, J.A., et al., "Lighting Appraisal, Well-Being, and Performance in Open-Plan Offices: A Linked Mechanisms Approach," Lighting Research and Technology 40(2) (June 2008): 133-151.*
4. *DiLaura, David, Kevin Houser, Richard Mistrick, and Gary Steff, eds., The Lighting Handbook, 10th edition (New York: Illuminating Engineering Society of North America, 2011).*

If the project has multiple tenants or reduced occupancy, see *Getting Started* and consider any potential challenges with meeting the credit requirements.

- Option 1 requires lighting controls for 50% of the individual occupant spaces and 100% of shared, multioccupant spaces. Standard on-off switches are not acceptable; at least three lighting levels or scenes must be provided. Project teams that are familiar with previous versions of LEED may prefer this option.

  However, installing lighting controls may not be straightforward, depending on how easily the existing controls and their associated lighting can be upgraded. A wireless control system might allow all fixtures to be retrofit so that they can be individually addressed and controlled.

  Lighting for individual occupant spaces may be provided with task lighting. Outlet-powered task lighting provides a simple and effective way to add additional control in existing buildings. Even greater control can be achieved with larger ambient lighting zones that are subswitched to create smaller lighting zones.

- Option 2 offers eight strategies (Table 1), of which four must be implemented to meet the requirements.

  Strategies A–D are based on characteristics of the lighting fixtures, light sources, and luminaires. For strategies A, B, and C, the performance of lamps in a specific luminaire may need to be evaluated, either in the building or by a qualified lighting laboratory, to determine compliance. Project teams pursuing MR Credit Purchasing—Lamps may find synergies between the two credits. For strategies C and D, the total connected lighting load for the building needs to be determined.

  Strategies E–H are based on characteristics of the surfaces in the building and the illuminance levels that fall on those surfaces.

  This option requires changing wall color, furniture or flooring, and/or lighting fixtures if the project does not have sufficient surface reflectances and/or illuminance ratios. Evaluate the existing surfaces and determine whether modifications are feasible. Changing the reflectance values significantly may also save energy because fewer lumens are required to deliver the same illumination levels at the work surface.

TABLE 1. Strategies for Option 2, Lighting Quality

Strategy	Scope	Exceptions, exclusions
A. Light fixture luminance	All light fixtures located in regularly occupied spaces	• Wallwash fixtures properly aimed at walls, as specified by manufacturer • Indirect uplighting fixtures, provided there is no view down into these uplights from a regularly occupied space above • Any other specific applications (e.g., adjustable fixtures)
B. Color rendering index (CRI)	All light fixtures	• Lamps or fixtures specifically designed to provide colored lighting for effect • Site lighting • Any other special use
C. Lamp life	75% connected lighting load	—
D. Direct overhead lighting	25% connected lighting load	—
E. Surface reflectance: ceilings, walls, floors	90% of regularly occupied floor area	—
F. Surface reflectance: furnishings	All furniture used for work surfaces	—
G. Surface illuminance ratio: wall to work surface	75% regularly occupied floor area	—
H. Surface illuminance ratio: ceiling to work surface	75% regularly occupied floor area	—

STEP 3. COMPLY WITH OPTION REQUIREMENTS E

Perform upgrades to the building as necessary. For the option(s) selected, follow the appropriate set of steps to confirm compliance.

Option 1. Lighting Control

Identify all individual occupant and shared, multioccupant spaces in the project (see *EQ Overview*).

- Confirm that the lighting controls for individual and multioccupant spaces meet requirements listed in the credit requirements. Task lighting may be used to meet the credit requirements for individual occupant spaces. Task lights are not required to be hardwired.
- All lighting controls must provide at least three lighting levels or scenes: on, off, and a midlevel, defined as 30% to 70% of the maximum illumination level (not including daylight contributions). Daylight does not qualify as a separate lighting level.
- For multioccupant spaces that can be subdivided by movable walls or partitions, provide the required lighting controls for each subdivision of the space.
- Tabulate all individual and multioccupant spaces and their respective lighting controls. Confirm that at least 50% of individual occupant spaces and 100% of multioccupant spaces meet the credit requirements. The percentage of compliant individual occupant spaces is based on the number of spaces, not floor area.

Option 2.

Lighting Quality Strategy A

Identify all regularly occupied spaces in the project and all light fixtures in these spaces (see EQ Overview). The following fixtures may be excluded:

- Wallwash fixtures properly aimed at walls, as specified by manufacturer's data
- Indirect uplighting fixtures, provided there is no view down into these uplights from a regularly occupied space above
- Any other specific applications (e.g., adjustable fixtures)

For the light fixtures, review luminaire cutsheets, Illuminating Engineering Society photometric files, or other documentation to identify luminance between 45 degrees and 90 degrees from nadir and select products that meet the credit requirements. The luminance must be below 2,500 candela per square meter.

Compile documentation that confirms compliance with the credit requirements for luminance.

Lighting Quality Strategy B

Identify all light sources used in the building.

- The following light sources may be excluded: lamps or fixtures specifically designed to provide colored lighting for effect, site lighting, and lamps or fixtures designed for some other special use.
- For the light sources, determine the CRI, not to be confused with correlated color temperature (CCT), which refers to the spectrum of warm to cool. A light source can have a high or low CRI regardless of its CCT.
- Replace all light sources with a CRI below 80.
- Compile documentation about the light sources that confirms compliance with the credit requirements for the lighting's CRI.

Lighting Quality Strategy C

Calculate the total connected lighting load for all lighting within the building, in watts or kilowatts.

- Tabulate luminaires quantities and wattages. For guidance on determining connected lighting load, see ASHRAE 90.1–2010, Sections 9.1.3 and 9.1.4. Plug-in lighting is included in the calculation for connected load.
- For lamp life, review luminaire cutsheets or other documentation. Lamp life depends on the type of source. For traditional light sources, the lamp life is based on the time at which 50% of the test samples have burned out. For LED light sources, the lamp life criterion L70 is based on the time at which the light source has a 30% reduction in light output. Review the IES *Lighting Handbook* for more information on lamp life.
- Calculate the amount of connected lighting load with compliant light source; it must be 75% or greater. If necessary, replace light sources so that at least 75% of the connected lighting load is compliant.
- Compile documentation that confirms compliance with the credit requirements for lamp life.

Lighting Quality Strategy D

Identify all regularly occupied spaces in the project and the total connected lighting load associated with these spaces (see *EQ Overview*).

Tabulate luminaires quantities and wattages. For guidance on determining connected lighting load, see ASHRAE 90.1–2010, Sections 9.1.3 and 9.1.4. Plug-in lighting is included in the calculation for connected load.

- Determine the connected lighting load that is associated with direct-only overhead lighting. If necessary, replace direct-only overhead lighting so that it contributes to 25% or less of the connected lighting load.
- Compile documentation that confirms compliance with the credit requirements for overhead lighting.

Surface Reflectance, E and F

Evaluate whether high-reflectance finish materials exist in the building as applicable to the strategy pursued: ceilings, walls, and floors for strategy E, and work surfaces and movable partitions for strategy F.

- If available, review manufacturers' cutsheets to identify reflectance, typically expressed as a fraction or percentage LR (light reflectance) or LRV (light reflectance value). If manufacturers' data do not include reflectance, or if the manufacturer data is unknown, measure the reflectance of the product using the methodology described in IES *Lighting Handbook*, Section 9.12.2, Measuring Reflectance and Transmittance. Or use reflectance charts, such as Lighting Guide 11, Surface Reflectance and Colour.[5]
- For strategy E, 10% of the regularly occupied floor area may be excluded.
- For strategy F, work surfaces include desk and table surfaces where individuals perform tasks. The surface area for movable partitions is limited to opaque surfaces of the partition; transparent or partially transparent surfaces are not included in the calculation.
- Use Equation 1 to calculate the average surface reflectance for walls, ceilings, and floors (strategy E) and work surfaces and movable partitions (strategy F).

EQUATION 1. Average surface reflectance

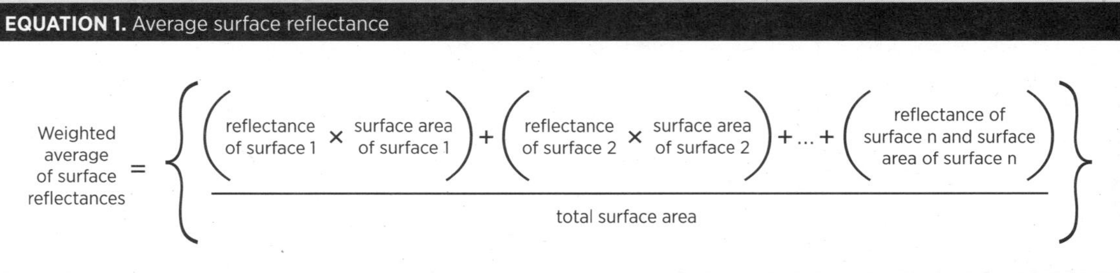

$$\text{Weighted average of surface reflectances} = \left\{ \frac{(\text{reflectance of surface 1} \times \text{surface area of surface 1}) + (\text{reflectance of surface 2} \times \text{surface area of surface 2}) + \ldots + (\text{reflectance of surface n and surface area of surface n})}{\text{total surface area}} \right\}$$

- Confirm that the average surface reflectance of the specified surfaces meets or exceeds the values in the credit requirements.

Illuminance, Strategies G and H

- Identify all regularly occupied spaces in the project and the associated floor area (see *EQ Overview*).
- Take measurements to determine the average illuminance levels on work, wall, and ceiling surfaces. If illuminance values vary widely throughout the space, either subdivide or use the predominant illuminance level. The illuminance of a given surface is measured with a light meter, with the sensor facing away from the surface for which the measurement is being taken. Work surfaces include desk and table surface where individuals perform tasks.
- Use Equation 2 (for Strategy G) and Equation 3 (for Strategy H) to calculate an illuminance ratio for each regularly occupied space. Determine the percentage of regularly occupied area that achieves an illuminance ratio of 1:10 or less, it must be at least 75%.

EQUATION 2. Wall to work plane illuminance ratio

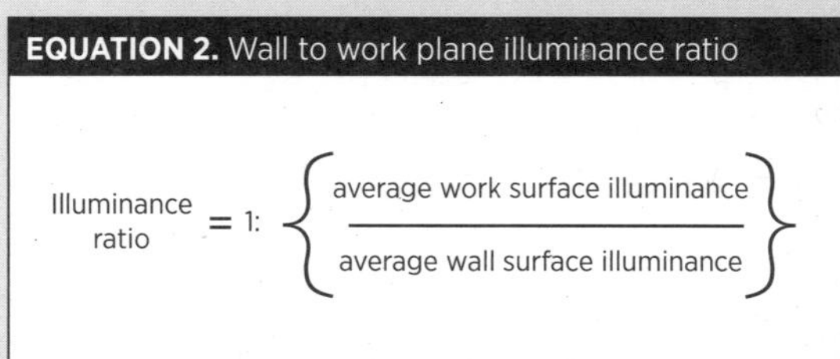

$$\text{Illuminance ratio} = 1{:} \left\{ \frac{\text{average work surface illuminance}}{\text{average wall surface illuminance}} \right\}$$

EQUATION 3. Ceiling to work plane illuminance ratio

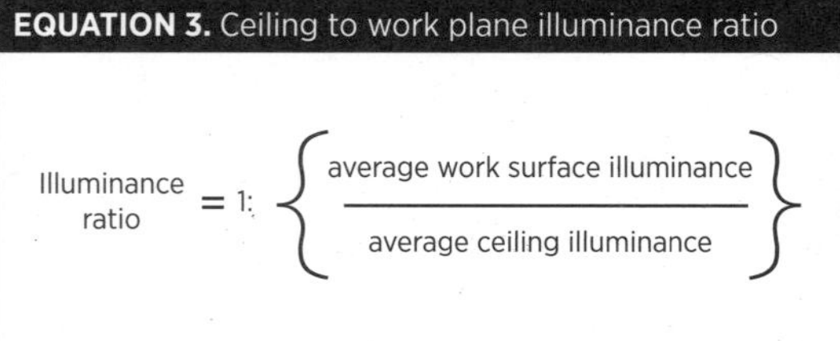

$$\text{Illuminance ratio} = 1{:} \left\{ \frac{\text{average work surface illuminance}}{\text{average ceiling illuminance}} \right\}$$

5. *cibseknowledgeportal.co.uk (accessed June 11, 2013).*

- Spaces with similar ratios of wall surface and/or ceiling surface illuminance to work surface illuminance can be assessed through a single representative measurement and calculation.
- Compile documentation that confirms compliance with the credit requirements for illuminance, As applicable, include confirmation that one of the following has also been met: strategy E, strategy F, area-weighted surface reflectances of at least 60% for walls, or area-weighted surface reflectances of at least 85% for ceilings.

If upgrades are needed to improve the illuminance ratio, consider the following design strategies:

- Use ceiling and wall finishes that are light colored or have high surface reflectance.
- Modify the lighting system to intentionally light the walls or ceiling.
- Consider luminaires that throw 20% to 30% of light on ceiling and/or wall, such as direct-indirect lighting.
- Arrange luminaires to provide wall wash.

FURTHER EXPLANATION

CALCULATIONS

See calculations in *Step-by-Step Guidance*.

EXAMPLES

Example 1. Option 1

An office has individual occupant spaces (workstations), private offices, and a conference room. The workstations have task lighting that is part of the furniture system; the control allows for four distinct light levels. The private offices have overhead lighting with manual dimming controls. The conference room can be divided into two spaces, each with its own set of manual controls for overhead lighting. The overhead lighting is divided into two separate zones and is also fully dimmable. There are separate controls for lighting the presentation wall. Because this office has the appropriate lighting controls for at least 90% of the individual occupant spaces and all shared, multioccupant spaces, the project earns 1 point under Option 1 of the credit.

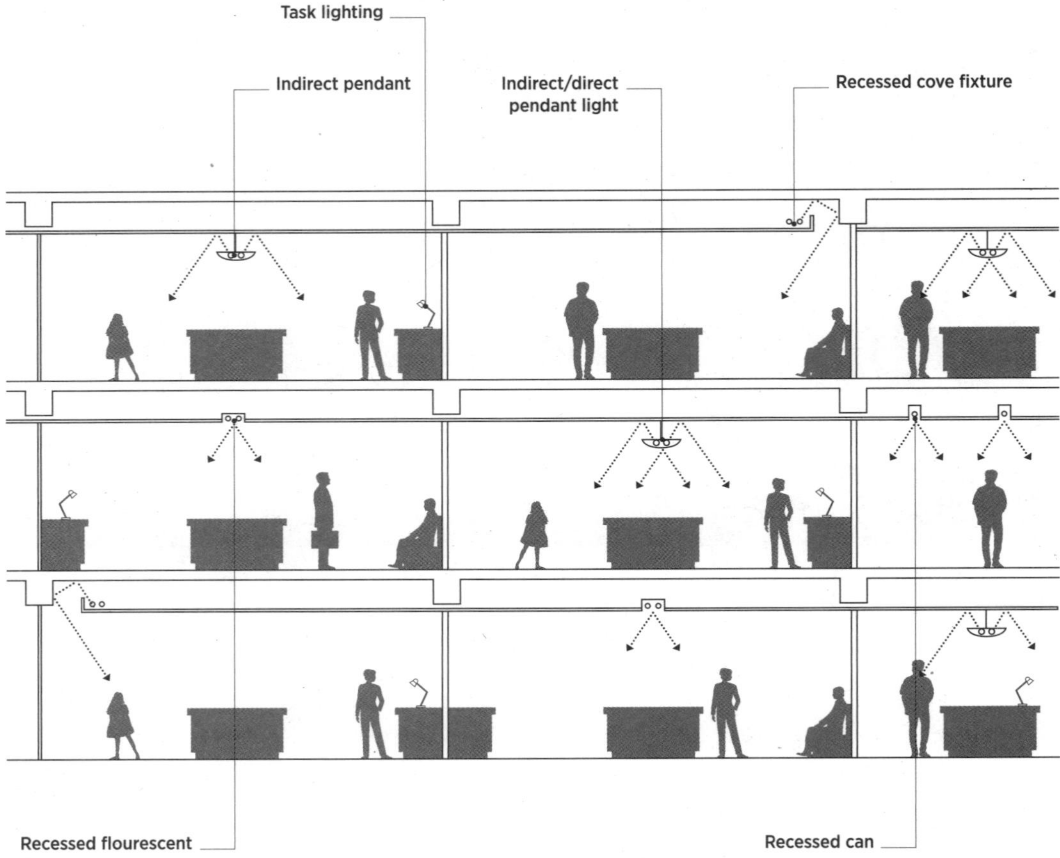

Figure 1. Example 1

Example 2. Option 2, lighting quality, strategies A and D

The building engineer has inventoried the installed lighting in the project's regularly occupied spaces and summarized applicable lighting data in Table 2.

For strategy A, two luminaire types (indirect pendant and indirect-direct pendant) are excluded because there is no view of these luminaires from above. There is one luminaire type that does not meet the requirement, the surface-mounted luminaires. For this reason, the project does not achieve strategy A.

For strategy D, there are two direct-only overhead lights: recessed and surface mounted. The percentage of connected lighting load attributed to these lights is 5.7 % which is well below the 25% threshold. For this reason, the project achieves strategy D.

TABLE 2. Luminaire information for Example 2

Description	Connected load per luminaire (W)	Luminaires	Total connected load (W)	Luminance <2,500 cd/m^2 between 45° and 90° from nadir	Excluded from strategy A	Direct-only?
Indirect pendant	112	8	896	N	Y	N
Recessed	56	4	224	Y	N	Y
Surface mounted	32	1	32	N	N	Y
Indirect-direct pendant	168	20	3,360	N	Y	N
Total connected lighting load (W): 4,512						
Percentage of connected lighting load that is direct-only: 5.7% (256 W)						

Example 3. Option 2, lighting quality, strategies B and C

Data for all light sources in the building are summarized in Table 3.

For strategy B, all three light sources have a CRI above 80. For this reason, the project achieves strategy B.

For strategy C, the lamp life for the linear fluorescent T8 and linear LED cove light both meet the lamp life requirement of 24,000 hours or more rated life or L70. The percentage of connected lighting load attributed to the light fixtures with these lamps is 96.2 % which is well above the 75% threshold. For this reason, the project achieves strategy C.

TABLE 3. Example 3, light source information

Light source description	Total connected load for fixtures (W)	CRI	Lamp life (hours)
Linear fluorescent T8	5,320	82	26,000
Halogen	250	99	5,000
Linear LED cove light	1,000	81	L70
Total connected load (W): 6,570			
Percentage of connected lighting load that meets lamp life requirement: 96.2% (6,320 W)			

Example 4. Option 2, lighting quality, strategies E and F

The values of the reflectance for the building ceilings, walls, floors, work surfaces, and partitions were determined. The results are summarized in Figure 2 below.

Figure 2. Supplemental calculator

Surface Information		Surface Reflectance for Ceilings, Walls, Floors			Surface Reflectance for Furnishings	
		Pctg. total regularly occupied floor area included below (%)		100%		
Description of Surface High reflectance ceiling	Reflectance (%) 90.00%	Ceiling Area (sq ft)	Wall Area (sq ft)	Floor Area (sq ft)	Work Surface Area (sq ft)	Moveable Partition Area (sq ft)
high reflectance ceiling	90.00%	26786.00				
generic ceiling	80.00%	216.00				
wall type 1	65.00%		7312.00			
wall type 2	55.00%		500.00			
light wood floor	27.00%			500.00		
dark carpet	12.00%			216.00		
light carpet	25.00%			26286.00		
workstation type 1	60.00%				2000.00	
workstation type 2	50.00%				20.00	
workstation type 3	10.00%				500.00	
partition type 1	50.00%					80.00
partition type 2	55.00%					40.00
Total area incl. in calculation		**27002.00**	**7812.00**	**27002.00**	**2520.00**	**120.00**
E. Surface Reflectance for Ceilings, Walls, Floors	Average surface reflectance for ceilings					90%
	Average surface reflectance for walls					64%
	Average surface reflectance for floors					25%
F. Surface Reflectance for Furnishings	Average surface reflectance for work surfaces					50%
	Average surface reflectance for moveable partitions					52%

Example 5. Option 2, lighting quality, strategies G and H

The illuminance values for all wall, ceiling, and work surfaces in the regularly occupied spaces have been measured and documented (Table 4). Private office 2 was excluded from the calculation because the office has low wall and ceiling illuminance values.

The project team wishes to use strategies G and H. The wall to work surface illuminance ratio exceeds 1:10 in the open office, which constitutes the majority of the floor area in the project, so the project does not attain strategy G.

However, the ceiling to work surface illuminance ratio is below 1:10 for the open office, private office 1, and the conference room. The project has also achieved strategy E, so the project complies with strategy H.

TABLE 4. Illuminance information for Example 5

Space	Floor area (ft^2)	Average illuminance (footcandles)			Illuminance ratio	
		Work surface	Wall	Ceiling	Wall to work surface	Ceiling to work surface
Open office	26,284	80 (861 lux)	7 (75 lux)	20 (214 lux)	1:11.4	1:4
Private office 1	96	75 (807 lux)	10 (107 lux)	25 (267 lux)	1:7.5	1:3
Conference room	500	60 (642 lux)	10 (107 lux)	15 (160 lux)	1:6	1:4
Private office 2	120	n/a	n/a	n/a	n/a	n/a
Total regularly occupied floor area (ft^2): 27,000						
Percentage of regularly occupied floor area that meets wall to work surface illuminance ratio of 1:10 or less (must be 75%): 2.2% (596 ft^2)						
Percentage of regularly occupied floor area that meets ceiling to work surface illuminance ratio of 1:10 or less (must be 75%): 99.6% (26,880 ft^2)						

ADDITIONAL LIGHTING RESOURCES

Studies of the effect of lighting on visual performance and comfort can be found in the following sources:

Peter R. Boyce, *Human Factors in Lighting*, 2nd edition (Taylor and Francis, 2003).

Lighting and Human Performance II (available at no cost from EPRI): my.epri.com/portal/server.pt?

Lighting Guide 11: Surface Reflectance and Colour: cibseknowledgeportal.co.uk/

Lighting Research Center, Rensselaer Polytechnic Institute: lrc.rpi.edu/

National Research Council Canada Institute for Research in Construction: nrc-cnrc.gc.ca/eng/ibp/irc.html

J.A. Veitch, "Psychological Processes Influencing Lighting Quality," *Journal of the Illuminating Engineering Society* 30(1) (2001): 124–40

The Lighting Handbook, 10th edition (Illuminating Engineering Society of North America, 2011): ies.org

RATING SYSTEM VARIATIONS

Retail

For Option 1, follow the steps for Option 1 for office and administration areas. In addition, provide at least three lighting levels: on, off, and a midlevel in sales areas.

Hospitality

For Option 1, exclude guest rooms from lighting control calculations.

PROJECT TYPE VARIATIONS

Residential

For Option 1, residential units must have one lighting control for each individual occupant and multioccupant space. For example, a bedroom is listed as individual occupancy. A task light in the bedroom or an overhead light with manual dimmable control would be acceptable. See *EQ Overview* for a detailed list of individual and multioccupant space types in residential buildings.

CAMPUS

Group Approach

All buildings in the group may be documented as one.

Campus Approach

Ineligible. Each LEED project may pursue the credit individually.

REQUIRED DOCUMENTATION

	Documentation	Option 1	Option 2							
			A	B	C	D	E	F	G	H
E	Table of individual occupant and multioccupant spaces and lighting controls in each space	X								
E	List of light fixtures for all regularly occupied spaces and luminance information.		X							
E	List of all light sources in project and light source CRI			X						
E	List of all light sources in project with lamp life rated 24,000 hours (or L70 for LED sources) and connected load information				X					
E	List of light fixtures for all regularly occupied spaces, indicating percentage of connected load for any direct-only overhead lights					X				
E	Calculations of total connected lighting load				X	X				
E	List of ceiling, wall, and floor surfaces in regularly occupied spaces and their associated surface reflectance values						X			
E	List of work surfaces and movable partitions in regularly occupied spaces and their associated surface reflectance values							X		
E	Average surface reflectance calculations						X	X		
E	List of work surfaces in regularly occupied spaces and illuminance values (lux)								X	
E	List of wall or ceiling surfaces in regularly occupied spaces with illuminance values (lux)									X
E	Illuminance ratio calculations								X	X
E	Confirmation that strategy E, strategy F, or an acceptable surface reflectance value has been met.								X	X

RELATED CREDIT TIPS

EQ Credit Thermal Comfort. Individual and multioccupant spaces for this credit must be consistent with those for the related credit.
EA Credit Existing Building Commissioning—Analysis and EA Credit Existing Building Commissioning—Implementation. Inventory and replacement of luminaires, lamps, and lighting controls may be considered as a part of the existing building commissioning and/or energy audit.

MR Credit Purchasing—Lamps. Lamps purchased through the lighting purchasing plan should be consistent with the strategies selected in this credit.

CHANGES FROM LEED 2009

- An additional point and option for lighting quality have been added.
- The requirements for lighting control have been revised to require at least three lighting levels: on, off, and a midlevel.

REFERENCED STANDARDS

The Lighting Handbook, 10th edition, Illuminating Engineering Society of North America: ies.org

EXEMPLARY PERFORMANCE

Not available.

DEFINITIONS

color rendering index a measurement from 0 to 100 that indicates how accurately an artificial light source, as compared with an incandescent light, displays hues. The higher the index number, the more accurately the light is rendering colors. Incandescent lighting has a color rendering index above 95; standard high-pressure sodium lighting (such as orange-hued roadway lights) measures approximately 25; many fluorescent sources using rare earth phosphors have a color rendering index of 80 and above. (Adapted from U.S. ENERGY STAR)

illuminance the incident luminous flux density on a differential element of surface located at a point and oriented in a particular direction, expressed in lumens per unit area. Since the area involved is differential, it is customary to refer to this as illuminance at a point. The unit name depends on the unit of measurement for area: footcandles if square feet are used for area, and lux if square meters are used. (Adapted from Illuminating Engineering Society) In lay terms, illuminance is a measurement of light striking a surface. It is expressed in footcandles in the U.S. (based on square feet) and in lux in most other countries (based on square meters).

individual occupant space an area where an occupant performs distinct tasks. Individual occupant spaces may be within multioccupant spaces and should be treated separately where possible.

shared multioccupant space a place of congregation, or where occupants pursue overlapping or collaborative tasks

INDOOR ENVIRONMENTAL QUALITY CREDIT

Daylight and Quality Views

This credit applies to:

Existing Buildings (2–4 points)
Schools (2–4 points)
Retail (2–4 points)
Data Centers (2–4 points)
Hospitality (2–4 points)
Warehouses and Distribution Centers (2–4 points)

INTENT

To connect building occupants with the outdoors, reinforce circadian rhythms, and reduce the use of electrical lighting by introducing daylight and views into the space.

REQUIREMENTS

ESTABLISHMENT E

OPTION 1. DAYLIGHT MEASUREMENT (2 POINTS)

Achieve illuminance levels between 300 lux and 3,000 lux for at least 50% of the regularly occupied floor area.

With furniture, fixtures, and equipment in place, measure illuminance levels as follows:

- Measure at appropriate work plane height during any hour between 9 a.m. and 3 p.m.
- Take one measurement in any regularly occupied month, and take a second as indicated in Table 1.
- For spaces larger than 150 square feet (14 square meters), take measurements on a maximum 10 foot (3 meter) square grid.
- For spaces 150 square feet (14 square meters) or smaller, take measurements on a maximum 3 foot (900 millimeter) square grid.

TABLE 1. Timing of measurements for illuminance

If first measurement is taken in ...	take second measurement in ...
January	May-September
February	June-October
March	June-July, November-December
April	August-December
May	September-January
June	October-February
July	November-March
August	December-April
September	December-January, May-June
October	February-June
November	March-July
December	April-August

AND/OR

OPTION 2. QUALITY VIEWS (2 POINTS)

Achieve a direct line of sight to the outdoors via vision glazing for 50% of all regularly occupied floor area. View glazing in the contributing area must provide a clear image of the exterior, not obstructed by frits, fibers, patterned glazing, or added tints that distort color balance.

Additionally, 50% of all regularly occupied floor area must have at least two of the following four kinds of views:

- multiple lines of sight to vision glazing in different directions at least 90 degrees apart;
- views that include at least two of the following: (1) flora, fauna, or sky; (2) movement; and (3) objects at least 25 feet (7.5 meters) from the exterior of the glazing;
- unobstructed views located within the distance of three times the head height of the vision glazing; and
- views with a view factor of 3 or greater, as defined in "Windows and Offices; A Study of Office Worker Performance and the Indoor Environment."

Include in the calculations any permanent interior obstructions (e.g., lab hoods, fixed partitions, demountable opaque full- or partial-height partitions). Movable furniture and partitions may be excluded.

Views into interior atria may be used to meet up to 30% of the required area.

WAREHOUSES AND DISTRIBUTION CENTERS ONLY

For the office portion of the building, meet the requirements above.

For the bulk storage, sorting, and distribution portions of the building, meet the requirements above for 25% of the regularly occupied floor area.

PERFORMANCE P

None.

BEHIND THE INTENT

Increased access to daylight has positive human behavioral and health effects because it reinforces our circadian rhythms.[1] Access to sufficient daylight has been shown to increase healing times in hospitals, improve students' performance,[2] increase productivity in the workplace,[3] fight depression and lethargy, and even increase sales in retail environments.[4] A well-designed daylit building also uses less electric lighting energy, conserving natural resources and reducing air pollution.

Building occupants who can visually connect with outdoor environments while performing everyday tasks experience greater satisfaction, attentiveness, and productivity. Outside views that incorporate natural elements are more enticing and offer better visual respite. Workers seated at computers, who often develop eye strain or dry eyes from looking at their screens for extended periods without a break, find relief in attractive distance views.[5]

Views to the outdoors also connect the occupants with natural environmental cues, such as diurnal changes from light to dark and the changes in light from season to season, which are important for maintaining natural circadian rhythms. Disruption of these rhythms can lead to long-term health care problems, including mental disorders.[6]

For the daylighting portion of this credit, compliance is based on actual daylight measurements—the easiest and best method for determining the level of daylight in an existing building. For the views portion, compliance is based on the quality of views from inside the building. Specifically, glazing color, frit, and patterns have been restricted to ensure that quality views are maintained. Additionally, the type of objects visible in the view (e.g., vegetation, sky, brick wall, busy street) is now an important factor. Four credit paths give teams flexibility in achieving compliance. Also, the credit atriums may now account for up to 30% of the required area with access to quality views—a change based on industry recognition that atriums can not only increase daylight and views for interior spaces but also reduce the need for electrical lighting in spaces that would otherwise likely require it.

STEP-BY-STEP GUIDANCE

STEP 1. IDENTIFY REGULARLY OCCUPIED SPACES E

Identify all regularly occupied spaces in the project (see *EQ Overview, Regularly Occupied Spaces*). Highlight regularly occupied spaces on the floor plan or furniture plan and create a tracking table (Table 2) that lists all regularly occupied spaces floor area (square footage or square meters).

1. *Kellert, Stephen R., Judith H. Heerwagen, and Martin L. Mador, Biophilic Design: The Theory, Science and Practice of Bringing Life into Buildings (New York: Wiley, 2008), p. 99.*
2. *Boyce, Peter, Reviews of Technical Reports on Daylight and Productivity (Rensselaer Polytechnic Institute, 2004); Heschong Mahone Group, Daylighting in Schools: An Investigation into the Relationship between Daylighting and Human Performance (1999).*
3. *Edwards, L., and P. Torcellini, A Literature Study of the Effects of Natural Light on Building Occupants. (Golden, Colorado: NREL, 2002).*
4. *Peet, Ramona, Lisa Heschong, Roger Wright, and Don Aumann, Daylighting and Productivity in the Retail Sector (2004), eceee.org/conference_proceedings/ACEEE_buildings/2004/Panel_7/p7_24/paper (accessed June 12, 2013).*
5. *California Energy Commission, Windows and Offices: A Study of Office Worker Performance and Indoor Environment: Technical Report (2003), pp. 8–9, ff. 1–8, energy.ca.gov/2003publications/CEC-500-2003-082/CEC-500-2003-082-A-09.PDF (accessed June 12, 2013); Oklahoma State University Healthy and Safety Office, You Can Do Something about Eyestrain (2011), ehs.okstate.edu/kopykit/eyestrain.htm (accessed June 12, 2013).*
6. *Kellert, Stephen R., Judith H. Heerwagen, and Martin L. Mador, Biophilic Design: The Theory, Science and Practice of Bringing Life into Buildings (New York: Wiley, 2008), p. 91.*

TABLE 2. Example tracking table for quality views

Regularly occupied space ID	Space type	Floor area (ft^2 or m^2)	Quality views		
			Floor area with direct line of sight to outdoors via vision glazing	View types	
				1	2

Determine whether any regularly occupied spaces should be excluded from the daylight and/or views requirements (see *Further Explanation, Project Type Variations*).

- For daylight, spaces where tasks would be hindered by the use of daylight may be excluded.
- For views, spaces whose functional requirements prohibit the incorporation of glazing for direct access to views may be excluded.
- Spaces may not be excluded for security or noise concerns.

STEP 2. SELECT ONE OR BOTH OPTIONS E

Determine which option(s) the project will pursue.

- Option 1 may be appropriate for narrow buildings, since the majority of their regularly used spaces are likely to be within 10 to 15 feet (3 to 4.5 meters) of glazing. Taking preliminary spot daylight measurements can help the team determine the feasibility of achieving this option. Consider the required measurement schedule: the second measurement must be taken at least five months after the first.
- Option 2 is most easily achieved by projects with open floor plans, low partitions, transparent enclosures, and vision glazing on multiple exposures.

Option 1. Daylight Measurement

STEP 1. PREPARE FOR MEASUREMENTS E

Determine when the first and second measurements will be taken.

- Review Table 1 in the credit requirements to determine timing of the second measurement. Both measurements must occur during regularly occupied months. For example, measurements may not be taken in a school during unoccupied recesses.
- Review regularly occupied space floor area to determine the measurement grid according to the credit requirements.
- Draw the measurement grid and the measurement nodes (usually at the center of each grid space) on a floor plan. Alternatively, use tape to mark off the measurement grid on the floor of the actual space and document the grid with photos or a video.

STEP 2. PERFORM MEASUREMENTS E

Use a light meter to take a daylight illuminance measurement at workplane height (30 inches [750 millimeters] above finished floor, unless otherwise defined) between 9 A.M. and 3 P.M. (see *Further Explanation, Solar Time* and *Examples*).

- Refer to the IESNA Reference Guide, 10th edition, Section 9.7, for more information on light meters.
- Locate each measurement node in the actual space.
- Record the measured illuminance at each node on the floor plan or in a tracking table.

- If measurements cannot be completed for the entire project in one day, continue the following day between 9 A.M. and 3 P.M.
- Repeat the process using the same nodes for the second measurement.

STEP 3. EVALUATE ILLUMINANCE COMPLIANCE E

Review the measurement results and determine the illuminance values for all regularly occupied floor area.

- Record the areas that have illuminance levels between 300 lux and 3,000 lux for both measurements and the associated floor area.
- Confirm that the project meets or exceeds the requirements for at least 50% of the regularly occupied floor area.

STEP 4. PLAN TO MAINTAIN COMPLIANCE P

Develop a plan to confirm that daylight access is maintained when more than 50% of a space undergoes alteration.

Option 2. Quality Views

STEP 1. EVALUATE PROJECT SITE E

Review the project's surroundings to identify the presence of elements that meet the view quality requirements of this credit, such as parks, green roofs and walls, nearby buildings, and pedestrian and vehicle movement.

STEP 2. IDENTIFY SIGHTLINES TO EXTERIOR VIEWS E

On floor plans or furniture plans, identify the locations of perimeter and interior glazing and all permanent interior obstructions.

- Determine whether the perimeter and interior glazing qualifies as vision glazing (see *Further Explanation, Vision Glazing*).
- Identify permanent interior obstructions (see *Definitions*). Movable furniture and partitions as well as movable glare control devices may be included in the calculations, but this is not required.
- Consider performing an initial rough assessment before performing the detailed assessment of view quality. Determine whether the regularly occupied floor area with proximity to vision glazing is at least 50% of the total regularly occupied floor area. If necessary, modify space placement to meet the 50% threshold.

STEP 3. ASSESS VIEW QUALITY E

Identify which kinds of view will be used to demonstrate view quality. For each regularly occupied space or area of the floor plan, select two view types and add the selection to the tracking table. Eligible view types are as follows:

1. Multiple lines of sight to vision glazing in different directions at least 90 degrees apart
2. Views that include at least two of the following: (1) flora, fauna, or sky; (2) movement; and (3) objects at least 25 feet (7.5 meters) from the exterior of the glazing
3. Unobstructed views located within the distance of three times the head height of the vision glazing
4. Views with a view factor of 3 or greater, as defined in *Windows and Offices: A Study of Office Worker Performance and the Indoor Environment.*[7]

The view types may be mixed and matched, but documentation will be simpler if the same view types are used consistently across spaces.

If the entire regularly occupied space or area does not meet the requirements of the selected view type, include only the regularly occupied floor area that complies. To assess the regularly occupied space for each view type selected, perform the following applicable steps (also see *Further Explanation, Examples*).

7. *California Energy Commission, Windows and Offices: A Study of Office Worker Performance and Indoor Environment: Technical Report (2003), pp. 8–9, ff. 1–8, energy.ca.gov/2003publications/CEC-500-2003-082/CEC-500-2003-082-A-09.PDF (accessed June 12, 2013).*

View type 1. Multiple lines of sight to vision glazing in different directions at least 90 degrees apart

On the floor plan or furniture plans, draw two lines of sight to the vision glazing for each location within the space.

- The space or location qualifies if the lines of sight are at least 90 degrees apart and if they are not intercepted by any permanent interior obstructions. If necessary, draw sight lines on section or elevation plans to confirm that permanent interior obstructions do not block the lines of sight.
- It may be easiest to determine the boundary of qualifying areas to nonqualifying areas (Figure 1).
- In lieu of floor plan or furniture plans, use photographs or other documentation to demonstrate multiple lines of sight.

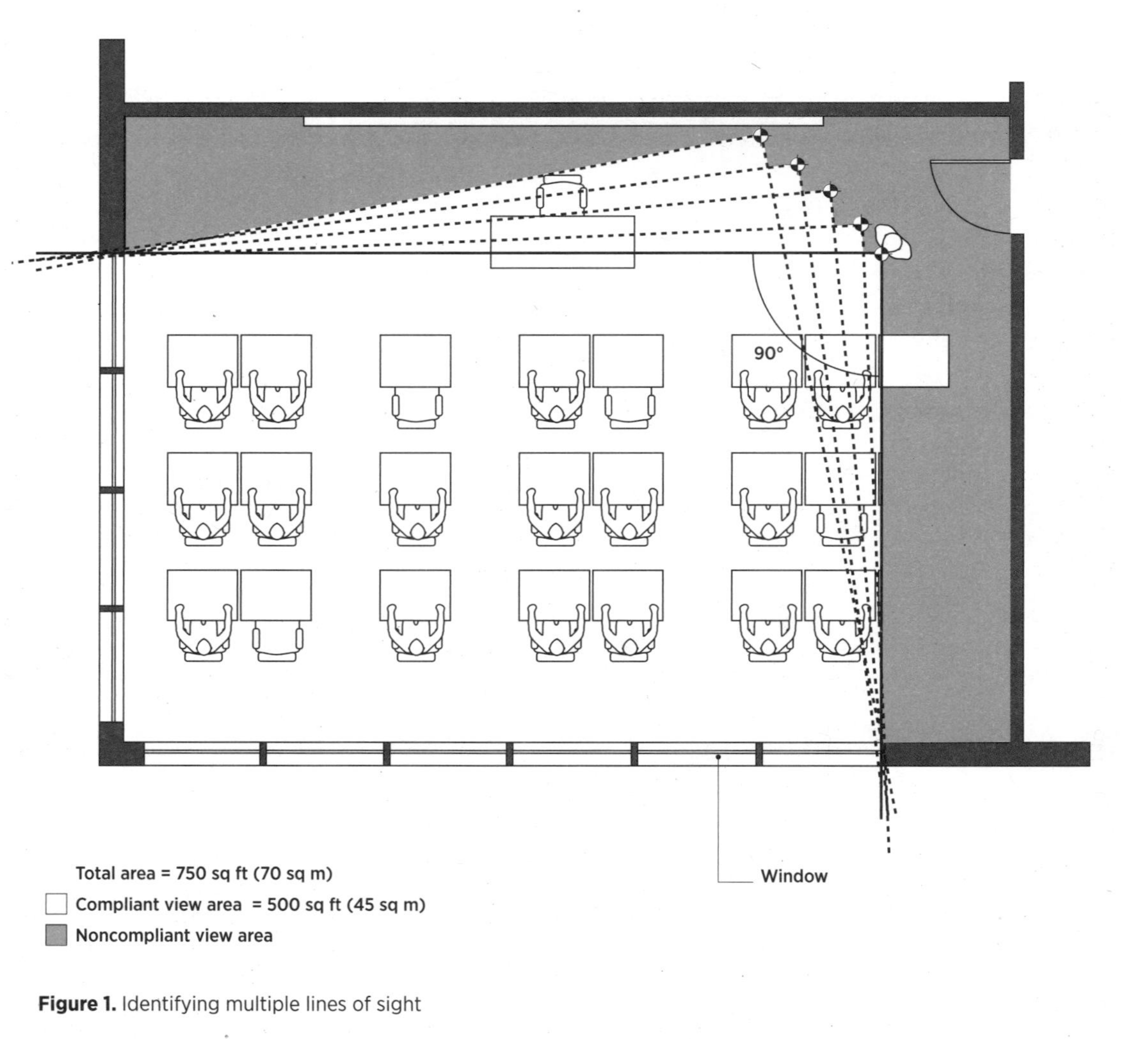

Figure 1. Identifying multiple lines of sight

View type 2. Views that include at least two of the following: (1) flora, fauna, or sky; (2) movement; and (3) objects at least 25 feet (7.5 meters) from the exterior of the glazing

In plan, label the qualifying features located at the vision glazing.

- Two features must be indicated.
- Movement (feature 2) includes such activities as people walking, cars driving on the street, and boats moving through the water. Movement of plants and trees from wind does not qualify.
- Account for any changes in exterior views as floor elevation changes.
- In plan, draw one line of sight to the vision glazing for each location in the space. The space or location qualifies if the line of sight is not intercepted by any permanent interior obstructions. If necessary, draw sight lines on section or elevation plans to confirm permanent interior obstructions do not block the lines of sight.

- In lieu of plans or sections, use photographs or other documentation to demonstrate the features for each view.

View type 3. Unobstructed views located within the distance of three times the head height of the vision glazing

In section, determine the head height of the vision glazing for each regularly occupied space. In plan, identify all regularly occupied floor area that is within three times the head height of the perimeter.

- The space or location qualifies if there are no permanent interior obstructions present in the area. No permanent interior obstructions are allowed, regardless of their height.
- Any regularly occupied floor area not in the identified area does not qualify.
- In lieu of floor plans and sections, use photographs or other documentation to demonstrate unobstructed views.

View type 4. Views with a view factor of 3 or greater, as defined in *Windows and Offices: A Study of Office Worker Performance and the Indoor Environment*

On the floor plan or furniture plan, identify occupants' typical locations in each regularly occupied space (e.g., open-office workstation, enclosed office, conference room seat, counter). Indicate whether the location is the primary view location or a break view location (see *Further Explanation, View Factor*).

- Assess the view factor for each of these locations, based on either the primary view or the break view.
- In section or elevation, or through drawings or images, demonstrate how the view factor was determined.
- In lieu of floor plans or furniture plans and sections, use photographs or other documentation to demonstrate view factors.

STEP 4. CONFIRM COMPLIANCE E

Complete the tracking table to confirm that at least 50% of the regularly occupied floor area has two qualifying view types.

STEP 5. PLAN TO MAINTAIN COMPLIANCE P

Develop a plan to confirm that views are maintained when more than 50% of a space undergoes alteration.

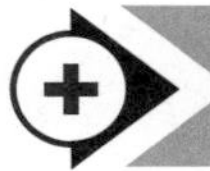

FURTHER EXPLANATION

SOLAR TIME OR LOCAL TIME

When performing daylight measurements, determine whether the measurements will be taken at solar or local time. Both are acceptable, but solar time may be more appropriate because it is based on the position of the sun in the sky.

Solar time varies from the local standard time because of eccentricities in Earth's orbit and because of time zones and daylight saving adjustments. Solar time is typically calculated using a third-party calculator, such as the National Oceanic and Atmospheric Administration's solar calculator.

VIEW FACTOR

View factor is a measure of the amount and quality of views within a 90-degree cone of vision from an individual workstation. View factor is rated from 0 (poor quality) to 5 (high quality).

To achieve this credit, teams may determine the view factor for either primary view, what an occupant would see while working on the phone or computer, or break view, what occupants would see while taking a short break by turning their heads or moving their chairs while remaining seated.

View factor is determined for each workstation by assessing the vertical and lateral viewing angle for either the primary or the break view (Figure 2). To determine view factor, first find the smaller of the vertical or lateral view angle. Use the angle to identify the preliminary view factor (Table 3). If the view angle falls within the gray zone, assess the content of the view. View angles in the gray zone are rated up one level when the view has very high vegetation content, and down one level if the view has no vegetation content.

Alternatively, use Figure 3, which demonstrates examples of different view factors, to visually assess the view factor of a given space.

Figure 2. Assessing view angles

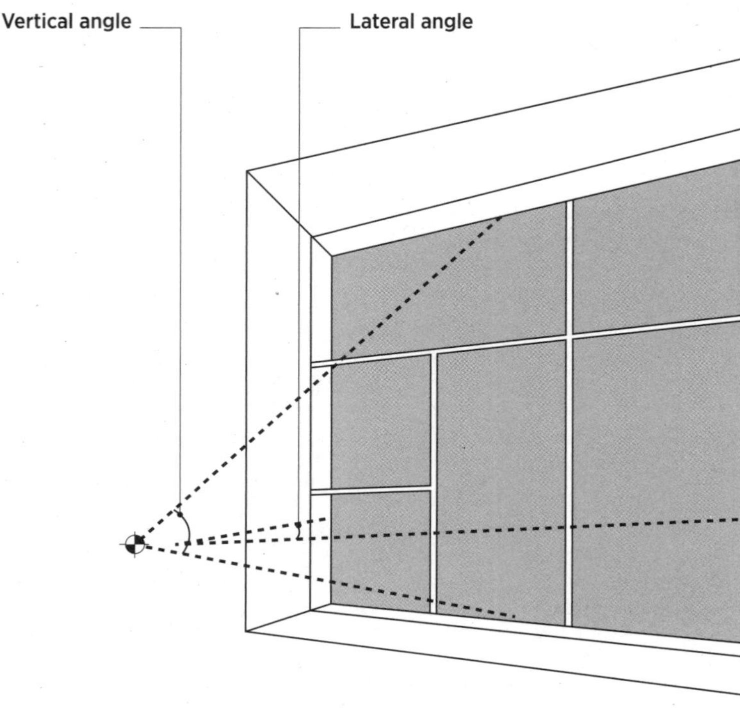

TABLE 3. View factor		
Preliminary view factor	**View angle**	
	Min–max (degrees)	**Gray-zone range (degrees)**
1	1–4	
1 or 2		4–5
2	5–9	
2 or 3		9–11
3	11–15	
3 or 4		15–20
4	20–40	
4 or 5		40–30
5	50–90	

Figure 3 illustrates the view quality associated with each view factor level.

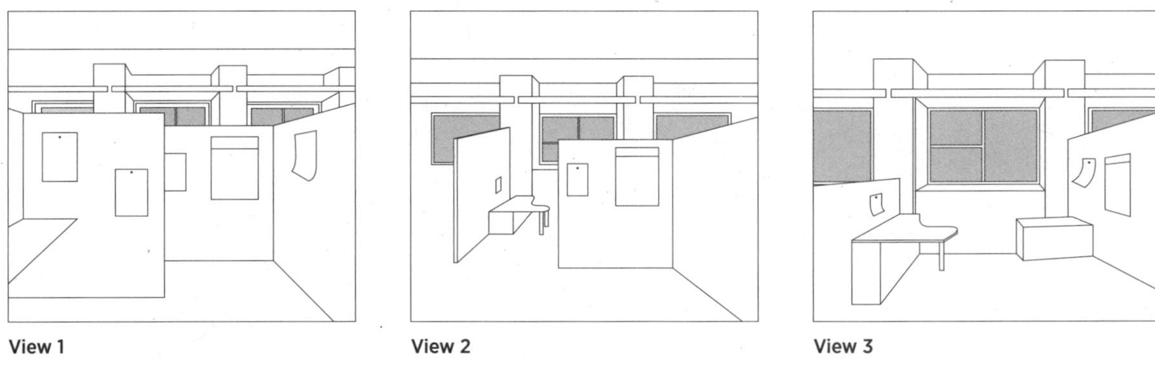

View 1 View 2 View 3

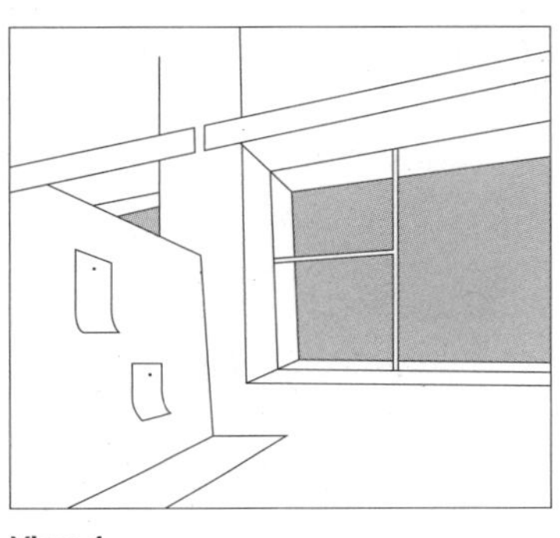

View 4

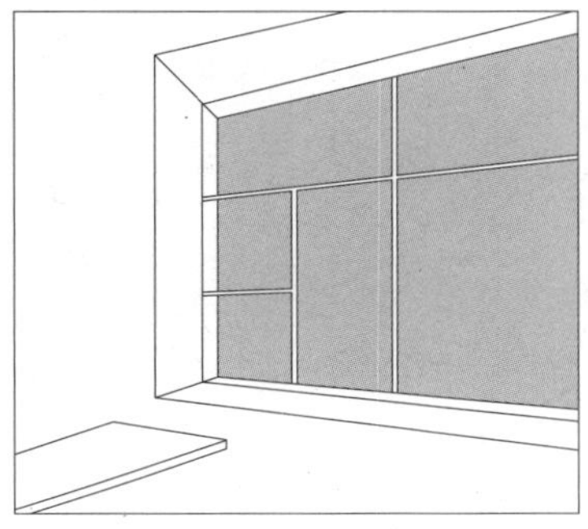

View 5

Figure 3. View factor illustrations

VISION GLAZING

Vision glazing is defined as that portion of exterior windows that permits views to the exterior (or an atrium). Vision glazing must have a clear image of the exterior, not obstructed by frits, fibers, patterned glazing, or added tints that distort color balance (Figures 4–8). Some patterns are acceptable if they preserve the view.

The glazing does not have to be located between 30 and 90 inches (750 and 2 300 millimeters) above the finished floor.

Figures 4–7 illustrate examples of glazing solutions that are eligible for this credit.

Figure 4. Fritted glass with horizontal strips of clear glazing. The area between the upper and lower portions of fritted glass is acceptable vision glazing. Photo by Michael Spillers.

Figure 5. Fritted glass with vertical panels of clear glazing. The glazing between the fritted panels is acceptable vision glazing. Photo by Michael Spillers.

Figure 6. Frosted glass above, clear glazing below. The area below the frosted glazing is acceptable vision glazing. This space also has multiple views more than 90 degrees apart. Photo by Todd Reed.

Figure 7. Lightly tinted glazing. The gray tint darkens the view but does not distort color balance, so it is acceptable vision glazing.

Figure 8 is an example of glazing that is ineligible for this credit.

Figure 8. Partial-height partitions with frosted glass. Frosted glass is not acceptable because it interferes with occupants' views to the vision glazing. Photo by Marcus Sheffer.

EXAMPLES

Example 1. Option 1

An open office with core areas is assessed for compliance with Option 1. Daylight Measurements. The office is in New York City and has six regularly occupied spaces (Table 4) plus several nonregularly occupied spaces, such as mechanical, elevator, and restroom space. The office has equally spaced ribbon glazing on all four sides and a window-to-wall ratio of 63%.

In mid June, the project team took daylight measurements in all regularly occupied spaces. A second set of daylight measurements was taken in October. The two measurements for each space were compared to determine the areas that are compliant at both times. The measurement results for the third-floor private office (301) are displayed in Figures 9 and 10.

TABLE 4. Regularly occupied spaces in example office

Regularly occupied space ID	Floor area (ft^2)	Floor area with daylight illuminance of 300–3,000 lux
2nd-floor open office	9,000	7,200
3rd-floor conference room	500	420
3rd-floor private office 301	96	72
3rd-floor private office 302	120	88
3rd-floor open office	8,284	6,900
4th-floor open office	9,000	7,200
Total regularly occupied area (ft^2)	**27,000**	
Daylighted regularly occupied area (ft^2)	**21,880**	
Regularly occupied area that is daylighted	**81%**	

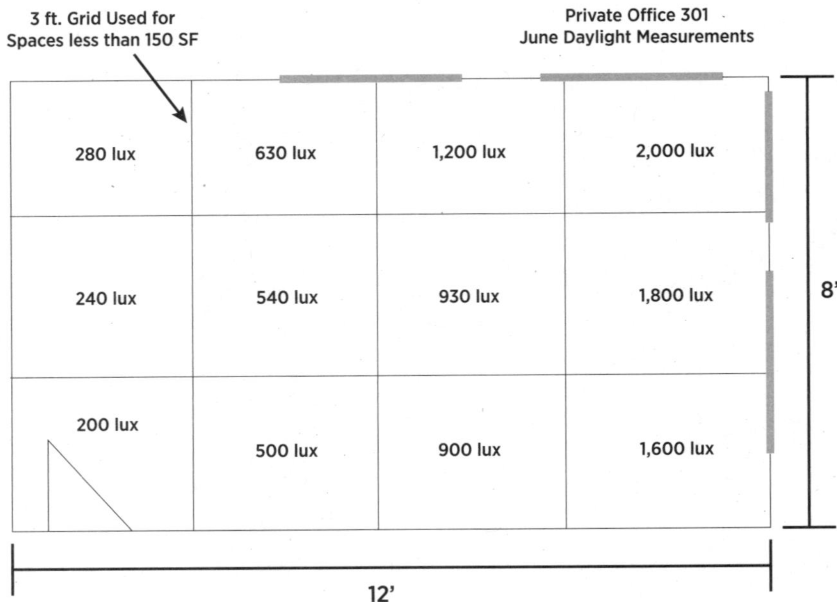

Figure 3. Measurements recorded in June

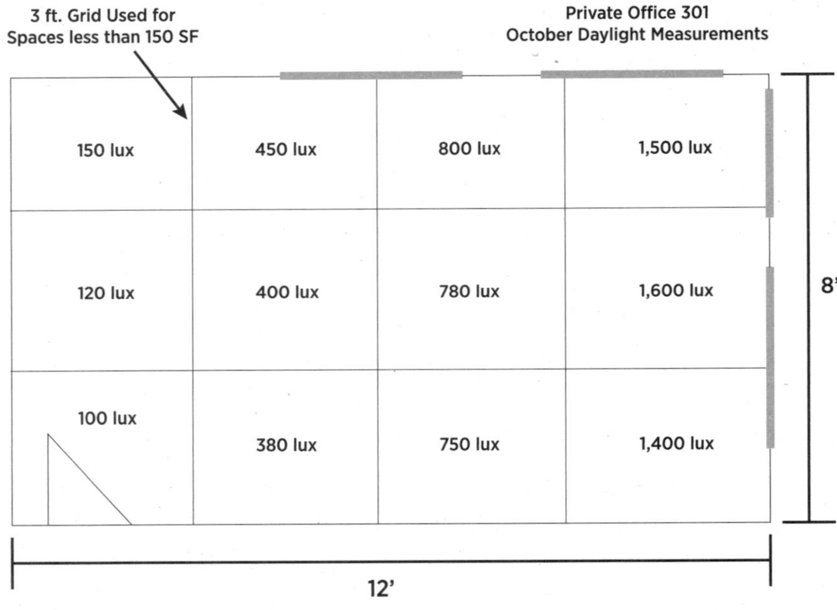

Figure 4. Measurements recorded in October

Example 2. Option 2, quality views, view type 1. Multiple lines of sight to vision glazing in different directions at least 90 degrees apart.

A classroom is assessed for compliance with the requirement for view type 1. The classroom has a total floor area of 750 square feet (70 square meters) and no permanent interior obstructions. To identify compliant areas within the classroom, the team has identified representative points on the classroom floor plan with two lines of sight at least 90 degrees apart (Figure 11) and determined that 500 square feet (45 square meters) of the classroom complies with the requirement.

Figure 11. Lines of sight in classroom

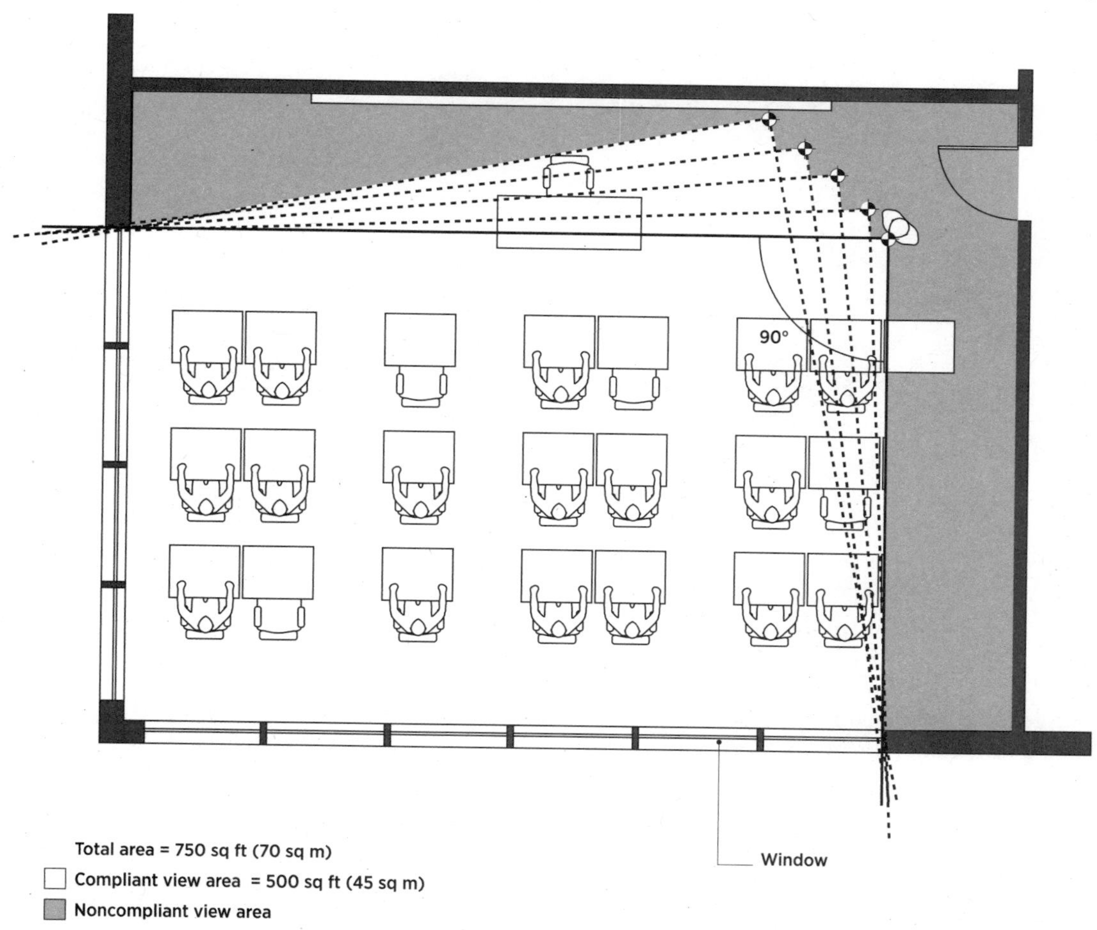

Example 3. Option 2, quality views, view type 2. Views that include at least two of the following: (1) flora, fauna, or sky; (2) movement; and (3) objects at least 25 feet (7.5 meters) from the exterior of the glazing. A regularly occupied space on the southeast side of the project building is assessed for compliance with requirements for view type 2. A section drawing of the building and adjacent properties is prepared to demonstrate that the space has views of trees close to the building and objects 25 feet (7.5 meters) from the exterior glazing (Figure 12). The section also shows that the space, which is an office, has no permanent interior obstructions, so this regularly occupied area meets the requirements.

Figure 12. Flora within sight of space

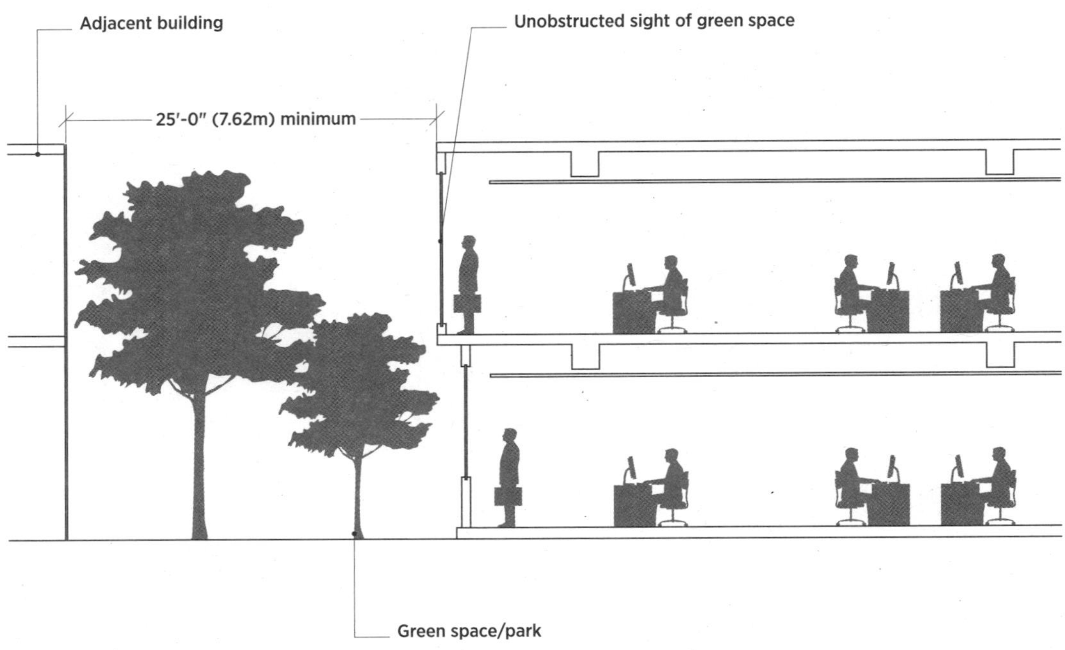

Example 4. Option 2, quality views, view type 2. Views that include at least two of the following: (1) flora, fauna, or sky; (2) movement; and (3) objects at least 25 feet (7.5 meters) from the exterior of the glazing. Figure 13 illustrates an example of a view with flora.

Figure 13. Planters outside a school. Photo by Marcus Sheffer.

Example 5. Option 2, quality views, view type 3. Unobstructed views located within the distance of three times the head height of the vision glazing.

An open-plan office space (Figure 14, Open Office 1) is assessed for compliance with the quality view requirement to have unobstructed views located within the distance of three times the head height of the vision glazing. A section view of the space is prepared to demonstrate that there are no permanent interior obstructions within 29 feet 3 inches (8.9 meters) of the vision glazing, which has a head height of 9 feet 9 inches (3 meters). The office space is compliant with the requirement (Figure 14).

In the same building, a similar open office space is also assessed for compliance. A section view of the space is prepared, but in this case, there are permanent interior obstructions within 29 feet 3 inches (8.9 meters) of the vision glazing, which has a head height of 9 feet 9 inches (3 meters). The fixed workstation with partitions and separate partition are both considered permanent interior obstructions. Open Office 2 is not compliant with the requirement (Figure 14).

Figure 14. Compliant and noncompliant office spaces

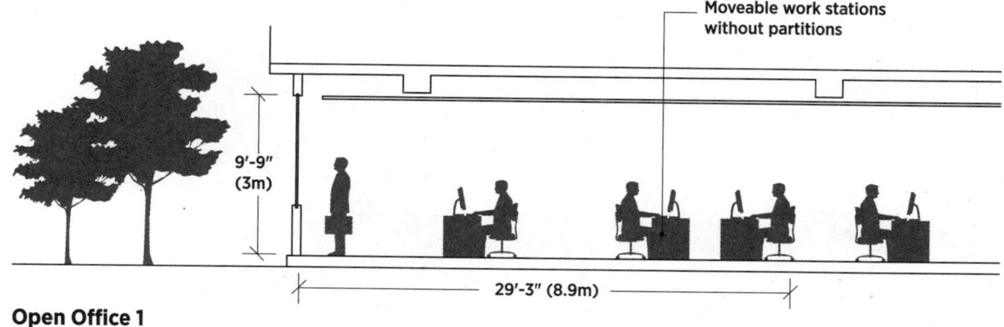

Open Office 1

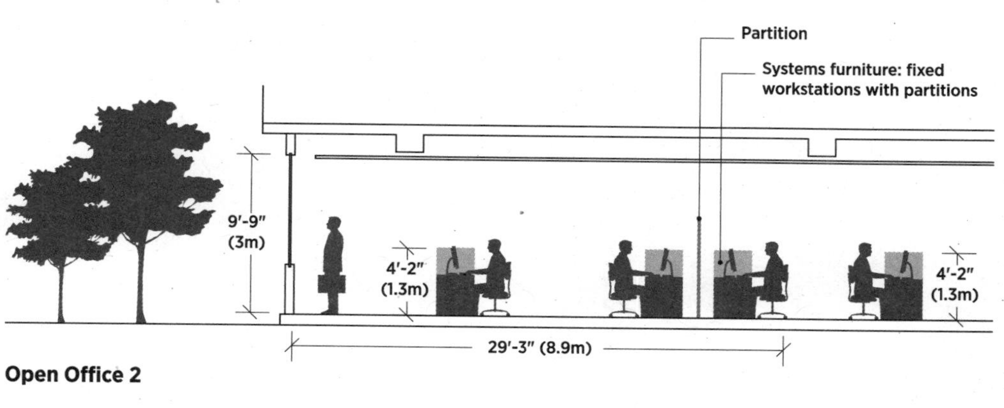

Open Office 2

SCALE: 1' (.3m) 5' (1.5m) 10' (3m)

Example 6. Option 2, quality views, view type 4. Views with a view factor of 3 or greater, as defined in *Windows and Offices: A Study of Office Worker Performance and the Indoor Environment*

The primary view for a workstation in an open-plan office (Figure 15) is evaluated and assigned a view factor of 5, based on the view factor illustrations provided in Figure 3. The view factor is rated 5 because the workstation is directly in front of two large windows, with no obstructions or odd angles disrupting the view to the outdoors.

Figure 15. Workstation with view factor of 5. Photo by Marcus Sheffer.

Example 7. Option 2, quality views, views into atrium

Figure 16 illustrates how views into a sunlit interior space can be an alternative to views to the outdoors. This approach can be used for up to 30% of the regularly occupied floor area. The requirements for direct line of sight and two view types still apply.

Figure 16. Image of view into interior atrium. The Christman Building: Photo by Gene Meadows.

RATING SYSTEM VARIATIONS

Warehouses and Distribution Centers

For bulk storage, sorting, and distribution portions of the building, only 25% of regularly occupied areas must meet the credit criteria.

PROJECT TYPE VARIATIONS

Auditoriums

Auditoriums must be included in the daylight requirements, but a lower illuminance level is acceptable (see recommended illuminance values in *The Lighting Handbook*, Table 24.2).[8] Auditoriums may be excluded from the view requirements.

Conference rooms dedicated to video conferencing

Conference rooms that are dedicated to video conferencing may be excluded from the daylight requirements and the view requirements.

Gymnasiums

Gymnasiums must be included in the daylight requirements. Gymnasiums may be excluded from the view requirements.

CAMPUS

Group Approach

Submit separate documentation for each building.

Campus Approach

Ineligible. Each LEED project may pursue the credit individually.

REQUIRED DOCUMENTATION

	Documentation	Option 1	Option 2			
			View type			
			1: multiple lines of sight	2: exterior features	3: unobstructed views within 3H	4: view factor
E	List of all regularly occupied spaces, with total area and qualifying floor area in each space	X	X	X	X	X
E	Sample daylight measurement report with measured illuminance values for at least one space, height of measurement point, measurement grid size, and results for first and second measurements	X				
E	Calculations demonstrating percentage of compliant space with 300 lux to 3,000 lux.	X				
E	Sample documentation showing how project meets credit requirements for each view type attempted and illustrating at least one space		X	X	X	X

8. *Illuminating Engineering Society, The Lighting Handbook, 10th edition.*

RELATED CREDIT TIPS

None.

CHANGES FROM LEED 2009

- Simulation and prescriptive options for daylighting compliance have been eliminated.
- Option 1 now requires daylight measurements at two times of the year.
- Glazing must provide a clear view to the outdoors. The glazing does not have to be located between 30 and 90 inches (750 mm and 2 300 mm).
- Atriums now qualify for up to 30% of the total area for views.
- View quality is now a component of the credit requirements.

REFERENCED STANDARDS

The Lighting Handbook, 10th edition, Illuminating Engineering Society: ies.org

Windows and Offices: A Study of Office Worker Performance and the Indoor Environment: h-m-g.com

EXEMPLARY PERFORMANCE

Achieve both options for 75% of all regularly occupied floor area.

DEFINITIONS

annual sunlight exposure (**ASE**) a metric that describes the potential for visual discomfort in interior work environments. It is defined as the percentage of an analysis area that exceeds a specified direct sunlight illuminance level more than a specified number of hours per year. (Illuminating Engineering Society)

$ASE_{1,000,250}$ reports the percentage of sensors in the analysis area, using a maximum 2-foot spacing between points, that are found to be exposed to more than 1000 lux of direct sunlight for more than 250 hours per year, before any operable blinds or shades are deployed to block sunlight, considering the same 10 hour/day analysis period as sDA and using comparable simulation methods

clear glazing glass that is transparent and allows a view through the fenestration. Diffused glazing allows only daylighting.

color rendering index a measurement from 0 to 100 that indicates how accurately an artificial light source, as compared with an incandescent light, displays hues. The higher the index number, the more accurately the light is rendering colors. Incandescent lighting has a color rendering index above 95; standard high-pressure sodium lighting (such as orange-hued roadway lights) measures approximately 25; many fluorescent sources using rare earth phosphors have a color rendering index of 80 and above. (Adapted from U.S. ENERGY STAR)

direct sunlight an interior horizontal measurement of 1,000 lux or more of direct beam sunlight that accounts for window transmittance and angular effects, and excludes the effect of any operable blinds, with no contribution from reflected light (i.e., a zero bounce analysis) and no contribution from the diffuse sky component. (Adapted from Illuminating Engineering Society)

movable furniture and partitions items that can be moved by the users without the need of tools or assistance from special trades and facilities management

permanent interior obstruction a structure that cannot be moved by the user without tools or assistance from special trades and facilities management. Examples include lab hoods, fixed partitions, demountable opaque full- or partial-height partitions, some displays, and equipment.

spatial daylight autonomy (sDA) a metric describing annual sufficiency of ambient daylight levels in interior environments. It is defined as the percentage of an analysis area (the area where calculations are performed, typically across an entire space) that meets a minimum daylight illuminance level for a specified fraction of the operating hours per year (i.e., the Daylight Autonomy value following Reinhart & Walkenhorst, 2001). The illluminance level and time fraction are included as subscripts, as in $sDA_{300,50\%}$. The sDA value is expressed as a percentage of area. (Illuminating Engineering Society)

$sDA_{300/50\%}$ the percentage of analysis points across the analysis area that meet or exceed this 300 lux value for at least 50% of the analysis period

vision glazing the glass portion of an exterior window that permits views to the exterior or interior. Vision glazing must allow a clear image of the exterior and must not be obstructed by frits, fibers, patterned glazing, or added tints that distort color balance.

INDOOR ENVIRONMENTAL QUALITY CREDIT

Green Cleaning—Custodial Effectiveness Assessment

This credit applies to:

Existing Buildings (1 point)
Schools (1 point)
Retail (1 point)
Data Centers (1 point)
Hospitality (1 point)
Warehouses and Distribution Centers (1 point)

INTENT

To reduce levels of chemical, biological, and particulate contaminants, which can compromise human health, building finishes and systems, and the environment, by implementing effective cleaning procedures.

REQUIREMENTS

ESTABLISHMENT E

None.

PERFORMANCE P

Implement the strategies set forth in the facility's green cleaning policy and perform routine inspection and monitoring. This inspection must verify that the specified strategies have been implemented and must identify areas in need of improvement.

Additionally, conduct an annual audit in accordance with APPA Leadership in Educational Facilities' Custodial Staffing Guidelines, or a local equivalent, whichever is more stringent, to determine the appearance level of the facility. The facility must score 2.5 or better.

BEHIND THE INTENT

Studies conducted by the U.S. Environmental Protection Agency, World Health Organization, and Building Owners and Managers Association have shown that the use of deep-cleaning procedures reduces the amount of dust, volatile organic compounds, bacteria, and fungi in a building by 40% to 60%.[1] Additional studies by North Shore University Hospital and Cornell University Medical College link these improvements directly to reductions in total illnesses, doctors' visits, and absenteeism by 24% to 46%.[2]

Audits of custodial effectiveness are an effective means to measure cleaning performance. They allow the building managers to verify that the building is clean, cleaning procedures are being followed, and custodial staff training is current. These audits also enable managers to identify areas that may need improvement to protect the health and well-being of the cleaning staff and occupants.

The Association of Physical Plant Administrators (APPA) has developed a standard auditing procedure that managers can follow to monitor cleaning performance over time. Trends can thus be identified and best practices shared with custodial staff, creating a continuous improvement process.

STEP-BY-STEP GUIDANCE

STEP 1. REVIEW GREEN CLEANING POLICY CREATED FOR PROJECT P

Requirements for routine inspection and monitoring are part of the project's green cleaning policy, developed for EQ Prerequisite Green Cleaning Policy.

For projects pursing Option 2 in EQ Prerequisite Green Cleaning Policy, the audits performed for certification compliance do not qualify as audits for the purpose of this credit, since they are not necessarily specific to the project building.

STEP 2. CREATE AUDIT FORMS P

Create customized audit forms or scorecards for the building based on APPA Operational Guidelines for Educational Facilities: Custodial, Chapter 7, or use another method at least as stringent as APPA (see *Further Explanation, Performing a Non-APPA Audit*).

The forms or scorecards must contain three pieces of information (Figure 1):

- **Space type.** Categorize spaces in the project according to the 33 types listed in the APPA guidelines, Appendix B. Using the building floor plan, group similar spaces to reduce the number of forms needed. Closed, private offices and open offices are different space types. Mechanical rooms and parking garages do not need to be audited. If the building contains space types not listed in Appendix B, select the closest category.
- **Appearance items.** Each space category has a set of appearance items, listed in Appendix D of the APPA guidelines, that will be scored by the auditor. For example, staff may spend more time classroom cleaning floors than wiping chalkboards, so an auditor should note the cleanliness of those items accordingly. For an effective and time-efficient audit, use no more than six appearance items per space category.
- **Time-averaged weighting factors.** The weighting factor assigns relative importance of each appearance item in maintaining a healthful and clean environment. The higher the weighting factor, the more important the appearance item is relative to the others. Weighting factors may be determined by the average percentage of time that should be spent cleaning the item in the space. Refer to APPA guidelines, Appendix D, for additional suggestions on weighting factors.

1. *Berry, Michael, Contaminant Reduction Study (UNC at Chapel Hill, Frank Graham Child Center, 1998).*
2. *Krilov, Leonard R., Stephen R. Barone, Francine S. Mandel, Timothy M. Cusack, Donna J. Gaber, Joseph R. Rubino, et al., Impact of an Infection Control Program in a Specialized Preschool, American Journal of Infection Control 24(3) (1996): 167–173.*

Appearance Item	Weighting Factor	Appearance Level					Raw Score (factor x level)
		Best 1	2	3	4	Worst 5	
Floors	55		X				110
Horizontal surfaces	12				X		48
Lighting, light fixtures	3			X			9
Trash containers	23		X				46
Vertical surfaces	7				X		28
Total Raw Score							241
Level = Raw Score / 100							2.41

Figure 1. Example audit scorecard

STEP 3. IMPLEMENT STANDARD OPERATING PROCEDURES OF GREEN CLEANING POLICY P

To prepare for a random audit, the building management team should ensure that all staff are trained, routines are firmly reinforced, and best practices are shared at team meetings.

- Periodic check-ins with individuals or the entire custodial staff can help identify weaknesses and opportunities, such as the need for more staff training, adjustments to the staffing plan, or clearer expectations in the green cleaning policy.
- Managers can conduct spot-checks to find specific areas that need improvement and those that exceed expectations.
- A feedback loop enables those responsible for implementing the procedures to reflect on lessons learned and use their successes to continuously improve custodial effectiveness.

See EQ Prerequisite Green Cleaning Policy for additional information on how to establish standard cleaning procedures for the building.

STEP 4. ESTABLISH AUDIT PROCESS P

Determine the procedures for routine monitoring and inspection of the work performed by the custodial staff. Decide on three components:

- **Audit personnel.** The audit may be conducted by a third party. Seek an auditor with in-depth custodial experience and ascertain his or her professional credentials and experience. Alternatively, two individuals associated with the building management team can conduct the audit. Ensure that they are trained in the procedures in the APPA guidelines, Chapter 7.
- **Timing.** The audit should be performed during normal business operations when occupancy activities reflect normal levels and patterns. No advance notice of the audit should be given to the custodial staff or contractors.
- **Quality assessment feedback.** Determine how to notify staff that an audit has occurred, how to communicate the score, and what process will be used to make improvements based on the audit findings.

STEP 5. PERFORM CUSTODIAL EFFECTIVENESS AUDIT P

During the performance period, perform a custodial effectiveness audit according to the APPA guidelines, Chapter 7.

- **Determine the sampling group.** Randomly select 10% of the rooms in each space category identified in Step 1. If 10% is fewer than five rooms, audit at least five rooms. If a space type has fewer than five rooms, audit all of those rooms.
- **Evaluate the selected rooms.** Use one audit form for each room. Assign an appearance level score ranging from 1 (highest cleanliness) to 5 (most unkempt), based on the definitions in the APPA guidelines, Chapter 1.
- **Score the audit.** Average the appearance level for each space type, and then averaging across all space types to determine the building's appearance level score. A score of 2.5 or better is required to achieve this credit. See Figure 2 for an example of this tabulation methodology, and see the APPA guidelines, Chapter 7, for more information.
- **Identify areas for improvement.** Based on the audit results, develop strategies for implementing improvements where needed.

- Continue to implement the green cleaning policy and conduct an APPA audit every year.

Space Use	APPA Category	Total (sf)	Rooms by Type	Rooms by Classification	10%	Audited (sf)	Average Score for Space Type
Office	Office	16,981	71	73	8	1,200	2.41
Hallway	Circulation	7,851	14	14	5	1,510	2.37
Lobby	Entry	312	1	1	1	312	3.00
Research lab	Research lab	1,643	9	9	5	780	2.95
Storage	Storeroom	1,858	10	12	5	925	2.32
Elevator	Office	80	1	—			
Custodial closet	Storeroom	190	2	—			
Washroom	Washroom	1,092	6	6	5	912	2.25
Stairwell	Stairwell	468	3	3	3	468	3.12
Conference room	Classroom	566	2	—			
Reception	Office	256	1	—			
Teaching lab	Classroom	1,640	2	—			
Lecture hall	Classroom	3,594	5	9	5	2,698	3.48
Totals	**36,531**	**127**	**127**	**37**	**8,805**	**21.90**	
Overall appearance level = 21.9 / 8							**2.74**

Figure 2. Example building level score tabulation

FURTHER EXPLANATION

PERFORMING A NON-APPA AUDIT

Some building management teams already have audit procedures for determining the effectiveness of the custodial staff. In these situations, alternative audit procedures may be used, provided the alternative procedures are at least as robust as the APPA procedures. The alternative audit procedures must examine all the space types in the building, evaluate all the different surfaces that are cleaned in each space type, and rate each space on a scale.

For documentation, provide a side-by-side comparison of the alternative audit procedure and the APPA audit requirements.

CAMPUS

Group Approach

Submit separate documentation for each building.

Campus Approach

Ineligible. Each LEED project may pursue the credit individually.

REQUIRED DOCUMENTATION

	Documentation	All projects
P	Description of procedures for routine monitoring and inspection of work performed by cleaning staff	X
P	Overall score and date of audit	X
P	Report of audit results	X
P	Description of audit procedures	X
P	Description of improvement opportunities	X

RELATED CREDIT TIPS

EQ Prerequisite Green Cleaning Policy. This credit is driven by the policy requirements established in the related prerequisite.

CHANGES FROM LEED 2009

- The credit directly links implementation of the Green Cleaning Policy to the audit process.
- The credit achievement threshold of the audit score has been tightened, from 3 to 2.5.

REFERENCED STANDARDS

Association of Physical Plant Administrators (APPA), Operational Guidelines for Educational Facilities: Custodial: appa.org/bookstore

EXEMPLARY PERFORMANCE

Not available.

DEFINITIONS

None.

INDOOR ENVIRONMENTAL QUALITY CREDIT

Green Cleaning—Products and Materials

This credit applies to:

Existing Buildings (1 point)
Schools (1 point)
Retail (1 point)
Data Centers (1 point)
Hospitality (1 point)
Warehouses and Distribution Centers (1 point)

INTENT

To reduce the environmental effects of cleaning products, disposable janitorial paper products, and trash bags.

REQUIREMENTS

ESTABLISHMENT E

None.

PERFORMANCE P

Purchase green cleaning materials and products such as floor finishes and strippers, disposable janitorial paper products, and trash bags. Include items used by in-house staff or outsourced service providers.

At least 75%, by cost, of the total annual purchases of these products must meet at least one of the following standards.

Cleaning products must meet one or more of the following standards, or a local equivalent for projects outside the U.S.:

- Green Seal GS-37, for general-purpose, bathroom, glass and carpet cleaners used for industrial and institutional purposes;
- Environmental Choice CCD-110, for cleaning and degreasing compounds;
- Environmental Choice CCD-146, for hard-surface cleaners;
- Environmental Choice CCD-148, for carpet and upholstery care;
- Green Seal GS-40, for industrial and institutional floor care products;
- Environmental Choice CCD-147, for hard-floor care;
- EPA Design for the Environment Program's Standard for Safer Cleaning Products; and/or

- Cleaning devices that use only ionized water or electrolyzed water and have third-party-verified performance data equivalent to the other standards mentioned above (if the device is marketed for antimicrobial cleaning, performance data must demonstrate antimicrobial performance comparable to EPA Office of Pollution Prevention and Toxics and Design for the Environment requirements, as appropriate for use patterns and marketing claims).

Disinfectants, metal polish, or other products not addressed by the above standards must meet one or more of the following standards (or a local equivalent for projects outside the U.S.):

- Environmental Choice CCD-112, for digestion additives for cleaning and odor control;
- Environmental Choice CCD-113, for drain or grease trap additives;
- Environmental Choice CCD-115, for odor control additives;
- Green Seal GS-52/53, for specialty cleaning products;
- California Code of Regulations maximum allowable VOC levels for the specific product category;
- EPA Design for the Environment Program's standard for safer cleaning products; and/or
- Cleaning devices that use only ionized water or electrolyzed water and have third-party-verified performance data equivalent to the other standards mentioned above (if the device is marketed for antimicrobial cleaning, performance data must demonstrate antimicrobial performance comparable to EPA Office of Pollution Prevention and Toxics and Design for the Environment requirements, as appropriate for use patterns and marketing claims).

Disposable janitorial paper products and trash bags must meet the minimum requirements of one or more of the following programs, or a local equivalent for projects outside the U.S.:

- EPA comprehensive procurement guidelines, for janitorial paper;
- Green Seal GS-01, for tissue paper, paper towels and napkins;
- Environmental Choice CCD-082, for toilet tissue;
- Environmental Choice CCD-086, for hand towels;
- Janitorial paper products derived from rapidly renewable resources or made from tree-free fibers;
- FSC certification, for fiber procurement;
- EPA comprehensive procurement guidelines, for plastic trash can liners; and/or
- California integrated waste management requirements, for plastic trash can liners (California Code of Regulations Title 14, Chapter 4, Article 5, or SABRC 42290-42297 Recycled Content Plastic Trash Bag Program).

Hand soaps and hand sanitizers must meet one or more of the following standards, or a local equivalent for projects outside the U.S.:

- no antimicrobial agents (other than as a preservative) except where required by health codes and other regulations (e.g., food service and health care requirements);
- Green Seal GS-41, for industrial and institutional hand cleaners;
- Environmental Choice CCD-104, for hand cleaners and hand soaps;
- Environmental Choice CCD-170, for hand sanitizers;
- EPA Design for the Environment Program's standard for safer cleaning products.

For projects outside the U.S., any Type 1 eco-labeling program as defined by ISO 14024: 1999 developed by a member of the Global Ecolabelling Network may be used in lieu of Green Seal or Environmental Choice standards.

BEHIND THE INTENT

Most cleaning products use agents that have the potential to harm human health and damage interior finishes. When used over time, these chemicals can build up and be present in the indoor air environment or be transferred via contact with fixtures and surfaces. In worst cases, prolonged and improper handling of cleaning chemicals can lead to sick building syndrome or create unhealthful working environments.

Third-party standards were selected for this credit because they require a higher degree of environmental compliance than are typical of cleaning products and materials commonly used in the industry. Owners and managers who use third-party verification programs can claim a leadership position in addressing the environmental and health concerns of chemical use in their buildings through the use of rigorous, consensus-based, and transparent industry standards.

STEP-BY-STEP GUIDANCE

STEP 1. REVIEW GREEN CLEANING POLICY CREATED FOR PROJECT P

Requirements for cleaning products and materials purchases are part of the project's green cleaning policy, developed for EQ Prerequisite Green Cleaning Policy. Ensure that the policy and the purchasing strategy for this credit account for all of the following:

- All known green cleaning product purchases for the building, including those made by the property management group, a janitorial vendor, and tenants
- Janitorial paper products (addressed in this credit, not MR Credit Purchasing—Ongoing Consumption)
- All product and material types listed in the credit requirements, including commonly overlooked items like hand soaps

Project teams pursing Option 2 in EQ Prerequisite Green Cleaning Policy may find that the certification program has a different threshold or scope than that required by this credit. Confirm that the selected program covers at least 75% of cleaning products, by cost.

Any cleaning products and material class not covered by one of the applicable standards may be excluded.

STEP 2. DEVELOP AND IMPLEMENT TRACKING SYSTEM P

Create a tracking system that allows all purchasing parties to log and indicate compliance of purchases.

Tracking systems should be user friendly, readily accessible, and allow for coordination of multiple purchases from various sources. Issues to consider when developing a tracking system include computer skills and accessibility, language barriers, and the need to merge information from multiple sources (see *Further Explanation, Selecting an Appropriate Tracking System*).

The tracking tool should catalogue the following information (Table 1):

- Date of purchase
- Purchaser
- Product name
- Cost
- Quantity
- Applicable referenced standard

TABLE 1. Example tracking tool

Purchase Date	Purchaser	Product Manufacturer and Name and URL	Cost per Item ($)	Number of Items	Total Cost	Product Category	Sustainability Criterion	Sustainability Value ($)
7/15/2014	Vendor	01960 Scott White L Fold Towel	$20.05	10	$200.50	Paper product or trash bag	EPA's CPG	$200.50
7/15/2014	Vendor	P24206N Roll Liner Natural	$11.56	4	$46.24	Paper product or trash bag	None	$-
7/15/2014	Property Manager	3904 Johnson Stride Citrus Gal	$16.41	1	$16.41	Cleaning product	GS-37	$16.41
7/15/2014	Property Manager	4995295 Johnson Emerel Creme Cl	$34.88	1	$34.88	Cleaning product	CCD-146	$34.88
7/15/2014	Tenant	4192 Johnson Gen'l Purpose Spot	$24.85	1	$24.85	Cleaning product	None	$-
8/15/2014	Property Manager	3904 Johnson Stride Citrus Gal	$16.71	1	$16.71	Cleaning product	GS-37	$16.71
8/15/2014	Property Manager	4995295 Johnson Emerel Creme Cl	$35.52	1	$35.52	Cleaning product	CCD-146	$35.52
8/15/2014	Property Manager	4192 Johnson Gen'l Purpose Spot	$25.31	1	$25.31	Cleaning product	None	$-
8/15/2014	Vendor	01960 Scott White L Fold Towel	$20.05	15	$300.75	Paper product or trash bag	EPA's CPG	$300.75
8/15/2014	Vendor	13217 KC Recycled Bath Tissue	$31.50	10	$315.00	Paper product or trash bag	GS-01	$315.00
8/15/2014	Vendor	Tradex International TSC5000 Toilet Seat Cover	$39.55	1	$39.55	Paper product or trash bag	None	$-
9/15/2013	Vendor	01960 Scott White L Fold Towel	$20.05	15	$300.75	Paper product or trash bag	EPA's CPG	$300.75
9/15/2013	Vendor	13217 KC Recycled Bath Tissue	$31.50	10	$315.00	Paper product or trash bag	GS-01	$315.00
9/15/2013	Property Manager	3062637 RTD Virex 256 Cleaner	$34.35	1	$34.35	Disinfectant, metal polish, etc	None	$-
9/15/2013	Property Manager	4995295 Johnson Emerel Creme Cl	$35.52	1	$35.52	Cleaning product	CCD-146	$35.52
9/15/2013	Tenant	3361936 Johnson RTD Glance NA	$34.78	1	$34.78	Cleaning product	GS-37	$34.78
					$-			$-
					$-			$-
Total cost of cleaning products and materials purchased								**$1,776.12**
Total value of sustainable cleaning products and materials ($)								**$1,605.82**
Sustainable cleaning products and materials as a percentage of total cost of cleaning products and materials								**90.41%**

Complete the table by identifying each cleaning product and material in use, the date of purchase, and the applicable sustainability criteria met by each product, if any.

STEP 3. EVALUATE CURRENT CLEANING PURCHASES P

The responsible party identified in the green cleaning policy should evaluate the current purchasing performance before the start of the performance period. Start by collecting and cataloging the information and comparing the results with the credit criteria.

- If the current purchasing levels do not meet the performance threshold for this credit, substitute compliant for noncompliant products and materials (see *Further Explanation, Meeting the Performance Thresholds* and *Nonchemical Cleaners* and *Products with Disinfectants*).
- Testing new products before switching over on a large scale may be desirable but will affect the timeline in the performance period.

STEP 4. COMMUNICATE PURCHASING REQUIREMENTS TO STAKEHOLDERS P

Communicate the green cleaning policy to building occupants, tenant representatives, and relevant vendors. Any party who may purchase cleaning products and materials should understand that purchases must meet the criteria listed in the green cleaning policy and be tracked on an ongoing basis.

To promote compliance, consider the following best practices:

- Provide a list of products and materials that meet the criteria of the referenced standards.
- Establish a protocol for evaluating additional products and materials.
- Have a single knowledgeable person review potential purchases for compliance, even if multiple individuals are involved in ordering.

STEP 5. TRACK PURCHASES DURING PERFORMANCE PERIOD P

All cleaning products and materials purchases must be tracked throughout the entire performance period or recertification period using the tracking system established in Step 2.

The spreadsheet must include purchases made by tenants and vendors as well as building staff, demonstrate the percentage of sustainable cleaning products and materials purchased, and state which criteria the product or material meets (see *Further Explanation, Project Type Variations*).

STEP 6. MAINTAIN RECORD OF MANUFACTURER DOCUMENTATION P

To demonstrate compliance, the responsible party must collect material safety data sheets (MSDS) or other product documentation for sustainable purchases made during the performance period or recertification period (Figure 1). This documentation should clearly show how the product meets the criteria (e.g., VOC limits, certification) of the referenced standards.

The MSDS or other product literature, often available online, may indicate what third-party standards the product meets. Or ask the product vendor or manufacturer for the information. Some standards, such as Green Seal and Design for the Environment, have online databases that can be used to look up products to verify their certification status. Circling or highlighting the relevant lines in the product documentation will make this information easier to find in the review process.

SECTION 1: Identification

1.1. Product identifier
3M™ 3-IN-1 FLOOR CLEANER CONCENTRATE (Product No. 24, Twist 'n Fill™ System)

Product Identification Numbers

ID Number	UPC	ID Number	UPC
70-0713-1133-9	00-48011-23553-5	70-0713-1134-7	00-48011-23914-4

1.2. Recommended use and restrictions on use

Recommended use
Versatile, low-foaming cleaner can be used in automatic scrubbers or in mop-on applications., This product meets Green Seal™ Standard GS-37 based on effective performance, concentration of product, minimized/recycled packaging, and protective limits on VOCs and human & environmental toxicity. Acute toxicity and skin/eye damage met requirements at the as-used dilution, as specified for closed dilution systems. GreenSeal.org. Fragrance Added., Hard Surface Cleaner

1.3. Supplier's details

MANUFACTURER:	3M
DIVISION:	Building & Commercial Services Division
ADDRESS:	3M Center, St. Paul, MN 55144-1000, USA
Telephone:	1-888-3M HELPS (1-888-364-3577)

1.4. Emergency telephone number
1-800-364-3577 or (651) 737-6501 (24 hours)

Figure 1. Example MSDS. 3M and Twist 'n Fill are trademarks of 3M Company. Used under license in Canada. © 3M 2013. All rights reserved. Green Seal is a trademark of Green Seal, Inc.

FURTHER EXPLANATION

MEETING THE PERFORMANCE THRESHOLDS

Project teams are encouraged to develop a product and materials inventory before the performance period. This inventory can be used to gauge performance and will be helpful when switching out noncompliant products for ones that meet the sustainability criteria. Possible tactics include the following:

- List products and materials that will ensure that the performance threshold is met and distribute copies to those with purchasing responsibilities; keep the list up-to-date.
- Focus first on high-cost or high-volume noncompliant items, since these will drive credit compliance.
- Testing several alternatives before purchasing new products in bulk. Most compliant alternatives are competitively priced, though research may be needed to find them.

SELECTING AN APPROPRIATE TRACKING SYSTEM

When deciding on a tracking system, ensure that the strategy works for the entire project team. For example, if many individuals make purchases, an electronic tracking system will make it easier to combine purchase data. Providing standardized tracking tools will ease the process for project teams that must coordinate tracking across different purchasing parties and aggregate data. Keep in mind that cleaning personnel may not have ready access to computers for logging product deliveries.

It is recommended that the team test the tracking system before the performance period, when the system will need to work smoothly. A one- to two-month trial period creates an opportunity to identify and address any problems and thus increase the project's chances of exceeding the threshold.

NONCHEMICAL CLEANERS

Cleaning devices that use steam, ionized or electrolyzed water, or other nonchemical processes may be counted toward credit achievement, since they eliminate the need for standard cleaning chemicals. Examples of alternative products include vinegar, lemon juice, olive oil, and baking soda. Using nonchemical cleaners and devices may help lower purchasing costs and reduce occupants' exposure to cleaning chemicals. Determine whether nonchemical cleaners are effective for the cleaning task.

To account for the use of nonchemical cleaners and devices towards compliance, use the following steps:

1. Provide a narrative description of the nonchemical cleaning product or method and describe what cleaning chemicals it replaces.
2. Analyze the value of using the nonchemical alternative based on one year of cost data. Account for any changes in occupancy between the baseline year and the performance period or other factors that affect the need for cleaning products.
3. Track the total cost of all cleaning products and materials purchased during the performance period, as is required by the credit, and add the amortized cost for the nonchemical cleaning alternative for the performance period.
4. Perform credit threshold calculations, as described in Step 3, by using the assumed value of the nonchemical cleaning alternatives.

PRODUCTS WITH DISINFECTANTS

Some facilities, such as hospitals, require the use of cleaning products with disinfectants. Most of the referenced standards do not certify these products. In these instances, teams may need to work directly with the manufacturer to obtain documentation showing that the product complies with all applicable requirements of a referenced standard even though it does not carry its label.

EXPLANATION OF STANDARDS

TABLE 2. Explanation of standards

Standard	Description	Cleaning products, materials types
Design for Environment (DfE) EPA epa.gov/dfe/	Labeling program for cleaning products demonstrated to be less damaging to human health and environment. Only products listed on DfE website without double daggers (‡) may contribute to this credit. Listing indicates product has completed DfE audit.	All-purpose cleaners, dish soaps, hand soaps, odor removers, degreasers, metal cleaners and polishes, bathroom cleaners
Forest Stewardship Council (FSC) fsc.org/	Labeling program that identifies wood products grown and harvested with responsible forest management practices	Fiber-based products: tissue paper, paper towels, paper napkins
Green Seal greenseal.org/	Third-party certification of products based on life-cycle sustainability standards	Cleaning products: general-purpose, bathroom, glass, carpet, floor cleaners; disinfectants; metal polishes. Paper products: tissue paper, paper towels, paper napkins
Environmental Choice (EcoLogo) ecologo.org/en/	Certification program that lists products with others in same category and awards certification to products that meet program's criteria as verified by third-party	Cleaning and degreasing compounds, hard-surface cleaners, carpet and upholstery care, hard-floor care, digestive additives for cleaning and odor, drain or grease trap additives, odor control additives, toilet tissue, hand towels, hand cleaners, hand soaps, hand sanitizers

PROJECT TYPE VARIATIONS

Multifamily Projects

All cleaning product and material purchases must be included in the percentage of total cleaning purchases during the performance period, whether the products and materials were purchased by the residents or by building staff (see Multitenant Buildings).

Multitenant Buildings

This credit applies to all cleaning products and materials used in the project building, including those purchased by individual tenants, cleaning vendors, and property or building managers and owners. If cleaning products and materials are supplied by multiple parties, all purchasing data must be tracked and aggregated to demonstrate compliance.

If additional tenants beyond those in the excluded 10% of gross floor area choose not to provide purchasing data, the purchases for those tenant spaces must be estimated and assumed to be noncompliant. To estimate the purchases made by nonparticipating tenants, extrapolate the purchasing rate from elsewhere in the building on a per occupant or square foot (square meter) basis and multiply the result by the number of occupants or floor area of the nonparticipating tenant. Integrate the estimated data from the nonparticipating tenants into the whole-building purchasing data (for both participating and nonparticipating tenants) to determine compliance for the whole building.

Project teams may exclude up to 10% of the project building's total floor area from the credit calculations if those spaces are under separate management (see *Getting Started, Tenant Space Exclusion Allowance*).

TABLE 3. Example compliance calculation with nonparticipating tenants

Actual purchase rate for participating tenants			
Tenant	**Floor area (ft²)**	**Total purchases**	**Compliant purchases**
Jones Hotelier	75,000	$2,000	$1,500
Big Red Offices	60,000	$1,000	$750
TOTAL	135,000	$3,000	$2,250
	Total purchases / ft² of participating tenants		**$0.022**
Estimated purchase rate for nonparticipating tenants			
Tenant	**Floor area (ft²)**	**Estimated total purchases**	**Estimated compliant purchases**
Cranky's Depot	15,000	$0.022 x 15,000 ft² = $330	$0
Whole-building results			
Tenant	**Floor area (ft²)**	**Total purchases**	**Compliant purchases**
Jones Hotelier	75,000	$2,000	$1,500
Big Red Offices	60,000	$1,000	$750
Cranky's Depot (estimated)	15,000	$330	$0
TOTAL	150,000	$3,330	$2,250
	Percentage compliant purchases		**67.57%**

INTERNATIONAL TIPS

For projects outside the U.S., any Type 1 ecolabeling program as defined by ISO 14024–1999 developed by a member of the Global Ecolabelling Network may be used in lieu of Green Seal or Environmental Choice standards. Examples of European green cleaning programs that meet the criteria include the following:

- EU Ecolabel
- Bra Miljöval (Good Environmental Choice), Sweden
- Der Blaue Engel (The Blue Angel), Germany
- Ekologicky Šetrný Výrobek, Czechoslovakia
- Svanen (The Swan), Nordic countries
- Листок жизни (Vitality Leaf), Russia
- Жжива планета (Living Planet), Ukraine

CAMPUS

Group Approach
All buildings in the group may be documented as one.

Campus Approach
Eligible.

REQUIRED DOCUMENTATION

	Documentation	All projects
P	Purchasing spreadsheet for all products	X
P	MSDS or other documentation for each product	X
P	Executed contract language requiring that purchases achieve threshold (optional)	X

RELATED CREDIT TIPS

SS Prerequisite Site Management Policy. The related prerequisite addresses cleaning products and materials used on the exterior of buildings; these products may need to meet additional requirements to contribute to this credit.

EQ Prerequisite Green Cleaning Policy. This credit goes beyond the green cleaning policy created for the related prerequisite by establishing performance targets for cleaning products and materials. The policy applies to spaces under the building management's control; this credit applies to the entire building, including tenants.

EQ Credit Green Cleaning—Equipment. The related credit addresses equipment, such as cleaners that use ionized water, that can replace chemical cleaners.

EQ Credit Integrated Pest Management. The related credit addresses sprays, gels, and other products that deter pests; these products may need to meet additional requirements to contribute to this credit.

CHANGES FROM LEED 2009

- The performance threshold for purchases has been raised from 30% to 75%.
- A provision for nonchemical and ionized water cleaning has been added.
- Design for the Environment has been added as an acceptable standard.

REFERENCED STANDARDS

See *Further Explanation, Explanation of Standards.*

EXEMPLARY PERFORMANCE

Meet the criteria for 100% of purchased cleaning products and materials.

DEFINITIONS

None.

INDOOR ENVIRONMENTAL QUALITY CREDIT

Green Cleaning—Equipment

This credit applies to:

Existing Buildings (1 point)
Schools (1 point)
Retail (1 point)
Data Centers (1 point)
Hospitality (1 point)
Warehouses and Distribution Centers (1 point)

INTENT

To reduce chemical, biological, and particulate contaminants from powered cleaning equipment.

REQUIREMENTS

ESTABLISHMENT E

Create an inventory of existing interior and exterior equipment, including what is brought on site by vendors. At least 40% of all powered janitorial equipment (purchased, leased, or used by contractors) must meet the following criteria. For existing equipment that does not meet the criteria, develop a phase-out plan for its replacement with environmentally preferable products at the end of its useful life.

All powered equipment must have the following features:

- safeguards, such as rollers or rubber bumpers, to avoid damage to building surfaces;
- ergonomic design to minimize vibration, noise, and user fatigue, as reported in the user manual in accordance with ISO 5349-1 for arm vibrations, ISO 2631–1 for vibration to the whole body, and ISO 11201 for sound pressure at operator's ear; and
- as applicable, environmentally preferable batteries (e.g., gel, absorbent glass mat, lithium-ion) except in applications requiring deep discharge and heavy loads where performance or battery life is reduced by the use of sealed batteries.

Vacuum cleaners must be certified by the Carpet and Rug Institute Seal of Approval/Green Label Vacuum Program and operate with a maximum sound level of 70 dBA or less in accordance with ISO 11201.

Carpet extraction equipment, for restorative deep cleaning, must be certified by the Carpet and Rug Institute's Seal of Approval Deep Cleaning Extractors and Seal of Approval Deep Cleaning Systems program.

Powered floor maintenance equipment, such as vacuums, guards, or other devices for capturing fine particulates, must operate with a maximum sound level of 70 dBA, in accordance with ISO 11201.

Propane-powered floor equipment must have high-efficiency, low-emissions engines with catalytic converters and mufflers that meet the California Air Resources Board or EPA standards for the specific engine size and operate with a sound level of 90 dBA or less, in accordance with ISO 11201.

Automated scrubbing machines must be equipped with variable-speed feed pumps and either (1) on-board chemical metering to optimize the use of cleaning fluids or (2) dilution control systems for chemical refilling. Alternatively, scrubbing machines may use tap water only, with no added cleaning products.

PERFORMANCE P

At least 40% of all powered janitorial equipment (purchased, leased, or used by contractors) must meet the above criteria. For existing equipment that does not meet the criteria, develop a phase-out plan for its replacement with environmentally preferable products at the end of its useful life.

BEHIND THE INTENT

Conventional cleaning equipment can be noisy, inefficient, and even injurious because of poor ergonomic design. High-performance green cleaning equipment typically uses less energy and water and often requires less abrasive cleaning compounds or less toxic cleaning chemicals, thereby protecting the indoor air quality of a building and limiting occupants' exposure to chemicals. In addition, it may require fewer repairs, be more effective, and cause less damage to building surfaces.

This credit requires the purchase and use of green cleaning equipment that is certified for efficiency and ergonomic design to minimize vibration, noise, and user fatigue and thus reduce the incidence of musculoskeletal or repetitive stress injuries.[1]

STEP-BY-STEP GUIDANCE

STEP 1. REVIEW GREEN CLEANING POLICY CREATED FOR PROJECT E

Requirements for cleaning equipment are part of the project's green cleaning policy, developed for EQ Prerequisite Green Cleaning Policy. Ensure that the policy and the purchasing strategy for this credit account for all powered cleaning equipment used on site, whether supplied by the owner or a vendor, that is covered by the referenced standards.

- Types of equipment not covered by the standards, such as wet-dry vacuums, can be excluded from compliance documentation.
- Project teams pursing Option 2 in EQ Prerequisite Green Cleaning Policy may find that the certification program has a different threshold or scope than that required by this credit. Confirm that the selected program covers at least 40% of eligible cleaning equipment, by count. The contract with the service provider must also include a phase-out plan for replacing noncompliant equipment at the end of its useful life with compliant equipment.

STEP 2. INVENTORY CURRENT EQUIPMENT E

Take inventory of all the existing powered janitorial equipment used to clean the building, including outdoor cleaning equipment (Table 1). Existing equipment refers to purchases made before the start of the performance period.

1. *Public Services Health and Safety Association, Fast Fact: Musculoskeletal Disorders* (2010), *healthandsafetyontario.ca/HSO/media/PSHSA/pdfS/MSDs/MSDs.pdf.*

TABLE 1. Equipment

Purchase Date	Purchaser	Product Manufacturer and Name	Number of Items or Cost	Product Category	Sustainability Criterion	Includes safeguards, ergonomic design?	Includes environmentally preferable batteries?	Maximum Operating Sound Level (dBA)	Credit Compliance
10/22/2013	Acme Inc	Quiet Vaccums Model X123	5	Vacuum cleaner	CRI certified	Yes	N/A	60	Yes
12/27/2013	Acme Inc	Squeaky Clean Floors AutoScrubber 2000	2	Powered floor maintenance equipment	N/A	Yes	N/A	45	Yes
									No
									No
									No
									No
									No
									No
									No
									No
Total number of equipment products purchased									**7**
Total number of equipment products meeting sustainability criteria									**7**

Complete the table by identifying each piece of powered cleaning equipment in use, the date of equipment purchase, and the applicable sustainability criteria met by each equipment, if any. Estimated purchase dates may be used for equipment purchased before the performance period.

If cleaning is performed by a vendor, ask the vendor to provide a list of all the powered equipment used on the building. Consider the following strategies to collect data from vendors:

- Provide the tracking tool for the vendor to complete.
- Request photographs of the equipment model tags.
- Check and record equipment as it is brought on site.

STEP 3. CALCULATE CURRENT EQUIPMENT COMPLIANCE E P

With the information from the tracking tool, calculate compliance with the credit requirements based on either equipment cost or quantity of items, using Equation 1.

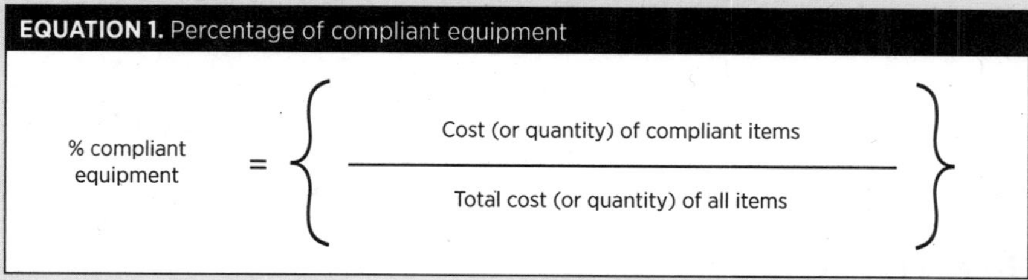

EQUATION 1. Percentage of compliant equipment

$$\text{\% compliant equipment} = \left\{ \frac{\text{Cost (or quantity) of compliant items}}{\text{Total cost (or quantity) of all items}} \right\}$$

- Include any new purchases made during the performance period in the calculation.
- If costs for any existing equipment are unavailable, the project team may use the replacement value of existing equipment.
- Any equipment with incomplete data should be considered noncompliant.

STEP 4. PURCHASE COMPLIANT EQUIPMENT E P

Ensure that at least 40% (by quantity) of all powered equipment meets the applicable credit requirements.

- Powered equipment must meet the specific referenced standards for each equipment category as well as the more general criteria in the credit requirements.
- Evaluate equipment by reviewing product data sheets. If sustainability information is not given, obtain letters or testing reports from the manufacturer to verify compliance.
- Consider developing a list of equipment that meets credit requirements and requiring the individuals with purchasing authority to seek approval for substitutions (see EQ Prerequisite Green Cleaning Policy).
- Consider giving the responsible individuals a tracking tool (e.g., Table 1) to document any new equipment purchases. Close collaboration with vendors may be required to ensure that new equipment used on the project meets credit requirements. This is particularly important the vendor's cleaning crews use different equipment to serve different clients.
- Purchase requirements in cleaning vendor contracts can be an effective way to ensure that equipment used on the project meets credit criteria (see EQ Prerequisite Green Cleaning Policy).
- There are currently no international standards that are equivalent to the Carpet and Rug Institute (CRI) standards.

STEP 5. CREATE EQUIPMENT PHASE-OUT PLAN E P

Determine how to meet the 40% threshold and create a phase-out plan for noncompliant equipment. If a phase-out plan has already been implemented, update it to include the sustainability criteria in this credit.

- If the threshold has been met, project teams are encouraged to continue to use equipment that still has significant remaining useful life (see *Changes from LEED 2009*).
- The phase-out plan should be based on the remaining useful life of noncompliant equipment as well as the value of new equipment that meets sustainability criteria.
- Determine which equipment will be phased out and when.

STEP 6. IMPLEMENT PHASE-OUT PLAN P

Track equipment replacement schedules against the plan.

- Work with cleaning vendors, if applicable, to appropriately track replacement of their equipment.
- Confirm that new equipment identified to replace phased-out equipment will meet the credit requirements.

FURTHER EXPLANATION

CALCULATIONS

See calculations in *Step-by-Step Guidance*.

CAMPUS

Group credit
All buildings in the group may be documented as one.

Campus credit
Eligible.

REQUIRED DOCUMENTATION

	Documentation	All Projects
E	List of equipment and manufacturers' urls or cutsheets indicating compliance with sustainability criteria	X
E	Contributing equipment calculation	X
E	Phase-out plan, as applicable	X
E	Updated contributing equipment calculation, as applicable	X
P	Phase-out plan, as applicable	X

RELATED CREDIT TIPS

SS Prerequisite Site Management Policy. Powered exterior cleaning equipment addressed in the related credit's site management policy may need to meet additional requirements for this credit.

EQ Prerequisite Green Cleaning Policy. This credit goes beyond the green cleaning policy created for the related prerequisite by establishing performance targets for cleaning equipment. The policy applies to spaces under the building management's control; this credit applies to the entire building, including tenants.

EQ Credit Integrated Pest Management. Vacuums or other powered equipment used in integrated pest management strategies may need to meet the requirements of this credit.

CHANGES FROM LEED 2009

- The performance threshold for credit achievement has been raised from 20% to 40%.
- A phase-out plan can now be used in lieu of discarding equipment that has useful life remaining.

REFERENCED STANDARDS

Carpet and Rug Institute (CRI): carpet-rug.org

- Seal of Approval, Green Label Vacuum Program
- Seal of Approval, Deep Cleaning Extractors
- Seal of Approval, Deep Cleaning Systems Program

EXEMPLARY PERFORMANCE

Meet the credit requirements for 100% of powered janitorial equipment.

DEFINITIONS

powered floor maintenance equipment electric and battery-powered floor buffers and burnishers. It does not include equipment used in wet applications

INDOOR ENVIRONMENTAL QUALITY CREDIT

Integrated Pest Management

This credit applies to:

Existing Buildings (2 points)
Schools (2 points)
Retail (2 points)
Data Centers (2 points)
Hospitality (2 points)
Warehouses and Distribution Centers (2 points)

INTENT

To minimize pest problems and exposure to pesticides.

REQUIREMENTS

ESTABLISHMENT E

Have in place an integrated pest management (IPM) plan for the building and grounds within the project boundary. The IPM plan must include the following elements.

- Identification of an IPM team. Identify roles for building management, pest management contractors, maintenance staff, and liaisons with building occupants.
- Provisions for identifying and monitoring pests. Specify inspections, pest population monitoring, and a reporting system that allows occupants, maintenance staff, and others to report evidence of pest infestations.
- Action thresholds for all pests likely encountered in the building. Also describe a process for modifying action thresholds, if necessary, through active communication between occupants and the IPM team.
- Nonchemical pest preventive measures, either designed into the structure or implemented as part of pest management activities.
- Pest control methods to be used when action thresholds are exceeded. For each pest, list all potential control methods considered and adopt the lowest-risk options, considering the risks to the applicator, building occupants, and the environment. The plan must preferentially require nonchemical approaches, with pesticides registered for the site applied only if those approaches fail. Give preference to the use of least-risk pesticides based on inherent toxicity and exposure potential. If a pesticide that is not in the least-risk category is selected, document the reason.
- A mechanism for documentation of inspection, monitoring, prevention, and control methods and for evaluation of the effectiveness of the IPM plan. Specify the metrics by which performance will be measured, and describe the quality assurance process to evaluate and verify successful implementation of the plan.

- A strategy for communications between the IPM team and the building occupants (for schools, faculty and staff). This strategy should include education about the IPM plan, participation in problem solving, feedback mechanisms (e.g., a system for recording pest complaints), and provision for notification of pesticide applications. At a minimum, the facility manager must notify any building occupant or employee who requests it and post a sign at the application site, which must remain in place for 24 hours. Notifications must include the pesticide name, EPA registration number, treatment location, and date of application. Applications of least-risk pesticides do not require notification. For an emergency application of a pesticide, anyone who requested notice must be notified within 24 hours of the application and given an explanation of the emergency.

PERFORMANCE P

Implement the strategies set forth in the IPM plan and evaluate the plan annually. This evaluation must verify that the strategies specified in the IPM plan have been implemented and identify any chemical applications that did not comply with the plan.

Perform recordkeeping and documentation required under the IPM plan. Maintain records of IPM team participation and decisions, as well as pesticide applications.

A project meets the requirements if the IPM service is provided by a certified member in good standing of GreenPro, EcoWise, or GreenShield, or a program with equivalent IPM standards, who complies with the program's standards.

BEHIND THE INTENT

Pests in and around a building can carry disease or cause allergic reactions. They can also cost costly property damage by harming landscaped areas, damaging structural components, or compromising the building envelope. Improper or misguided attempts to control pests can cause problems, too: overapplication or use of inappropriate chemicals wastes money and does not prevent future infestations.

The U.S., the Federal Healthy Homes Work Group, which includes the Department of Housing and Urban Development, Department of Health and Human Services (HHS), and Environmental Protection Agency, has identified a pest-free environment as one of the eight top characteristics of a safe and healthful home. A pest-free environment is achieved by taking a common-sense approach to pest management: focusing on exclusion, using pest control methods and products judiciously, and working in partnership with qualified and licensed pest professionals.

Integrated pest management (IPM) is an approach to managing pests in ways that protect human health and the surrounding environment while avoiding unnecessary use of pesticides. IPM, the most effective, least-risk option, is often more effective than the typical preventive application of pesticides because it addresses the underlying causes of pest problems rather than simply treating the symptoms.

IPM begins with accurately identifying and monitoring pests and the conditions conducive to pest infestations. IPM also involves exclusion and sanitation to keep pest populations below a predetermined action threshold. Pesticide applications can then be limited to targeted species in specific locations. Although IPM may require additional upfront maintenance costs, it ultimately lowers costs because it prevents and reduces pest problems and limits pesticide applications.

STEP-BY-STEP GUIDANCE

STEP 1. DETERMINE PHYSICAL SCOPE OF IPM PROGRAM E

Identify the applicable areas of the building and site.

- For individually owned buildings, include all areas of the building and site that are within the LEED project boundary.
- For projects that include tenant spaces, include all areas of the building and site that are under the building management's control and at least 90% of the tenant spaces within the LEED boundary.
- As a best practice, teams should consider how to engage tenants in developing and implementing the IPM plan in their spaces. IPM requirements and best management practices can be shared with tenants whose spaces are cleaned and maintained by vendors separate from those of the building management.

STEP 2. CREATE IPM TEAM E

Identify roles for stakeholders. The IPM plan can be outsourced to a qualified vendor or developed by a qualified member of the management staff. The person responsible for implementing the IPM plan should have the authority to do the following:

- Manage the creation of the IPM plan
- Maintain and update the IPM plan
- Track performance
- Coordinate with pest management contractors
- Coordinate with the purchasing department
- Communicate pest control schedules and methods to the building occupants

STEP 3. CREATE IPM TRACKING TOOL E

Set up a spreadsheet tracking tool for the following items:

- Pest name
- Monitoring method
- Monitoring schedule

- Responsible party
- Pest prevention
- Prevention measures
- Threshold for action
- Product applied (name)
- Toxicity of product (least?)
- Date and time of product application
- Date and time of occupant notification
- Emergency application? (If so, explain emergency)

STEP 4. SELECT COMPLIANCE OPTION(S) E

Select one of the following two options or a combination of both.

- Option 1 is for projects that will implement a customized in-house IPM policy. Ensure that those who will perform the work are licensed or trained in accordance with state standards (refer to the Association of Structural Pest Control Officials).
- Option 2 is for projects that will use contracted services certified by one of the following third parties: GreenPro, EcoWise, or GreenShield.
- A combination of Options 1 and 2 may be appropriate, provided all pest management procedures, products, and services within the LEED project boundary are addressed by the IPM plan.

Option 1. In-House IPM Policy

STEP 1. IDENTIFY POTENTIAL PESTS AND CONTROL THRESHOLDS E

For each pest, identify an action threshold—the point beyond which the property must take some remedial action. For many pests, like bedbugs, rats, and cockroaches, the threshold may be very low.

- Discuss with the building maintenance team the possible or known pests in the building and grounds. List those pests and determine the action threshold for each in different portions of the project.
- There should be action thresholds for each pest and structural environment. For example, the action threshold for German cockroaches in a food preparation or storage area will be much lower than for a smoky brown cockroach in a foyer or parking area.

Development of an in-house IPM plan requires properly trained and experienced staff. Identification of pests and conducive conditions must be accurate for an IPM plan to work. Monitoring of pest populations also requires training and experience. For the in-house option to succeed, training of staff in pest identification, monitoring, and control will be necessary.

STEP 2. CREATE IPM PLAN E

Work with the building management team to create an IPM plan that includes the components identified in the credit requirements (see *Getting Started, Effective Policy Development*).

STEP 3. IMPLEMENT IPM PLAN P

During the performance period, implement the strategies included in the IPM plan (see *Further Explanation, IPM Plan Implementation Best Practices*).

- Track the IPM team's participation and decision-making process.
- Perform annual evaluations of the program.
- Track compliance and noncompliance of pest management methods and the certification of any service providers.

Option 2. Certified IPM Service

STEP 1. VERIFY VENDOR CERTIFICATION

Determine whether the existing vendor has current certification from GreenPro, EcoWise, or GreenShield (see *Further Explanation, Third Party Certification Programs*).

- If the vendor is not currently certified, request that the company obtain certification.
- If the vendor cannot or will not obtain certification, initiate a new contract with an eligible vendor, or pursue Option 1.
- Ensure that the service provided is done in accordance with GreenPro, EcoWise or GreenShield standards.

STEP 2. COLLECT DOCUMENTATION

Obtain a copy of the GreenPro, EcoWise, or GreenShield certification from the vendor. Ensure that the vendor's certification was valid for the duration of the performance period.

FURTHER EXPLANATION

IPM PLAN REQUIREMENTS

IPM plans must include all the requirements in the rating system and address all of the following items.

Pest identification. Establish a process by which building occupants and building maintenance team can report evidence of pest infestations.

Pest monitoring. Outline the monitoring method and frequency for each potential pest. This enables the IPM team to be proactive and address pest infestations before they require use of chemical pesticides. In the IPM tracking tool, list each pest to be monitored, the monitoring method and schedule, and the person in charge of monitoring. Using the person's job title instead of name avoids revising the log to accommodate staff changes.

Pest prevention. Research pest prevention measures. Establish an inspection method and frequency to ensure that these measures are in place. Determine when traps, baits, and other structural control methods should be replaced and link the frequency to the monitoring schedule. Differentiate building zones if appropriate.

Pesticide application. Identify who will apply the selected products and ensure that they are properly credentialed. Establish a protocol for approval to deviate from the use of least-risk pesticides (see *Further Explanation, Least-Toxic Eligible Pesticides*). If application of any pesticide not considered least-risk could result in inadvertent human exposure (e.g., through broadcast, spray, fog, mist), establish reentry intervals based on the registered label of the product and activate the communication plan (below). For each application, track the date, time, and product are used.

Outside expertise. If a pest population exceeds the action threshold and least-risk products are not sufficiently effective, it may be necessary to use other pesticides. In the plan, list specialists or contractors who can be called in if required. Consult with pest management professionals or university extension specialists on what product to use.

Communications plan. Set up a communications plan to notify occupants before the application of a pesticide that does not meet the definition of a least-risk pesticide. Use the IPM tracking tool to determine whether the communications plan was implemented as designed (see *Further Explanation, Pesticide Application Communications Plan*).

BEST PRACTICE INTEGRATED PEST MANAGEMENT CONTROL METHODS

Sanitation. Occupants may inadvertently attract pests into the building. Perform a walk-through assessment and identify problem areas or activities and devise a plan to address them. Eliminate or control all potential food and water sources. Food service areas and break rooms should be thoroughly cleaned, food and waste should be kept in airtight containers, and empty beverage containers should be rinsed or isolated. Clean all spills promptly and eliminate clutter to simplify cleaning and minimize hiding places for pests. Fix dripping faucets and leaking pipes.

Exclusion. Because landscaping can offer safe havens for pests, including rodents, keep shrubs and other plants at least 18 inches (450 mm) from the building, and fill that space with small stones or similar substrate. Install barriers to prevent pests from entering the building. Seal cracks, crevices, and holes in external walls and inspect the seals around doors and windows. If the building does not already have window screens, consider adding screens.

Traps. Install traps for both insects and rodents only where needed, rather than throughout the building. Use rodent baits that are solid blocks placed in locked outdoor dispensers. No second-generation (single-feed) rodent baits should be used if the building is adjacent to parkland, wild areas, or other spaces where wildlife may be unintentionally affected. Rodent baits are not considered least toxic under any circumstances.

PESTICIDE APPLICATION COMMUNICATIONS PLAN

The IPM plan must include a strategy for the IPM team to communicate with building occupants about pesticide problems and control measures. Create a way for occupants to opt into notifications.

Notify occupants about pesticide applications or pest problems. Ensure that the information reaches those who have opted into notifications and all occupants who could be affected. For example, use e-mail for office workers, posted signs for maintenance staff, and translations as necessary.

For pesticide application notifications, include the pesticide product name, active ingredient, product label signal word (e.g., "caution," "danger"), the time and location of the application, and contact information for anyone seeking additional details.

ELIGIBLE LEAST-TOXIC PESTICIDES

Any product that meets San Francisco's Tier 3 hazard criteria (least hazardous) is considered a least-toxic pesticide. Most active ingredients are covered in San Francisco's system, and additional screenings can be done using Internet resources.

Nonrodent pesticides that exceed the Tier 3 criteria are considered least toxic if they are used in self-contained baits and placed in inaccessible locations. Rodent baits are not considered least toxic under any circumstances.

RESOURCES

Integrated pest management plan template, available on the USGBC website

EPA's Integrated Pest Management in Buildings. This reference guide defines IPM, describes proper IPM implementation in buildings, and outlines the roles and responsibilities necessary for success.
http://www.epa.gov/pesp/publications/ipm/ipm_in_buildings.pdf

San Francisco's Department of the Environment (SF Environment) explains the listing criteria and process and has an updated 2007 reduced-risk pesticide list for screened pesticide active ingredients.
http://www.sfenvironment.org/ipmchecklist

IPM PLAN IMPLEMENTATION

Best practices for implementing an IPM plan include holding a kick-off meeting, engaging the building's staff and occupants, and ensuring regular progress updates.

IPM kick-off meeting. A few weeks before the start of the performance period, consider scheduling an IPM kick-off meeting for all entities involved in the project's maintenance process. The following people should attend the meeting:

- Representative from the purchasing department
- Building manager
- Custodial staff and/or janitorial contractors
- Designated members from the operations and maintenance team and pest management providers who will be responsible for pesticide product applications

The meeting can be used to familiarize everyone on the intent and requirements of the IPM plan and the importance of tracking IPM activities. Highlight changes from previous pest management practices. Demonstrate the IPM tracking tool that will be used to track performance, and review the responsibilities and process for tracking.

Stakeholder involvement. Before the performance period begins, consider posting copies of the approved list of least-toxic chemicals and products in visible locations (e.g., janitor's closet and staff break room). Include major parts of the IPM plan, such as the monitoring and inspection schedule, approved product lists, and a copy of the tracking tool, in custodial staff training materials, such as binders, online resource pages, and best management practice documents. Maintain a list of staff who have read the IPM plan.

Regular progress updates. Set up a process for the IPM team to review the IPM tracking tool. This can be a simple half-hour meeting every few weeks for the building maintenance staff to update the IPM team on pest inspections, maintenance activities, and any pesticide applications. The IPM team can then update the IPM tracking tool and measure progress against the performance metrics in the IPM plan. The team can also use the information collected to improve performance before the next check-in meeting. Regularly report progress to managers, occupants, and staff to communicate success and establish new best practices.

THIRD-PARTY CERTIFICATION PROGRAMS

TABLE 1. Third-party certification programs

Program	Definition of "green" pest management	Administrative components	Enforcement, regulatory components	Additional information
Green Pro National Pest Management Association npmagreenpro.org	Practices that include development and implementation of IPM, documentation of monitoring and nonchemical approaches, documentation of treatments used, documentation of "exceptions" to treatment standard. Use of baits, crack-and-crevice, and spot treatments is standard. Certain methods prohibited: nonblock rodent baits in bait stations, fogging or broadcast sprays, perimeter sprays.	Certification of pest management companies is provided by NPMA via Quality Pro program. Requires membership in Quality Pro, training and testing of technicians, filing a written commitment to Green Pro service standard, submission of audits including providing records to independent auditor.	Independent auditor hired by advisory committee. Paper audits of all companies in first year consisting of 15% of branches (up to 30 total). 20% of companies are field-audited each year. Deficiencies identified allowed to be corrected. Disqualification if not corrected.	Funded by fees collected from participants. Not limited geographically.
Green Shield IPM Institute of North America greenshieldcertified.org	Application of IPM and advanced IPM, with criteria established for approaches to pest management using corrective measures to reduce pest-conducive conditions. Requires use of "least toxic" pesticides when pesticides when nonchemical measures are ineffective. Certain methods prohibited: fogging, baseboard treatments, residual pesticides used inside buildings. Restrictions on baits and rodenticides. Written IPM plan is not required but strongly recommended (for LEED, written plan is required).	IPM Institute administers program and credentials pest management companies or dedicated portions of companies, conducts initial and follow up evaluations and makes recommendations for improvements. Requires training of staff and documentation of pest management methods and pest problems.	IPM Institute determines compliance with program via on-site audits every three years and annual update to maintain certification. Participants who do not resolve criteria violations are removed from program. No provision for removing credential if criteria are not met.	Funded by fees collected by participants. Not limited geographically.

TABLE 1 (CONTINUED). Third-party certification programs				
Program	**Definition of "green" pest management**	**Administrative components**	**Enforcement, regulatory components**	**Additional information**
Eco Wise **Bay Area Council of Governments, San Fransisco** ecowisecertified.org	Prevention-based pest control using corrective measures to reduce conducive conditions, and minimizing use of pesticides. Pesticide applications based on pest presence, applied only as directed treatment to voids and inaccessible areas, crack or crevice treatments, or spot treatments to exterior, contained in bait stations, with no fogging and no exterior perimeter treatments allowed. Written IPM protocol required. Establishes program materials list.	Candidates for program must document 20 IPM service visits in at least 7 different customer sites within one year of application. Eco Wise reviews records and performs field evaluations to determine whether certification requirements are met. Certification is granted to companies that employ at least one Eco Wise–certified IPM practitioner who supervises the certified IPM service. Requires 15 hours of IPM continuing education every 3 years.	Eco Wise determines compliance with program. Notification of noncompliance can be issued and certification denied, with opportunities for reapplication.	Limited to pest management firms in California. Funded by state.

PROJECT TYPE VARIATIONS

Multifamily Residential

Multifamily residential projects can earn this credit by implementing the IPM plan in the areas under the control of the building management.

International Tips

Projects outside the U.S. must use the San Francisco pesticide hazard screening list of least-toxic pesticides. For pesticide brands and names not available in other countries, use the listed active ingredients as a guide. Hazard criteria can be determined by using the San Francisco pesticide hazard screening methodology.

CAMPUS

Group Approach

All buildings in the group may be documented as one. One log and one plan can be used for multiple buildings, provided all buildings adhere to the plan 100% of the time.

Campus Approach

Eligible. The IPM plan may be implemented on a campus-wide basis. One log and one plan can be used for multiple buildings, provided all buildings adhere to the plan 100% of the time.

REQUIRED DOCUMENTATION

	Documentation	Option 1	Option 2
E	IPM plan	X	
E P	IPM tracking tool	X	X
E P	Pesticide application list	X	
E P	GreenPro, EcoWise, or GreenShield certificate		X

RELATED CREDIT TIPS

None.

CHANGES FROM LEED 2009

- The exterior pest management from SS Credit 3 and the interior pest management requirements from IEQ Credit 3.7 have been combined into one credit.
- The 72-hour window for alerting building occupants that a non-least-risk pesticide application was going to occur has been shortened to 24 hours.
- The required log has been expanded to include pest population tracking. Teams must now conduct a pest inventory and establish pest population thresholds.

REFERENCED STANDARDS

None.

EXEMPLARY PERFORMANCE

Not available.

DEFINITIONS

integrated pest management a method of pest management that protects human health and the surrounding environment, and improves economic returns through the most effective, least-risk option

least-risk pesticide a registered pesticide in the Tier III (lowest toxicity) category, using the San Francisco Hazard Ranking system, or a pesticide that meets the requirements in the San Francisco Pesticide Hazard Screening Protocol and is sold as a self-contained bait or as a crack-and-crevice treatment used in areas inaccessible to building occupants. Rodenticides are never considered least-risk pesticides.

INDOOR ENVIRONMENTAL QUALITY CREDIT

Occupant Comfort Survey

This credit applies to:

Existing Buildings (1 point)
Schools (1 point)
Retail (1 point)
Data Centers (1 point)
Hospitality (1 point)
Warehouses and Distribution Centers (1 point)

INTENT

To assess building occupants' comfort.

REQUIREMENTS

ESTABLISHMENT E

None.

PERFORMANCE P

Administer at least one occupant comfort survey to collect anonymous responses regarding at least the following:

- acoustics;
- building cleanliness;
- indoor air quality;
- lighting; and
- thermal comfort.

The responses must be collected from a representative sample of building occupants making up at least 30% of the total occupants.

Document survey results. Develop and implement a corrective action plan to address comfort issues if the results indicate that more than 20% of occupants are dissatisfied.

Perform at least one survey and implement corrective actions. At a minimum, perform one new survey at least once every 2 years.

BEHIND THE INTENT

Soliciting feedback from occupants on their satisfaction with the building's thermal comfort, lighting and acoustic quality, indoor air quality, and cleanliness helps building managers improve the indoor environment. Gathering feedback in a systematic way can reveal problems that may not otherwise be observed during the course of typical building operations.

If occupants indicate dissatisfaction, taking corrective action will contribute toward ongoing improvement of a building's indoor environmental quality. Comfortable, satisfied occupants are more productive, delivering substantial benefits for building owners and operators.

STEP-BY-STEP GUIDANCE

STEP 1. DEVELOP ANONYMOUS SURVEY P

To ensure that the survey is sufficiently specific, consider involving the building property manager, facility manager, and/or chief engineer in its development.

The survey response format should rate satisfaction against the occupant comfort criteria using a seven-point scale, ranging from very satisfied (+3) to very dissatisfied (–3), with a value of zero signifying a neutral response. The survey may include follow-up questions to identify the nature and cause of any problems (see *Further Explanation, Example Follow-Up Questions for Dissatisfaction*.)

Project teams are not required to create their own surveys. Survey templates or a third-party survey tool may be used, provided the survey responses remain anonymous and all required occupant comfort areas are addressed.

STEP 2. ADMINISTER SURVEY P

Administer the survey to the regular building occupants.

- The survey must be made available to all regular building occupants. This may be accomplished through any form of communication from building management or tenant contact that alerts all building occupants to the opportunity to participate in the survey.
- The survey responses must be representative of regular building occupants working in all major space types and from a variety of areas on the building floor plate (see *Further Explanation, Regular Building Occupants*).
- Project teams may use incentives to increase the survey response rate, provided the individual responses remain anonymous. For example, surveys may be numbered and the numbers entered in a drawing.
- Surveys may be conducted in person, over the phone, online, or on paper. To ensure anonymity, in-person surveys may be conducted by a third party or in such a way that the survey administrator cannot connect a set of responses to a specific building occupant.

STEP 3. COLLECT AND SUMMARIZE SURVEY RESULTS P

Summarize the survey results to determine the average level of satisfaction in each area of occupant comfort.

- Dissatisfied responses are defined as any response that is negative. On the recommended seven-point scale, this would include very dissatisfied (–3), mostly dissatisfied (–2), and somewhat dissatisfied (–1).
- The summary must include the total number of regular building occupants, the number and percentage of survey respondents, and the average rate of satisfaction for each component of occupant comfort (see *Further Explanation, Example Survey Summary*).

STEP 4. DEVELOP CORRECTIVE ACTION PLAN P

The plan must address any areas with a dissatisfaction rate above 20%.

- The corrective action plan should include no-cost measures (e.g., operational or procedural changes, adjustments to equipment run-time or setpoints) and may include capital improvements, such as minor equipment repairs or major retrofits or upgrades.

- Describe the no-cost measures and implementation date for any corrective action taken to address comfort issues. All no-cost measures included in the corrective action plan must be implemented before the completion of the performance period.
- Project teams are encouraged to include capital improvement measures in the corrective action plan when appropriate, but their implementation is not required.

FURTHER EXPLANATION

EXAMPLE FOLLOW-UP QUESTIONS FOR DISSATISFACTION

The survey should ask respondents who indicate dissatisfaction to identify the nature and cause of the problem. Specific follow-up questions are not prescribed by the credit; the following are examples illustrate some possibilities.

For the following statements and questions, please indicate yes or no.

1. In warm or hot weather, the temperature in my workspace is
   Often too hot ____
   Often too cold ____
2. In warm or hot weather,
   My hands are too cold ____
   My feet are too cold ____
3. In cool or cold weather, the temperature in my workspace is
   Often too hot ____
   Often too cold ____
4. In cool or cold weather,
   My hands are too cold ____
   My feet are too cold ____
5. When is this most often the problem?
   Morning ____
   Midday ____
   Afternoon ____
   Evening ____
6. How would you best describe the source of the problem?
   Humidity is too high (damp) ____
   Humidity is too low (dry) ____
   Air movement is too high ____
   Air movement is too low ____
   Sun heats my workspace ____
   Surfaces (wall, floor, etc.) are hot or cold ____
   Heat is coming from office equipment ____
   Drafts are coming from vents ____
   Thermostat is inaccessible ____
   Thermostat is adjusted by others ____
   Heating or cooling system is not responsive ____

Alternatively, provide an open-ended format to solicit feedback on specific sources of thermal discomfort.

1. Please describe the specific issues that you have experienced related to thermal comfort in your workspace.

REGULAR BUILDING OCCUPANTS

See *Getting Started, Occupancy*, for a general description of regular building occupants. Also review *Getting Started, Tenant Space Exclusion Allowances*, and *Getting Started, Variable Occupancy*, for any special situations or allowed exclusions. For this credit, the following modifications apply.

K-12 students (ages 5–18). Only students in grade 6 (or age 12) and above need to be surveyed.

Hotel guests. Hotel guests do not need to be surveyed, though teams are encouraged to solicit feedback from hotel guests if possible. Suggested methods include sending an email survey to guests after their stay or providing a paper copy of the survey in the guest room.

Regular building occupants in warehouses and distribution centers. Any occupant meeting the definition of a regular building occupant must be included in the survey, except for occupants in areas that are necessarily maintained at conditions outside the typical range for occupant comfort (e.g., refrigerated warehouses).

EXAMPLE SURVEY SUMMARY

The project team has summarized the following results from a survey conducted for a building with 300 regular occupants. The team received 100 responses, for a response rate of 33%.

TABLE 1. Example survey results

Occupant comfort area	3 Very satisfied	2 Mostly satisfied	1 Somewhat satisfied	0 Neutral	-1 Somewhat dissatisfied	-2 Mostly dissatisfied	-3 Very dissatisfied	% Dissatisfied (-1 to -3)
Thermal comfort	20	15	30	5	15	10	5	30%
Lighting quality	35	30	15	10	2	4	4	10%
Acoustic quality	41	30	6	10	10	3	0	13%
Building cleanliness	30	15	10	20	12	8	5	25%
Air quality	20	30	40	5	3	2	0	5%

This project team must develop corrective action plans for the occupant comfort areas that scored more than 20% dissatisfied: thermal comfort and building cleanliness.

CAMPUS

Group Approach

All buildings in the group may be documented as one.

Campus Approach

Eligible.

REQUIRED DOCUMENTATION

	Documentation	All projects
P	Copy of survey addressing acoustics, building cleanliness, indoor air quality, lighting, and thermal comfort	X
P	Summary of survey results and description of corrective actions taken	X

RELATED CREDIT TIPS

LT Credit Alternative Transportation. If attempting either Option 1 or Option 2 of the related credit, consider combining the surveys to generate higher response rates.

EQ Credit Indoor Air Quality Management Program. The I-BEAM audit conducted to meet the requirements of the related credit may be used to investigate indoor air quality issues and determine corrective actions.

EQ Credit Green Cleaning-Custodial Effectiveness. The audit required by the related credit may be used to investigate cleanliness issues and determine corrective actions.

CHANGES FROM LEED 2009

Corrective action for any area with a dissatisfaction rate higher than 20% is now required.

REFERENCED STANDARDS

None.

EXEMPLARY PERFORMANCE

Not available.

DEFINITIONS

None.

Innovation (IN)

OVERVIEW

Strategies for sustainable building operations are constantly evolving and improving. New technologies that improve building operations and maintenance are continually introduced to the marketplace. The purpose of this LEED category is to recognize projects for innovative and exemplary building features or practices that generate environmental benefits beyond those addressed or specified in the other credit categories.

Occasionally, a strategy results in building performance that greatly exceeds what is required in an existing LEED credit. Other strategies may not be addressed by any LEED prerequisite or credit but warrant consideration for their sustainability benefits. In addition, LEED is most effectively implemented as part of a cohesive team, and this category addresses the role of a LEED Accredited Professional in facilitating that process.

INNOVATION CREDIT

Innovation

This credit applies to:

Existing Buildings (1-5 points)
Schools (1-5 points)
Retail (1-5 points)
Data Centers (1-5 points)
Hospitality (1-5 points)
Warehouses and Distribution Centers (1-5 points)

INTENT

To encourage projects to achieve exceptional or innovative performance.

REQUIREMENTS

Project teams can use any combination of innovation, pilot, and exemplary performance strategies.

OPTION 1. INNOVATION (1 POINT)

Achieve significant, measurable environmental performance using a strategy not addressed in the LEED green building rating system.

Identify the following:

- the intent of the proposed innovation credit;
- proposed requirements for compliance;
- proposed submittals to demonstrate compliance; and
- the design approach or strategies used to meet the requirements.

AND/OR

OPTION 2. PILOT (1 POINT)

Achieve one pilot credit from USGBC's LEED Pilot Credit Library

AND/OR

OPTION 3. ADDITIONAL STRATEGIES

Innovation (1-3 **points**)

- Defined in Option 1 above.

Pilot (1–3 **points**)

- Meet the requirements of Option 2.

Exemplary Performance (1–2 **points**)

- Achieve exemplary performance in an existing LEED v4 prerequisite or credit that allows exemplary performance, as specified in the LEED Reference Guide, v4 edition. An exemplary performance point is typically earned for achieving double the credit requirements or the next incremental percentage threshold.

BEHIND THE INTENT

Sustainable operations come from innovative strategies and thinking. Institutional measures that reward such thinking—such as the achievement of this credit—benefit our environment. Recognition of exceptional efforts will spur further innovation.

When project teams innovate and go beyond LEED requirements, they not only achieve measurable environmental benefits beyond those specified by the LEED rating system, they also have the opportunity to explore cutting-edge pilot credits and contribute to the development of future LEED credits. When they can demonstrate that the project exceeds the standard level of performance associated with one or more LEED credits, their innovations can be adopted by other teams in the future.

STEP-BY-STEP GUIDANCE

STEP 1. IDENTIFY INNOVATIVE STRATEGIES

Innovation may begin at a project's conception, but it can enter at any step of the process and come from any member of the project team.

- During initial meetings, explore opportunities to incorporate innovative strategies, achieve exemplary performance for existing LEED credits, and develop pilot credits, based on the project scope.
- Review the project goals and targeted credits to determine whether the project is likely to meet any exemplary performance criteria.
- Identify any environmental strategies included in the project's operations and protocols that are not addressed by existing LEED credits.
- Discuss pilot credits, green housekeeping, public education, and other opportunities for innovation.

STEP 2. DEVELOP INNOVATION POINT STRATEGY

Projects may earn up to 5 points through any combination of the following:

- Innovation (up to 4 points). This option is appropriate for strategies that are not addressed by any existing credits in the LEED rating system under which the project will be certified. Strategies must demonstrate a comprehensive approach, have significant, measurable environmental benefits, and be better than standard practice. Points can also be earned by achieving selected credits from other LEED rating systems.
- Pilot credits (up to 4 points). This option requires project teams to achieve, document, and provide feedback on pilot credit strategies developed by USGBC members and committees.
- Exemplary performance (up to 2 points). This option is achieved by demonstrating performance that greatly exceeds the level or scope required by existing LEED prerequisites or credits.

Innovation (up to 4 points)

STEP 1. CONFIRM CREDIT ELIGIBILITY

For innovations that are not addressed by existing LEED credits, confirm that the proposed strategy meets the following three basic criteria:

- The project must demonstrate quantitative environmental performance improvement by identifying or establishing a baseline of standard performance and comparing with the final design.
- The strategy must be comprehensive. Measures that address a limited portion of a project or are not comprehensive in other ways are not eligible. The project team must demonstrate that the proposed innovation credit applies to the entire project being certified under LEED and has at least two components (i.e., it is not limited to use of a single product).
- The strategy must be significantly better than standard building operations and maintenance practices.

Innovation credit can also be earned by achieving selected credits from other LEED rating systems.

Strategies that integrate building operations practices across LEED categories are encouraged. Strategies must not contribute to earning any existing prerequisites or credits. Project teams should provide a narrative supporting why their strategies are innovative and not duplicative of existing prerequisites or credits. See *Further Explanation, Suggested Topics for Innovation Credits,* and *Ineligible Strategies.*

STEP 2. DEVELOP DOCUMENTATION

Document credit eligibility as outlined above, and note any project-specific strategies.

STEP 3. IMPLEMENT CREDIT

Develop and execute the innovative strategy or program in a manner that yields a meaningful environmental benefit. Retain documentation and calculations to validate the project team's approach and implementation.

Pilot credits (up to 4 points)

STEP 1. SELECT CREDIT

Select a credit from the LEED Pilot Credit Library on the USGBC website. The Pilot Credit Library includes credit intent and requirements, submittals, and specific feedback questions for each pilot credit.

- Pilot credits open and close at varying intervals. Check the USGBC website for a current list of available pilot credit strategies.
- Pilot credits are applicable to specific rating systems. Review the listing on the website to identify pilot credits for the applicable LEED rating system.

STEP 2. REGISTER PILOT CREDIT

Register for the selected pilot credit through the Pilot Credit Library.

- Since pilot credit availability changes over time, register for a credit as soon as the project team decides to pursue it, rather than waiting until documentation review.
- Once a project has registered for a pilot credit, the project team may continue to pursue it even if it is closed to new registrants.

STEP 3. IMPLEMENT CREDIT

Follow the required steps to implement the credit as outlined in the pilot credit. Visit the LEEDuser forums for the selected pilot credit to ask questions or get advice on strategy.

STEP 4. PROVIDE FEEDBACK

Complete the credit's feedback survey, found on the USGBC website. Include any information that might be helpful in future revisions of the credit.

STEP 5. DOCUMENT CREDIT

Complete all credit-specific documentation as outlined in the pilot credit.

- Some pilot credits will have documentation forms or calculators.
- Pilot credits may be attempted in any review stage and can be replaced before the next review if the initial credit is not accepted.

Exemplary Performance (up to 2 points)

STEP 1. IDENTIFY TARGET EXEMPLARY PERFORMANCE CREDITS

During initial planning, review exemplary performance criteria and select credits for which exemplary performance will be pursued. Credits that allow exemplary performance through a predetermined approach are noted throughout this reference guide.

STEP 2. CONFIRM IMPLEMENTATION

Incorporate operational elements and specifications requirements to ensure that the selected exemplary performance criteria are met. Provide the required documentation as noted in the base credit.

FURTHER EXPLANATION

SUGGESTED TOPICS FOR INNOVATION CREDITS

Project teams are encouraged to explore the full range of innovative opportunities in their buildings. Refer to the online Innovation database for examples of successful innovation credits. The examples do not constitute preapproval of any Innovation strategy, however, and Innovation credit awarded for a project today does not imply automatic approval for similar strategies in the future. A team seeking formal preapproval should submit a project credit interpretation request (CIR).

The following example was submitted for an Innovation credit:

Public education. *Provide an educational program on the environmental and human health benefits of green building practices and how building occupants or the public can help improve green performance within the LEED space (such as recycling and appropriate use of efficient fixtures and equipment). The program must be actively instructional and include at least two instructional initiatives that have ongoing components, such as a signage program, case study, guided tours, educational outreach program through periodic events covering green building topics, and/or a website or electronic newsletter.*

Office garden. *Dedicate a permanent and viable growing space and/or facility (such as a greenhouse) within the project boundary, with at least 1 square foot of garden space per occupant. Provide solar access, fencing, watering systems, garden bed enhancements (such as raised beds), secure storage space for tools, and pedestrian access.*

INELIGIBLE STRATEGIES

Innovation credits are not awarded for the use of a particular product or design strategy if the technology aids in the achievement of an existing LEED credit, even if the project is not attempting to earn that credit.

Innovation strategies that are closed pilot credits are not available unless they are listed in the online Innovation database.

No strategy can achieve more than 1 point under Innovation. That is, a single strategy cannot be double-counted for both exemplary performance and innovation (or both exemplary performance and a pilot credit, or both a pilot credit and innovation).

Corporate strategies are not considered innovative. The innovation strategy must be specific to the LEED project under review.

CAMPUS

Group Approach

All buildings in the group may be documented as one. Documentation for campus-wide strategies must represent the total combined performance for all buildings and site areas.

Campus Approach

Eligible. Documentation for campus-wide strategies must represent the total combined performance for all master site buildings and site areas, but strategies that apply to individual buildings must be documented for every building.

REQUIRED DOCUMENTATION

Documentation	Innovation	Pilot credit	Exemplary Performance
Innovation narrative	X		
Supporting documentation	X	X	X
Pilot credit registration		X	
Pilot credit survey		X	
Pilot credit specific submittals		X	
Exemplary performance credit and level			X

RELATED CREDIT TIPS

None.

CHANGES FROM LEED 2009

The maximum number of exemplary performance strategies eligible for IN credits has changed from three to two.

REFERENCED STANDARDS

None.

DEFINITIONS

None.

INNOVATION CREDIT

LEED Accredited Professional

This credit applies to:

Existing Buildings (1 point)
Schools (1 point)
Retail (1 point)
Data Centers (1 point)
Hospitality (1 point)
Warehouses and Distribution Centers (1 point)

INTENT

To encourage the team integration required by a LEED project and to streamline the application and certification process.

REQUIREMENTS

At least one principal participant of the project team must be a LEED Accredited Professional (AP) with a specialty appropriate for the project.

BEHIND THE INTENT

A LEED Accredited Professional (LEED AP) with specialty can be a valuable resource in the LEED certification process. The presence of a LEED AP with specialty helps project team members understand the rating system, the importance of interactions among the prerequisites and credits, and the LEED application process.

STEP-BY-STEP GUIDANCE

STEP 1. ENGAGE LEED AP WITH SPECIALTY

Identify a project team member who is a LEED AP with specialty, or engage a LEED AP with specialty to support the project and participate in the certification process.

- Select a team member with a LEED AP Operations + Maintenance (LEED AP O+M) credential.
- The LEED AP with specialty identified for this credit must have an active credential at the time of certification review (see *Further Explanation, Maintaining a LEED Credential*).
- LEED APs without specialty (legacy LEED APs) do not qualify for this credit.

FURTHER EXPLANATION

MAINTAINING A LEED CREDENTIAL

The LEED AP with specialty credential can be maintained through either of the following methods:

- Retaking and passing the LEED accreditation exam
- Earning 30 continuing education hours per credentialing period

A credential is considered active (and eligible for this credit) only if the credential holder has completed his or her credential maintenance through the GBCI Credential Maintenance Program. For more information, visit USGBC's website.

CAMPUS

Group Approach

Submit separate documentation for each building.

Campus Approach

Ineligible. Each LEED project may pursue the credit individually.

REQUIRED DOCUMENTATION

Documentation	All projects
Full name and specialty credential of LEED AP	X

RELATED CREDIT TIPS

None.

CHANGES FROM LEED 2009

LEED APs without specialty (legacy LEED APs) are no longer eligible for this credit.

REFERENCED STANDARDS

None.

EXEMPLARY PERFORMANCE

Not available.

DEFINITIONS

None.

Regional Priority (RP)

OVERVIEW

Because some environmental issues are particular to a locale, volunteers from USGBC chapters and the LEED International Roundtable have identified distinct environmental priorities within their areas and the credits that address those issues. These Regional Priority credits encourage project teams to focus on their local environmental priorities.

USGBC established a process that identified six RP credits for every location and every rating system within chapter or country boundaries. Participants were asked to determine which environmental issues were most salient in their chapter area or country. The issues could be naturally occurring (e.g., water shortages) or man-made (e.g., polluted watersheds) and could reflect environmental concerns (e.g., wa-ter shortages) or environmental assets (e.g., abundant sunlight). The areas, or zones, were defined by a combination of priority issues—for example, an urban area with an impaired watershed versus an urban area with an intact watershed.

The participants then prioritized credits to address the important issues of given locations. Because each LEED project type (e.g., a data center) may be associated with different environmental impacts, each rat-ing system has its own RP credits.

The ultimate goal of RP credits is to enhance the ability of LEED project teams to address critical environmental issues across the country and around the world.

REGIONAL PRIORITY CREDIT

Regional Priority

This credit applies to:

Existing Buildings (1–4 points)
Schools (1–4 points)
Retail (1–4 points)
Data Centers (1–4 points)
Hospitality (1–4 points)
Warehouses and Distribution Centers (1–4 points)

INTENT

To provide an incentive for the achievement of credits that address geographically specific environmental, social equity, and public health priorities.

REQUIREMENTS

Earn up to four of the six Regional Priority credits. These credits have been identified by the USGBC regional councils and chapters as having additional regional importance for the project's region. A database of Regional Priority credits and their geographic applicability is available on the USGBC website, http://www.usgbc.org.

One point is awarded for each Regional Priority credit achieved, up to a maximum of four.

BEHIND THE INTENT

LEED projects are designed, built, and operated in many different contexts. Climate, population density, and local regulations can differ significantly from one location to another, making certain environmental issues more critical than others. Examples include water conservation in arid climates versus rainwater management in wet climates.

LEED projects can be more transformative if teams recognize their location's priority environmental issues and address them through design, construction, and operation choices. LEED encourages a focus on regional issues through RP credits—existing LEED credits that USGBC volunteers have determined to be especially important in a given area. For every location in the U.S., six credits are prioritized. The ultimate intent is to motivate project teams to earn the credits that address an area's priority issues.

STEP-BY-STEP GUIDANCE

STEP 1. IDENTIFY APPLICABLE RP CREDITS

Review the credits flagged for regional priority in the project's area (see USGBC's website). Consider how achievement of these credits will affect the project.

STEP 2. DETERMINE PERFORMANCE REQUIRED TO EARN RP POINTS

- For credits with multiple thresholds (e.g., percentage improvement in energy efficiency), points are awarded at particular levels of achievement.
- If such a credit is flagged as RP for the project's location, confirm the threshold the project must meet to earn the bonus point.

FURTHER EXPLANATION

None.

REQUIRED DOCUMENTATION

Documentation
No additional documentation is required to earn Regional Priority credits. Document compliance for the selected credits, and the related RP bonus points for their achievement will be awarded automatically.

RELATED CREDIT TIPS

None.

CHANGES FROM LEED 2009

The RP credits for a given region may be different than they were for LEED 2009.

REFERENCED STANDARDS

Not available.

EXEMPLARY PERFORMANCE

Not available.

DEFINITIONS

None.

APPENDICES

APPENDIX 1. USE TYPES AND CATEGORIES

TABLE 1. Use Types and Categories

Category	Use type
Food retail	Supermarket
	Grocery with produce section
Community-serving retail	Convenience store
	Farmers market
	Hardware store
	Pharmacy
	Other retail
Services	Bank
	Family entertainment venue (e.g., theater, sports)
	Gym, health club, exercise studio
	Hair care
	Laundry, dry cleaner
	Restaurant, café, diner (excluding those with only drive-thru service)
Civic and community facilities	Adult or senior care (licensed)
	Child care (licensed)
	Community or recreation center
	Cultural arts facility (museum, performing arts)
	Education facility (e.g., K—12 school, university, adult education center, vocational school, community college)
	Government office that serves public on-site
	Medical clinic or office that treats patients
	Place of worship
	Police or fire station
	Post office
	Public library
	Public park
	Social services center
Community anchor uses (BD+C and ID+C only)	Commercial office (100 or more full-time equivalent jobs)

Adapted from Criterion Planners, INDEX neighborhood completeness indicator, 2005.

APPENDIX 2. DEFAULT OCCUPANCY COUNTS

Use Table 1 to calculate default occupancy counts. Only use the occupancy estimates if occupancy is unknown.

For the calculation, use gross floor area, not net or leasable floor area. Gross floor area is defined as the sum of all areas on all floors of a building included within the outside faces of the exterior wall, including common areas, mechanical spaces, circulation areas, and all floor penetrations that connect one floor to another. To determine gross floor area, multiply the building footprint (in square feet or square meters) by the number of floors in the building. Exclude underground or structured parking from the calculation.

TABLE 1. Default Occupancy Numbers

	Gross square feet per occupant		Gross square meters per occupant	
	Employees	Transients	Employees	Transients
General office	250	0	23	0
Retail, general	550	130	51	12
Retail or service (e.g., financial, auto)	600	130	56	12
Restaurant	435	95	40	9
Grocery store	550	115	51	11
Medical office	225	330	21	31
R&D or laboratory	400	0	37	0
Warehouse, distribution	2,500	0	232	0
Warehouse, storage	20,000	0	1860	0
Hotel	1,500	700	139	65
Educational, daycare	630	105	59	10
Educational, K-12	1,300	140	121	13
Educational, postsecondary	2,100	150	195	14

Sources:

- ANSI/ASHRAE/IESNA Standard 90.1–2004 (Atlanta, GA, 2004).
- 2001 Uniform Plumbing Code (Los Angeles, CA)
- California Public Utilities Commission, 2004–2005 Database for Energy Efficiency Resources (DEER) Update Study (2008).
- California State University, Capital Planning, Design and Construction Section VI, Standards for Campus Development Programs (Long Beach, CA, 2002).
- City of Boulder Planning Department, Projecting Future Employment—How Much Space per Person (Boulder, 2002).
- Metro, 1999 Employment Density Study (Portland, OR 1999).
- American Hotel and Lodging Association, Lodging Industry Profile Washington, DC, 2008.
- LEED for Core & Shell Core Committee, personal communication (2003 - 2006).
- LEED for Retail Core Committee, personal communication (2007)
- OWP/P, Medical Office Building Project Averages (Chicago, 2008).
- OWP/P, University Master Plan Projects (Chicago, 2008).
- U.S. General Services Administration, Childcare Center Design Guide (Washington, DC, 2003).

APPENDIX 3. RETAIL PROCESS LOAD BASELINES

TABLE 1A. Commercial kitchen appliance prescriptive measures and baseline for energy cost budget (IP units)

	Baseline energy usage for energy modeling path				Levels for prescriptive path	
Appliance Type	**Fuel**	**Function**	**Baseline Efficiency**	**Baseline Idle Rate**	**Prescriptive Efficiency**	**Prescriptive Idle Rate**
Broiler, underfired	Gas	Cooking	30%	16,000 Btu/h/ft² peak input	35%	12,000 Btu/h/ft² peak input
Combination ovens, steam mode (P = pan capacity)	Elec	Cooking	40% steam mode	0.37P+4.5 kW	50% steam mode	0.133P+0.6400 kW
Combination ovens, steam mode	Gas	Cooking	20% steam mode	1,210P+35,810 Btu/h	38% steam mode	200P+6,511 Btu/h
Combination ovens, convection mode	Elec	Cooking	65% convection mode	0.1P+1.5 kW	70% convection mode	0.080P+0.4989 kW
Combination ovens, convection mode	Gas	Cooking	35% convection mode	322P+13,563 Btu/h	44% convection mode	150P+5,425 Btu/h
Convection oven, full-size	Elec	Cooking	65%	2.0 kW	71%	1.6 kW
Convection oven, full-size	Gas	Cooking	30%	18,000 Btu/h	46%	12,000 Btu/h
Convection oven, half-size	Elec	Cooking	65%	1.5 kW	71%	1.0 kW
Conveyor oven, > 25-inch belt	Gas	Cooking	20%	70,000 Btu/h	42%	57,000 Btu/h
Conveyor oven, ≤ 25-inch belt	Gas	Cooking	20%	45,000 Btu/h	42%	29,000 Btu/h
Fryer	Elec	Cooking	75%	1.05 kW	80%	1.0 kW
Fryer	Gas	Cooking	35%	14,000 Btu/h	50%	9,000 Btu/h
Griddle (based on 3 ft model)	Elec	Cooking	60%	400 W/ft²	70%	320 W/ft²
Griddle (based on 3 ft model)	Gas	Cooking	30%	3,500 Btu/h/ft²	38%	2,650 Btu/h/ft²
Hot food holding cabinets (excluding drawer warmers and heated display) 0 < V < 13 ft³ (V = volume)	Elec	Cooking	na	40 W/ft³	na	21.5V Watts
Hot food holding cabinets (excluding drawer warmers and heated display) 13 ≤ V < 28 ft³	Elec	Cooking	na	40 W/ft³	na	2.0V + 254 Watts
Hot food holding cabinets (excluding drawer warmers and heated display) 28 ft³ ≤ V	Elec	Cooking	na	40 W/ft³	na	3.8V + 203.5 Watts
Large vat fryer	Elec	Cooking	75%	1.35 kW	80%	1.1 kW

TABLE 1A (CONTINUED). Commercial kitchen appliance prescriptive measures and baseline for energy cost budget (IP units)						
	Baseline energy usage for energy modeling path				Levels for prescriptive path	
Appliance Type	Fuel	Function	Baseline Efficiency	Baseline Idle Rate	Prescriptive Efficiency	Prescriptive Idle Rate
Large vat fryer	Gas	Cooking	35%	20,000 Btu/h	50%	12,000 Btu/h
Rack oven, double	Gas	Cooking	30%	65,000 Btu/h	50%	35,000 Btu/h
Rack oven, single	Gas	Cooking	30%	43,000 Btu/h	50%	29,000 Btu/h
Range	Elec	Cooking	70%		80%	
Range	Gas	Cooking	35%	na	40% and no standing pilots	na
Steam cooker, batch cooking	Elec	Cooking	26%	200 W/pan	50%	135 W/pan
Steam cooker, batch cooking	Gas	Cooking	15%	2,500 Btu/h/pan	38%	2,100 Btu/h/pan
Steam cooker, high production or cook to order	Elec	Cooking	26%	330 W/pan	50%	275 W/pan
Steam cooker, high production or cook to order	Gas	Cooking	15%	5,000 Btu/h/pan	38%	4,300 Btu/h/pan
Toaster	Elec	Cooking	na	1.8 kW average operating energy rate	na	1.2 kW average operating energy rate
Ice machine, IMH (ice-making head, H = harvest ice), H ≥ 450 lb/day	Elec	Ice	6.89 – 0.0011H kWh/100 lb ice	na	$37.72*H^{-0.298}$ kWh/100 lb ice	na
Ice machine, IMH (ice-making head), H < 450 lb/day	Elec	Ice	10.26 – 0.0086H kWh/100 lb ice	na	$37.72*H^{-0.298}$ kWh/100 lb ice	na
Ice machine RCU (remote condensing unit, w/o remote compressor), H < 1,000 lb/day	Elec	Ice	8.85 – 0.0038H kWh/100lb ice	na	$22.95*H^{-0.258}$ + 1.00 kWh/100 lb ice	na
Ice machine RCU (remote condensing unit), 1600 > H ≥ 1000 lb/day	Elec	Ice	5.10 kWh/100 lb ice	na	$22.95*H^{-0.258}$ + 1.00 kWh/100 lb ice	na
Ice machine RCU (remote condensing unit), H ≥ 1600 lb/day	Elec	Ice	5.10 kWh/100 lb ice	na	-0.00011*H + 4.60 kWh/100 lb ice	na
Ice machine SCU (self-contained unit), H < 175 lb/day	Elec	Ice	18.0 – 0.0469H kWh/100 lb ice	na	$48.66*H^{-0.326}$ + 0.08 kWh/100 lb ice	na
Ice machine self-contained unit, H ≥ 175 lb/day	Elec	Ice	9.80 kWh/100 lb ice	na	$48.66*H^{-0.326}$ + 0.08 kWh/100 lb ice	na

TABLE 1A (CONTINUED). Commercial kitchen appliance prescriptive measures and baseline for energy cost budget (IP units)

	Baseline energy usage for energy modeling path				Levels for prescriptive path	
Appliance Type	**Fuel**	**Function**	**Baseline Efficiency**	**Baseline Idle Rate**	**Prescriptive Efficiency**	**Prescriptive Idle Rate**
Ice machine, water-cooled ice-making head, H ≥ 1436 lb/day (must be on chilled loop)	Elec	Ice	4.0 kWh/100 lb ice	na	3.68 kWh/100 lb ice	na
Ice machine, water-cooled ice-making head, 500 lb/day < H < 1436 (must be on chilled loop)	Elec	Ice	5.58 – 0.0011H kWh/100 lb ice	na	5.13 – 0.001H kWh/100 lb ice	na
Ice machine, water-cooled ice-making head, H < 500 lb/day (must be on chilled loop)	Elec	Ice	7.80 – 0.0055H kWh/100 lb ice	na	7.02 – 0.0049H kWh/100 lb ice	na
Ice machine water-cooled once-through (open loop)	Elec	Ice	Banned	Banned	Banned	Banned
Ice machine, water-cooled SCU (self-contained unit), H < 200 lb/day (must be on chilled loop)	Elec	Ice	11.4 – 0.0190H kWh/100 lb ice	na	10.6 – 0.177H kWh/100 lb ice	na
Ice machine, water-cooled self-contained unit, H ≥ 200 lb/day (must be on chilled loop)	Elec	Ice	7.6 kWh/100 lb ice	na	7.07 kWh/100 lb ice	na
Chest freezer, solid or glass door	Elec	Refrig	0.45V + 0.943 kWh/day	na	≤ 0.270V + 0.130 kWh/day	na
Chest refrigerator, solid or glass door	Elec	Refrig	0.1V + 2.04 kWh/day	na	≤ 0.125V + 0.475 kWh/day	na
Glass-door reach-in freezer 0 < V < 15 ft^3	Elec	Refrig	0.75V + 4.10 kWh/day	na	≤ 0.607V + 0.893 kWh/day	na
Glass-door reach-in freezer 15 ≤ V < 30 ft^3	Elec	Refrig	0.75V + 4.10 kWh/day	na	≤ 0.733V – 1.00 kWh/day	na
Glass-door reach-in freezer, 30 ≤ V < 50 ft^3	Elec	Refrig	0.75V + 4.10 kWh/day	na	≤ 0.250V + 13.50 kWh/day	na
Glass-door reach-in freezer, 50 ≤ V ft^3	Elec	Refrig	0.75V + 4.10 kWh/day	na	≤ 0.450V + 3.50 kWh/day	na
Glass-door reach-in refrigerator, 0 < V < 15 ft^3	Elec	Refrig	0.12V + 3.34 kWh/day	na	≤ 0.118V + 1.382 kWh/day	na
Glass-door reach-in refrigerator, 15 ≤ V < 30 ft^3	Elec	Refrig	0.12V + 3.34 kWh/day	na	≤ 0.140V + 1.050 kWh/day	na
Glass-door reach-in refrigerator, 30 ≤ V < 50 ft^3	Elec	Refrig	0.12V + 3.34 kWh/day	na	≤ 0.088V + 2.625 kWh/day	na

TABLE 1A (CONTINUED). Commercial kitchen appliance prescriptive measures and baseline for energy cost budget (IP units)						
	Baseline energy usage for energy modeling path				Levels for prescriptive path	
Appliance Type	Fuel	Function	Baseline Efficiency	Baseline Idle Rate	Prescriptive Efficiency	Prescriptive Idle Rate
Glass-door reach-in refrigerator, 50 ≤ V ft^3	Elec	Refrig	0.12V + 3.34 kWh/day	na	≤ 0.110V + 1.500 kWh/day	na
Solid-door reach-in freezer, 0 < V < 15 ft^3	Elec	Refrig	0.4V + 1.38 kWh/day	na	≤ 0.250V + 1.25 kWh/day	na
Solid-door reach-in freezer, 15 ≤ V < 30 ft^3	Elec	Refrig	0.4V + 1.38 kWh/day	na	≤ 0.400V – 1.000 kWh/day	na
Solid-door reach-in freezer, 30 ≤ V < 50 ft^3	Elec	Refrig	0.4V + 1.38 kWh/day	na	≤ 0.163V + 6.125 kWh/day	na
Solid-door reach-in freezer, 50 ≤ V ft^3	Elec	Refrig	0.4V + 1.38 kWh/day	na	≤ 0.158V + 6.333 kWh/day	na
Solid-door reach-in refrigerator, 0 < V < 15 ft^3	Elec	Refrig	0.1V + 2.04 kWh/day	na	≤ 0.089V + 1.411 kWh/day	na
Solid-door reach-in refrigerator, 15 ≤ V < 30 ft^3	Elec	Refrig	0.1V + 2.04 kWh/day	na	≤ 0.037V + 2.200 kWh/day	na
Solid-door reach-in refrigerator, 30 ≤ V < 50 ft^3	Elec	Refrig	0.1V + 2.04 kWh/day	na	≤ 0.056V + 1.635 kWh/day	na
Solid-door reach-in refrigerator, 50 ≤ V ft^3	Elec	Refrig	0.1V + 2.04 kWh/day	na	≤ 0.060V + 1.416 kWh/day	na
Clothes washer	Gas	Sanitation	1.72 MEF	na	2.00 MEF	na
Door-type dish machine, high temp	Elec	Sanitation	na	1.0 kW	na	0.70 kW
Door-type dish machine, low temp	Elec	Sanitation	na	0.6 kW	na	0.6 kW
Multitank rack conveyor dish machine, high temp	Elec	Sanitation	na	2.6 kW	na	2.25 kW
Multitank rack conveyor dish machine, low temp	Elec	Sanitation	na	2.0 kW	na	2.0 kW
Single-tank rack conveyor dish machine, high temp	Elec	Sanitation	na	2.0 kW	na	1.5 kW
Single-tank rack conveyor dish machine, low temp	Elec	Sanitation	na	1.6 kW	na	1.5 kW
Undercounter dish machine, high temp	Elec	Sanitation	na	0.9 kW	na	0.5 kW
Undercounter dish machine, low temp	Elec	Sanitation	na	0.5 kW	na	0.5 kW

The energy efficiency, idle energy rates, and water use requirements, where applicable, are based on the following test methods:

ASTM F1275 Standard Test Method for Performance of Griddles

ASTM F1361 Standard Test Method for Performance of Open Deep Fat Fryers

ASTM F1484 Standard Test Methods for Performance of Steam Cookers

ASTM F1496 Standard Test Method for Performance of Convection Ovens

ASTM F1521 Standard Test Methods for Performance of Range Tops

ASTM F1605 Standard Test Method for Performance of Double-Sided Griddles

ASTM F1639 Standard Test Method for Performance of Combination Ovens

ASTM F1695 Standard Test Method for Performance of Underfired Broilers

ASTM F1696 Standard Test Method for Energy Performance of Single-Rack Hot Water Sanitizing, ASTM Door-Type Commercial Dishwashing Machines

ASTM F1704 Standard Test Method for Capture and Containment Performance of Commercial Kitchen Exhaust Ventilation Systems

ASTM F1817 Standard Test Method for Performance of Conveyor Ovens

ASTM F1920 Standard Test Method for Energy Performance of Rack Conveyor, Hot Water Sanitizing, Commercial Dishwashing Machines

ASTM F2093 Standard Test Method for Performance of Rack Ovens

ASTM F2140 Standard Test Method for Performance of Hot Food Holding Cabinets

ASTM F2144 Standard Test Method for Performance of Large Open Vat Fryers

ASTM F2324 Standard Test Method for Prerinse Spray Valves

ASTM F2380 Standard Test Method for Performance of Conveyor Toasters

ARI 810-2007: Performance Rating of Automatic Commercial Ice Makers

ANSI/ASHRAE Standard 72–2005: Method of Testing Commercial Refrigerators and Freezers with temperature setpoints at 38°F for medium-temp refrigerators, 0°F for low-temp freezers, and -15°F for ice cream freezers

TABLE 1B. Commercial Kitchen Appliance Prescriptive Measures and Baseline for Energy Cost Budget (SI units)

	Baseline energy usage for energy modeling path				Levels for prescriptive path	
Appliance type	**Fuel**	**Function**	**Baseline Efficiency**	**Baseline idle Rate**	**Prescriptive Efficiency**	**Prescriptive idle Rate**
Broiler, underfired	Gas	Cooking	30%	50.5 kW/m²	35%	37.9 kW/m²
Combination oven, steam mode (P = pan capacity)	Elec	Cooking	40% steam mode	0.37P + 4.5 kW	50% steam mode	0.133P + 0.6400 kW
Combination oven, steam mode	Gas	Cooking	20% steam mode	(1 210P + 35 810)/3 412 kW	38% steam mode	(200P + 6 511)/ 3 412 kW
Combination oven, convection mode	Elec	Cooking	65% convection mode	0.1P + 1.5 kW	70% convection mode	0.080P + 0.4989 kW
Combination oven, convection mode	Gas	Cooking	35% convection mode	(322P + 13 563)/3 412 kW	44% convection mode	(150P + 5 425)/ 3 412 kW
Convection oven, full-size	Elec	Cooking	65%	2.0 kW	71%	1.6 kW
Convection oven, full-size	Gas	Cooking	30%	5.3 kW	46%	3.5 kW
Convection oven, half-size	Elec	Cooking	65%	1.5 kW	71%	1.0 kW
Conveyor oven, > 63.5-cm belt	Gas	Cooking	20%	20.5 kW	42%	16.7 kW
Conveyor oven, < 63.5-cm belt	Gas	Cooking	20%	13.2 kW	42%	8.5 kW
Fryer	Elec	Cooking	75%	1.05 kW	80%	1.0 kW
Fryer	Gas	Cooking	35%	4.1 kW	50%	2.64 kW
Griddle (based on 90-cm model)	Elec	Cooking	60%	4.3 kW/m²	70%	3.45 kW/m²

TABLE 1B (CONTINUED). Commercial Kitchen Appliance Prescriptive Measures and Baseline for Energy Cost Budget (SI units)

	Baseline energy usage for energy modeling path				Levels for prescriptive path	
Appliance type	**Fuel**	**Function**	**Baseline Efficiency**	**Baseline idle Rate**	**Prescriptive Efficiency**	**Prescriptive idle Rate**
Griddle (based on 90-cm model)	Gas	Cooking	30%	11 kW/m^2	33%	8.35 kW/m^2
Hot food holding cabinets (excluding drawer warmers and heated display) 0 < V < 0.368 m^3 (V = volume)	Elec	Cooking	na	1.4 kW/m^3	na	(21.5*V)/0.0283 kW/m^3
Hot food holding cabinets (excluding drawer warmers and heated display) 0.368 ≤ V < 0.793 m^3	Elec	Cooking	na	1.4 kW/m^3	na	(2.0*V + 254)/0.0283 kW/m^3
Hot food holding cabinets (excluding drawer warmers and heated display) 0.793 m^3 ≤ V	Elec	Cooking	na	1.4 kW/m^3	na	(3.8*V + 203.5)/0.0283 kW/m^3
Large vat fryer	Elec	Cooking	75%	1.35 kW	80%	1.1 kW
Large vat fryer	Gas	Cooking	35%	5.86 kW	50%	3.5 kW
Rack oven, double	Gas	Cooking	30%	19 kW	50%	10.25 kW
Rack oven, single	Gas	Cooking	30%	12.6 kW	50%	8.5 kW
Range	Elec	Cooking	70%	na	80%	na
Range	Gas	Cooking	35%	na	40% and no standing pilots	na
Steam cooker, batch cooking	Elec	Cooking	26%	200 W/pan	50%	135 W/pan
Steam cooker, batch cooking	Gas	Cooking	15%	733 W/pan	38%	615 W/pan
Steam cooker, high production or cook to order	Elec	Cooking	26%	330 W/pan	50%	275 W/pan
Steam cooker, high production or cook to order	Gas	Cooking	15%	1.47 kW/pan	38%	1.26 kW/pan
Toaster	Elec	Cooking	na	1.8 kW average operating energy rate	na	1.2 kW average operating energy rate
Ice machine IMH (ice-making head, H = ice harvest) H ≥ 204 kg/day	Elec	Ice	0.0015 – 5.3464E^{-07} kWh/kg ice	na—	$\leq 13.52*H^{-0.298}$ kWh/100 kg ice	na
Ice machine IMH (ice making head) ice-making head, H < 204 kg/day	Elec	Ice	0.2262 – 4.18E^{-04} kWh/kg ice	na	$\leq 13.52*H^{-0.298}$ kWh/100 kg ice	na
Ice machine, RCU (remote condensing unit, w/o remote compressor) H < 454 kg/day	Elec	Ice	0.1951 – 1.85E^{-04} kWh/kg ice	na	$\leq 111.5835*H^{-0.258} + 2.205$ kWh/100 kg ice	na

TABLE 1B (CONTINUED). Commercial Kitchen Appliance Prescriptive Measures and Baseline for Energy Cost Budget (SI units)						
	Baseline energy usage for energy modeling path				Levels for prescriptive path	
Appliance type	Fuel	Function	Baseline Efficiency	Baseline idle Rate	Prescriptive Efficiency	Prescriptive idle Rate
Ice machine RCU (remote condensing unit) 726 > H ≥ 454 kg/day	Elec	Ice	0.1124 kWh/kg ice	na	≤ 111.5835*H$^{-0.258}$ + 2.205 kWh/100 kg ice	na
Ice machine RCU (remote condensing unit) H ≥ 726 kg/day	Elec	Ice	0.1124 kWh/kg ice	na	≤ -0.00024H + 4.60 kWh/100 kg ice	na
Ice machine SCU (self contained unit), H < 79 kg/day	Elec	Ice	0.3968 – 2.28E^{-03} kWh/kg ice	na	236.59*H$^{-0.326}$ + 0.176 kWh/100 kg ice	na
Ice machine SCU (self-contained unit), H ≥ 79 kg/day	Elec	Ice	0.2161 kWh/kg ice	na	236.59*H$^{-0.326}$ + 0.176 kWh/100 kg ice	na
Ice machine, water-cooled ice-making head, H ≥ 651 kg/day (must be on a chilled loop)	Elec	Ice	0.0882 kWh/kg ice	na	≤ 8.11 kWh/100 kg ice	na
Ice machine, water-cooled ice-making head, 227 ≤ H < 651 kg/day (must be on a chilled loop)	Elec	Ice	0.1230 – 5.35E^{-05} kWh/kg ice	na	≤ 11.31 – 0.065H kWh/100 kg ice	na
Ice machine, water-cooled ice-making head, H < 227 kg/day (must be on a chilled loop)	Elec	Ice	0.1720 – 2.67E^{-04} kWh/kg ice	na	≤ 15.48 – 0.0238H kWh/100 kg ice	na
Ice machine, water-cooled once-through (open loop)	Elec	Ice	Banned	Banned	Banned	Banned
Ice machine water-cooled SCU (self-contained unit) H < 91 kg/day (must be on a chilled loop)	Elec	Ice	0.2513 – 29.23E^{-04} kWh/kg ice	na	≤ 23.37 – 0.086H kWh/100 kg ice	na
Ice machine, water-cooled SCU (self-contained unit) H ≥ 91 kg/day (must be on a chilled loop)	Elec	Ice	0.1676 kWh/kg ice	na	15.57 kWh/100 kg ice	na
Chest freezer, solid or glass door	Elec	Refrig	15.90V + 0.943 kWh/day	na	9.541V + 0.130 kWh/day	na
Chest refrigerator, solid or glass door	Elec	Refrig	3.53V + 2.04 kWh/day	na	≤ 4.417V + 0.475 kWh/day	na
Glass-door reach-in freezer, 0 < V < 0.42 m^3	Elec	Refrig	26.50V + 4.1 kWh/day	na	≤ 21.449V + 0.893 kWh/day	na
Glass-door reach-in freezer, 0.42 ≤ V < 0.85 m^3	Elec	Refrig	26.50V + 4.1 kWh/day	na	≤ 25.901V – 1.00 kWh/day	na
Glass-door reach-in freezer, 0.85 ≤ V < 1.42 m^3	Elec	Refrig	26.50V + 4.1 kWh/day	na	≤ 8.834V + 13.50 kWh/day	na
Glass-door reach-in freezer, 1.42 ≤ V m^3	Elec	Refrig	26.50V + 4.1 kWh/day	na	≤ 15.90V + 3.50 kWh/day	na

TABLE 1B (CONTINUED). Commercial Kitchen Appliance Prescriptive Measures and Baseline for Energy Cost Budget (SI units)

	Baseline energy usage for energy modeling path				Levels for prescriptive path	
Appliance type	**Fuel**	**Function**	**Baseline Efficiency**	**Baseline idle Rate**	**Prescriptive Efficiency**	**Prescriptive idle Rate**
Glass-door reach-in refrigerator, 0 < V < 0.42 m³	Elec	Refrig	4.24V + 3.34 kWh/day	na	≤ 4.169V + 1.382 kWh/day	na
Glass-door reach-in refrigerator, 0.42 ≤ V < 0.85 m³	Elec	Refrig	4.24V + 3.34 kWh/day	na	≤ 4.947V + 1.050 kWh/day	na
Glass-door reach-in refrigerator, 0.85 ≤ V < 1.42 m³	Elec	Refrig	4.24V + 3.34 kWh/day	na	≤ 3.109V + 2.625 kWh/day	na
Glass-door reach-in refrigerator, 1.42 ≤ V m³	Elec	Refrig	4.24V + 3.34 kWh/day	na	≤ 3.887V + 1.500 kWh/day	na
Solid-door reach-in freezer, 0 < V < 0.42 m³	Elec	Refrig	14.13V + 1.38 kWh/day	na	≤ 8.834V + 1.25 kWh/day	na
Solid-door reach-in freezer, 0.42 < V < 0.85 m³	Elec	Refrig	14.13V + 1.38 kWh/day	na	≤ 4.819V – 1.000 kWh/day	na
Solid-door reach-in freezer, 0.85 ≤ V < 1.42 m³	Elec	Refrig	14.13V + 1.38 kWh/day	na	≤ 5.760V + 6.125 kWh/day	na
Solid-door reach-in freezer, 1.42 ≤ V m³	Elec	Refrig	14.13V + 1.38 kWh/day	na	≤ 5.583V + 6.333 kWh/day	na
Solid-door reach-in refrigerator, 0 < V < 0.42 m³	Elec	Refrig	3.53V + 2.04 kWh/day	na	≤ 3.145V + 1.411 kWh/day	na
Solid-door reach-in refrigerator, 0.42 ≤ V < 0.85 m³	Elec	Refrig	3.53V + 2.04 kWh/day	na	≤ 1.307V + 2.200 kWh/day	na
Solid-door reach-in refrigerator, 0.85 ≤ V < 1.42 m³	Elec	Refrig	3.53V + 2.04 kWh/day	na	≤ 1.979V + 1.635 kWh/day	na
Solid-door reach-in refrigerator, 1.42 ≤ V m³	Elec	Refrig	3.53V + 2.04 kWh/day	na	≤ 2.120V + 1.416 kWh/day	na
Clothes washer	Gas	Sanitation	1.72 MEF		2.00 MEF	
Door-type dish machine, high temp	Elec	Sanitation	na	1.0 kW	na	0.70 kW
Door-type dish machine, low temp	Elec	Sanitation	na	0.6 kW	na	0.6 kW
Multitank rack conveyor dish machine, high temp	Elec	Sanitation	na	2.6 kW	na	2.25 kW
Multitank rack conveyor dish machine, low temp	Elec	Sanitation	na	2.0 kW	na	2.0 kW
Single-tank rack conveyor dish machine, high temp	Elec	Sanitation	na	2.0 kW	na	1.5 kW

TABLE 1B (CONTINUED). Commercial Kitchen Appliance Prescriptive Measures and Baseline for Energy Cost Budget (SI units)

	Baseline energy usage for energy modeling path				Levels for prescriptive path	
Appliance type	**Fuel**	**Function**	**Baseline Efficiency**	**Baseline idle Rate**	**Prescriptive Efficiency**	**Prescriptive idle Rate**
Single-tank rack conveyor dish machine, low temp	Elec	Sanitation	na	1.6 kW	na	1.5 kW
Undercounter dish machine, high temp	Elec	Sanitation	na	0.9 kW	na	0.5 kW
Undercounter dish machine, low temp	Elec	Sanitation	na	0.5 kW	na	0.5 kW

The energy efficiency, idle energy rates, and water use requirements, where applicable, are based on the following test methods:

ASTM F1275 Standard Test Method for Performance of Griddles

ASTM F1361 Standard Test Method for Performance of Open Deep Fat Fryers

ASTM F1484 Standard Test Methods for Performance of Steam Cookers

ASTM F1496 Standard Test Method for Performance of Convection Ovens

ASTM F1521 Standard Test Methods for Performance of Range Tops

ASTM F1605 Standard Test Method for Performance of Double-Sided Griddles

ASTM F1639 Standard Test Method for Performance of Combination Ovens

ASTM F1695 Standard Test Method for Performance of Underfired Broilers

ASTM F1696 Standard Test Method for Energy Performance of Single-Rack Hot Water Sanitizing, ASTM Door-Type Commercial Dishwashing Machines

ASTM F1704 Standard Test Method for Capture and Containment Performance of Commercial Kitchen Exhaust Ventilation Systems

ASTM F1817 Standard Test Method for Performance of Conveyor Ovens

ASTM F1920 Standard Test Method for Energy Performance of Rack Conveyor, Hot Water Sanitizing, Commercial Dishwashing Machines

ASTM F2093 Standard Test Method for Performance of Rack Ovens

ASTM F2140 Standard Test Method for Performance of Hot Food Holding Cabinets

ASTM F2144 Standard Test Method for Performance of Large Open Vat Fryers

ASTM F2324 Standard Test Method for Prerinse Spray Valves

ASTM F2380 Standard Test Method for Performance of Conveyor Toasters

ARI 810-2007: Performance Rating of Automatic Commercial Ice Makers

ANSI/ASHRAE Standard 72–2005: Method of Testing Commercial Refrigerators and Freezers with temperature setpoints at 3°C for mediumtemp refrigerators, -18°C for low-temp freezers, and -26°C for ice cream freezers.

TABLE 2. Supermarket refrigeration prescriptive measures and baseline for energy cost budget

Item	Attribute	Prescriptive Measure	Baseline for Energy Modeling Path
Commercial Refrigerator and Freezers	Energy Use Limits	ASHRAE 90.1-2010 Addendum g. Table 6.8.1L	ASHRAE 90.1-2010 Addendum g. Table 6.8.1L
Commercial Refrigeration Equipment	Energy Use Limits	ASHRAE 90.1-2010 Addendum g. Table 6.8.1M	ASHRAE 90.1-2010 Addendum g. Table 6.8.1M

TABLE 3. Walk-in coolers and freezers prescriptive measures and baseline for energy cost budget			
Item	**Attribute**	**Prescriptive Measure**	**Baseline for Energy Modeling Path**
Envelope	Freezer insulation	R-46	R-36
	Cooler insulation	R-36	R-20
	Automatic closer doors	Yes	No
	High-efficiency low- or no-heat reach-in doors	40W/ft (130W/m) of door frame (low temperature), 17W/ft (55W/m) of door frame (medium temperature)	40W/ft (130W/m) of door frame (low temperature), 17W/ft (55W/m) of door frame (medium temperature)
Evaporator	Evaporator fan motor and control	Shaded pole and split phase motors prohibited; use PSC or EMC motors	Constant-speed fan
	Hot gas defrost	No electric defrosting	Electric defrosting
Condenser	Air-cooled condenser fan motor and control	Shaded pole and split phase motors prohibited; use PSC or EMC motors; add condenser fan controllers	Cycling one-speed fan
	Air-cooled condenser design approach	Floating head pressure controls or ambient subcooling	10°F (-12°C) to 15°F (-9°C) dependent on suction temperature
Lighting	Lighting power density (W/sq.ft.)	0.6 W/sq.ft. (6.5 W/sq. meter)	0.6 W/sq.ft. (6.5 W/sq. meter)
Commercial Refrigerator and Freezers	Energy Use Limits	na	Use an Exceptional Calculation Method if attempting to take savings
Commercial Refrigerator and Freezers	Energy Use Limits	na	Use an Exceptional Calculation Method if attempting to take savings

TABLE 4. Commercial kitchen ventilation prescriptive measures and baseline for energy cost budget		
Strategies	**Prescriptive Measure**	**Baseline**
Kitchen hood control	ASHRAE 90.1-2010 Section 6.5.7.1, except that Section 6.5.7.1.3 and Section 6.5.7.1.4 shall apply if the total kitchen exhaust airflow rate exceeds 2,000 cfm (960 L/s) (as opposed to 5,000 cfm (2,400 L/s) noted in the ASHRAE 90.1-2010 requirements)	ASHRAE 90.1-2010 Section 6.5.7.1 and Section G3.1.1 Exception (d) where applicable